ATOMY &
YSIOLOGY

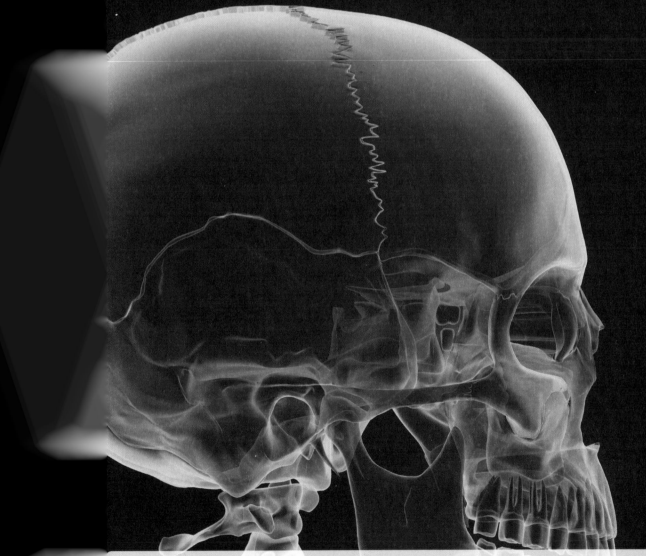

THIS BOOK IS THE PROPERTY OF

Name _____

Class _____

School _____

Copyright © 2023 Richard Allan
First published 2023 by BIOZONE International Ltd

Third edition 2023
ISBN 978-1-99-101408-5

Printed by Replika Press Pvt. Ltd using paper produced from renewable and waste materials

Acknowledgements

BIOZONE wishes to thank and acknowledge the team for their efforts and contributions to the production of this title.

Cover Photograph

Photo: istockphoto.com Credit: Raycat

The human skull
The skull consists of 22 bones in total. All are fused together except for the mandible (jaw). The neurocranium consists of 8 bones and houses and protects the brain. The facial skeleton consists of 14 bones.
The skull balances on the cervical vertebrae that form the neck.

Disclaimer

The external weblinks (URLs) referenced in this book were correct at the time of publishing. However, due to the dynamic nature of the internet, some addresses may have changed, or cease to exist. While BIOZONE regrets any inconvenience that this may cause readers, no responsibility for any such changes or unforeseeable errors can be accepted by BIOZONE.

North & South America	✉ sales@biozone.com
UK & Rest of World	✉ sales@biozone.co.uk
Australia	✉ sales@biozone.com.au
New Zealand	✉ sales@biozone.co.nz

BIOZONE.com

ANATOMY & PHYSIOLOGY

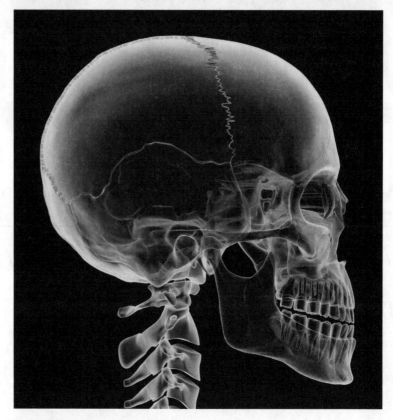

About the Authors

Jillian Mellanby *Editor*

Jill began her science career with a degree in biochemistry and, after a short spell in research labs, became a science teacher both in the UK and then New Zealand. She spent many years managing the Royal Society of New Zealand's academic publishing programme of eight science journals which allowed her to hone her project management and editorial skills. She was also a part of the Expert Advice writing team at the Royal Society of New Zealand, producing science pieces for a public audience. She joined the BIOZONE team in late 2021, as editor.

Kent Pryor *Author*

Kent has a BSc from Massey University, majoring in zoology and ecology and taught secondary school biology and chemistry for 9 years before joining BIOZONE as an author in 2009.

Sarah Gaze *Author*

Sarah has 16 years' experience as a Science and Chemistry teacher, recently completing MEd. (1st class hons) with a focus on curriculum, science, and climate change education.
She has a background in educational resource development, academic writing, and art. Sarah joined the BIOZONE team at the start of 2022.

Lissa Bainbridge-Smith *Author*

Lissa graduated with a Masters in Science (hons) from the University of Waikato. After graduation she worked in industry in a research and development capacity for eight years. Lissa joined BIOZONE in 2006 and is hands-on developing new curricula. Lissa has also taught science theory and practical skills to international and ESL students.

Contents

CODING: **Activity** is marked: ☐ to be done   ✓ when completed

Contents

Contents

Using This Worktext

This worktext is designed as a resource that will help to increase your understanding of the content and skill requirements of your anatomy and physiology course, and reinforce and extend the ideas developed by your teacher. This worktext includes many useful features outlined below, and over the next few pages, to help you locate activities and information.

Interacting systems
Summarizes the interactions of the body system or systems with other body systems.

Concept maps
Summary of how disease, medicine, age, and exercise relate to the system or systems.

Chapter introduction
Identifies the activities relating to the guiding questions.

Chapter summary
Test what you know about the ideas, connections, and skills you have explored in the chapter.

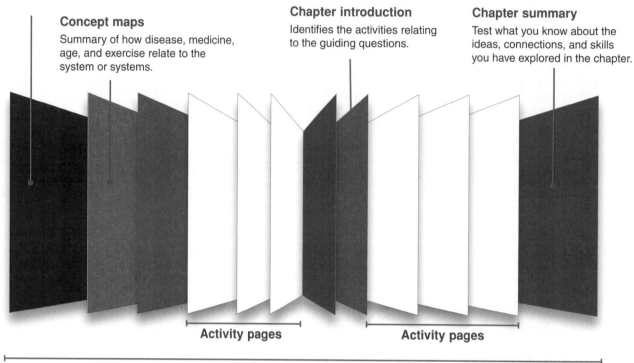

Activity pages   Activity pages

System or systems
Some systems can be grouped together, e.g. systems for control, or systems for support and movement.

Chapter Introductions

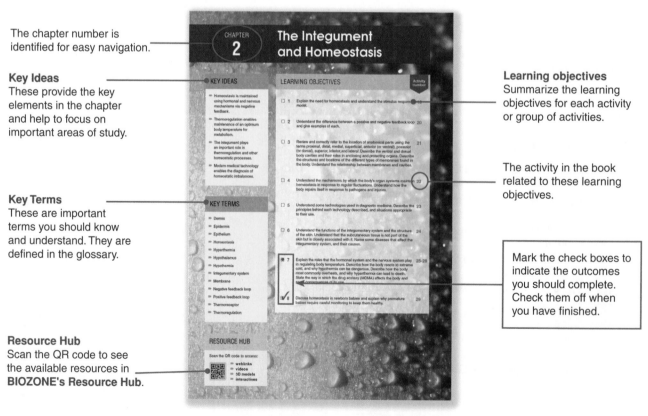

The chapter number is identified for easy navigation.

Key Ideas
These provide the key elements in the chapter and help to focus on important areas of study.

Key Terms
These are important terms you should know and understand. They are defined in the glossary.

Resource Hub
Scan the QR code to see the available resources in **BIOZONE's Resource Hub.**

Learning objectives
Summarize the learning objectives for each activity or group of activities.

The activity in the book related to these learning objectives.

Mark the check boxes to indicate the outcomes you should complete. Check them off when you have finished.

Activity Page

The activities make up most of the content of this worktext. The components of the activity page, including the tab system, are described below.

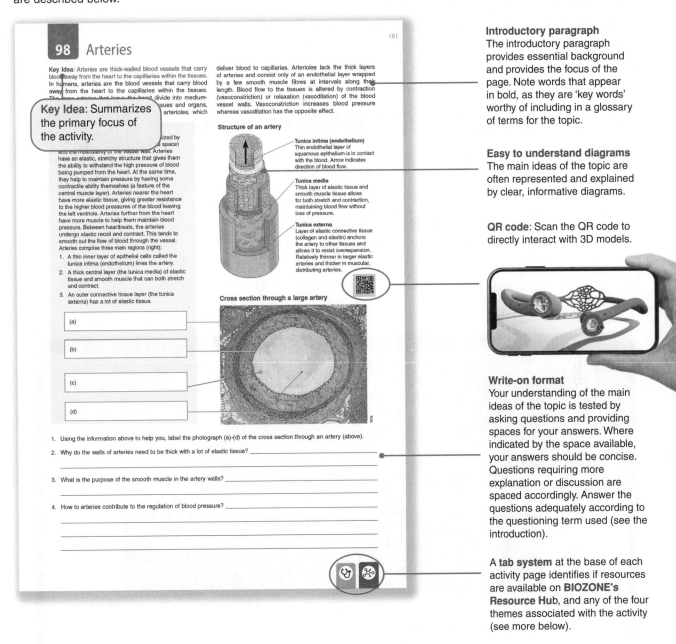

Key Idea: Summarizes the primary focus of the activity.

Introductory paragraph
The introductory paragraph provides essential background and provides the focus of the page. Note words that appear in bold, as they are 'key words' worthy of including in a glossary of terms for the topic.

Easy to understand diagrams
The main ideas of the topic are often represented and explained by clear, informative diagrams.

QR code: Scan the QR code to directly interact with 3D models.

Write-on format
Your understanding of the main ideas of the topic is tested by asking questions and providing spaces for your answers. Where indicated by the space available, your answers should be concise. Questions requiring more explanation or discussion are spaced accordingly. Answer the questions adequately according to the questioning term used (see the introduction).

A **tab system** at the base of each activity page identifies if resources are available on **BIOZONE's Resource Hub**, and any of the four themes associated with the activity (see more below).

Page Tabs

The tab system identifies which of the four related anatomy and physiology themes: disease, medicine and technology, effects of aging, or exercise, are covered in the activity. The tab panel also indicates whether or not the activity is supported online on **BIOZONE's Resource Hub**.

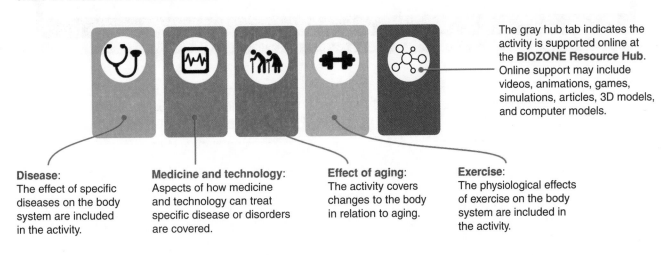

The gray hub tab indicates the activity is supported online at the **BIOZONE Resource Hub**. Online support may include videos, animations, games, simulations, articles, 3D models, and computer models.

Disease:
The effect of specific diseases on the body system are included in the activity.

Medicine and technology:
Aspects of how medicine and technology can treat specific disease or disorders are covered.

Effect of aging:
The activity covers changes to the body in relation to aging.

Exercise:
The physiological effects of exercise on the body system are included in the activity.

Using BIOZONE's Resource Hub

▶ BIOZONE's Resource Hub provides links to online content that supports the activities in the book. From this page, you can also check for any corrections or clarifications to the book since printing.

▶ The Resource Hub provides a range of different resources to help explain or support the activity in the worktext. They provide great support to help your understanding of a topic.

 www.BIOZONEhub.com

Then enter the code in the text field **ANP3-4085**

Or scan this QR code

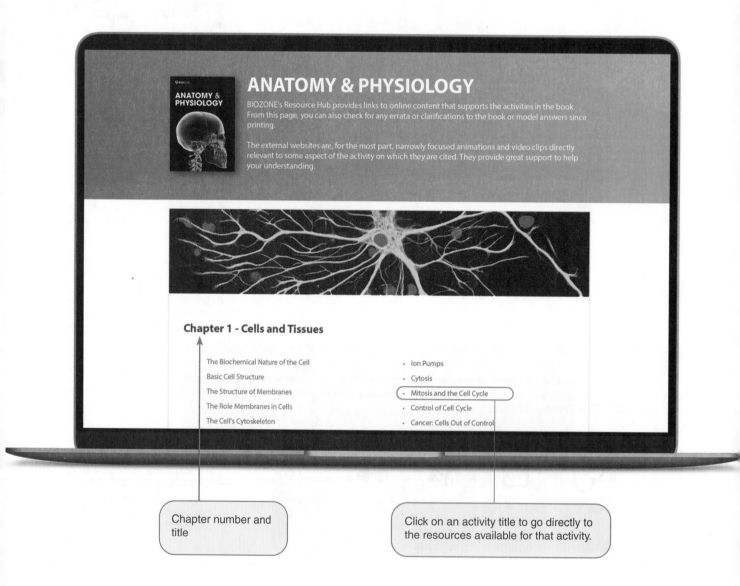

ANATOMY & PHYSIOLOGY

BIOZONE's Resource Hub provides links to online content that supports the activities in the book. From this page, you can also check for any errata or clarifications to the book or model answers since printing.

The external websites are, for the most part, narrowly focused animations and video clips directly relevant to some aspect of the activity on which they are cited. They provide great support to help your understanding.

Chapter 1 - Cells and Tissues

The Biochemical Nature of the Cell
Basic Cell Structure
The Structure of Membranes
The Role Membranes in Cells
The Cell's Cytoskeleton

- Ion Pumps
- Cytosis
- Mitosis and the Cell Cycle
- Control of Cell Cycle
- Cancer: Cells Out of Control

Chapter number and title

Click on an activity title to go directly to the resources available for that activity.

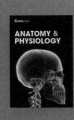

Using BIOZONE's Resource Hub

BIOZONE's Resource Hub provides links to online content that supports the activities in the book. From this page, you can also check for any errata or clarifications to the book or model answers since printing.

The external websites are, for the most part, narrowly focused animations and video clips directly relevant to some aspect of the activity on which they are cited. They provide great support to help your understanding.

Anatomy & Physio...

Activity you are viewing

Activity

BIOZONE Resource Hub / The Integument and Homeostasis / 19 Principles of Homeostasis

19 Principles of Homeostasis

- Human body with organs
- What is homeostasis? I Biology
- PBS: Body control centre
- Live Science: What is homeostasis?
- Homeostasis- Definition, Types, Examples, Applications
- Sciencing: Organ systems involved in homeostasis

Supporting material is available for this activity. Hyperlink to an external resource.

The Resource Hub icons

 Games   Simulations   Weblinks   Slideshow   3D Models   PDF   Spreadsheet   Video   Reference

Explore videos

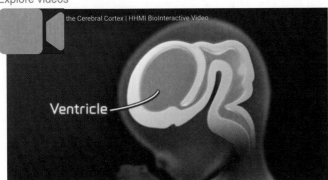

the Cerebral Cortex | HHMI BioInteractive Video

Ventricle

Explore interactive simulations

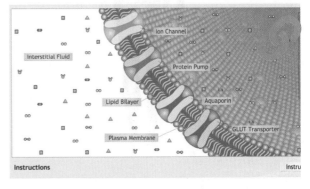

Ion Channel
Interstitial Fluid
Protein Pump
Lipid Bilayer
Aquaporin
Plasma Membrane
GLUT Transporter
Instructions

Explore web based resources

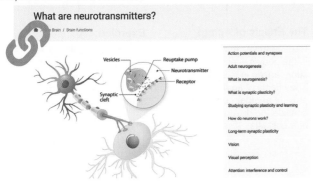

What are neurotransmitters?

Vesicles
Reuptake pump
Neurotransmitter
Receptor
Synaptic cleft

Action potentials and synapses
Adult neurogenesis
What is neurogenesis?
What is synaptic plasticity?
Studying synaptic plasticity and learning
How do neurons work?
Long-term synaptic plasticity
Vision
Visual perception
Attention: interference and control

Explore 3D models

Chapter Summary and Contexts

Homeostasis is a unifying theme throughout *Anatomy & Physiology*. Each chapter (or in some cases two chapters) is preceded by a two page summary of homeostatic interactions and contextual examples. The first of the two pages provides an overview of how the specific body system (or a pair of body systems) interacts with the other body systems to maintain homeostasis. A lower panel summarizes the general functions of the system. The second of the two pages continues this theme by showing how the selected body system can be affected by disease, aging, and exercise, and how medical knowledge can be applied to diagnosing and treating disorders of the body system. These contexts provide a relevant and interesting framework for understanding the subject matter.

A contextual framework

Interacting systems:

The purpose of this page is to summarize the interactions of the body system under study (in this case the nervous and endocrine system) with all other body systems in turn. This summary describes the way in which systems work together to maintain homeostasis.

Four-panel Focus:

Each of the four panels on this page focuses on one contextual theme to which you can apply your knowledge and understanding of the topic's content.

Disease:

A summary of some of the diseases affecting the body system. These provide a good context for examining departures from homeostasis.

Medicine and Technology:

A summary of how medicine and technology are used to study the chosen body system, and how new technologies can be used to diagnose and treat specific diseases.

Most systems are treated singly, although those systems that operate very closely (e.g. nervous and endocrine) are mapped together.

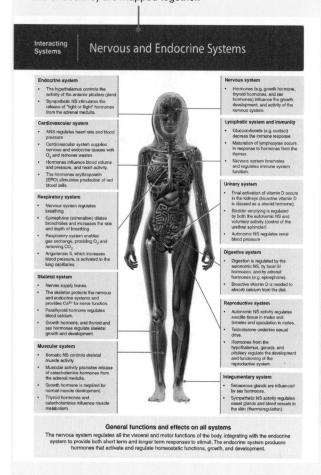

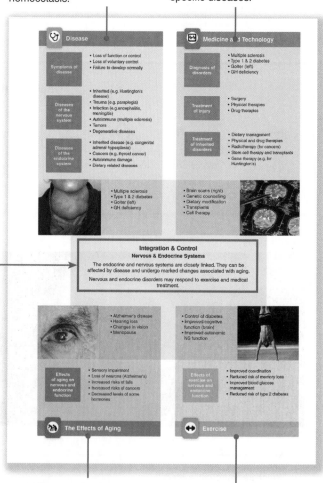

The intersecting regions of the center panel of the context map highlight topics of focus within each context. These are specifically addressed within the worktext.

The Effects of Aging:

Degenerative changes in the body system are summarized in this panel. The effects of aging provide another context for considering disruptions to homeostasis.

Exercise:

Exercise has different effects on different body systems. Some of the physiological effects of exercise are summarized here.

Concepts in Anatomy and Physiology

Cells and Tissues

Cell structure and function	• Cellular membranes and organelles • Cellular transport processes • Cell division and specialization
Tissues are made up of cells with different roles	• Epithelial tissues • Connective tissues • Muscle tissue • Nervous tissue
Organs are made up of different tissues. Organ systems have different roles	• Exchanges with the environment • Support and movement • Control and coordination • Internal transport • Internal defense • Reproduction and development • Excretion and fluid balance

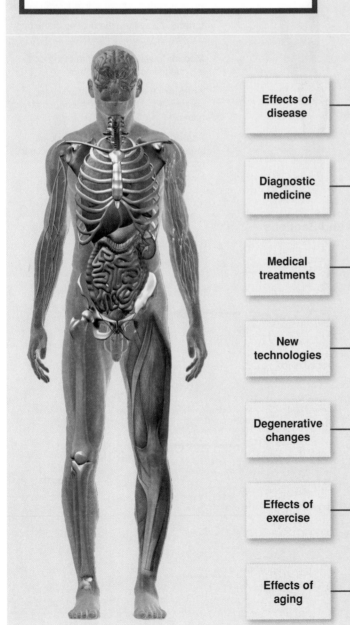

Effects of disease

Diagnostic medicine

Medical treatments

New technologies

Degenerative changes

Effects of exercise

Effects of aging

The Integumentary System
The skin and its accessory structures

The Skeletal System
The bones, cartilage, and ligaments

The Muscular System
Smooth, cardiac, and skeletal muscle

The Nervous System
Neurons, glial cells, sensory receptors, and sense organs

The Endocrine System
Endocrine glands and hormones, including the hypothalamus

The Cardiovascular System
The heart, blood vessels, and blood

The Lymphatic System
The lymphoid tissues and organs, the leukocytes

The Digestive System
The digestive tract and accessory organs, including the liver

The Respiratory System
The lungs and associated structures

The Urinary System
The kidneys, bladder, and accessory structures

The Reproductive System
The sex organs and associated structures

Direction and Planes

The location and orientation of structures is important when studying human anatomy. Descriptions and locations of structures assume the body is in the **anatomical position** in which the body stands erect facing the observer with feet flat on the floor and hands at the side, palms turned forward. Directional terms describe the orientation and position of organs and structures from this position.

Directional Terms

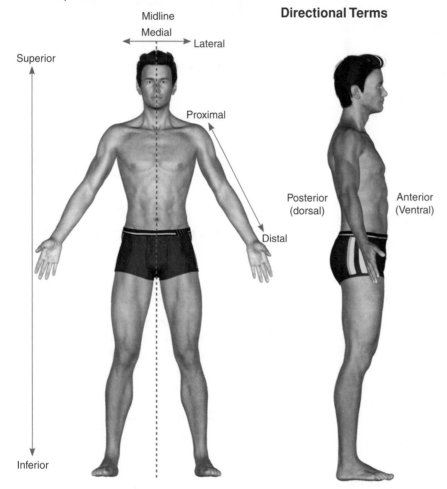

Specific terms are used to give the location and orientation of structures in the body. Many of these terms come in pairs. It is easier to locate and describe structures and movements accurately if you understand these terms.

Proximal: An area towards the attached end of a limb or the origin of a structure, e.g. proximal convoluted tubule.

Distal: An area farthest from the point of attachment of a limb or origin of a structure e.g. distal convoluted tubule.

Superior: Above or over another structure. Towards the head e.g superior vena cava

Inferior: Below or under another structure. Away from the head e.g. inferior vena cava.

Lateral: Away from the midline of the body e.g. lateral collateral ligament.

Medial: Towards the midline of the body e.g. medial collateral ligament

Anterior: Towards the front or ventral surface of the body e.g anterior pituitary gland.

Posterior: Towards the back or dorsal surface of the body e.g. posterior pituitary gland.

Planes and Sections

Planes (flat surfaces) may be cut through a body or organ to a produce section. The plane is named according to the relative direction of the cut surface to the orientation of the organ or structure in the body.

A **frontal plane** (also known as a coronal plane) divides the body into anterior (ventral) and posterior (dorsal) sections.

A **sagittal plane** divides the body into left and right halves. A midsagittal plane does this down the midline of the body (or organ), producing equal sections.

A **transverse plane** divides the body into superior and inferior sections.

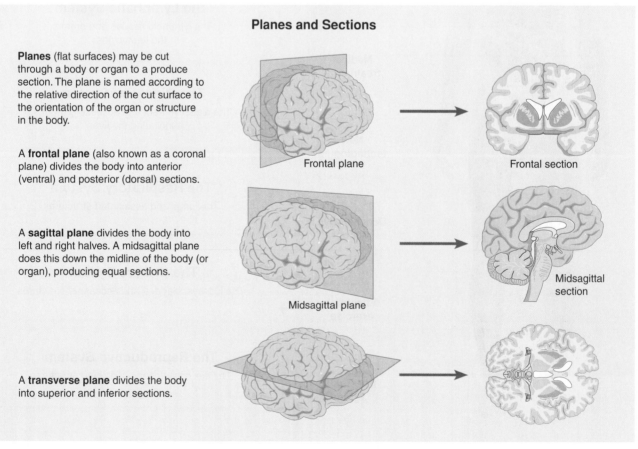

Cells and Tissues

KEY IDEAS

- Cells are the basic units of life. Microscopy can be used to understand cellular structure.

- Cellular metabolism depends on the transport of substances across cellular membranes.

- Cell size is limited by surface area to volume ratio.

- New cells arise through cell division.

- Cellular diversity arises through specialization from stem cell progenitors.

KEY TERMS

- Active transport
- Cell
- Cell cycle
- Diffusion
- Hypertonic
- Hypotonic
- Ion pump
- Isotonic
- Membrane
- Mitosis
- Organ
- Organelle
- Organ system
- Osmosis
- Plasma membrane
- Tissue

RESOURCE HUB

Scan the QR code to access:

- weblinks
- videos
- 3D models
- interactives

LEARNING OBJECTIVES

Activity number

☐ 1 Identify the main components of cells and their functions. Understand the main chemical elements found in the body and give examples of their biological roles. Describe the structure of a generic animal cell and appreciate that different types of cells have specialized features, depending on their function.
1-2

☐ 2 Describe the fluid mosaic model of membrane structure, including the role of phospholipids, cholesterol, glycolipids, proteins, and glycoproteins. Describe the functions of membranes, including the plasma membrane, in cells.
3-4

☐ 3 Understand what is meant by metabolism. Explain the role of the cytoskeleton and identify and describe the following cell organelles.
5-7

- plasma membrane, nucleus, nuclear envelope, nucleolus
- mitochondria, rough/smooth endoplasmic reticulum, ribosomes
- Golgi apparatus, lysosomes, peroxisomes
- cytoplasm, cytoskeleton (of microtubules), centrioles, cilia (if present)

☐ 4 Explain passive transport across membranes by diffusion and osmosis. Explain the terms hypotonic, isotonic, and hypertonic with reference to water fluxes in cells. Describe facilitated diffusion (facilitated transport) involving carrier or channel proteins. Identify when and where facilitated diffusion might occur in a cell.
8

☐ 5 Using examples, explain active transport in cells, including ion pumps, endocytosis, and exocytosis.
9-11

☐ 6 Describe the cell cycle in eukaryotes such as humans. Include reference to mitosis, growth (G1, G2), and DNA replication (S). Explain how the cell cycle is regulated and issues that can arise when regulation goes wrong. Describe the structure and role of the nucleus and its contents, including the DNA and chromosomes.
12-14

☐ 7 Recognize the hierarchy of organization in multicellular organisms (including humans). Appreciate the role of cooperation between cells, tissues, organs, and organ systems in the structure and function of human body.
15

☐ 8 With reference to specific examples, explain how cells are organized into tissues. Recognize structural and functional diversity in the cells that make up human tissues. Recognize the characteristic features and functional roles of the four main tissue types in humans.
16

Background: Human skin cells

1 The Biochemical Nature of the Cell

Key Idea: Carbon, hydrogen, oxygen, and nitrogen are the key elements of life. Together, they combine into the various key molecules of life, including nucleotides, carbohydrates, lipids, and proteins.

Water is the main component of organisms and provides an equable environment in which metabolic reactions can occur. Apart from water, most other substances in **cells** are compounds of carbon, hydrogen, oxygen, and nitrogen.

The combination of carbon atoms with the atoms of other elements provides a huge variety of molecular structures, collectively called organic molecules. The organic molecules that make up living things can be grouped into four broad classes: carbohydrates, lipids, proteins, and nucleic acids. In addition, a small number of elements and inorganic ions are also essential for life, as components of larger molecules or extracellular fluids.

The elements of life

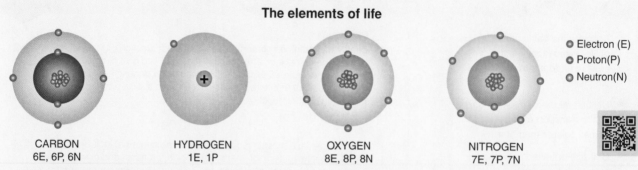

● Electron (E)
● Proton(P)
● Neutron(N)

CARBON
6E, 6P, 6N

HYDROGEN
1E, 1P

OXYGEN
8E, 8P, 8N

NITROGEN
7E, 7P, 7N

Carbon is abundant. It has four valence (outer shell) electrons that can form up to four covalent (shared electron) bonds with other atoms. Complex biological molecules consist of carbon atoms bonded with other elements, especially oxygen and hydrogen, but also nitrogen, phosphorus, and sulfur. Carbon readily forms stable polymers that can participate in chemical reactions.

The components of cells

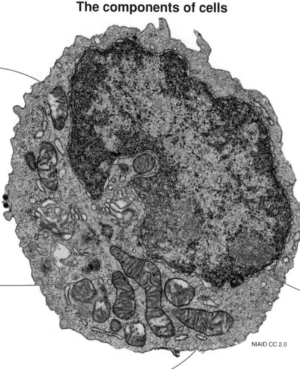

NIAID CC 2.0

Chromosome

Nucleic acids (DNA and RNA) encode information for the construction and functioning of an organism. Most of a eukaryotic cell's DNA is found in the nucleus. The nucleotide called ATP is the energy currency of the cell.

VMRCVM

Carbohydrates act as energy stores, e.g. glycogen, arrowed above, and are involved in cellular recognition, cell signaling, and **membrane** stability (as glycoproteins and glycolipids).

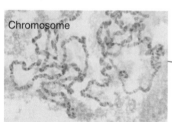

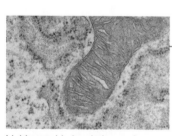

Lipids provide insulation and a concentrated source of energy. Phospholipids are a major component of cellular membranes, including the membranes of **organelles**.
Above: Mitochondrion

Water is a major component of cells. Many substances dissolve in it, metabolic reactions occur in it, and it provides support and turgor.

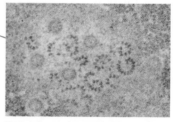

Proteins may be catalytic (enzymes), structural (collagen in skin), proteins in ribosomes, or they may be involved in movement, message signaling, internal defense and transport, or storage.
Above: ribosomes in translation

1. Identify the most four common chemical elements in living organisms: _____

_____

2. Explain why carbon is so important for building the molecular components of an organism: _____

_____

_____

Functions of atoms and ions in the body

Certain elements and inorganic ions are important for the structure and metabolism of all living organisms. An ion is simply an atom (or group of atoms) that has gained or lost one or more electrons. Many of these ions are soluble in water. Some of these elements and inorganic ions required by organisms and their biological roles are listed in the table below.

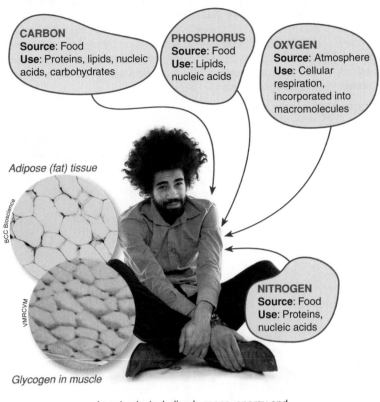

CARBON
Source: Food
Use: Proteins, lipids, nucleic acids, carbohydrates

PHOSPHORUS
Source: Food
Use: Lipids, nucleic acids

OXYGEN
Source: Atmosphere
Use: Cellular respiration, incorporated into macromolecules

Adipose (fat) tissue

Glycogen in muscle

NITROGEN
Source: Food
Use: Proteins, nucleic acids

In animals, including humans, energy and carbon are stored as fat and glycogen.

Ion or element	Name	Example of biological roles
Ca^{2+}	Calcium	Component of bones and teeth, required for muscle contraction.
NO_3^-	Nitrate	Component of amino acids.
Fe^{2+}	Iron (II)	Component of hemoglobin and cytochromes.
S	Sulfur	Component of the thiol (-SH) functional group and part of many organic molecules, e.g. coenzyme A and some amino acids.
P	As phosphate	Component of phospholipids and nucleotides, including ATP.
Na^+	Sodium	Component of extracellular fluid and needed for nerve function.
K^+	Potassium	Important intracellular ion, needed for heart and nerve function.
Cl^-	Chloride	Component of extracellular fluid in multicellular organisms.

3. Identify the biological role of each of the following elements or ions in the body:

   (a) Calcium: _____

   _____

   (b) Nitrate: _____

   _____

   (c) Sulfur: _____

   _____

   (d) Iron: _____

   _____

   (e) Sodium: _____

   _____

4. Summarize the role of each of the following cell components:

   (a) Carbohydrates: _____

   (b) Lipids: _____

   (c) Proteins: _____

   (d) Nucleic acids: _____

   (e) Inorganic ions: _____

   (f) Water: _____

5. State the main source of carbon, phosphorus, and nitrogen for animals: _____

2 Basic Cell Structure

Key Idea: All animal cells have a similar basic structure, although they may vary in size, shape, and function. Cells can be specialized to carry out specific functions.

Features common to almost all eukaryotic **cells** include the nucleus (often near the cell's center), surrounded by a watery cytoplasm, which is itself enclosed by the **plasma membrane**. Animal cells do not have a regular shape, and some (such as phagocytes) are quite mobile. The diagram below shows

the ultrastructure of a liver cell (hepatocyte). It contains **organelles** common to most relatively unspecialized human cells. Hepatocytes make up 70-80% of the liver's mass. They are metabolically active, with a large central nucleus, many mitochondria, and large amounts of rough endoplasmic reticulum. Thin, cellular extensions called microvilli increase the surface area of the cell, increasing its capacity for absorbing nutrients.

The structure of a liver cell

Mitochondria (sing. mitochondrion): 1.5 µm X 2–8 µm. Ovoid organelles bounded by a double membrane. They are the cell's energy transformers, and convert chemical energy into ATP.

Transverse section through a mitochondrion

Peroxisomes: Self-replicating organelles containing oxidative enzymes, which function to rid the body of toxic substances. They are distinguished from lysosomes by the crystalline core.

Each cell has small projections, called microvilli, which increase the surface area for absorption.

Lysosome: A sac bounded by a single membrane. Lysosomes are pinched off from the Golgi and contain and transport enzymes that break down foreign material. Lysosomes show little internal structure but often contain fragments of degraded material.

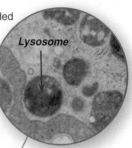
Lysosome

Tight junction: impermeable junction binding neighboring cells together (common in epithelial cells).

Plasma membrane: 3-10 nm thick phospholipid bilayer with associated proteins and lipids.

Nuclear pore: A hole in the nuclear membrane. It allows communication between the nucleus and the rest of the cell.

Rough endoplasmic reticulum showing ribosomes (dark spots)

Rough ER: Endoplasmic reticulum with ribosomes attached to its surface. It is where the proteins destined for transport outside of the cell are synthesized.

Ribosomes: These small (20 nm) structures manufacture proteins. Ribosomes are made of ribosomal RNA and protein. They may be free in the cytoplasm or associated with the surface of the endoplasmic reticulum.

Cytoplasm: A watery solution containing dissolved substances, enzymes, and the cell organelles and structures. The cytoplasm of liver cells contains stored carbohydrate as glycogen.

Golgi apparatus (above): A series of flattened, disk-shaped sacs, stacked one on top of the other and connected with the ER. The Golgi stores, modifies, and packages proteins. It 'tags' proteins so that they go to their correct destination.

Nucleus (above): 5 µm diameter. A large organelle containing most of the cell's DNA. Within the nucleus, the nucleolus (n) is a dense structure of crystalline protein and nucleic acids involved in ribosome synthesis.

Centrioles: Microtubular structures associated with nuclear division. Under a light microscope, they appear as small, featureless particles, 0.25 µm diameter.

Endoplasmic reticulum (ER): Comprises a network of tubules and flattened sacs. ER is continuous with the nuclear membrane. Smooth ER, as shown here, is a site for lipid and carbohydrate metabolism, including hormone synthesis.

©2023 **BIOZONE** International
ISBN: 978-1-99-101408-5
Photocopying Prohibited

Specializations of animal cells

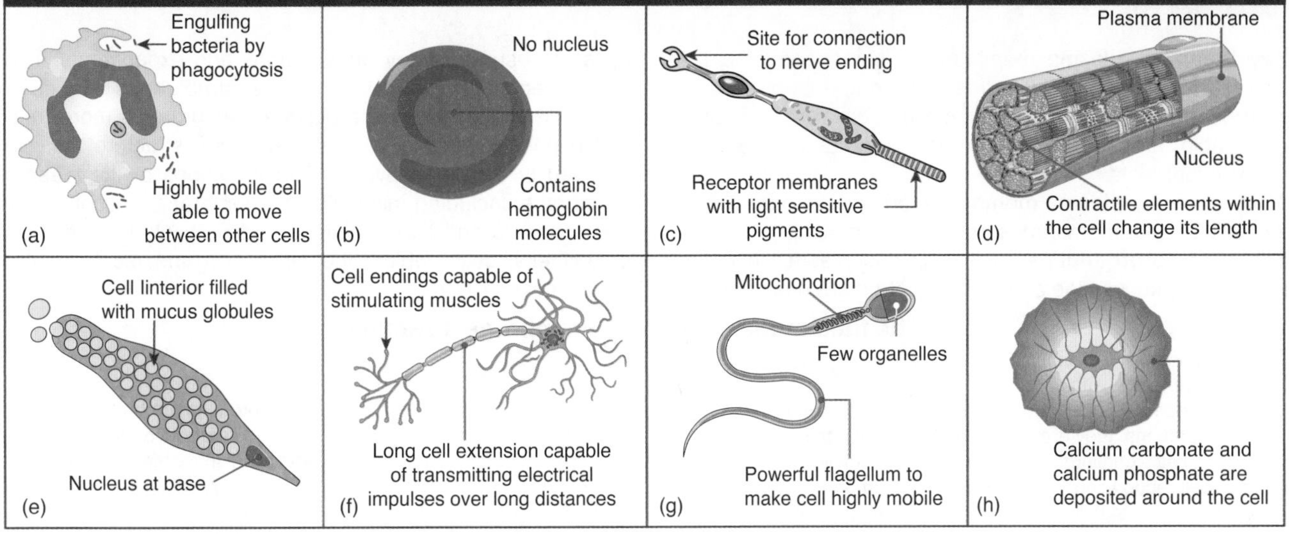

(a) Engulfing bacteria by phagocytosis. Highly mobile cell able to move between other cells	(b) No nucleus. Contains hemoglobin molecules	(c) Site for connection to nerve ending. Receptor membranes with light sensitive pigments	(d) Plasma membrane. Nucleus. Contractile elements within the cell change its length
(e) Cell linterior filled with mucus globules. Nucleus at base	(f) Cell endings capable of stimulating muscles. Long cell extension capable of transmitting electrical impulses over long distances	(g) Mitochondrion. Few organelles. Powerful flagellum to make cell highly mobile	(h) Calcium carbonate and calcium phosphate are deposited around the cell

1. Explain what you understand by the term generalized cell: _____

_____

_____

2. Each of the cells (a) to (h) above exhibits specialized features specific to its functional role in the body. For each, describe one specialized feature of the cell and its purpose:

(a) Phagocytic white blood cell: _____

_____

(b) Red blood cell (erythrocyte): _____

_____

(c) Rod cell of the retina: _____

_____

(d) Skeletal muscle fiber (part of): _____

_____

(e) Intestinal goblet cell: _____

_____

(f) Motor neuron: _____

_____

(g) Spermatozoon: _____

_____

(h) Osteocyte: _____

_____

3. Discuss how the shape and size of a specialized cell, as well as the number and types of organelles it has, is related to its functional role. Use examples to illustrate your answer:

_____

_____

_____

_____

3 The Structure of Membranes

Key Idea: The plasma membrane is composed of a lipid bilayer with proteins moving freely within it. It is the partially permeable (also called semi-permeable or selectively permeable) boundary between the internal and external cell environments.

All **cells** have a **plasma membrane** forming the outer limit of the cell. Cellular membranes are also found inside eukaryotic cells as part of **organelles**, such as the endoplasmic reticulum. Present day knowledge of membrane structure has been built

up as a result of many observations and experiments. The now-accepted model of membrane structure is the fluid-mosaic model (below). The plasma membrane is more than just a passive envelope; it is a dynamic structure actively involved in cellular activities. Specializations of the plasma membrane, including microvilli and membrane junctions, e.g. desmosomes and tight junctions, are particularly numerous in epithelial cells, which line hollow **organs,** such as the small intestine.

The fluid mosaic model of membrane structure

Glycolipids in membranes are **phospholipids** with attached carbohydrate. Like glycoproteins, they are involved in cell signaling and cell-cell recognition. They also help to stabilize membrane structure.

Cholesterol is a packing molecule and interacts with the phospholipids to regulate membrane consistency, keeping it firm but fluid.

Water molecules pass between the phospholipid molecules by **osmosis**.

Glycoproteins are proteins with attached carbohydrate. They are important in membrane stability, in cell-cell recognition, and in cell signaling, acting as receptors for hormones and neurotransmitters.

Attached carbohydrate

CO_2

Phospholipids naturally form a bilayer.

Some integral proteins do not span the lipid bilayer.

Channel proteins form a pore through the hydrophobic interior of the membrane to enable water soluble molecules to pass by facilitated diffusion.

Fatty acid tail is hydrophobic

Phosphate head is hydrophilic

Carrier proteins permit the passage of specific molecules by facilitated diffusion or **active transport**.

α-helical transmembrane glycoprotein

Lipid soluble molecules, e.g. gases and steroids, can move through the membrane by **diffusion**, down their concentration gradient.

Intracellular environment

Based on a diagram in Biol. Sci. Review, Nov. 2009, pp. 20-21

1. (a) Explain how phospholipids organize themselves into a bilayer in an aqueous environment:

_____

_____

_____

_____

_____

(b) Explain how the fluid mosaic model accounts for the observed properties of cellular membranes:

_____

_____

_____

_____

Membrane specializations

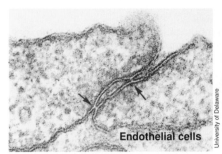

Endothelial cells

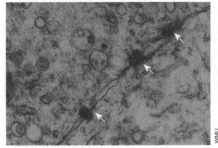

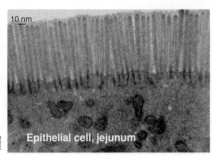

Epithelial cell, jejunum

Tight junctions bind the membranes of neighboring cells together to form a virtually impermeable barrier to fluid. Tight junctions prevent molecules passing through the spaces between cells.

Desmosomes (arrowed) are anchoring junctions that allow cell-to-cell adhesion. Desmosomes help to resist shearing forces in **tissues** subjected to mechanical stress (such as skin cells).

Microvilli are microscopic protrusions of the plasma membrane that increase the surface area of cells. Microvilli are involved in a wide variety of functions, including absorption, e.g. in the intestine.

2. Explain how the membrane surface area is increased within cells and organelles: _____
_____

3. Discuss the importance of each of the following to cellular function:

   (a) High membrane surface area: _____
   _____

   (b) Channel proteins and carrier proteins in the plasma membrane: _____
   _____

4. (a) Name a cellular organelle that possesses a membrane: _____

   (b) Describe the membrane's purpose in this organelle: _____
   _____

5. Describe the purpose of cholesterol in the plasma membrane: _____
_____

6. Describe the role of each of the following membrane junctions and give an example of where they commonly occur. The first example is completed for you:

   (a) Gap junctions: _Communicating junctions linking the cytoplasm of neighboring cells. They allow rapid passage_
   of signals between cells, e.g. electrical messages in cardiac muscle cells.

   (b) Tight junctions: _____
   _____

   (c) Desmosomes: _____
   _____

7. Explain why tight junctions are especially abundant in epithelial cells, e.g. in the skin and intestine: _____
_____

8. On the diagram below, label the hydrophobic and hydrophilic ends of the phospholipid and indicate which end is attracted to water:

   (a) _____   (b) _____

4 The Role of Membranes in Cells

Key Idea: Many of the important structures and organelles in cells are composed of, or are enclosed by, membranes. These include the endoplasmic reticulum, mitochondria, nucleus, Golgi apparatus, and the plasma membrane itself. All membranes within eukaryotic **cells** share the same basic structure as the **plasma membrane** around the cell.

They perform a number of critical functions in the cell: compartmentalizing regions of different function within the cell, controlling the entry and exit of substances, and fulfilling a role in recognition and communication between cells. Some of these roles are described below and electron micrographs of the **organelles** involved are on the following page.

What membranes do in a cell

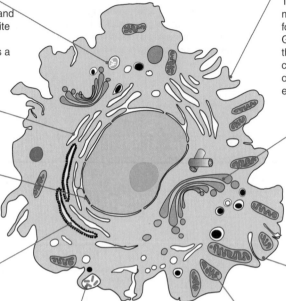

Isolation of enzymes
Membrane-bound lysosomes contain enzymes for the destruction of wastes and foreign material. Peroxisomes are the site for destruction of the toxic and reactive molecule hydrogen peroxide, formed as a result of some cellular reactions.

Role in lipid synthesis
The smooth ER is the site of lipid and steroid synthesis.

Containment of DNA
The nucleus is surrounded by a nuclear envelope of two membranes, forming a separate compartment for the cell's genetic material.

Role in protein and membrane synthesis
Some protein synthesis occurs on free ribosomes, but much occurs on membrane-bound ribosomes on the rough endoplasmic reticulum. Here, the protein is synthesized directly into the space within the ER membranes. The rough ER is also involved in membrane synthesis, growing in place by adding proteins and **phospholipids**.

Entry and export of substances
The plasma membrane may take up fluid or solid material and form membrane-bound vesicles (or larger vacuoles) within the cell. Membrane-bound transport vesicles move substances to the inner surface of the cell where they can be exported from the cell by exocytosis.

Cell communication and recognition
The proteins embedded in the membrane act as receptor molecules for hormones and neurotransmitters. Glycoproteins and glycolipids stabilize the plasma membrane and act as cell identity markers, helping cells to organize themselves into **tissues**, and enabling foreign cells to be recognized.

Packaging and secretion
The Golgi apparatus is a specialized, membrane-bound organelle which produces lysosomes and compartmentalizes the modification, packaging, and secretion of substances, such as proteins and hormones.

Transport processes
Channel and carrier proteins are involved in selective transport across the plasma membrane. The level of cholesterol in the membrane influences permeability and transport functions.

Energy transfer
The reactions of cellular respiration (and photosynthesis in plants) take place in the membrane-bound energy transfer systems occurring in mitochondria and chloroplasts respectively. See the example explained below.

Compartmentation within membranes

Cisternae (membrane-bound sacs)

Vesicles transporting material to the Golgi

Vesicles leaving the Golgi

Membranes play an important role in separating regions within the cell (and within organelles) where particular reactions occur. Specific enzymes are, therefore, often located in particular organelles. The reaction rate is controlled by the rate at which substrates enter the organelle and therefore the availability of the raw materials required for the reactions.

The Golgi *(diagram left and TEM right) modifies, sorts, and packages macromolecules for cell secretion. Enzymes within the cisternae modify proteins by adding carbohydrates and phosphates. To do this, the Golgi imports the substances it needs from the cytosol.*

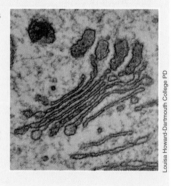

Louisa Howard-Dartmouth College PD

1. Discuss the importance of membrane systems and organelles in providing compartments within the cell:

_____

_____

_____

_____

_____

©2023 **BIOZONE** International
ISBN: 978-1-99-101408-5
Photocopying Prohibited

Functional roles of membranes in cells

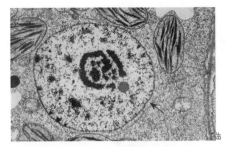
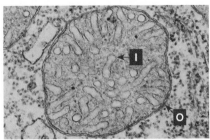
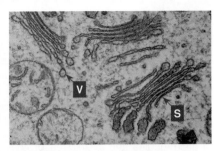

The nuclear membrane, which surrounds the nucleus, regulates the passage of genetic information to the cytoplasm and may also protect the DNA from damage.

Mitochondria have an outer membrane (**O**) which controls the entry and exit of materials involved in aerobic respiration. Inner membranes (**I**) provide attachment sites for enzyme activity.

The Golgi apparatus comprises stacks of membrane-bound sacs (**S**). It is involved in packaging materials for transport or export from the cell as secretory vesicles (**V**).

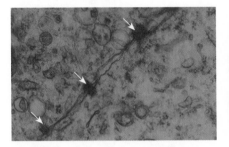
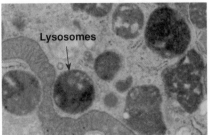
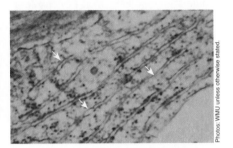

The plasma membrane surrounds the cell. In this photo, intercellular junctions called desmosomes, which connect neighboring cells, are indicated with arrows.

Lysosomes are membrane-bound organelles containing enzymes capable of digesting worn-out cellular structures and foreign material. They are abundant in phagocytes.

This EM shows stacks of rough endoplasmic reticulum (arrows). The membranes are studded with ribosomes, which synthesize proteins into the intermembrane space.

2. Match each of the following organelles with the correct description of its functional role in the cell:

   peroxisome, rough endoplasmic reticulum, lysosome, smooth endoplasmic reticulum, mitochondrion, Golgi apparatus

   (a) Active in synthesis, sorting, and secretion of cell products: _____

   (b) Digestive organelle where macromolecules are hydrolyzed: _____

   (c) Organelle where most cellular respiration occurs and most ATP is generated: _____

   (d) Active in membrane synthesis and synthesis of secretory proteins: _____

   (e) Active in lipid and hormone synthesis and secretion: _____

   (f) Small organelle responsible for the destruction of toxic substances: _____

3. (a) Explain why non-polar (lipid-soluble) molecules diffuse more rapidly through membranes than polar molecules:

   _____
   _____
   _____

   (b) Explain the implications of this to the transport of substances into the cell through the plasma membrane:

   _____
   _____
   _____

4. Identify three substances that need to be transported into all kinds of human cells, in order for them to survive:

   _____

5. Identify two substances that need to be transported out of all kinds of human cells, in order for them to survive:

   (a) _____ (b) _____

5 The Cell's Cytoskeleton

Key Idea: The cytoskeleton provides structural support for the cell. The **cell's** cytoplasm is not a fluid-filled space. It contains a complex network of fibers called the cytoskeleton. The cytoskeleton provides tension and so provides structural support to maintain the cell's shape. The cytoskeleton is made up of three proteinaceous elements: microfilaments, intermediate filaments, and microtubules. Each has a distinct size, structure, and protein composition, and a specific role in cytoskeletal function. Cilia and flagella are made up of microtubules and for this reason they are considered to be part of the cytoskeleton. The elements of the cytoskeleton are dynamic, and move and change to alter the cell's shape, move materials within the cell, and move the cell itself. Movement of materials is achieved through the action of motor proteins, which transport material by 'walking' along cytoskeletal 'tracks', hydrolyzing ATP at each step.

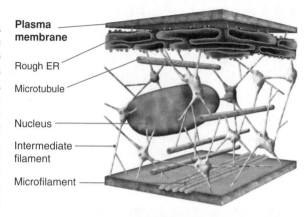

- Plasma membrane
- Rough ER
- Microtubule
- Nucleus
- Intermediate filament
- Microfilament

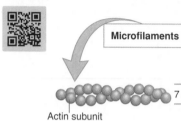

Microfilaments

7 nm

Actin subunit

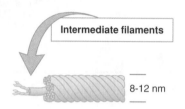

Intermediate filaments

8-12 nm

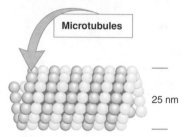

Microtubules

25 nm

β α Tubulin dimer

	Microfilaments	Intermediate filaments	Microtubules
Protein subunits	Actin	Fibrous proteins, e.g. keratin	α and β tubulin dimers
Structure	Two intertwined strands	Fibers wound into thicker cables	Hollow tubes
Functions	• Maintain cell shape • Motility (pseudopodia) • Contraction (muscle) • Cytokinesis of cell division	• Maintain cell shape • Anchor nucleus and **organelles**	• Maintain cell shape • Motility (cilia and flagella) • Move chromosomes (spindle) • Move organelles

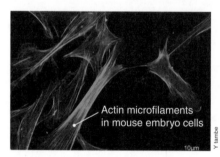

Actin microfilaments in mouse embryo cells

10μm

Y tambe

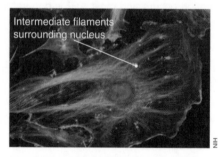

Intermediate filaments surrounding nucleus

NIH

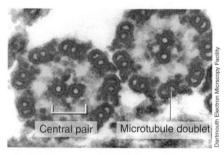

Central pair Microtubule doublet

Dartmouth Electron Microscopy Facility

Microfilaments are long polymers of the protein actin. Microfilaments can grow and shrink as actin subunits are added or taken away from either end. Networks of microfilaments form a matrix that helps to define the cell's shape. Actin microfilaments are also involved in cell division (during cytokinesis) and in muscle contraction.

Intermediate filaments can be composed of a number of different fibrous proteins and are defined by their size rather than composition. The protein subunits are wound into cables around 10 nm in diameter. Intermediate filaments form a dense network within and projecting from the nucleus, helping to anchor it in place.

Microtubules are the largest cytoskeletal components and grow or shrink in length as tubulin subunits are added or subtracted from one end. The are involved in movement of material within the cell and in moving the cell itself. This EM shows a cilia *Chlamydomonas*, with the 9+2 arrangement of microtubular doublets.

1. Describe the role that all components of the cytoskeleton have in common: _____

2. Explain the importance of the cytoskeleton being a dynamic structure: _____

_____

3. Explain how the presence of a cytoskeleton could aid in directing the movement of materials within the cell:

_____

_____

©2023 **BIOZONE** International
ISBN: 978-1-99-101408-5
Photocopying Prohibited

6 Cell Structures and Organelles

Key Idea: Organelles can be identified from their specific features.

This activity requires you to summarize information about the components of a typical eukaryotic **cell**. Complete the table using the list provided and by referring to other pages in this chapter. The first **organelle** has been completed for you as a guide and the log scale of measurements (next page) illustrates the relative sizes of some cells and cell structures. List of components: *nucleus, ribosome, centrioles, mitochondrion, lysosome (given), endoplasmic reticulum, Golgi apparatus, plasma membrane (given), cell cytoskeleton, flagella or cilia (given), cellular junctions (given).*

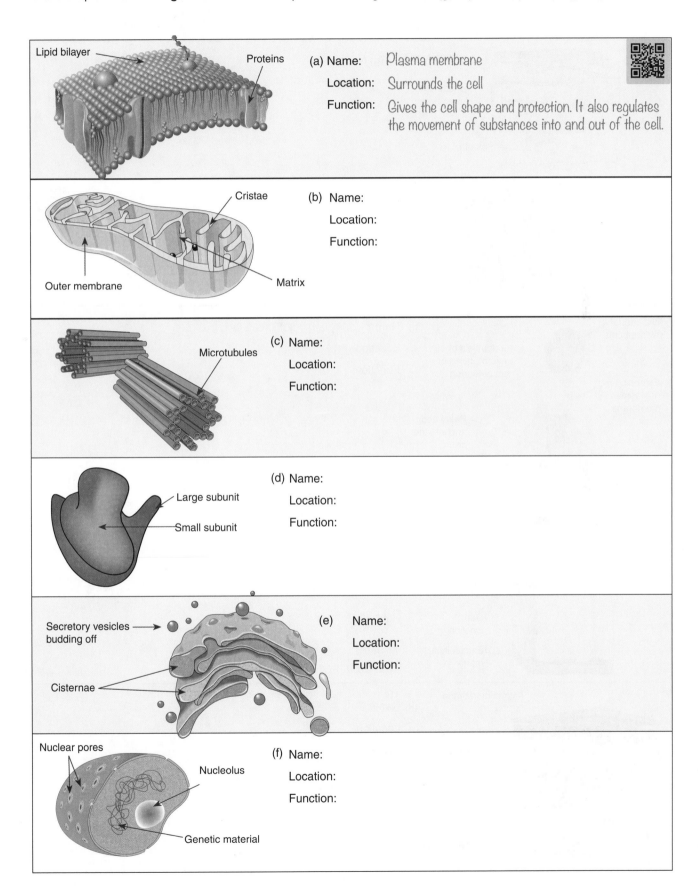

Lipid bilayer · Proteins

(a) Name: Plasma membrane
Location: Surrounds the cell
Function: Gives the cell shape and protection. It also regulates the movement of substances into and out of the cell.

Cristae · Outer membrane · Matrix

(b) Name:
Location:
Function:

Microtubules

(c) Name:
Location:
Function:

Large subunit · Small subunit

(d) Name:
Location:
Function:

Secretory vesicles budding off · Cisternae

(e) Name:
Location:
Function:

Nuclear pores · Nucleolus · Genetic material

(f) Name:
Location:
Function:

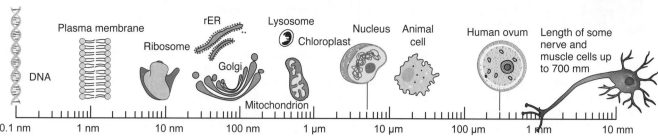

DNA — Plasma membrane — Ribosome — rER — Golgi — Lysosome — Chloroplast — Mitochondrion — Nucleus — Animal cell — Human ovum — Length of some nerve and muscle cells up to 700 mm

0.1 nm   1 nm   10 nm   100 nm   1 µm   10 µm   100 µm   1 mm   10 mm

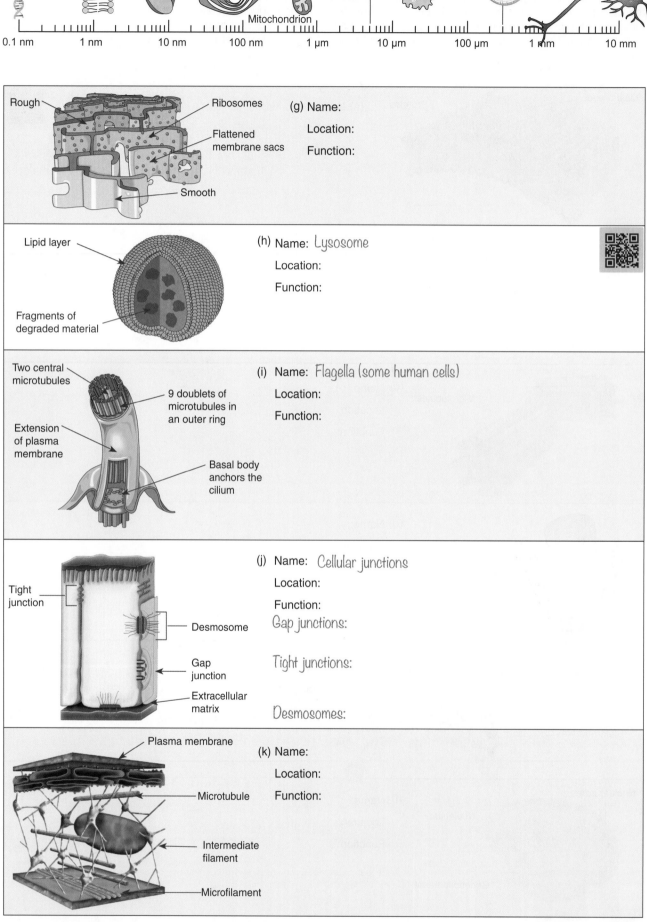

(g) Name:

Location:

Function:

(Rough, Ribosomes, Flattened membrane sacs, Smooth)

(h) Name: Lysosome

Location:

Function:

(Lipid layer, Fragments of degraded material)

(i) Name: Flagella (some human cells)

Location:

Function:

(Two central microtubules, 9 doublets of microtubules in an outer ring, Extension of plasma membrane, Basal body anchors the cilium)

(j) Name: Cellular junctions

Location:

Function:
Gap junctions:

Tight junctions:

Desmosomes:

(Tight junction, Desmosome, Gap junction, Extracellular matrix)

(k) Name:

Location:

Function:

(Plasma membrane, Microtubule, Intermediate filament, Microfilament)

7 Cell Processes

Key Idea: Having specific processes occurring in specific parts of the cell increases efficiency.

A **cell** can be compared to a factory with an assembly line. **Organelles** in the cell provide the equivalent of the power supply, assembly line, packaging department, repair and maintenance, transport system, and the control center. The sum total of all the processes occurring in a cell is known as metabolism. Some of these processes store energy in molecules (anabolism) while others release the stored energy (catabolism).

Containment of damaging oxidative reactions

peroxisomes
Isolate damaging oxidation reactions, such as beta oxidation. Peroxisomes are derived from the ER.

Protein synthesis

nucleus, rough endoplasmic reticulum, free ribosomes
Genetic information in the nucleus is translated into proteins by attached or free ribosomes.

Transport in and out of the cell

plasma membrane
Diffusion and **active transport** mechanisms move substances across the **plasma membrane**.

Cellular respiration

cytoplasm, mitochondria
Glucose is broken down, supplying the cell with energy to carry out the many other reactions involved in metabolism.

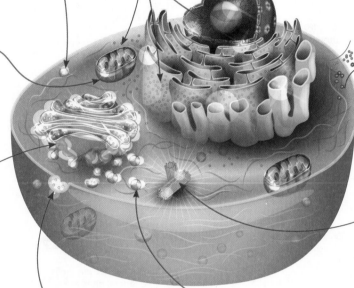

Cell division

nucleus, centrioles
Centrioles are microtubular structures involved in key stages of cell division. They are part of a larger organelle called the centrosome.

Secretion

Golgi apparatus, plasma membrane
The Golgi produces secretory vesicles (small membrane-bound sacs) that are used to modify and move substances around and export them from the cell, e.g. hormones, digestive enzymes.

Cytosis

plasma membrane, vacuoles
Material can be engulfed to bring it into the cell (endocytosis) or the plasma membrane can fuse with secretory vesicles to expel substances from the cell (exocytosis). In animal cells, cytosis may involve vacuoles.

Breakdown

lysosomes
Contain hydrolytic enzymes to destroy unwanted cell organelles and foreign material. Lysosomes are derived from the Golgi.

1. For each of the processes listed below, identify the organelles or structures associated with that process (there may be more than one associated with a process):

   (a) Secretion: _____

   (b) Respiration: _____

   (c) Endocytosis: _____

   (d) Exocytosis: _____

   (e) Protein synthesis: _____

   (f) Cell division: _____

   (g) Autolysis: _____

   (h) Transport in/out of cell: _____

2. (a) Explain what is meant by metabolism and describe an example of a metabolic process: _____

   _____

   _____

   (b) Identify the organelles in the diagram where catabolic processes occur: _____

   _____

   (c) Identify the organelles in the diagram where anabolic processes occur: _____

   _____

©2023 **BIOZONE** International
ISBN: 978-1-99-101408-5
Photocopying Prohibited

8 Cells Exchange Substances by Diffusion

Key Idea: Diffusion is the movement of molecules down a concentration gradient.

The molecules that make up substances are constantly moving about in a random way. This random motion causes them to disperse from areas of high to low concentration. This dispersal, called **diffusion,** requires no energy. Each type of molecule moves down its own concentration gradient. In biological systems, most diffusion occurs across **membranes**. Some molecules move freely (unassisted) across the membrane by simple diffusion. For other molecules, their diffusion is helped by proteins in the membrane. Diffusion is important in allowing cells to make exchanges with their extracellular environment, e.g. the blood and fluids that bathe them, and is crucial to the regulation of water content.

What is diffusion?

Diffusion is the movement of particles down a concentration gradient. Diffusion is a passive process, meaning it needs no input of energy to occur. During diffusion, molecules move randomly about, eventually becoming evenly dispersed.

If molecules can move freely, they move from high to low concentration (down a concentration gradient) until evenly dispersed. Each molecule moves down its own concentration gradient, independent of the concentration of other types of molecule (diagram, right).

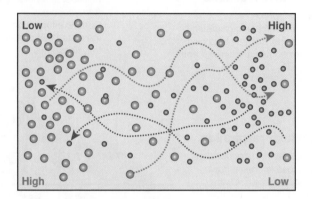

Diffusion through membranes

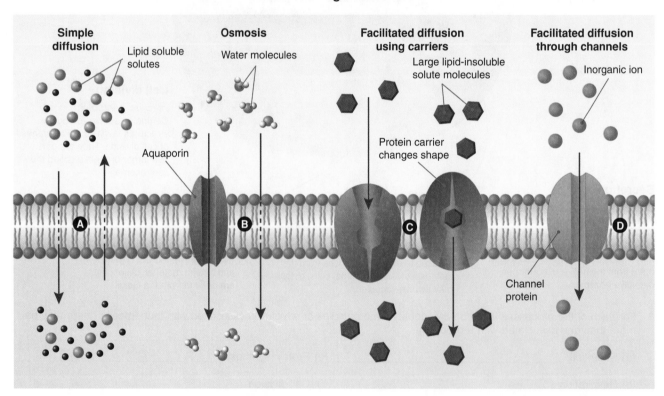

Simple diffusion — Lipid soluble solutes

Osmosis — Water molecules — Aquaporin

Facilitated diffusion using carriers — Large lipid-insoluble solute molecules — Protein carrier changes shape

Facilitated diffusion through channels — Inorganic ion — Channel protein

A: Some molecules, e.g. gases and lipid soluble molecules, diffuse directly across the **plasma membrane**. Two-way diffusion is common in biological systems, e.g. at the alveolar surface of the lung, CO_2 diffuses out and oxygen diffuses into the blood.

B: **Osmosis** describes the diffusion of water across a partially permeable membrane (in this case, the plasma membrane). Some water can diffuse directly through the lipid bilayer, but movement is also aided by specific protein channels called aquaporins.

C: In carrier-mediated facilitated diffusion, a lipid-insoluble molecule is aided across the membrane by a transmembrane carrier protein specific to the molecule being transported, e.g. glucose transport into red blood cells.

D: Small polar molecules and ions diffuse rapidly across the membrane by channel-mediated facilitated diffusion. Protein channels create hydrophilic pores that allow some solutes, usually inorganic ions, to pass through.

1. Describe how the following would affect the rate of diffusion (see opposite page):

   (a) Increasing the surface area: _____

   (b) Decreasing the temperature: _____

©2023 **BIOZONE** International
ISBN: 978-1-99-101408-5
Photocopying Prohibited

Factors affecting the rate of diffusion

Concentration gradient	The rate of diffusion is higher when there is a greater difference between the concentrations of two regions.	Temperature	Particles at a high temperature diffuse at a greater rate than at a low temperature.
The distance moved	Diffusion over shorter distance occurs at a greater rate than over a larger distance.	Solubility	Lipid-soluble or non-polar molecules pass across membranes more easily than polar materials, so their rates of diffusion are faster.
The surface area involved	The larger the area across which diffusion occurs, the greater the rate of diffusion.	Solvent density	As the density of a solvent increases, the rate of diffusion decreases. Cellular dehydration adversely affects diffusion rates within cells.
Barriers to diffusion	Thick barriers have a slower rate of diffusion than thin barriers.		

These factors are expressed in Fick's law, which governs the rate of diffusion of substances across membranes. It is described by:

Fick's law

$$\text{Rate of diffusion} \sim \frac{\text{Surface area of membrane} \times \text{Difference in concentration across the membrane}}{\text{Length of the diffusion path (thickness of the membrane)}}$$

2. Suggest how a cell could regulate the rate of facilitated diffusion of specific molecules: _____

_____

_____

_____

3. Why is a molecule like glucose able to continually diffuse into a cell? _____

_____

_____

_____

_____

4. Study the images below. Place them in order of first event to last event. Explain your order of events in terms of diffusion:

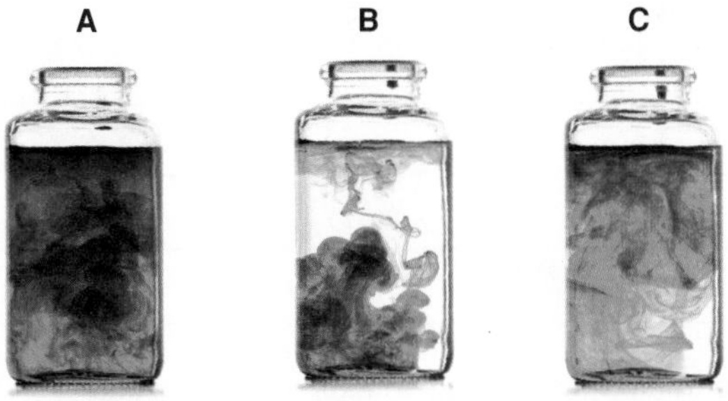

A   **B**   **C**

_____

_____

_____

_____

_____

_____

_____

5. Explain how concentration gradients across membranes are maintained: _____

_____

_____

6. Explain the role of aquaporins in the rapid movement of water through some cells: _____

_____

_____

Cellular tonicity and osmotic pressure

In physiology, it is important to understand the consequences of changes to the solute concentrations of cellular environments. The tendency of a solution to 'pull' water into it is called the osmotic pressure and it is directly related to the concentration of solutes in the solution. The higher the solute concentration, the greater the osmotic pressure and the greater the tendency of water to move into the solution. In biology, relative tonicity (**isotonic**, **hypotonic**, or **hypertonic**) is used to describe the difference in osmotic pressure between solutions. Only solutes that cannot cross the plasma membrane affect tonicity.

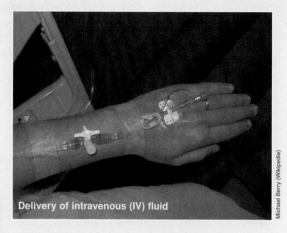

Delivery of intravenous (IV) fluid

Michael Berry (Wikipedia)

Tonicity of solution relative to the cytosol	Extracellular environment (solution)	Intracellular environment (cytosol)	Consequence to a cell in the solution
Isotonic	Equal osmotic environment		Normal shape and form
Hypotonic	Lower solute concentration	Higher solute concentration	Water enters cell, causing the cell to burst (cell lysis)
Hypertonic	Higher solute concentration	Lower solute concentration	Water leaves cell, causing shrinkage (crenation)

The relative tonicity of **cells** can be used to predict the consequences of changes in solute concentration either side of a partially permeable membrane, e.g. the plasma membrane around each body cell. Such predictions have practical importance. For example, when delivering intravenous fluid to patients (intravenous means within vein), the intravenous (IV) fluids must have the same osmotic environment as the blood cells they will be surrounding when delivered, i.e. 0.9% saline solution. This prevents life-threatening changes to cell volumes.

7. Describe how facilitated diffusion is achieved for:

(a) Small polar molecules and ions: _____

_____

_____

(b) Glucose: _____

_____

_____

8. Fluid replacements are usually provided for heavily perspiring athletes after endurance events.

(a) Identify the preferable tonicity of these replacement drinks (isotonic, hypertonic, or hypotonic): _____

(b) Give a reason for your answer: _____

_____

_____

_____

9. Describe what would happen to a patient's red blood cells if they were treated with an intravenous drip containing:

(a) Pure water: _____

_____

(b) A hypertonic solution: _____

_____

(c) A hypotonic solution: _____

_____

9 Active Transport

Key Idea: Active transport uses energy to transport molecules against their concentration gradient across a partially permeable membrane.

Active transport is the movement of molecules (or ions) by a transport protein from regions of low concentration to regions of high concentration across a cellular **membrane**. Active transport needs energy to proceed because molecules are being moved against their concentration gradient.

▸ The energy for active transport comes from ATP (adenosine triphosphate). Energy is released when ATP is hydrolyzed (water is added) forming ADP (adenosine diphosphate) and inorganic phosphate (Pi).

▸ Transport (carrier) proteins in the membrane are used to actively transport molecules from one side of the membrane to the other (diagram below).

▸ Active transport can be used to move molecules into and out of a **cell**.

▸ Active transport can be either primary or secondary. Primary active transport directly uses ATP for the energy to transport molecules. In secondary active transport, energy is stored in a concentration gradient. The transport of one molecule is coupled to the movement of another down its concentration gradient; ATP is not directly involved in the transport process.

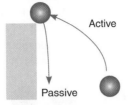
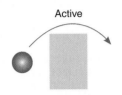

A ball falling is a passive process (it requires no energy input). Replacing the ball requires active energy input.

It requires energy to actively move an object across a physical barrier.

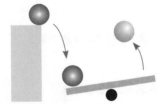

Sometimes the energy of a passively moving object can be used to actively move another. For example, a falling ball can be used to catapult another (left).

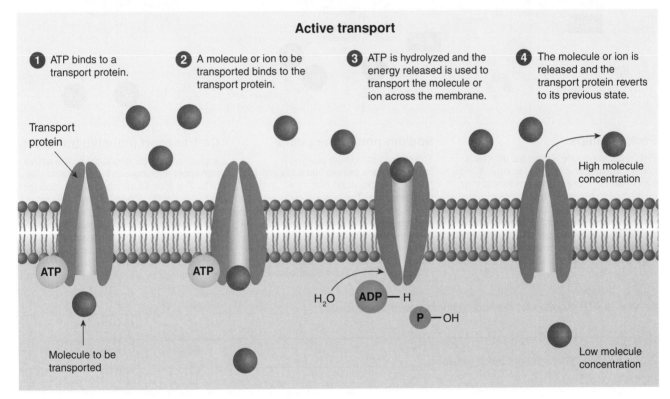

Active transport

1 ATP binds to a transport protein.

2 A molecule or ion to be transported binds to the transport protein.

3 ATP is hydrolyzed and the energy released is used to transport the molecule or ion across the membrane.

4 The molecule or ion is released and the transport protein reverts to its previous state.

Transport protein

High molecule concentration

ATP

ATP

H_2O ADP — H

P — OH

Molecule to be transported

Low molecule concentration

1. (a) What is the essential feature of active transport? _____

   (b) How is active transport used in the cell? _____
   _____

2. Where does the energy for active transport come from? _____

3. Explain the difference between primary active transport and secondary active transport: _____
   _____
   _____
   _____
   _____

©2023 **BIOZONE** International
ISBN: 978-1-99-101408-5
Photocopying Prohibited

10 Ion Pumps

Key Idea: Ion pumps are transmembrane proteins that use energy to move ions and molecules across a membrane against their concentration gradient.

Sometimes molecules or ions are needed in concentrations that **diffusion** alone cannot supply to the **cell**, or they cannot diffuse through the **plasma membrane**. In this case, **ion** **pumps** move ions (and some molecules) across the plasma membrane. The sodium-potassium pump (below) is found in almost all animal cells and is common in plant cells also. The concentration gradient created by ion pumps is often coupled to the transport of other molecules, such as glucose, across the membrane.

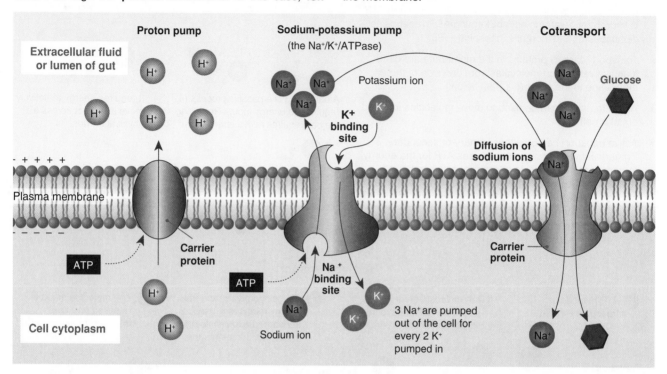

Proton pumps

Proton pumps create a potential difference across a membrane by using energy (ATP or electrons) to move H^+ from one side of the membrane to the other. This difference can be coupled to the transport of other molecules. In cell respiration, the energy for moving the H^+ comes from electrons, and the flow of H^+ back across the membrane drives ATP synthesis via the membrane-bound enzyme ATP synthase.

Sodium-potassium pump

The sodium-potassium pump is a transmembrane protein that uses energy from ATP to exchange Na^+ for K^+ across the membrane. The unequal balance of Na^+ and K^+ across the membrane creates large electrochemical gradients that can be used to drive transport of other substances, e.g. co-transport of glucose. The Na^+/K^+ pump also helps to maintain ion balance and so helps regulate the cell's water balance.

Co-transport (coupled transport)

A gradient in sodium ions drives the **active transport** of glucose in intestinal epithelial cells. The specific transport protein couples the return of Na^+ down its electrochemical gradient to the transport of glucose into the intestinal epithelial cell. Glucose diffuses from the epithelial cells and is transported away in the blood. A low intracellular concentration of Na^+ (and therefore the concentration gradient) is maintained by a sodium-potassium pump.

1. Why is ATP required for membrane pump systems to operate? _____

_____

2. (a) Explain what is meant by co-transport: _____

_____

   (b) How is co-transport used to move glucose into the intestinal epithelial cells? _____

_____

_____

   (c) What happens to the glucose that is transported into the intestinal epithelial cells? _____

_____

_____

3. Describe two consequences of the extracellular accumulation of sodium ions: _____

_____

_____

©2023 **BIOZONE** International
ISBN: 978-1-99-101408-5
Photocopying Prohibited

11 Cytosis

Key Idea: The folding of the plasma membrane enables the cell to import or export material.
Cytosis is an active process involving the **plasma membrane**.

In exocytosis, vesicles merge with the plasma membrane to export material from the **cell**. Endocytosis is a general term for engulfing of material by infolding of the plasma membrane.

Exocytosis

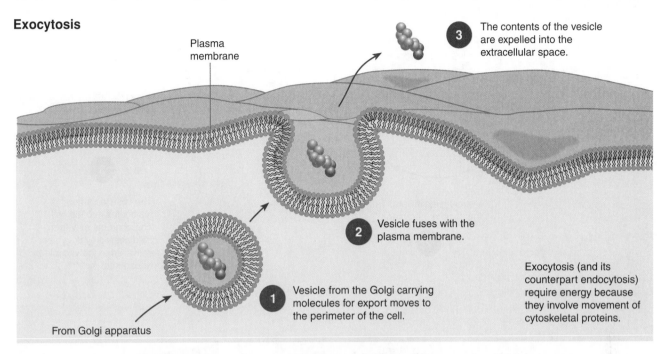

Plasma membrane

3 The contents of the vesicle are expelled into the extracellular space.

2 Vesicle fuses with the plasma membrane.

1 Vesicle from the Golgi carrying molecules for export moves to the perimeter of the cell.

From Golgi apparatus

Exocytosis (and its counterpart endocytosis) require energy because they involve movement of cytoskeletal proteins.

Exocytosis (above) is an **active transport** process in which a secretory vesicle fuses with the plasma **membrane** and expels its contents into the extracellular space. In multicellular organisms, various types of cells, e.g. endocrine cells and nerve cells, are specialized to manufacture products, such as proteins, and then export them from the cell to elsewhere in the body or outside it.

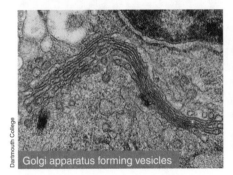

Golgi apparatus forming vesicles

Dartmouth College

The transport of Golgi vesicles to the edge of the cell and their expulsion from the cell occurs through the activity of the cytoskeleton. This requires energy (ATP).

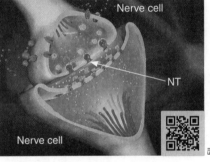

Nerve cell

NT

Nerve cell

Exocytosis is important in the transport of neurotransmitters (NT) into the junction (synapse) between nerve cells to transmit nervous signals, as shown in this illustration.

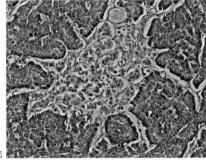

Alpha cells in the pancreas secrete the hormone glucagon via exocytosis. Secretion is stimulated by hypoglycemia (low blood sugar levels)

1. (a) What is the purpose of exocytosis? _____

   _____

   (b) How does it occur? _____

   _____

   _____

2. Describe two examples of the role of exocytosis in cells:

   (a) _____

   _____

   (b) _____

   _____

©2023 **BIOZONE** International
ISBN: 978-1-99-101408-5
Photocopying Prohibited

Endocytosis

Endocytosis is a type of active transport in which the plasma membrane folds around a substance to transport it across the plasma membrane into the cell. The ability of cells to do this is a function of the fluid nature of the plasma membrane.

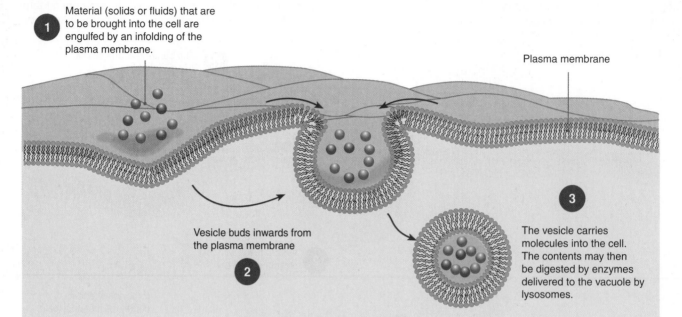

1 Material (solids or fluids) that are to be brought into the cell are engulfed by an infolding of the plasma membrane.

Plasma membrane

Vesicle buds inwards from the plasma membrane

2

3 The vesicle carries molecules into the cell. The contents may then be digested by enzymes delivered to the vacuole by lysosomes.

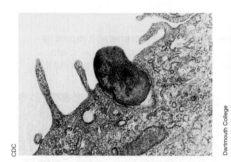

Phagocytosis (or 'cell-eating') involves the cell engulfing solid material to form large phagosomes or vacuoles, e.g. food vacuoles. It may be non-specific or receptor-mediated. Examples: phagocytosis of foreign material and cell debris by neutrophils and macrophages.

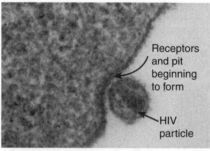

Receptors and pit beginning to form

HIV particle

Receptor mediated endocytosis is triggered when certain metabolites, hormones, or viral particles bind to specific receptor proteins on the membrane so that the material can be engulfed. Examples: the uptake of lipoproteins by mammalian cells and endocytosis of viruses.

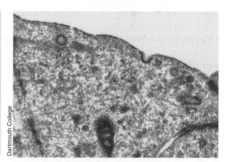

Pinocytosis (or 'cell-drinking') involves the non-specific uptake of liquids or fine suspensions into the cell to form small pinocytic vesicles. Pinocytosis is used primarily for absorbing extracellular fluid. Example: uptake in some cells of the liver.

3. What is the purpose of endocytosis? _____

_____

4. Is endocytosis active or passive transport? _____

5. Describe the following types of endocytosis:

(a) Phagocytosis: _____

_____

(b) Receptor mediated endocytosis: _____

_____

(c) Pinocytosis: _____

_____

6. Explain how the plasma membrane can form a vesicle: _____

_____

©2023 **BIOZONE** International
ISBN: 978-1-99-101408-5
Photocopying Prohibited

12 Mitosis and Cytokinesis

Key Idea: Several stages can be identified in mitosis, in which the nuclear material is replicated and divided into new cells. **Mitosis** refers to the division of the nuclear material and it is followed immediately by division of the cell. Although mitosis is part of a continuous **cell cycle**, it is divided into stages to help distinguish the processes occurring during its progression. Mitosis is one of the shortest stages of the cell cycle. Cytokinesis (the division of the newly formed cells) is part of M-phase but it is distinct from nuclear division. During cytokinesis, the **cell** divides into two.

The cell cycle and stages of mitosis in an animal cell

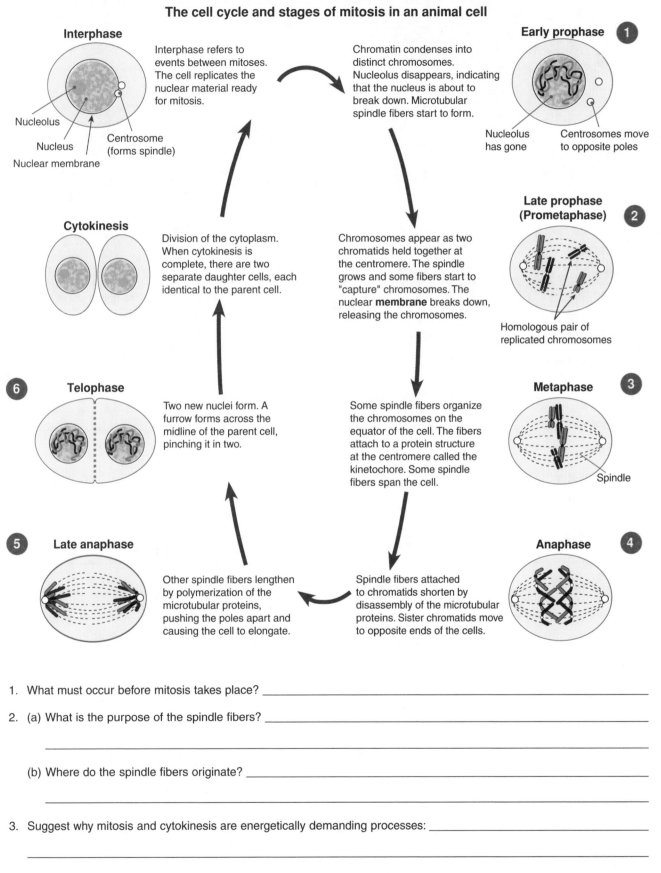

Interphase

Interphase refers to events between mitoses. The cell replicates the nuclear material ready for mitosis.

Nucleolus
Nucleus
Nuclear membrane
Centrosome (forms spindle)

Chromatin condenses into distinct chromosomes. Nucleolus disappears, indicating that the nucleus is about to break down. Microtubular spindle fibers start to form.

Early prophase 1

Nucleolus has gone
Centrosomes move to opposite poles

Cytokinesis

Division of the cytoplasm. When cytokinesis is complete, there are two separate daughter cells, each identical to the parent cell.

Chromosomes appear as two chromatids held together at the centromere. The spindle grows and some fibers start to "capture" chromosomes. The nuclear **membrane** breaks down, releasing the chromosomes.

Late prophase (Prometaphase) 2

Homologous pair of replicated chromosomes

6 **Telophase**

Two new nuclei form. A furrow forms across the midline of the parent cell, pinching it in two.

Some spindle fibers organize the chromosomes on the equator of the cell. The fibers attach to a protein structure at the centromere called the kinetochore. Some spindle fibers span the cell.

Metaphase 3

Spindle

5 **Late anaphase**

Other spindle fibers lengthen by polymerization of the microtubular proteins, pushing the poles apart and causing the cell to elongate.

Spindle fibers attached to chromatids shorten by disassembly of the microtubular proteins. Sister chromatids move to opposite ends of the cells.

Anaphase 4

1. What must occur before mitosis takes place? _____

2. (a) What is the purpose of the spindle fibers? _____

    _____

    (b) Where do the spindle fibers originate? _____

    _____

3. Suggest why mitosis and cytokinesis are energetically demanding processes: _____

    _____

    _____

©2023 **BIOZONE** International
ISBN: 978-1-99-101408-5
Photocopying Prohibited

Cytokinesis (division of the cytoplasm)

Cytokinesis (below left) begins shortly after the sister chromatids have separated in anaphase of mitosis. A ring of microtubules assembles in the middle of the cell, next to the **plasma membrane**, constricting it to form a cleavage furrow. In an energy-using process, the cleavage furrow moves inwards, forming a region where the two cells will separate.

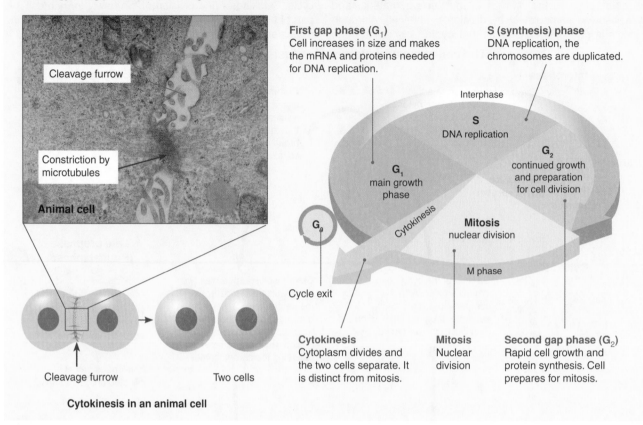

First gap phase (G_1)
Cell increases in size and makes the mRNA and proteins needed for DNA replication.

S (synthesis) phase
DNA replication, the chromosomes are duplicated.

Cleavage furrow

Constriction by microtubules

Animal cell

Interphase

S
DNA replication

G_1
main growth phase

G_2
continued growth and preparation for cell division

G_0

Cytokinesis

Mitosis
nuclear division

M phase

Cycle exit

Cytokinesis
Cytoplasm divides and the two cells separate. It is distinct from mitosis.

Mitosis
Nuclear division

Second gap phase (G_2)
Rapid cell growth and protein synthesis. Cell prepares for mitosis.

Cleavage furrow

Two cells

Cytokinesis in an animal cell

4. Summarize what happens in each of the following phases of mitosis:

    (a) Prophase: _____

    _____

    (b) Metaphase: _____

    _____

    (c) Anaphase: _____

    _____

    (d) Telophase: _____

    _____

    _____

5. Summarize the following steps in the cell cycle:

    (a) G1: _____

    _____

    (b) S phase: _____

    _____

    (c) G2: _____

    _____

    (d) Mitosis: _____

    _____

©2023 **BIOZONE** International
ISBN: 978-1-99-101408-5
Photocopying Prohibited

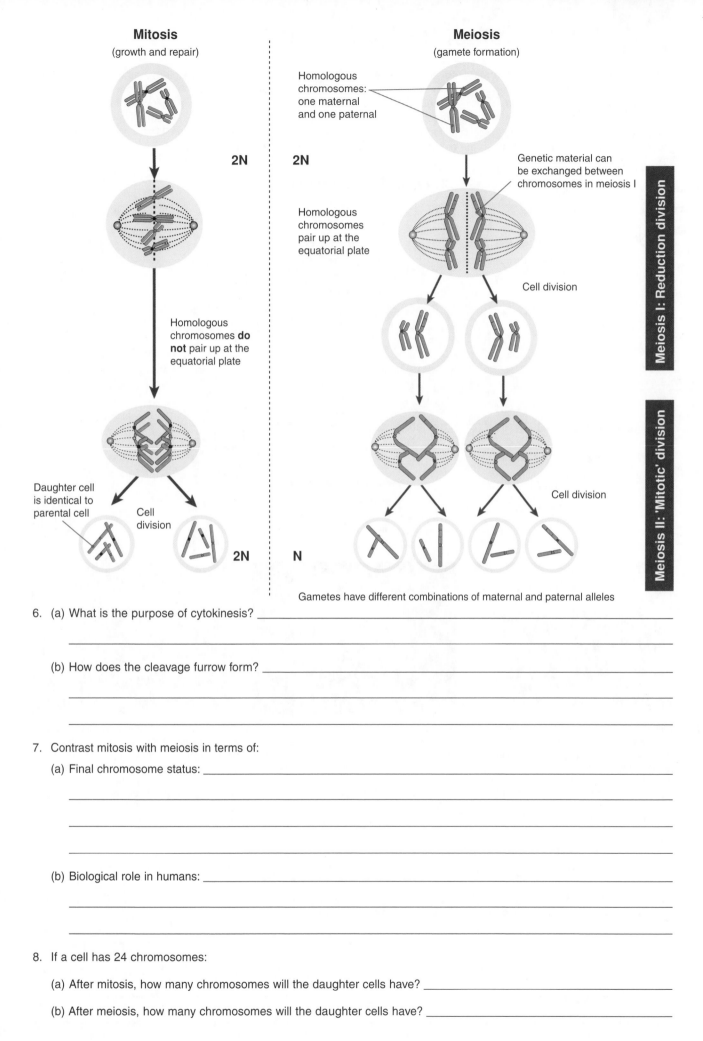

Mitosis
(growth and repair)

Meiosis
(gamete formation)

Homologous chromosomes: one maternal and one paternal

2N

2N

Homologous chromosomes pair up at the equatorial plate

Genetic material can be exchanged between chromosomes in meiosis I

Cell division

Meiosis I: Reduction division

Homologous chromosomes **do not** pair up at the equatorial plate

Daughter cell is identical to parental cell

Cell division

Cell division

Meiosis II: 'Mitotic' division

2N

N

Gametes have different combinations of maternal and paternal alleles

6. (a) What is the purpose of cytokinesis? _____

_____

(b) How does the cleavage furrow form? _____

_____

_____

7. Contrast mitosis with meiosis in terms of:

(a) Final chromosome status: _____

_____

_____

_____

(b) Biological role in humans: _____

_____

_____

8. If a cell has 24 chromosomes:

(a) After mitosis, how many chromosomes will the daughter cells have? _____

(b) After meiosis, how many chromosomes will the daughter cells have? _____

©2023 **BIOZONE** International
ISBN: 978-1-99-101408-5
Photocopying Prohibited

13 Regulation of the Cell Cycle

Key Idea: The cell makes sure the materials and processes needed to proceed are correct using regulatory checkpoints. **Cell cycle** checkpoints provide a way for **cells** to make sure that necessary processes at one stage have been completed successfully before the cell transitions to the next stage. There are three checkpoints in the cell cycle. At each checkpoint, a set of conditions determines whether or not the cell will continue into the next phase. Cancer can result when the pathways regulating the checkpoints fail. Non-dividing cells enter a resting phase (G_0), where they may remain for a few days or up to several years. Under specific conditions, they may re-enter the cell cycle.

Checkpoints during the cell cycle

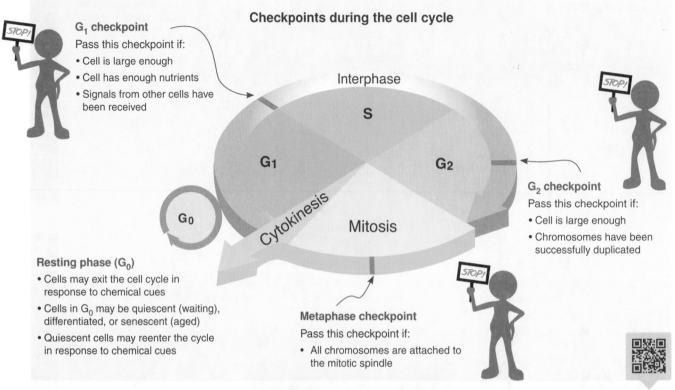

G_1 checkpoint
Pass this checkpoint if:
- Cell is large enough
- Cell has enough nutrients
- Signals from other cells have been received

G_2 checkpoint
Pass this checkpoint if:
- Cell is large enough
- Chromosomes have been successfully duplicated

Resting phase (G_0)
- Cells may exit the cell cycle in response to chemical cues
- Cells in G_0 may be quiescent (waiting), differentiated, or senescent (aged)
- Quiescent cells may reenter the cycle in response to chemical cues

Metaphase checkpoint
Pass this checkpoint if:
- All chromosomes are attached to the mitotic spindle

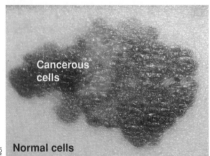

Skin cancer (melanoma). The cancer cells grow more rapidly than the normal skin cells because normal cell regulation checkpoints are ignored. This is why the cancerous cells sit higher than the normal cells and can rapidly spread (a process called metastasis).

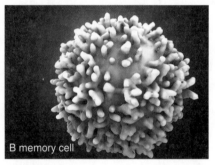

Most lymphocytes in human blood are in the resting G_0 phase and remain there unless they are stimulated by specific antigens to re-enter the cell cycle via G_1. G_0 phase cells are not completely dormant, continuing to carry out essential cell functions in reduced form.

Many fully differentiated (specialized) cells, e.g. neurons (above), exit the cell cycle permanently and stay in G_0. These cells continue their functional role in the body, but do not proliferate. Senescent cells have accumulated mutations, lose function, and die.

1. Explain the importance of cell cycle checkpoints: _____

_____

_____

2. In terms of the cell cycle and the resting phase (G_0), distinguish between the behavior of fully differentiated cells, such as neurons, and cells that are quiescent, such as B memory cells:

_____

_____

_____

_____

©2023 **BIOZONE** International
ISBN: 978-1-99-101408-5
Photocopying Prohibited

The trigger for mitosis

Experiments with the eggs of the African clawed frog (*Xenopus laevis*) provided evidence that a substance found in an M-phase cell could induce a G₂ cell to enter M phase. The substance was called M-phase promoting factor (MPF).

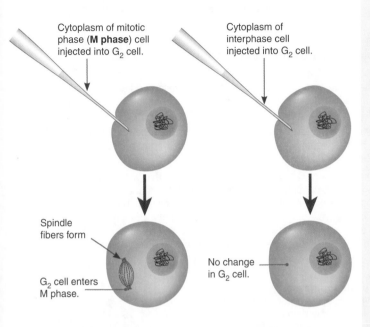

Cytoplasm of mitotic phase (**M phase**) cell injected into G₂ cell.

Cytoplasm of interphase cell injected into G₂ cell.

Spindle fibers form

G₂ cell enters M phase.

No change in G₂ cell.

Other studies have shown that MPF is made up of two subunits. The first subunit is a protein kinase, which activates proteins by transferring a phosphate group from ATP to the protein. The second subunit, called a cyclin, activates the first subunit. The first subunit, known as a cyclin-dependent kinase, or CdK, is constantly present in the cell, whereas cyclin is not.

Checkpoints and the role of cyclins

The cell cycle is driven by cyclin-CdK complexes. CdK without cyclin is inactive. Once cyclin is bound, it forms an active enzyme complex that can target the proteins involved in that phase of the cell cycle.

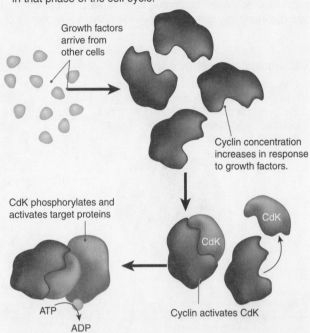

Growth factors arrive from other cells

Cyclin concentration increases in response to growth factors.

CdK phosphorylates and activates target proteins

CdK

CdK

ATP

ADP

Cyclin activates CdK

The cyclin-CdK complexes have periodic spikes of activity associated with orderly progression of the cell cycle. Cyclins are synthesized in response to growth factors from other cells and different cyclins are associated with each phase of the cell cycle. For example, M cyclins send CdKs to M phase protein targets, e.g. to cause breakdown of the nuclear membrane.

3. Explain why the cytoplasm from an M-phase cell could induce a G₂ cell to enter M phase: _____

_____

_____

_____

4. (a) Which checkpoint ensures that replicated chromosomes will separate correctly? _____

_____

(b) Why is this important? _____

_____

5. Suggest why signals (growth factors) from other cells play a part in regulating the cell cycle: _____

_____

_____

_____

6. Cyclin D is synthesized during G₁ and is important in the G₁ checkpoint and the G₁/S transition. Predict a likely consequence of errors resulting in an over-production of cyclin D:

_____

_____

_____

_____

14 Defective Gene Regulation in Cancer

Key Idea: When checkpoints fail, cancer may be the result. **Cells** that become damaged beyond repair normally undergo a controlled process of programmed cell death called apoptosis. However, cancerous cells evade this control and become immortal, continuing to divide without any checks on

their proliferation, even though they are faulty. Agents capable of causing cancer are called carcinogens. Most carcinogens are also mutagens (they damage DNA). Any one of a number of cancer-causing factors (including defective genes) may interact to disrupt the **cell cycle** and result in cancer.

Cancer: cells out of control

Cancerous transformation results from changes in the genes controlling normal cell growth and division. The resulting cells become immortal and no longer carry out their functional role.

Normal cell

If the damage is too serious to repair, the p53 gene activates other genes to cause the cell to enter apoptosis (programmed cell death).

Given a continual supply of nutrients, cancer cells can go on dividing indefinitely and are said to be immortal.

Cancer cells may have unusual numbers of chromosomes.

The bloated, lumpy shape is readily distinguishable from a healthy cell, which has a flat, scaly appearance.

Metabolism is disrupted and the cell ceases to function constructively.

Cancerous cells lose their attachments to neighboring cells.

Proto-oncogenes and tumor-suppressor genes

▶ Two types of gene are normally involved in controlling the cell cycle: proto-oncogenes, which start cell division and are essential for normal cell development, and tumor-suppressor genes, which switch off cell division.

▶ In their normal form, these types of gene work together, enabling the body to repair defective cells and replace dead ones. Mutations in these genes can disrupt this regulation.

▶ Proto-oncogenes, through mutation, can give rise to oncogenes, which cause uncontrolled cell division. Mutations to tumor-suppressor genes initiate most human cancers. The best studied tumor-suppressor gene is p53, which encodes a protein that halts the cell cycle so that DNA can be repaired before division. P53 acts at the G_1-S checkpoint and initiates DNA repair or apoptosis.

Tumor-suppressor genes
When damage occurs, the tumor suppressor gene p53 commands other genes to bring cell division to a halt. If repairs are made, then the p53 gene allows the cell cycle to continue.

DNA molecule

Damaged DNA

Proto-oncogenes
Genes that turn on cell division. The mutated form or oncogene leads to unregulated cell division. A mutation to one or two controlling genes might cause a benign (non-malignant) tumor. A large number of mutations can cause loss of control, causing a cell to become cancerous.

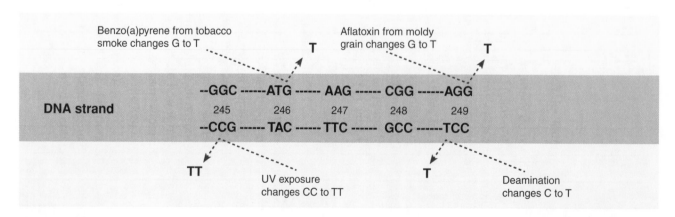

Benzo(a)pyrene from tobacco smoke changes G to T

Aflatoxin from moldy grain changes G to T

DNA strand

--GGC ------ ATG ------ AAG ------ CGG ------ AGG

245   246   247   248   249

--CCG ------ TAC ------ TTC ------ GCC ------ TCC

UV exposure changes CC to TT

Deamination changes C to T

©2023 **BIOZONE** International
ISBN: 978-1-99-101408-5
Photocopying Prohibited

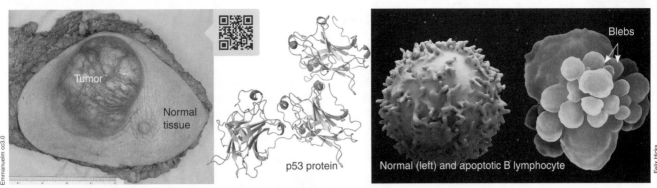

p53 protein

Blebs

Normal (left) and apoptotic B lymphocyte

The product of the gene BRCA1 is involved in repairing damaged DNA and BRCA1 deficiency is associated with abnormalities in cell cycle checkpoints. Mutations to this gene and another gene called BRCA2 are found in about 10% of all breast cancers and 15% of ovarian cancers.

One of the most important proteins in regulating the cell cycle is the protein produced by the gene p53. The p53 tumor-suppressor protein helps regulate the cell cycle, apoptosis, and genomic stability. Mutations to the p53 gene are found in about 50% of cancers. Apoptosis is a controlled process that involves cell shrinkage, blebbing (above), and DNA fragmentation. Apoptosis removes damaged or abnormal cells before they can multiply. When apoptosis malfunctions, it can cause disease, including cancer. When cell cycle checkpoints fail, the normal rate of apoptosis falls. This allows a damaged cell to divide without regulation.

Reduction in rates of apoptosis can cause cancer

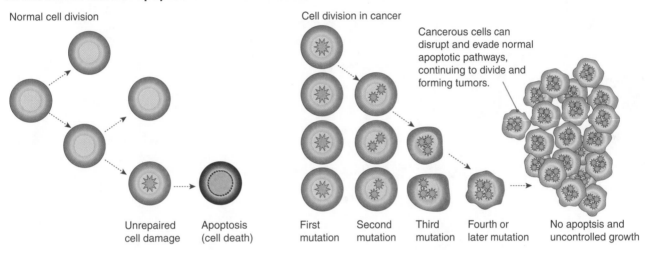

Normal cell division

Unrepaired cell damage — Apoptosis (cell death)

Cell division in cancer

Cancerous cells can disrupt and evade normal apoptotic pathways, continuing to divide and forming tumors.

First mutation — Second mutation — Third mutation — Fourth or later mutation — No apoptsis and uncontrolled growth

Tumor suppressor genes, e.g. the p53 gene, normally halt cell division of DNA damaged cells until the damage is repaired. If the damage cannot be repaired, apoptosis, a process of controlled cell death, is triggered.

Cancerous cells may inhibit the expression of the p53 gene. Around 50% of all human tumors contain p53 gene mutations. Factors known to disrupt normal cell cycle controls include defective genes, some viruses, and a number of chemical and environmental factors.

1. How do cancerous cells differ from normal cells? _____

_____

2. Describe the involvement of regulatory genes in control of the cell cycle: _____

_____

_____

_____

_____

_____

3. (a) Explain how the normal controls over the cell cycle can be lost: _____

_____

_____

   (b) How can these failures result in cancer? _____

_____

_____

15 Levels of Organization

Key Idea: Structural organization in animals, as in all multicellular organisms, is hierarchical.

Organization and the emergence of novel properties in complex systems are two of the defining features of living organisms. Multicellular organisms are organized according to a hierarchy of structural levels. At each level, new properties arise that were absent at the simpler level. Hierarchical organization allows specialized **cells** to group together into **tissues** and **organs** to perform a specific function. This improves efficiency in the organism.

The diagram below explains this hierarchical organization for a mammalian example - a human.

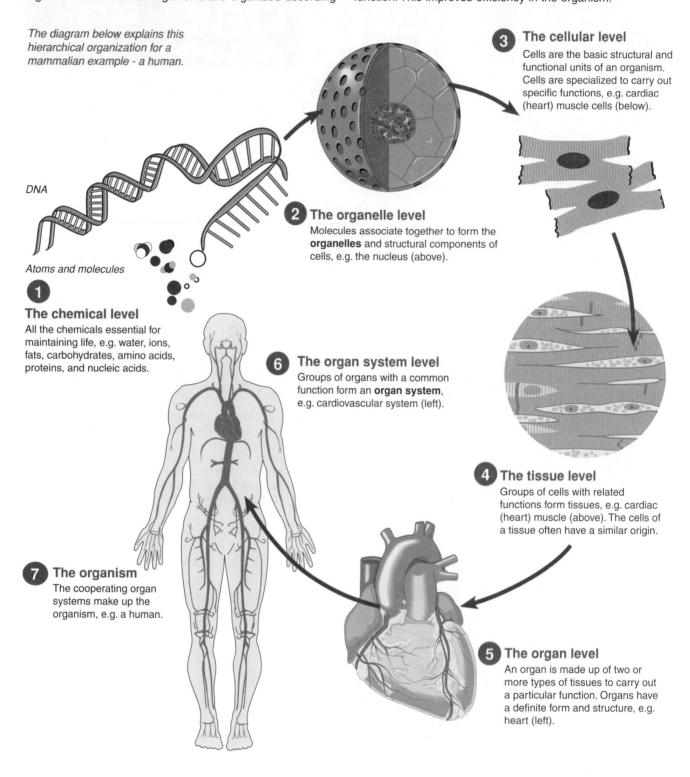

3 The cellular level

Cells are the basic structural and functional units of an organism. Cells are specialized to carry out specific functions, e.g. cardiac (heart) muscle cells (below).

2 The organelle level

Molecules associate together to form the **organelles** and structural components of cells, e.g. the nucleus (above).

DNA

Atoms and molecules

1 The chemical level

All the chemicals essential for maintaining life, e.g. water, ions, fats, carbohydrates, amino acids, proteins, and nucleic acids.

6 The organ system level

Groups of organs with a common function form an **organ system**, e.g. cardiovascular system (left).

4 The tissue level

Groups of cells with related functions form tissues, e.g. cardiac (heart) muscle (above). The cells of a tissue often have a similar origin.

7 The organism

The cooperating organ systems make up the organism, e.g. a human.

5 The organ level

An organ is made up of two or more types of tissues to carry out a particular function. Organs have a definite form and structure, e.g. heart (left).

---

1. Assign each of the following emergent properties to the level at which it first appears:

    (a) Metabolism: _____

    (b) Behavior: _____

    (c) Replication: _____

©2023 **BIOZONE** International
ISBN: 978-1-99-101408-5
Photocopying Prohibited

Specialized cells make up tissues and organs

Specialized cells often have modifications or exaggerations to a normal cell feature to help them perform a particular task. They may have more (or fewer) of a particular organelle in order to perform their role most efficiently.

  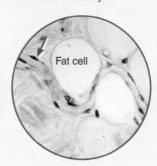 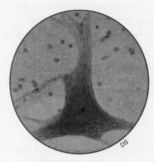

Muscle cells are able to contract (shorten) to bring about the movement of limbs and organs.

There are many types of blood cells; they each carry out a particular job.

Thin, flat, epithelial cells line the walls of blood vessels (arrow). Large fat cells store lipid.

Nerve cells conduct impulses around the body, enabling responses to the environment.

In the spaces provided below, assign each of the examples listed to one of the levels of organization, (a-f).

2. Examples: *blood, bone, brain, cardiac muscle, cartilage, epinephrine (adrenaline), collagen, DNA, heart, leukocyte, lysosome, pancreas, mast cell, nervous system, phospholipid, reproductive system, ribosomes, neuron, Schwann cell, spleen, squamous epithelium, astrocyte, respiratory system, muscular system, peroxisome, ATP, collagen, testis, liver.*

(a) Chemical level: _____

_____

(b) Organelles: _____

_____

(c) Cells: _____

_____

(d) Tissues: _____

_____

(e) Organs: _____

_____

(f) Organ system: _____

_____

3. You will learn about the organ systems and their roles in the course of working through this book. Organ systems don't work in isolation. Each is connected to multiple other organ systems in the body at different parts of the system. For the systems below, list or describe what you understand about how or where they interact. You can use this as a pretest of your current knowledge or review it later as you work your way through this book.

(a) Cardiovascular system and respiratory system: _____

_____

_____

_____

_____

(b) Cardiovascular system and digestive system: _____

_____

_____

_____

_____

©2023 **BIOZONE** International
ISBN: 978-1-99-101408-5
Photocopying Prohibited

16 Tissues of the Body

Key Idea: A tissue is a group of cells that are similar in structure and perform a specific function. There are four basic types of tissue in the body.

The microscopic study of **tissues** is called histology. The **cells** of a tissue, and their associated extracellular substances, are grouped together to perform particular functions. Tissues improve the efficiency of operation because they enable tasks to be shared amongst various specialized cells.

Epithelial tissue

Epithelial tissues make up one of the four broad groups of tissues found in humans and other animals. Epithelial tissues line internal and external surfaces, e.g. blood vessels, ducts, gut lining, and protect the underlying structures from wear and tear, infection, and pressure. They are found associated with other tissue types, e.g. muscle and connective tissues, in every **organ system** of the body

▶ Epithelium always has one free surface called the apical surface. On the lower, basal, surface the epithelial cells are anchored on a basement membrane of collagen fibers held together by a carbohydrate-based glue.

▶ Except for glandular epithelium, epithelial cells form fitted continuous sheets, held in place by desmosomes and tight junctions.

▶ Epithelial tissues are avascular, i.e. they have no blood supply and rely on **diffusion** from underlying capillaries.

▶ Epithelia are classified as simple (single layered) or stratified (two or more layers), and the cells may be squamous (flat), cuboidal, or columnar (rectangular). Thus, at least two adjectives describe any particular epithelium, e.g. stratified cuboidal.

▶ Pseudostratified epithelium is a type of simple epithelium that appears layered because the cells are of different heights. All cells rest on the basement membrane.

▶ Transitional epithelium is a type of stratified epithelium which is capable of considerable stretching. It lines **organs** such as the urinary bladder.

▶ Epithelia may be modified, e.g. ciliated, such as in the respiratory tract; or specialized for secretion, absorption, or filtration.

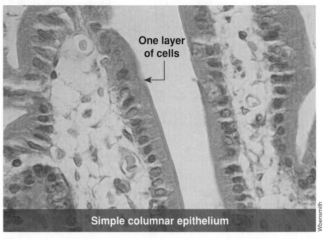

Simple columnar epithelium

The simple epithelium of the gastrointestinal tract is easily recognized by the regular, column-like cells. It is specialized for secretion and absorption.

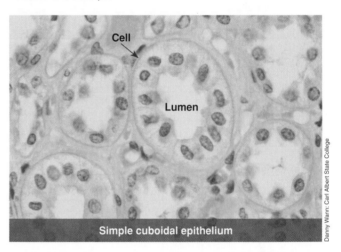

Cell

Lumen

Simple cuboidal epithelium

Simple, cuboidal epithelium is common in glands and their ducts and also lines the kidney tubules (above) and the surface of the ovaries.

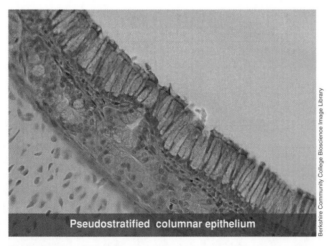

Pseudostratified columnar epithelium

This epithelium lines much of the respiratory tract (above). Mucus produced by goblet cells in the epithelium traps dust particles.

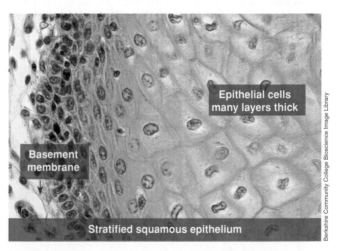

Epithelial cells many layers thick

Basement membrane

Stratified squamous epithelium

Stratified epithelium is more durable than simple epithelium because it has several layers. It has a protective role, e.g. in the vagina above.

©2023 **BIOZONE** International
ISBN: 978-1-99-101408-5
Photocopying Prohibited

1. (a) Describe the basic components of a tissue: _____

_____

_____

(b) Explain how the development of tissues improves functional efficiency: _____

_____

_____

_____

2. Describe the general functional role of epithelial tissue: _____

_____

3. Describe the particular features that contribute to the functional role of each of the following types of epithelial tissue:

(a) Transitional epithelium: _____

_____

_____

(b) Stratified epithelium: _____

_____

_____

Features of muscle tissue

The muscle tissue of the body is responsible for producing movement. This includes movement of the body, as in locomotion, and also internal movements, such as heartbeat, intestinal peristalsis, blood vessel constriction and dilation, and contraction and expansion of the iris of the eye. Muscle tissue is composed of specialized, elongated cells called fibers, held together by connective tissue. The contractile protein filaments within these fibers give the muscle cells their ability to contract. Muscle is classed as skeletal, cardiac, or smooth according to its structure, function, and location in the body. Each type is described below.

Skeletal muscle

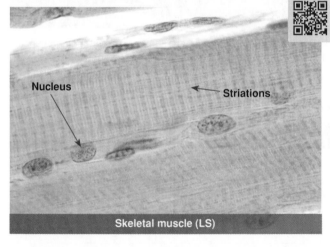

Skeletal muscle (LS)

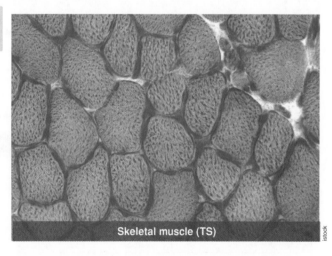

Skeletal muscle (TS)

▶ Skeletal muscle is the major muscle type in the body. It brings about voluntary movement of the skeleton as well as the facial skin, tongue, and eyeball. The contraction and relaxation of skeletal muscle is under conscious control (hence voluntary). The fibers are large, with many peripheral nuclei and the regular arrangement of the contractile elements gives them a striated appearance. Skeletal fibers are innervated by motor neurons. If they lose their nerve supply, they lose function and waste away.

4. (a) Identify the three types of muscle tissue: _____

(b) What is a muscle cell called? _____

(c) What is the purpose of muscle tissue? _____

5. What is the specific purpose of skeletal muscle? _____

_____

©2023 **BIOZONE** International
ISBN: 978-1-99-101408-5
Photocopying Prohibited

Smooth muscle

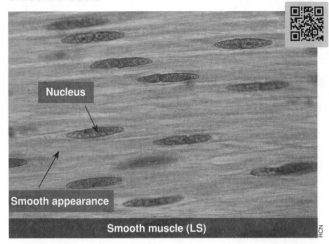

Smooth muscle (LS)

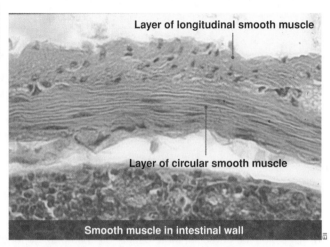

Layer of longitudinal smooth muscle

Layer of circular smooth muscle

Smooth muscle in intestinal wall

▶ The spindle-shaped cells of smooth muscle have only one nucleus per cell. The contractile elements are not regularly arranged so the tissue appears smooth. Smooth muscle is responsible for involuntary movements, e.g. peristalsis in the gut wall, and is found predominantly lining the visceral organs and blood vessels. Smooth muscle cells make contact with each other at specialized regions called gap junctions. They also receive input from the neurons of the autonomic nervous system.

Cardiac muscle

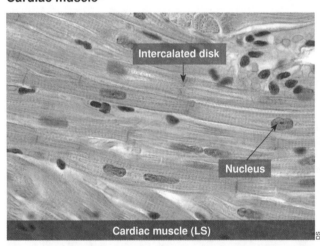

Intercalated disk

Nucleus

Cardiac muscle (LS)

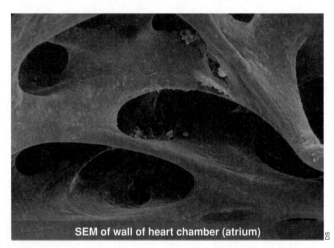

SEM of wall of heart chamber (atrium)

▶ Cardiac muscle is found only in the heart. It has striations, like skeletal muscle, but the fibers are short and branched and usually have only one, centrally located, nucleus. The fibers are joined at specialized intercalated disks with gap junctions to allow rapid communication between the cells. Contraction of cardiac muscle is involuntary - it contracts spontaneously and rhythmically throughout life, although the rate of beating is influenced by nervous input and hormones.

6. Summarize features of each type of muscle tissue in the following table:

	Skeletal muscle	Smooth muscle	Cardiac muscle
Appearance of cells	Large, striated		
Nuclei (number, location)		One, central	
Control			Involuntary

7. Compare and contrast the functional role of each type of muscle tissue, relating structure to function in each case:

_____

_____

_____

_____

_____

_____

_____

©2023 **BIOZONE** International
ISBN: 978-1-99-101408-5
Photocopying Prohibited

Connective tissues

Connective tissue (CT) is the major supporting tissue of the body. Connective tissues bind other structures together and provide support and protection against damage, infection, or heat loss. Most CTs have a plentiful blood supply, although tendons and ligaments are poorly vascularized and cartilage is avascular (lacking blood vessels). Connective tissues range from very hard to fluid and include so-called ordinary CTs (dense and loose CT) and special CTs, e.g. bone, cartilage, fat, and blood. In most ordinary CTs, collagen is the predominant fiber type. All CTs have three common elements: fibers, cells, and non-cellular matrix material. The most common cells in all CTs are fibroblasts, which synthesize the collagen and extracellular matrix.

Ordinary connective tissues

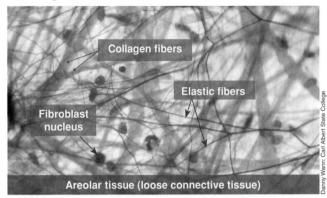

Areolar tissue (loose connective tissue)

Danny Wann: Carl Albert State College

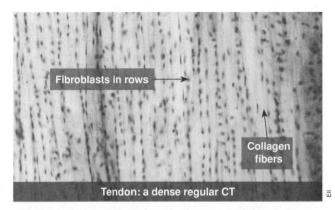

Tendon: a dense regular CT

▶ The so-called ordinary connective tissues are categorized as either loose or dense, depending on the relative abundance of cells, fibers, and ground substance. Loose connective tissues have more cells and fewer fibers than denser connective tissues. The fibers are loosely organized as the name suggests. A typical example is areolar tissue, which helps to hold internal organs in position. Dense regular CT is found where strength is required, such as in ligaments and tendons. The collagen fibers are arranged in compact bundles with rows of fibroblasts between.

Special connective tissues

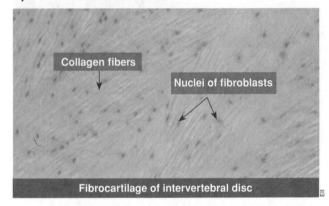

Fibrocartilage of intervertebral disc

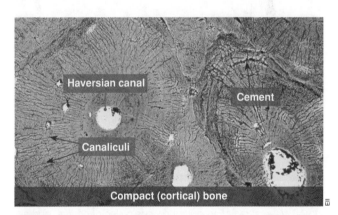

Compact (cortical) bone

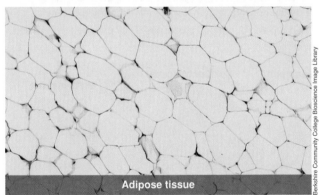

Adipose tissue

Berkshire Community College Bioscience Image Library

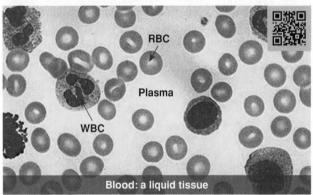

Blood: a liquid tissue

▶ Special connective tissues differ from proper CTs in being specialized for particular functions, e.g. elasticity or compression resistance. They are also more restricted in their distribution than the 'ordinary' CTs described above. Cartilage is more flexible than bone and forms supporting structures in the skeleton. Fibrocartilage forms the cushion-like disks between vertebrae. Bone is the hardest connective tissue. In compact bone, the bone cells are trapped within a hard layered matrix. Canals (canaliculi) penetrate the matrix, allowing the cells to make exchanges with the blood vessels supplying the bone tissue.

▶ Adipose (fat) tissue is made up of large cells, each containing a single large droplet of fat surrounded by a thin ring containing the cellular cytoplasm and nucleus. The adipose cells are surrounded by a fine supporting network of collagen fibers.

▶ Blood is a liquid tissue composed of cells floating in a liquid matrix, which includes soluble fibers. The cells (red blood cells or erythrocytes, white blood cells or leukocytes, and platelets) make up the formed elements of the blood. The liquid matrix or plasma makes up ~55% of the blood volume.

8. (a) Identify the most common cell type in connective tissue: _____

   (b) What is the role of these cells? _____

   (c) Identify a common fiber type in connective tissue: _____

9. Giving examples, discuss the roles of different connective tissues in the body: _____

   _____

   _____

   _____

   _____

   _____

   _____

   _____

Nervous tissue

Nervous tissue makes up the structures of the nervous system: the brain, spinal cord and all the peripheral nervous tissue, including sensory structures and sense organs. Nervous tissue contains densely packed neurons, which are specialized for receiving and transmitting electrochemical impulses. Neurons are usually associated with supporting cells (neuroglia) and connective tissue containing blood vessels.

A nerve (or nerve fiber) is a cable-like structure in the peripheral nervous system containing the axons of many neurons and their associated insulating sheaths. Nerves are enclosed and protected by connective tissue. The equivalent structure in the central nervous system is called a tract.

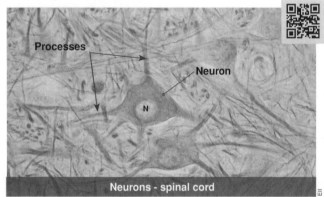
Neurons - spinal cord

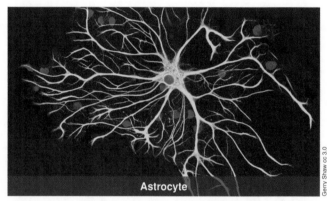
Astrocyte

▶ The large, multipolar (=many-processes) motor neurons of the central nervous system (above left) have a large central nucleus (N), several radiating cell processes called dendrites, and a long thin axon. The long processes allow nerve impulses to be transmitted over long distances. Note how the cell processes form a dense network, together with their supporting glial cells.

▶ Astrocytes (above right) are a type of glial cell. They have a small cell body and numerous processes. They provide physical and metabolic support to the neurons of the CNS and help maintain the composition of the extracellular fluid.

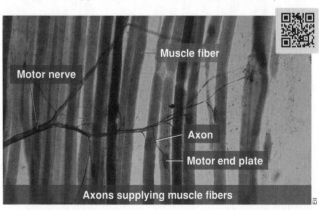
Axons supplying muscle fibers

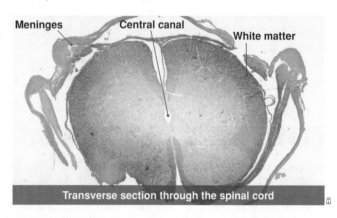
Transverse section through the spinal cord

▶ The photograph (above left) shows the terminating axons of a motor nerve. The nerve distributes its axons to the individual muscle fibers. Each axon ends in a specialized junction called the motor end plate.

▶ In the TS of the spinal cord (above right), staining reveals outer white matter (the myelinated axons of neurons) and inner gray matter (mostly the cell bodies of neurons). The gray matter is connected across the midline where the central canal is located. The central canal contains nutritive cerebrospinal fluid and is continuous with the ventricles of the brain. Like the brain, it is surrounded by connective tissue meninges.

©2023 **BIOZONE** International
ISBN: 978-1-99-101408-5
Photocopying Prohibited

10. (a) Describe the characteristic features of nervous tissue: _____

_____

_____

(b) What is the role of glial cells in nervous tissue? _____

_____

_____

(c) What is the role of the cerebrospinal fluid and how is it supplied to the tissue of the central nervous system?

_____

_____

_____

11. Discuss the role of neural tissue in the body: _____

_____

_____

_____

_____

_____

12. Identify the tissue types below from the list given (there are more tissue types in the list than images:
*Nervous tissue, smooth muscle tissue, simple columnar epithelium, skeletal muscle tissue,
simple cuboidal epithelium, adipose tissue.*

(a)
Berkshire Community College Bioscience Image Library

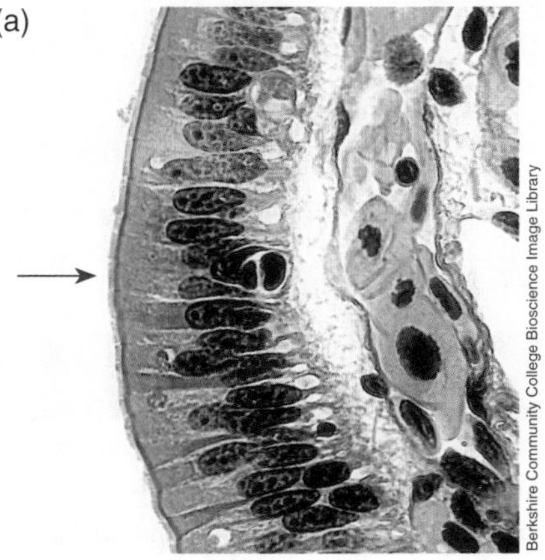

(b)
Doc. RNDr. Josef Reischig, CSc. CC 3.0

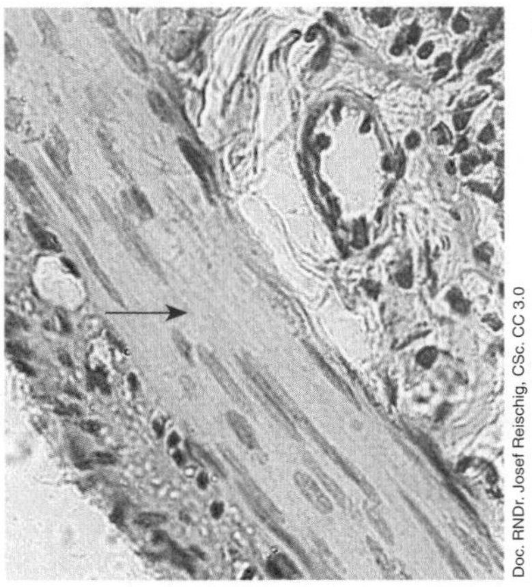

(c)

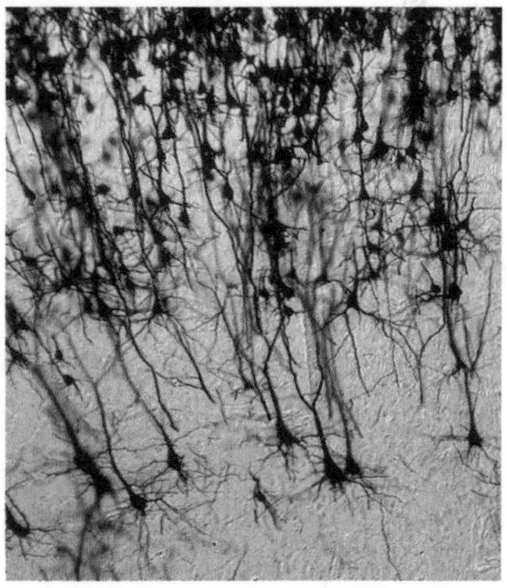

_____   _____   _____

13. Sort the tissues in the following list into epithelial, connective, muscle, or nervous tissue:
*Simple squamous epithelium, adipose tissue, blood, smooth muscle, cardiac muscle, spinal cord motor neurons,
myelinated axon, human bone, human elastic cartilage, simple cuboidal epithelium.*

(a) Epithelial tissue: _____

_____

(b) Muscle tissue: _____

_____

(c) Connective tissue: _____

_____

(d) Nervous tissue: _____

_____

17 Human Organ Systems

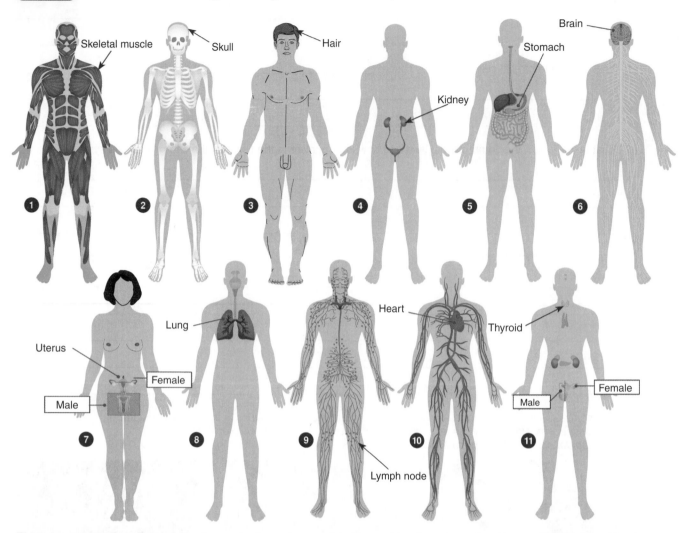

There are 11 **organ systems** in the human body, each comprising a number of components with specific functions. Match up the organ system with the image (1-11) above and the function given below. Some labels are given as clues and you can use **BIOZONE's Resource Hub**, your textbook, or other chapters in this workbook to help you.

Organ system number	Organ system name
1	
2	
3	
4	
5	
6	
7	
8	
9	
10	
11	

Organ system number	Organ system function
	Support and protection of tissues and **organs**, movement (with muscular system), blood cells production.
	Excretion of nitrogenous wastes and other metabolic waste products. Maintains fluid and electrolyte balance.
	Physical and chemical digestion and absorption of ingested food to provide the body's fuel.
	Movement of body (limbs, locomotion), and its component parts, e.g. gut.
	Circulates tissue fluid, internal defense against pathogens.
	Production of gametes and offspring.
	Delivers O_2 and nutrients to **tissues** and organs and removes CO_2 and other waste products.
	Physical and chemical protection of tissues, thermoregulation, synthesis of vitamin D precursor.
	Regulates all visceral and motor functions of the body.
	Produces hormones that activate and regulate homeostatic functions, growth, and development
	Interface for gas exchange with the internal environment obtaining O_2 and expelling CO_2.

©2023 **BIOZONE** International
ISBN: 978-1-99-101408-5
Photocopying Prohibited

18 Chapter Summary

1. Explain how the properties of the phospholipid molecule result in the bilayer structure of membranes:

_____

_____

_____

_____

2. The diagrams below depict what happens when a red blood cell is placed into three solutions with differing concentrations of solutes. Describe the tonicity of the solution (in relation to the cell) and describe what is happening:

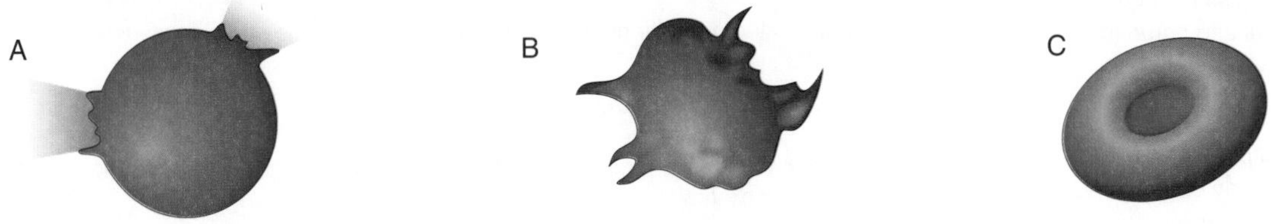

A   B   C

(a) _____   (b) _____   (c) _____

     _____   _____   _____

     _____   _____   _____

3. Consider the two diagrams below. For each, draw in the appropriate box what you would expect to see after one hour.

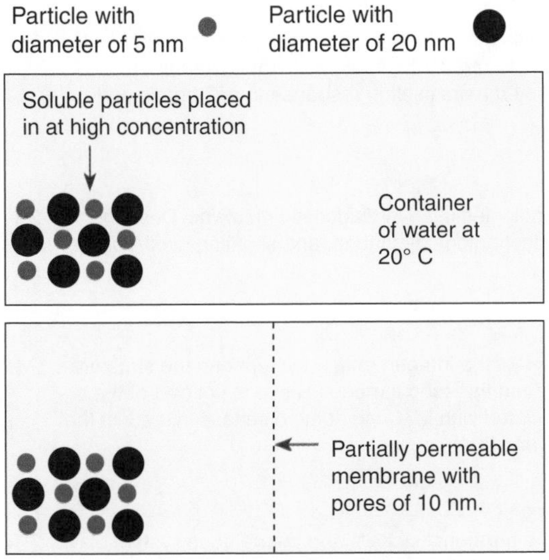

Particle with diameter of 5 nm   ●   Particle with diameter of 20 nm   ⬤   After one hour:

Soluble particles placed in at high concentration

Container of water at 20° C

Partially permeable membrane with pores of 10 nm.

4. Identify the four organelles shown in the image of the cell below:

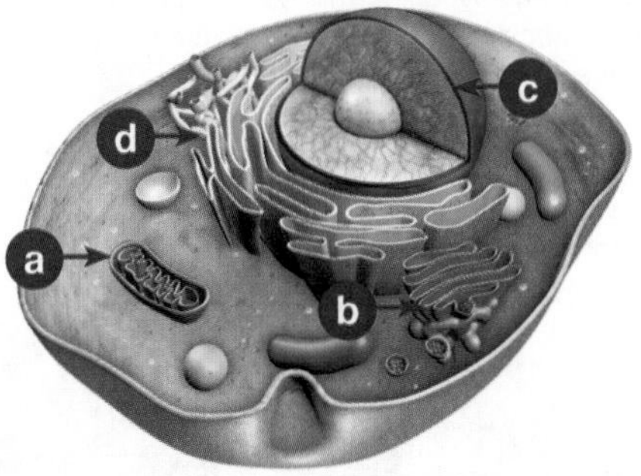

a: _____

b: _____

c: _____

d: _____

5. An observation of epithelial cells under a microscope shows the cells are arranged in a single layer and look tall and narrow, with the nucleus located close to the basal side (base) of the cell. Identify the type of epithelial tissue:

_____

6. What three essential components is connective tissue made of? _____

_____

The Integument and Homeostasis

KEY IDEAS

- Homeostasis is maintained using hormonal and nervous mechanisms via negative feedback.

- Thermoregulation enables maintenance of an optimum body temperature for metabolism.

- The integument plays an important role in thermoregulation and other homeostatic processes.

- Modern medical technology enables the diagnosis of homeostatic imbalances.

KEY TERMS

- Dermis
- Epidermis
- Epithelium
- Homeostasis
- Hyperthermia
- Hypothalamus
- Hypothermia
- Integumentary system
- Membrane
- Negative feedback loop
- Positive feedback loop
- Thermoreceptor
- Thermoregulation

RESOURCE HUB

Scan the QR code to access:

- weblinks
- videos
- 3D models
- interactives

LEARNING OBJECTIVES

Activity number

☐ 1   Explain the need for homeostasis and understand the stimulus response model.   **19**

☐ 2   Understand the difference between a positive and negative feedback loop and give examples of each.   **20**

☐ 3   Review and correctly refer to the location of anatomical parts using the terms proximal, distal, medial, superficial, anterior (or ventral), posterior (or dorsal), superior, inferior,and lateral. Describe the ventral and dorsal body cavities and their roles in enclosing and protecting organs. Describe the structures and locations of the different types of membranes found in the body. Understand the relationship between membranes and cavities.   **21**

☐ 4   Understand the mechanisms by which the body's organ systems maintain homeostasis in response to regular fluctuations in the environment. Understand how the body repairs itself in response to pathogens and injuries.   **22**

☐ 5   Understand some technologies used in diagnostic medicine. Describe the principles behind each technology described, and situations appropriate to their use.   **23**

☐ 6   Understand the functions of the integumentary system and the structure of the skin. Understand that the subcutaneous tissue is not part of the skin but is closely associated with it. Name some diseases that affect the integumentary system, and their causes.   **24**

☐ 7   Explain the roles that the hormonal system and the nervous system play in regulating body temperature. Describe how the body reacts to extreme cold, and why hypothermia can be dangerous. Describe how the body most commonly overheats, and why hyperthermia can lead to death. State the way in which the drug ecstasy (MDMA) affects the body and some consequences of its use.   **25-28**

☐ 8   Discuss homeostasis in newborn babies and explain why premature babies require careful monitoring to keep them healthy.   **29**

Background: Sweat on skin

19 Principles of Homeostasis

Key Idea: Homeostasis is the process of sustaining a constant physiological state within the body, regardless of fluctuations in the external environment.

Organisms maintain a relatively constant physiological state, called **homeostasis**, despite changes in their environment. Any change in the environment to which an organism responds is called a stimulus. Environmental stimuli are constantly changing, therefore organisms must adjust their behavior and physiology constantly to maintain homeostasis. This requires the coordinated activity of the body's organ systems. Homeostatic mechanisms prevent potentially harmful deviations from the steady state and keep the body's internal conditions within strict limits.

Homeostasis is required to maintain constant body temperature at around 37°C. Similarly, the body must regulate blood glucose levels, pH, and pressure as well as water and electrolyte balance. Your body's organ systems coordinate to carry out these tasks.

How homeostasis is maintained: the stimulus-response model

To maintain homeostasis, the body must detect stimuli through receptors, process this sensory information in a control center, and respond to it appropriately via an effector. The responses provide new feedback to the receptor. These three components are illustrated below.

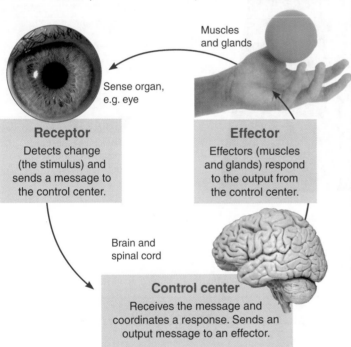

Muscles and glands

Sense organ, e.g. eye

Receptor
Detects change (the stimulus) and sends a message to the control center.

Effector
Effectors (muscles and glands) respond to the output from the control center.

Brain and spinal cord

Control center
Receives the message and coordinates a response. Sends an output message to an effector.

Homeostasis analogies

The analogy of a temperature setting on a home heating/cooling system explains how homeostasis is maintained. For example, a heat pump has sensors (receptor) to monitor room temperature as well as a control center to receive and process the data from the sensors. Depending on the data it receives, the control center activates the effector (heating/cooling unit), switching either on or off.

When the room is too cold, the heating unit switches on, and the cooling unit is off. When it is too hot, the heating unit switches off and the cooling unit is switched on. This system maintains a constant temperature, similar to homeostasis in the body.

The analogy of staying upright on a mountain bike using body weight, arms, pedals, brakes, and steering demonstrates that many homeostasis systems have multiple mechanisms to maintain a steady state.

1. Define homeostasis: _____

_____

2. What are the roles of the following components in maintaining homeostasis?

   (a) Receptor: _____

   _____

   (b) Control center: _____

   _____

   (c) Effector: _____

   _____

©2023 **BIOZONE** International
ISBN: 978-1-99-101408-5
Photocopying Prohibited

Exchanges with the environment

Organ systems work together to maintain the environment necessary for the functioning of the body's cells. A constant internal environment allows an organism to be somewhat independent of its external environment so that it can function normally as its external environment changes. The simplified example below illustrates how organ systems interact with each other to maintain a constant internal environment.

Organ systems maintain a constant internal environment that provides for the needs of all the body's cells, making it possible for animals to move through different and often highly variable external environments. This representation shows how organ systems permit exchanges with the environment. The exchange surfaces are usually internal, but may be connected to the environment via openings on the body surface.

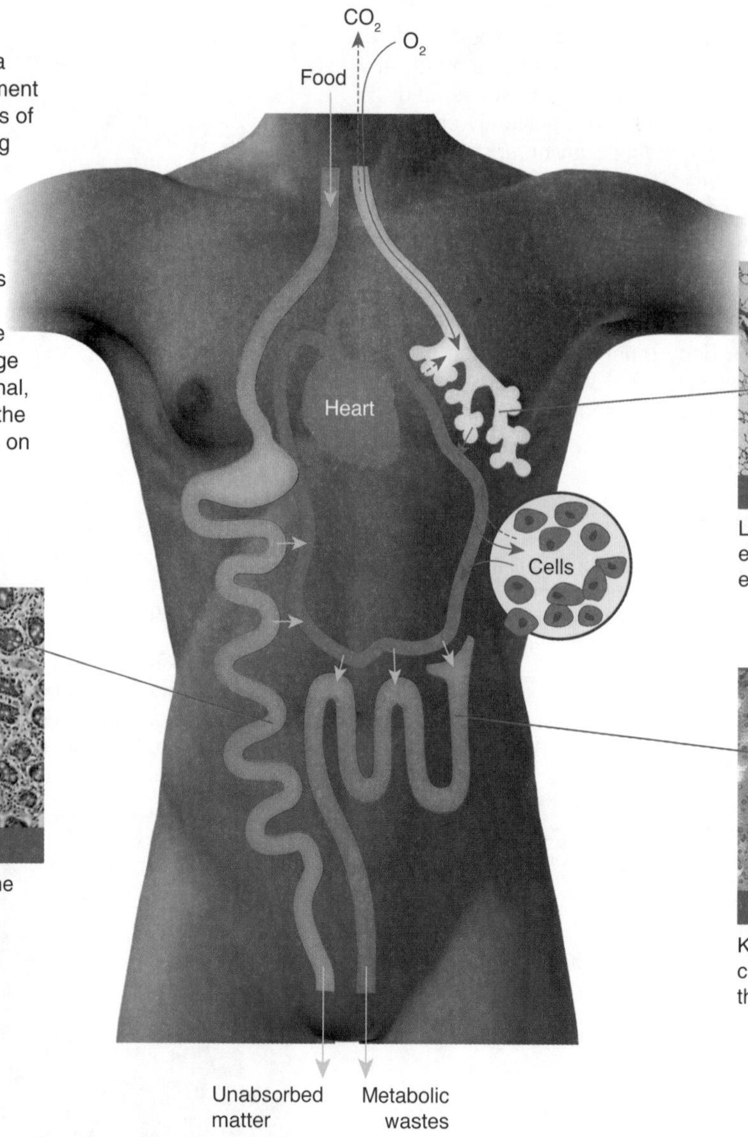

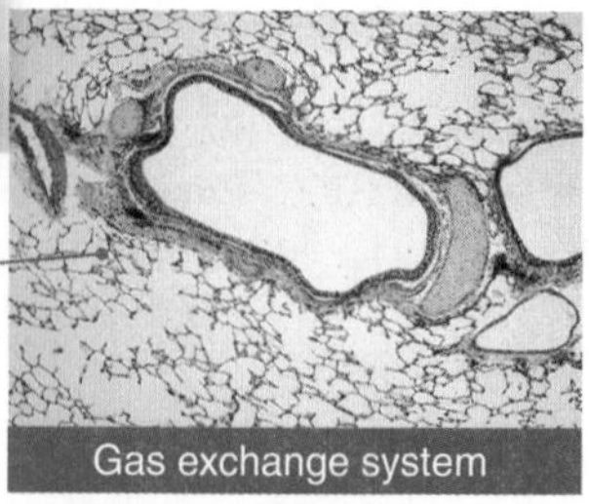

CO_2

O_2

Food

Heart

Cells

Gas exchange system

Lung tissue provides an expansive, moist surface for gas exchange.

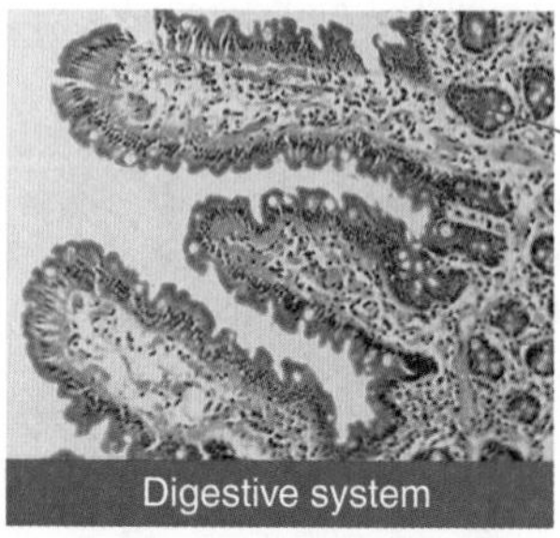

Digestive system

The villi of the small intestine increase surface area for nutrient absorption.

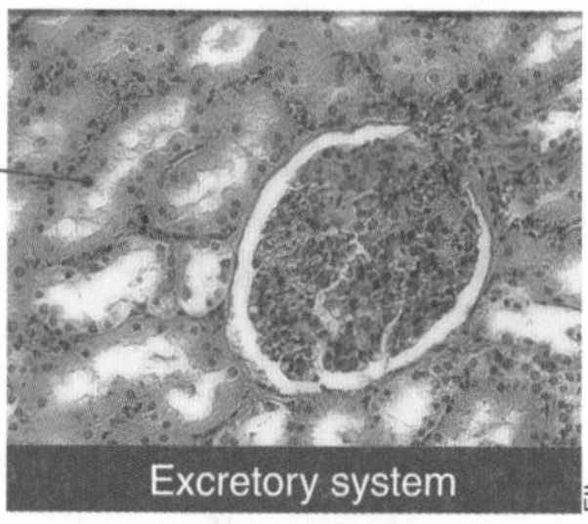

Excretory system

Kidney tubules exchange chemicals with the blood through capillaries.

Unabsorbed matter

Metabolic wastes

3. Why is it important that body systems are kept in balance? _____

_____

_____

_____

_____

4. Why is it important that the brain prioritizes the importance of incoming stimuli? _____

_____

_____

_____

5. Using an example, briefly explain why homeostasis often involves more than one body system: _____

_____

_____

_____

20 | Feedback Loops

Key Idea: Feedback loops, driven by various mechanisms, can stabilize biological systems or exaggerate deviations from the median condition.

Two types of feedback loop are used in the body, each producing specific outcomes. **Negative feedback loops** maintain **homeostasis**, e.g. regulation of body temperature. **Positive feedback loops** exaggerate any changes in the internal environment, moving the body away from a stable state by quickly amplifying changes in the internal environment e.g. blood clotting.

Negative feedback loops

▸ Negative feedback loops are control systems that maintain the body's internal environment at a relatively steady state.

▸ When variations from the norm are detected by the body's receptors, a response or output from the effectors that opposes the stimulus is classified as negative feedback.

▸ Negative feedback discourages variations from a set point and returns internal conditions to a steady state.

▸ Most physiological systems achieve homeostasis through negative feedback loops.

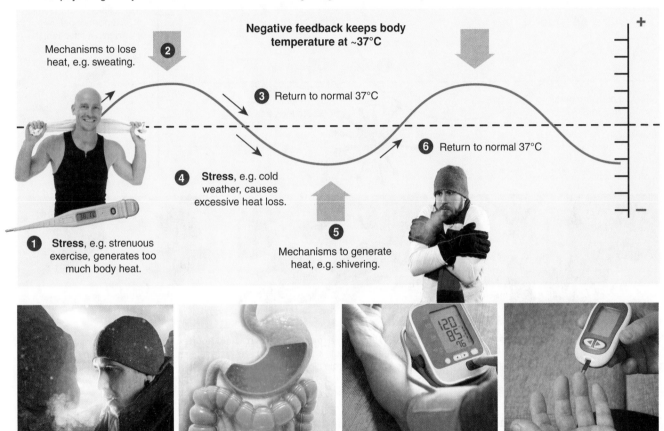

Negative feedback keeps body temperature at ~37°C

Mechanisms to lose heat, e.g. sweating.

2

3 Return to normal 37°C

6 Return to normal 37°C

4 **Stress**, e.g. cold weather, causes excessive heat loss.

5

Mechanisms to generate heat, e.g. shivering.

1 **Stress**, e.g. strenuous exercise, generates too much body heat.

We know when we are cold but we are unaware of most of the negative feedback loops operating in our bodies that keep our systems stable.

Food in the stomach activates stretch receptors, stimulating gastric secretion and motility. As the stomach empties, the stimulus for gastric activity declines.

Negative feedback loops control almost all the body's functioning processes including heart rate, blood glucose, blood pressure, and pituitary secretions.

Maintaining a stable blood glucose level is an important homeostatic function regulated by negative feedback. It involves two opposing hormones.

1. Using information and terms in this activity, construct a diagram of a negative feedback loop that models thermoregulation (homeostasis of constant body temperature):

Positive feedback loops

▶ Positive feedback loops amplify (increase) a response in order to achieve a particular result. Examples include fever, blood clotting, childbirth (labor), and lactation (production of milk).

▶ The mechanisms within a positive feedback loop will cease to function once the end result is achieved, e.g. the baby is born or a pathogen is destroyed by a fever. Positive feedback loops are less common than negative feedback loops in biological systems because the escalation in response is unstable. Unresolved positive feedback responses, e.g. high fevers, can be fatal.

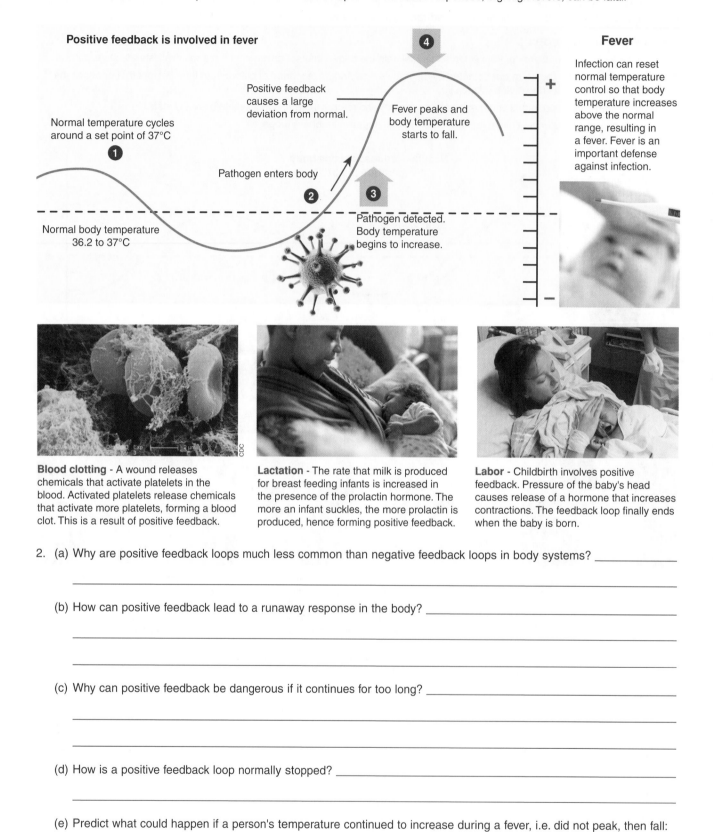

Positive feedback is involved in fever

Fever

Infection can reset normal temperature control so that body temperature increases above the normal range, resulting in a fever. Fever is an important defense against infection.

Positive feedback causes a large deviation from normal.

Fever peaks and body temperature starts to fall.

Normal temperature cycles around a set point of 37°C ❶

Pathogen enters body ❷

Pathogen detected. Body temperature begins to increase. ❸

Normal body temperature 36.2 to 37°C

Blood clotting - A wound releases chemicals that activate platelets in the blood. Activated platelets release chemicals that activate more platelets, forming a blood clot. This is a result of positive feedback.

Lactation - The rate that milk is produced for breast feeding infants is increased in the presence of the prolactin hormone. The more an infant suckles, the more prolactin is produced, hence forming positive feedback.

Labor - Childbirth involves positive feedback. Pressure of the baby's head causes release of a hormone that increases contractions. The feedback loop finally ends when the baby is born.

2. (a) Why are positive feedback loops much less common than negative feedback loops in body systems? _____
_____

(b) How can positive feedback lead to a runaway response in the body? _____
_____
_____

(c) Why can positive feedback be dangerous if it continues for too long? _____
_____
_____

(d) How is a positive feedback loop normally stopped? _____
_____

(e) Predict what could happen if a person's temperature continued to increase during a fever, i.e. did not peak, then fall:
_____
_____
_____

©2023 **BIOZONE** International
ISBN: 978-1-99-101408-5

21 Body Membranes and Cavities

Key Idea: The body is divided into cavities, and organs are surrounded by protective membranes.

The study of anatomy and physiology requires a basic understanding of anatomical terms. These include the directional and regional terms, e.g. distal / pelvic, used to describe the position of body parts, the location of the body's cavities (dorsal and ventral), and the way in which the body's membranes line those cavities and protect the organs within. A **membrane** is a thin layer of tissue that covers a structure or lines a cavity. The body's membranes fall into two broad categories: epithelial membranes (the skin, mucosa, and serosa), and synovial membranes, which lack **epithelium**. Membranes line and cover the internal and external surfaces of the body, protecting and, in some cases, lubricating them. Epithelial membranes are formed from epithelium and the connective tissue on which it rests. The skin (cutaneous membrane) is exposed to air and is a dry membrane but mucous membranes (mucosa) and serous membranes (serosa) are moist and bathed in secretions.

Body cavities

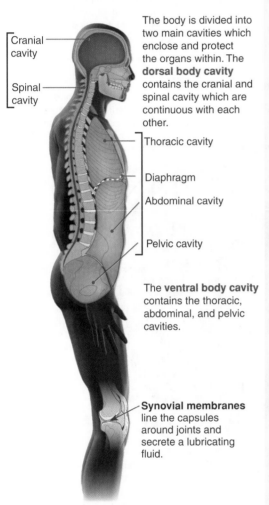

The body is divided into two main cavities which enclose and protect the organs within. The **dorsal body cavity** contains the cranial and spinal cavity which are continuous with each other.

Cranial cavity

Spinal cavity

Thoracic cavity

Diaphragm

Abdominal cavity

Pelvic cavity

The **ventral body cavity** contains the thoracic, abdominal, and pelvic cavities.

Synovial membranes line the capsules around joints and secrete a lubricating fluid.

Above: Location of dorsal and ventral body cavities in the human body. A knee joint shows a typical location of connective tissue (synovial) membranes.

Location of the body's membranes

Cutaneous membrane (the skin) forms a protective covering over the surface of the body.

Mucous membranes (muscosa) lines all body cavities that open to the exterior, i.e. the hollow organs of the respiratory, digestive, urinary, and reproductive tracts.

Serous membranes (serosa) line internal body cavities that are closed to the exterior. Serosa occur in pairs: the parietal layer lines the body wall and the visceral layer lines the organ within that cavity. The membranes are separated by a thin film of serous fluid.

They are named according to their location in the body:
• peritoneum (abdomen)
• pleura (lungs)
• pericardium (heart).

Cavity		Main contents	Membranous lining
Dorsal body cavity	Cranial cavity	Brain	Meninges
	Vertebral canal	Spinal cord	Meninges
Ventral body cavity	Thoracic cavity	Lungs Heart	Pleural cavities Pericardium
	Abdominal cavity	Digestive organs, spleen, kidneys	Peritoneum
	Pelvic cavity	Bladder, reproductive organs	Peritoneum

1. Use the information given above to name the serous membranes, labeled A-D, in the diagram above right:

   (a) A: _____   (c) C: _____

   (b) B: _____   (d) D: _____

2. (a) Describe the general role of epithelial membranes in the body: _____

   _____

   _____

   (b) Explain how epithelial membranes differ from synovial membranes: _____

   _____

   _____

©2023 **BIOZONE** International
ISBN: 978-1-99-101408-5
Photocopying Prohibited

Epithelial membranes			Synovial membranes
Serous membranes	**Mucous membranes**	**Cutaneous membrane**	
Moist - bathed in secretions.	Moist - bathed in secretions.	Dry - open to the air.	Moist - bathed in secretions.
Made of a thin layer of squamous epithelium resting on a thin layer of loose connective tissue.	Composed of some type of simple epithelium, e.g. columnar or squamous, resting on loose connective tissue.	It is made up of an **epidermis** of stratified squamous epithelium and an underlying **dermis** of connective tissue.	They are composed of connective tissue and contain no epithelial cells.
The parietal and visceral membranes are separated by a thin film of serous fluid.	The epithelium of mucosae is often absorptive or secretory. Many of them, but not all, produce mucus.	The outermost cells of skin are protected by a keratin layer, which varies in thickness.	They provide a smooth surface and cushion moving structures.
Line internal body cavities that are closed to the exterior. Occur in pairs and named according to their location, e.g. visceral pleura (see previous page).	Lines all body cavities that open to the exterior, i.e. the hollow organs of the respiratory, digestive, urinary, and reproductive tracts.	The skin forms a protective covering over the surface of the body.	Synovial membranes line the capsules around joints and secrete a lubricating synovial fluid.

The relationship between membranes and cavities

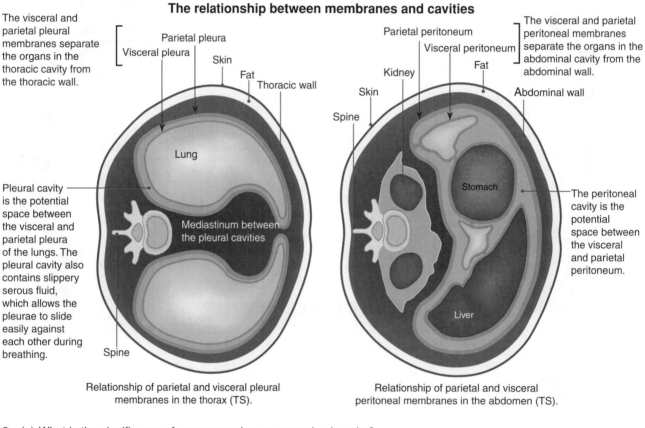

The visceral and parietal pleural membranes separate the organs in the thoracic cavity from the thoracic wall.

Pleural cavity is the potential space between the visceral and parietal pleura of the lungs. The pleural cavity also contains slippery serous fluid, which allows the pleurae to slide easily against each other during breathing.

The visceral and parietal peritoneal membranes separate the organs in the abdominal cavity from the abdominal wall.

The peritoneal cavity is the potential space between the visceral and parietal peritoneum.

Relationship of parietal and visceral pleural membranes in the thorax (TS).

Relationship of parietal and visceral peritoneal membranes in the abdomen (TS).

3. (a) What is the significance of serous membranes occurring in pairs? _____

_____

_____

(b) Describe the role of the serous fluid secreted by these membranes: _____

_____

4. (a) The stomach (labeled above, right) is covered in visceral peritoneum. What lines its inside surface (the lumen)?

_____

(b) What is the importance of the cutaneous membrane being a dry membrane? _____

_____

_____

_____

©2023 **BIOZONE** International
ISBN: 978-1-99-101408-5
Photocopying Prohibited

22 Maintaining Homeostasis

Key Idea: The various organ systems of the body act to maintain **homeostasis** through a combination of hormonal and nervous mechanisms.

In everyday life, the body must regulate respiratory gases, protect itself against agents of disease (pathogens), maintain fluid and salt balance, regulate energy and nutrient supply, and maintain a constant body temperature. All these must be coordinated and appropriate responses made to incoming stimuli. In addition, the body must be able to repair itself when injured and be capable of reproducing (leaving offspring).

Regulating respiratory gases

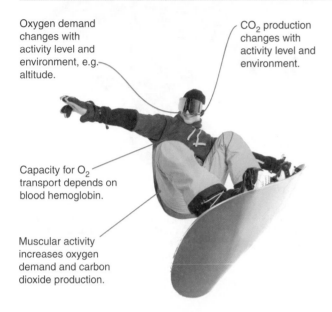

Oxygen demand changes with activity level and environment, e.g. altitude.

CO_2 production changes with activity level and environment.

Capacity for O_2 transport depends on blood hemoglobin.

Muscular activity increases oxygen demand and carbon dioxide production.

Oxygen (O_2) must be delivered to all cells and carbon dioxide (CO_2), a waste product of cellular respiration, must be removed. Breathing brings in O_2 and expels CO_2, and the cardiovascular and lymphatic systems circulate these respiratory gases (the O_2 mostly bound to hemoglobin). The rate of breathing is varied according to O_2 demands, as detected by levels in the blood.

Coping with pathogens

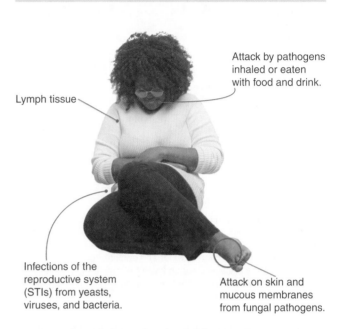

Lymph tissue

Attack by pathogens inhaled or eaten with food and drink.

Infections of the reproductive system (STIs) from yeasts, viruses, and bacteria.

Attack on skin and mucous membranes from fungal pathogens.

All of us are under constant attack from pathogens (disease causing organisms). The body has a number of mechanisms that help to prevent the entry of pathogens and limit the damage they cause if they do enter the body. The skin, the digestive system, and the immune system are all involved in the body's defense, while the cardiovascular and lymphatic systems circulate the cells and antimicrobial substances involved.

Maintaining nutrients and removing wastes

Digestion in the gut provides the building materials for the body to grow and repair tissue.

Food and drink provide energy and nutrients, but supply is pulsed at mealtimes with little in between.

Water must be reabsorbed from the digested material.

Metabolism generates waste products, including urea, which is formed in the liver and excreted by the kidneys.

The solid waste products of digestion must be eliminated. Nitrogenous wastes from protein metabolism are excreted by the kidney in the urine.

Food and drink is taken in to maintain energy supplies. The digestive system makes these nutrients available and the cardiovascular system distributes them throughout the body. Food intake is regulated largely through nervous mechanisms, while hormones control the cellular uptake of glucose. The liver metabolizes proteins to form urea, which is excreted by the kidneys.

Repairing injuries

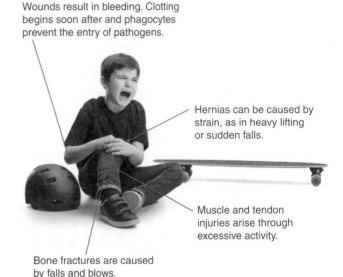

Wounds result in bleeding. Clotting begins soon after and phagocytes prevent the entry of pathogens.

Hernias can be caused by strain, as in heavy lifting or sudden falls.

Muscle and tendon injuries arise through excessive activity.

Bone fractures are caused by falls and blows.

Damage to body tissues triggers the inflammatory response and white blood cells move to the injury site. The inflammatory response is started (and ended) by chemical signals, e.g. from histamine and prostaglandins, released when tissue is damaged. The cardiovascular and lymphatic systems distribute the cells and molecules involved.

Regulating temperature, fluid, and electrolytes

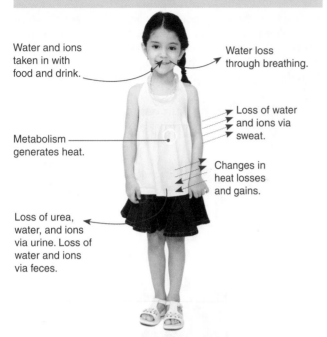

Water and ions taken in with food and drink.

Water loss through breathing.

Loss of water and ions via sweat.

Metabolism generates heat.

Changes in heat losses and gains.

Loss of urea, water, and ions via urine. Loss of water and ions via feces.

The balance of fluid and electrolytes and excretion of wastes is the job of the kidneys. Osmoreceptors monitor blood volume and bring about the release of the hormones ADH and aldosterone, which regulate reabsorption of water and sodium from blood via the kidneys. The cardiovascular and lymphatic systems distribute fluids around the body. The circulatory system and skin both help to maintain body temperature.

Coordinating responses

The brain monitors and regulates hormone levels and coordinates complex movements.

Glands, e.g. the adrenal, respond to messages from the brain to produce regulatory hormones.

Environmental stimuli bombard the senses through ears, nose, eyes, skin, and mouth.

Simple reflexes, such as pain withdrawal, allow rapid responses to stimuli.

The body is constantly bombarded by stimuli from the environment. The brain sorts these stimuli into those that require a response and those that do not. Responses are coordinated via nervous or hormonal controls. Simple nervous responses (reflexes) act quickly. Hormones, which are distributed by the cardiovascular and lymphatic systems, take longer to produce a response and the response is more prolonged.

1. Describe two mechanisms that operate to restore homeostasis after infection by a pathogen:

   (a) _____

   _____

   (b) _____

   _____

   _____

2. Describe two mechanisms by which responses to stimuli are brought about and coordinated:

   (a) _____

   _____

   (b) _____

   _____

   _____

3. Explain two ways in which water and ion balance are maintained. Name the organ(s) and any hormones involved:

   (a) _____

   _____

   _____

   _____

   (b) _____

   _____

   _____

   _____

©2023 **BIOZONE** International
ISBN: 978-1-99-101408-5
Photocopying Prohibited

23 Diagnostic Medicine

Key Idea: Sophisticated medical imaging has provided the means to look in detail at the tissues and organs of the body. This makes it possible to accurately and rapidly diagnose disorders, including use of complex computer systems and sometimes AI (artificial intelligence) to analyze data, and therefore treat people more effectively for medical problems. As well as imaging techniques, simpler methods, such as blood tests, are also widely used for diagnostic purposes.

X-ray imaging

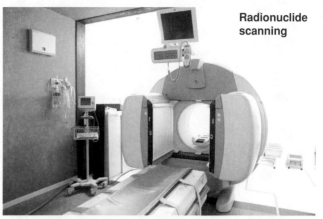
Radionuclide scanning

X-rays are a form of electromagnetic radiation that can pass through tissues and expose photographic film. The X-rays are absorbed by dense body tissues, e.g. bone, which appear as white areas, but they pass easily through less dense tissues, e.g. muscle, which appear dark. X-rays are used to identify fractures or abnormalities in bone. X-ray technology is also used in conjunction with computer imaging techniques.

Radionuclide (also called SPECT) scanning involves introducing a radioactive substance (the radionuclide) into the body, where it is taken up in different amounts by different tissues, e.g. radioactive iodine is taken up preferentially by the thyroid. The radiation emitted by the tissues that take up the radionuclide is detected by a gamma camera. Radionuclide scanning provides better detail of function than other techniques but gives less anatomical detail.

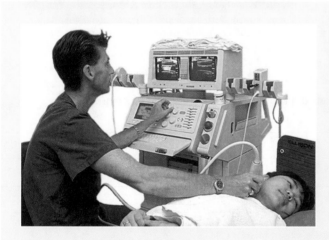

Diagnostic uses of ultrasound

Ultrasound is a diagnostic tool used to visualize internal structures without surgery or X-rays. Ultrasound imaging is based on the fact that tissues of different densities reflect sound waves differently. Sound waves are directed towards a structure, e.g. uterus, heart, kidney, liver, and the reflected sound waves are recorded. An image of the internal structures is analyzed by computer and displayed on a screen.

Echocardiography uses ultrasound to investigate heart disorders such as congenital heart disease and valve disorders. The liver and other abdominal organs can also be viewed with ultrasound for diagnosis of disorders such as cirrhosis, cysts, blockages, and tumors. Ultrasound scans of the uterus are commonly used during pregnancy to indicate placental position and aspects of fetal growth and development. This information aids better pregnancy management.

1. X-rays are a common tool to diagnose broken bones. Describe some advantages and disadvantages of this tool:

_____

_____

_____

2. Explain how radionuclide scanning differs from X-ray: _____

_____

_____

3. Discuss the advantages of ultrasound use in pregnancy:_____

_____

_____

_____

Computer imaging techniques

Computers are used extensively to examine the soft tissues and internal structures of the body for diagnostic purposes. Patients are moved into the tunnel of a special device and exposed to different types of electromagnetic waves, depending on the technique. The data is captured and analyzed by computers and medical staff to assist detection of abnormalities such as tumors.

Computerized tomography scans

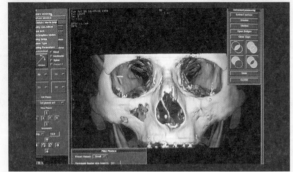

Computerized tomography (CT) scans make a series of X-rays through an organ and the picture from each X-ray slice is reconstructed into a 3-D image using computer software.

Magnetic resonance imaging

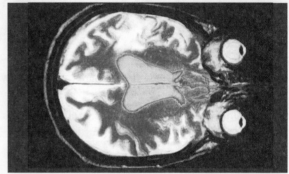

Magnetic resonance imaging (MRI) uses computer analysis of high frequency radio waves to map out variations in tissue density, especially of the central nervous system.

4. Describe the basic principle of the scanning technology behind each of the following imaging techniques:

   (a) Computerised Tomography (CT): _____

   _____

   (b) Magnetic Resonance Imaging (MRI): _____

   _____

5. Describe the benefits of using computer imaging techniques such as MRI or CT: _____

   _____

   _____

   _____

   _____

6. Describe some disadvantages of using computer imaging techniques such as MRI or CT:

   (a) CT scan: _____

   _____

   _____

   (b) MRI scan: _____

   _____

   _____

   _____

©2023 **BIOZONE** International
ISBN: 978-1-99-101408-5
Photocopying Prohibited

Endoscopy

An endoscope is an illuminated tube comprising fiber-optic cables with lenses attached. Endoscopy can be used for a visual inspection of the inside of organs or any body cavity to look for blockages or damage. Endoscopes can also be fitted with devices to remove foreign objects, temporarily stop bleeding, remove tissue samples (biopsy), and remove polyps or growths. The advantage of endoscopy use over tradition incision methods is a small entry site, leading to quicker healing.

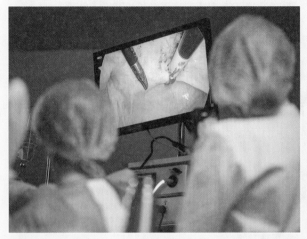

Laparoscopy is the endoscopic examination of the organs in the abdominal cavity, and is used during simple surgical operations, e.g. tubal ligation. Endoscopic examination of the stomach is called gastroscopy.

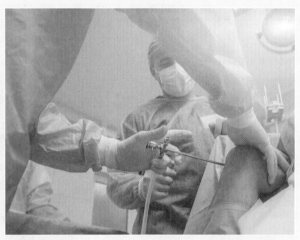

Arthroscopy is used for inspecting joints, usually knee joints (above), while the patient is under a general anesthetic. Using very small incisions, damaged cartilage can be removed from the joint using other instruments.

Biosensors

Biosensors are electronic monitoring devices that use biological material to detect the presence or concentration of a particular substance. Because of their specificity and sensitivity, enzymes are ideally suited for use in biosensors. The example below illustrates how the enzyme glucose oxidase is used to detect blood sugar level in diabetics.

The enzyme, glucose oxidase is immobilized in a semi-conducting silicon chip. It catalyzes the conversion of glucose (from the blood sample) to gluconic acid.

Hydrogen ions from the gluconic acid cause a movement of electrons in the silicon which is detected by a transducer. The strength of the electric current is directly proportional to the blood glucose concentration.

Results are shown on a liquid crystal display.

Plastic sleeve | Membrane permeable to glucose → | **Biological recognition layer** | **Transducer** | **Amplifier** | **932**

The signal is amplified

7. Describe the basic principle of a biosensor: _____

_____

_____

8. Endoscopy was originally developed as a diagnostic tool. Some types of surgery that used to use invasive techniques are increasingly using endoscopy as an alternative. Discuss some possible reasons for this trend:

_____

_____

_____

_____

_____

_____

_____

©2023 **BIOZONE** International
ISBN: 978-1-99-101408-5
Photocopying Prohibited

24 The Integumentary System

Key Idea: The skin, or cutaneous membrane, and its associated structures (hair, sweat glands, nails) collectively make the **integumentary system**.

The skin is the body's largest organ. Unlike other epithelial membranes, it is a dry **membrane**, made up of an outer **epidermis** and underlying **dermis**. The subcutaneous tissue beneath the dermis, which is largely fat (a loose connective tissue) is called the hypodermis. It is not part of the skin, but it does anchor the skin to underlying organs, thereby insulating and protecting them. The homeostatic interactions of the skin with other body systems are described below.

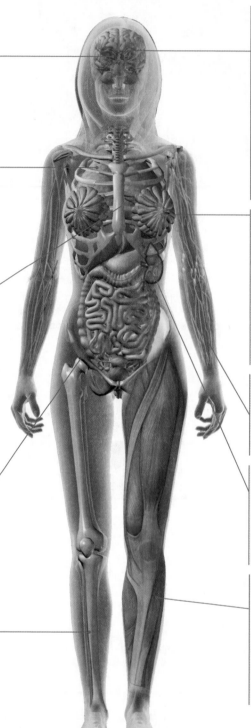

Endocrine system

- Estrogens help to maintain skin hydration.
- Androgens activate the sebaceous glands and help to regulate the growth of hair.
- Changes in skin pigmentation are associated with hormonal changes during pregnancy and puberty.

Respiratory system

- Provides oxygen to the cells of the skin via gas exchange with the blood.
- Removes carbon dioxide (metabolic waste from skin) via gas exchange.

Cardiovascular system

- Blood vessels transport O_2 and nutrients to the skin and remove wastes via the blood.
- The skin prevents fluid loss and acts as a reservoir for blood.
- Dilation and constriction of blood vessels is an important thermoregulatory mechanism.
- The blood supplies substances required for functioning of the skin's glands.

Digestive system

- Skin synthesizes vitamin D, which is required for absorption of calcium from the gut.
- The digestive system provides nutrients for growth, repair, and maintenance of the skin, delivered via the cardiovascular system.

Skeletal system

- Skin absorbs ultraviolet light and produces a vitamin D precursor. Vitamin D is involved in calcium and phosphorus metabolism, and is needed for normal calcium absorption and deposition of calcium salts in bone.

Nervous system

- Many sensory organs, e.g. Pacinian corpuscle, and simple receptors, e.g. thermoreceptors, are located in the skin.
- The nervous system regulates blood vessel dilation and sweat gland secretion.
- CNS interprets sensory information from the skin's sensory receptors.
- Nervous stimulation of arrector pili muscles causes erection of hair (thermoregulatory response).

Reproductive system

- Mammary glands, which are modified sweat glands, nourish the infant in lactating women.
- Skin stretches during pregnancy to accommodate enlargement of the uterus.
- Changes in skin pigmentation are associated with pregnancy and puberty.

Lymphatic system and immunity

- Tissue fluid nourishes skin cells. Lymphatic vessels prevent edema by collecting/returning tissue fluid to the general circulation.

Urinary system

- Vitamin D synthesis begins in the skin but final activation of vitamin D occurs in the kidneys.
- Urination controlled by a voluntary sphincter in the urethra.

Muscular system

- Muscular activity generates heat, which is dissipated via an increase in blood flow to the skin's surface.
- Muscular activity and increased blood flow increases secretion from the skin's glands, e.g. sweating.

General functions and effects on all systems

The skin is the body's largest organ and the integumentary system covers and provides physical and chemical protection for most parts of all other body systems. It has a critical role in thermoregulation and in the absorption of sunlight and synthesis of a vitamin D precursor.

©2023 **BIOZONE** International
ISBN: 978-1-99-101408-5
Photocopying Prohibited

The structure of the skin

1 The upper epidermis consists of stratified squamous **epithelium**. There are up to five layers of cells in the epidermis, with the regenerative basal layer furthest from the surface. The basal layer houses the melanocytes containing the pigment melanin, which gives skin a dark color. Cells divide at the basal layer and migrate towards the surface, becoming flatter and more keratinized. Like all epithelial tissue, the skin's epidermis lacks blood vessels.

2 The lower dermis of dense connective tissue contains collagen (strength), elastic fibers (flexibility), and reticular fibers (support). The dermis also contains the skin's sensory receptors. The upper papillary region is uneven, with small projections into the epidermis. The lower reticular layer contains blood vessels, sweat and oil glands, and deep dermal sensory receptors.

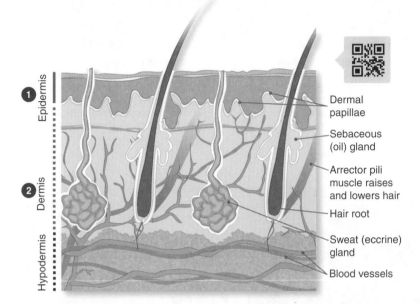

Epidermis **1**

Dermis **2**

Hypodermis

Dermal papillae

Sebaceous (oil) gland

Arrector pili muscle raises and lowers hair

Hair root

Sweat (eccrine) gland

Blood vessels

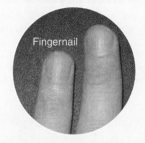

Fingernail

Fingernails (above) and toenails are modifications of the epidermis that protect the ends of the digits. Nails are formed from the horny layer of the epidermis (stratum corneum) that contains hard keratin, and they grow from the basal layer of cells in an area called the nail matrix.

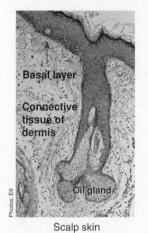

Basal layer

Connective tissue of dermis

Oil gland

Photos: Eii

Scalp skin

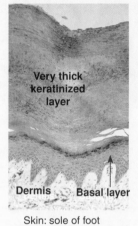

Very thick keratinized layer

Dermis   Basal layer

Skin: sole of foot

Moderately thick keratinized layer

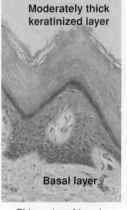

Basal layer

Skin: palm of hand

There are up to five layers of cells in the epidermis. The thickness of the layers, particularly the outermost heavily keratinized layer, varies, depending on where the skin is. Keratin protects the deeper cell layers. Skin subjected to regular wear and tear is heavily keratinized.

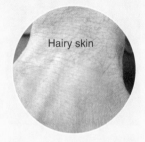

Hairy skin

Hair is found over almost all of the body. Each hair has a shaft, which protrudes above the skin's surface, and a root and hair bulb beneath. The root and shaft are made of dead, keratinized epithelial cells in three layers: a central medulla, thick inner cortex, and outer cuticle. As with skin, melanin is responsible for the color of the hair.

1. Describe two homeostatic functions of the skin: _____

   (a) _____

   (b) _____

2. Identify the location (dermis or epidermis) of each of the following and identify its role in the skin:

   (a) Basal layer (stratum basale): _____

   (b) Outermost keratinized layer (stratum corneum): _____

   (c) Sweat glands: _____

   (d) Collagen fibers: _____

©2023 **BIOZONE** International
ISBN: 978-1-99-101408-5
Photocopying Prohibited

Changes in skin

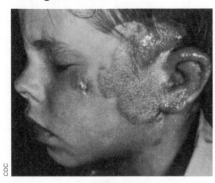

Ringworm is a fungal infection of the skin. It can affect any area of the body surface and causes raised, ring-like, scaly lesions, which may be itchy and inflamed. It can be prevented by keeping skin clean and dry, and treated with anti-fungal products.

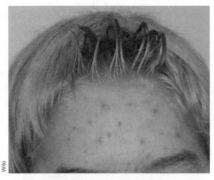

Acne is a common skin condition in adolescents in which the sebaceous glands become infected and pimples appear on the skin. Acne can be extremely severe, causing deep abscesses and scarring.

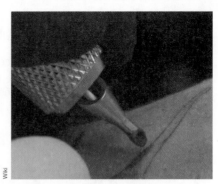

A tattoo is a permanent marking made by inserting ink into the layers of skin. The pigment remains stable in the upper layer of the dermis, trapped within fibroblasts but, in the long term, it tends to migrate deeper into the dermis and the tattoo degrades.

Mpox and skin changes

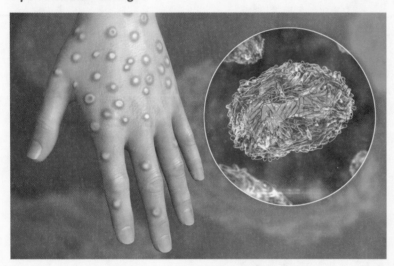

Mpox (formerly monkeypox) is a disease caused by the mpox virus producing similar, but much milder, symptoms to smallpox, a related virus. A significant mpox outbreak began in 2022, spreading beyond its origin into other continents. The virus spreads from direct human-to-human skin or secretion contact, and initially causes flu-like symptoms. 1-4 days later a rash will appear on the skin in various areas, including the hands. Anywhere from 1 to 200 round, rubbery, or firm lesions form on the skin. The lesions are painful and can often be seen with a dot on the top, called umbilication. The lesions eventually fill with pus and after 2-4 weeks a scab will form over the top, beginning the healing process.

3. Both ringworm and mpox are infectious but can be prevented with non-medical actions. Describe some of these:

(a) Ringworm: _____

_____

(b) Mpox: _____

_____

4. Why do some skin changes caused by ringworm and severe acne cause permanent scarring? _____

_____

_____

_____

_____

5. Why can a vaccine be used to prevent mpox, but not ringworm or acne? _____

_____

_____

_____

_____

_____

©2023 **BIOZONE** International
ISBN: 978-1-99-101408-5
Photocopying Prohibited

25 Thermoregulation

Key Idea: Thermoregulation is controlled both by the hormonal and nervous systems of the body.

In humans, the temperature regulation center is a region of the brain called the **hypothalamus**. The hypothalamus acts as the control center in the **thermoregulation** negative feedback loop. It contains **thermoreceptors** that monitor core body temperature and has a 'set-point' temperature of 36.7°C. The hypothalamus acts like a thermostat: it

registers changes in the core body temperature and also receives information about temperature changes from thermoreceptors in the skin. It then coordinates effector responses to counteract the changes and restore normal body temperature. Communication between components of the **negative feedback loop** uses both nervous and hormonal pathways. When normal body temperature is restored, the corrective mechanisms are switched off.

Regulating body temperature

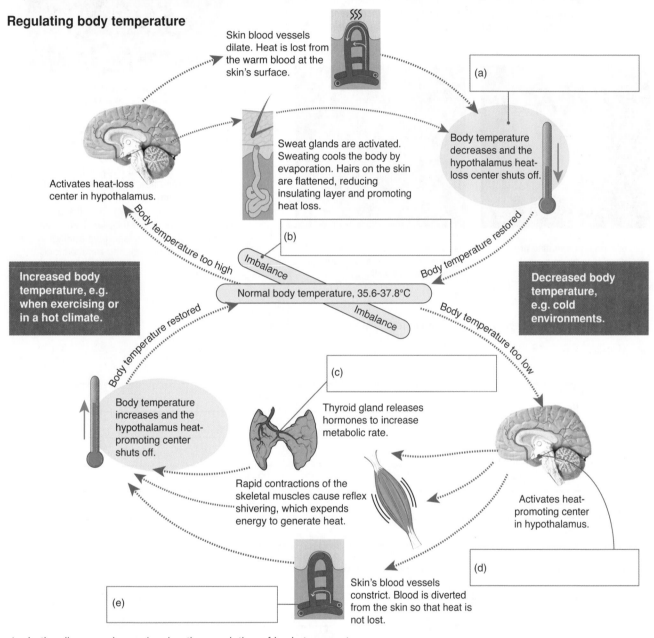

Skin blood vessels dilate. Heat is lost from the warm blood at the skin's surface.

(a)

Body temperature decreases and the hypothalamus heat-loss center shuts off.

Sweat glands are activated. Sweating cools the body by evaporation. Hairs on the skin are flattened, reducing insulating layer and promoting heat loss.

Activates heat-loss center in hypothalamus.

(b)

Body temperature too high

Imbalance

Normal body temperature, 35.6-37.8°C

Imbalance

Body temperature restored

Increased body temperature, e.g. when exercising or in a hot climate.

Decreased body temperature, e.g. cold environments.

Body temperature restored

Body temperature too low

(c)

Thyroid gland releases hormones to increase metabolic rate.

Body temperature increases and the hypothalamus heat-promoting center shuts off.

Rapid contractions of the skeletal muscles cause reflex shivering, which expends energy to generate heat.

Activates heat-promoting center in hypothalamus.

(d)

(e)

Skin's blood vessels constrict. Blood is diverted from the skin so that heat is not lost.

1. In the diagram above showing the regulation of body temperature:

   (a) Identify the stimulus: _____

   (b) Identify the effectors: _____

   (c) What structure(s) would you add to represent the receptors? _____

2. Label the diagram above by appropriately adding the labels: stimulus, receptors, control center, and effectors.

3. How do the effectors restore body temperature when it increases above the set point? _____

_____

_____

©2023 **BIOZONE** International
ISBN: 978-1-99-101408-5
Photocopying Prohibited

Thermoreceptors

▶ Thermoreceptors are simple sensory receptors located both inside the body and free nerve endings embedded in the skin. They respond to changes in temperature. When they detect a temperature change, they send information (as nerve impulses) to the hypothalamus. Heat thermoreceptors detect an increase in skin temperature above 37.5°C and cold thermoreceptors detect a fall below 35.8°C.

▶ The hair erector muscles, sweat glands, muscles, and blood vessels are the effectors for mediating a response to information from thermoreceptors.

▶ The temperature changes resulting from the actions of the effectors is communicated as negative feedback to the thermoreceptors, and relayed back to the hypothalamus to deactivate once normal body temperature is reached. Illness can 'set' the temperature higher, felt as a fever.

Regulating blood flow to the skin

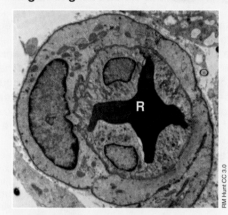

Constriction of a small blood vessel. A red blood cell (R) is in the vessel (TEM).

To regulate heat loss or gain from the skin, the blood vessels underneath become narrower (vasoconstriction) to reduce blood flow, or expand (vasodilation) to increase blood flow. When blood vessels are fully constricted, there may be as much as a 10°C gradient from the outer to the inner layers of the skin. Extremities such the hands and feet have additional vascular controls that can reduce blood flow to them in times of severe cooling.

Vasodilation and sweating are mechanisms in response to high temperature or exertion.

Vasoconstriction and 'goosebumps' (piloerection) are in response to low temperature or inactivity.

4. Describe the role of each of the following in regulating body temperature:

(a) Shivering: _____

_____

(b) The skin: _____

_____

(c) Nervous input to effectors: _____

_____

(d) Hormones: _____

_____

5. What is the purpose of sweating and how does it achieve its effect? _____

_____

_____

6. Explain how negative feedback is involved in the regulation of body temperature: _____

_____

_____

_____

_____

7. How do the blood vessels help to regulate the amount of heat lost from the skin and body? _____

_____

_____

©2023 **BIOZONE** International
ISBN: 978-1-99-101408-5
Photocopying Prohibited

Skin and sweating

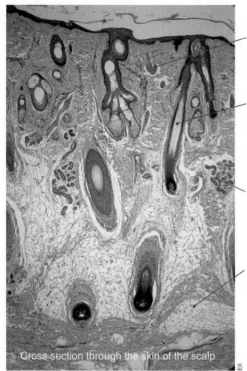

Blood vessels in the **dermis** dilate or constrict to promote or restrict heat loss.

Hairs raised or lowered to increase or decrease the thickness of the insulating air layer between the skin and the environment.

Sweat glands produce sweat, which cools through evaporation.

Fat in the sub-dermal layers insulates the organs against heat loss.

Cross section through the skin of the scalp

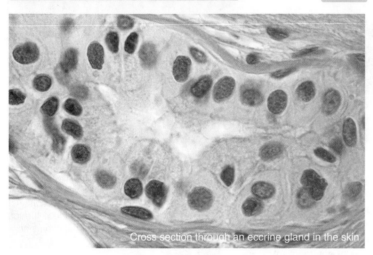

Cross section through an eccrine gland in the skin

Human skin contains two main types of sweat glands: apocrine glands secrete around the hair follicles, and eccrine glands (above) secrete directly to the skin's surface. Eccrine glands can be found on most areas of the body and, as well as secreting sweat to aid in cooling, they also release a range of compounds, such as lactate and urea, to help the skin retain a barrier to conserve moisture.

Sweat glands and the environment

Graham Crumb CC 2.0

▸ People are born with an excess of sweat glands but if they spend the first years of their life in a cold climate, most of these become permanently inactive.

▸ People acclimatized to a warm climate, such as the young Vanuatu boy above, produce sweat profusely (up to 3 L / h) and the sweat is distributed uniformly. This increases the efficiency of heat loss.

▸ People not acclimatized to warm climates may only sweat up to 1 L / h and the sweat usually beads up and drips off the body.

▸ Some people have a condition called anhidrosis, where the sweat glands do not function normally to produce sweat, putting sufferers at risk of heat stroke. This condition can be caused by environmental damage or injury to the skin, certain diseases, or be genetically inherited (Fabry disease).

8. Why does a person from a cool climate have difficulty regulating their body temperature when visiting a hot climate?

_____

_____

_____

9. How do sweat glands work to enable a person to maintain homeostasis in hot conditions? _____

_____

_____

_____

_____

26 Hypothermia

Key Idea: Hypothermia is a condition experienced when the core body temperature drops below 35°C.

Hypothermia is caused by exposure to low temperatures, and results from the body's inability to replace the heat being lost to the environment. The condition ranges from mild to severe, depending how low the body temperature has dropped. Severe hypothermia results in severe mental confusion, including inability to speak, and amnesia, organ and heart failure, and death.

A body temperature of around 37°C allows for optimal metabolic function. Below 35°C, metabolism slows, causing a loss of coordination, lethargy, and mental fatigue. Hypothermia can result from exposure to very low temperatures for a short time or to moderately low temperatures for a long time. Exposure to cold water produces symptoms of hypothermia far more quickly than exposure to the same temperature of air. This is because water is much more effective than air at conducting heat away from the body.

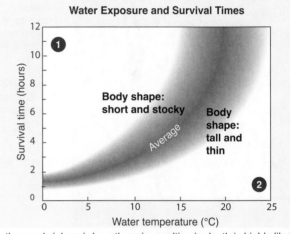

Water Exposure and Survival Times

In the graph (above), hypothermia resulting in death is highly likely in region 1 and highly unlikely in region 2.

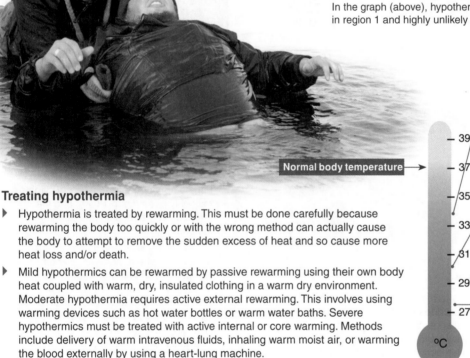

Normal body temperature →

Mild hypothermia: Shivering. Vasoconstriction reduces blood flow to the extremities. Hypertension and cold diuresis (increased urine production due to the cold).

Moderate hypothermia: Muscle coordination becomes difficult. Movements slow or laboured. Blood vessels in ears, nose, fingers, and toes constrict further resulting in these turning a blue color. Mental confusion sets in.

Severe hypothermia: Speech fails, mental processes become irrational, victim may enter a stupor. Organs and heart eventually fail, resulting in death.

Treating hypothermia

▸ Hypothermia is treated by rewarming. This must be done carefully because rewarming the body too quickly or with the wrong method can actually cause the body to attempt to remove the sudden excess of heat and so cause more heat loss and/or death.

▸ Mild hypothermics can be rewarmed by passive rewarming using their own body heat coupled with warm, dry, insulated clothing in a warm dry environment. Moderate hypothermia requires active external rewarming. This involves using warming devices such as hot water bottles or warm water baths. Severe hypothermics must be treated with active internal or core warming. Methods include delivery of warm intravenous fluids, inhaling warm moist air, or warming the blood externally by using a heart-lung machine.

1. What conditions might cause a person to become hypothermic? _____

_____

_____

_____

2. (a) With reference to the graph above, which body shape has best survival at 15°C? _____

   (b) Explain your choice: _____

3. Describe the methods used to rewarm hypothermic people safely: _____

_____

_____

_____

©2023 **BIOZONE** International
ISBN: 978-1-99-101408-5
Photocopying Prohibited

27 Hyperthermia

Key Idea: Hyperthermia is a physiological state in which the core body temperature exceeds 38.5°C without a change to the set-point of the heat control center in the **hypothalamus**. The most common cause is heat stroke caused by prolonged exposure to excessive heat or humidity, often associated with exertion. When the body produces more heat than it can dissipate, the heat regulating systems of the body can become overwhelmed and body temperature will rise uncontrollably. Prolonged elevation in body temperature is potentially fatal and is thus regarded as a medical emergency. **Hyperthermia** is different from a fever, which involves resetting the body's thermostat to a higher level in response to infection.

Causes of hyperthermia:
- Dehydration
- Hot environment
- Exercise
- Response to some drugs

Treating hyperthermia

Treating hyperthermia involves rapidly lowering the core body temperature. However, care must be taken to avoid causing vasoconstriction and shivering, as these produce heat and make the hyperthermic condition worse.

External treatments

Mild hyperthermia, e.g. exercising on a hot day, is treated by drinking water, removing excess clothing, and resting in a cool place. In more serious cases, cooling is achieved by sponging the body with cool water, or using cooling blankets or ice-packs. A person may also be wrapped in wet sheets and have a fan directed on them to increase evaporative cooling (sweating). Placing the patient in a bathtub of cool water removes a significant amount of heat in a short period of time.

Internal treatments

Internal cooling is required when the core temperature exceeds 40°C, or the patient is unconscious or confused. These methods are more aggressive and invasive. Treatments include administering cool intravenous fluids, flushing the stomach or rectum with cold water, or hemodialysis, where a machine cools the blood externally before it is returned to the body.

Phases in heat exhaustion and hyperthermia

Phase 1
Overexertion is usually accompanied with a flushed red face and rapid short breaths. Correction is by seeking shade and drinking plenty of fluid.

Phase 2
Heat exhaustion is a more serious problem. It is indicated by profuse sweating, a dry mouth, cramps, and nausea. The skin will appear red as blood is directed to the skin to reduce core temperature. Physical activity should be stopped immediately and shade should be sought. Cool drinks and ice packs on the skin may be needed.

Phase 3
Heat stroke is the final and most serious stage. The body's core temperature may have risen to 41°C. Thermoregulatory mechanisms fail. Sweat is no longer produced and the skin becomes hot and dry. Disorientation is followed by collapse and unconsciousness. Metabolic processes become uncoupled and enzymes denature. Death follows.

---

1. (a) What is hyperthermia? _____

_____

(b) How does hyperthermia differ from a fever? _____

_____

2. (a) Why is it dangerous to lower the temperature of a hyperthermia patient so quickly that they begin to shiver?

_____

(b) Why are internal cooling treatments used on patients with temperatures over 40°C? _____

_____

3. Explain why untreated heat stroke can rapidly lead to death: _____

_____

_____

28 Drugs and Thermoregulation

Key Idea: Consumption of some drugs can effect the body's ability to maintain **thermoregulation**.

Ecstasy, or MDMA, is an illegal stimulant, popular in the clubbing or dance party scene for the feelings of euphoria it induces. It has profound psychological and physiological effects, brought about by an increase in the levels of serotonin in the brain. These effects include changes to temperature regulation, heart rate, blood pressure, and appetite control. The effects of ecstasy start 20-60 minutes after taking it and last for six hours. It can take days or weeks for serotonin levels to return to normal.

Ecstasy induced hyperthermia

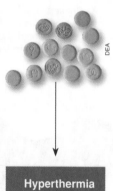

Hyperthermia

Physiological effect of ecstasy	Consequence
Reduces blood flow to skin	Reduces heat loss
Decreases sweating	
Increases metabolic rate	Increases heat generation
Decreases thirst recognition	Increases dehydration

Other contributing factors: Hot environment and dancing (= heat generation)

Hyperthermia is one of the major side effects of ecstasy use and can result in organ failure and death if it is not treated. It has been implicated in the deaths of people attending dance-parties.

To understand how humans may be affected by ecstasy, researchers investigated how it causes hyperthermia in rabbits. The data (right) shows a clear positive relationship between the ecstasy dose and body temperature (figure A). The same research also showed that blood flow to the skin decreases due to vasoconstriction after ecstasy is taken (figure B).

One of the body's main cooling mechanisms is to increase blood flow to the skin, so that heat can be lost. Ecstasy shuts down this mechanism, so it becomes more difficult to lose heat. In humans, the problems of ecstasy use are exacerbated by hot, crowded dance environments in parties or clubs, and the physical effort of dancing, which generates heat. The combination of these behavioral and physiological factors results in abnormal increases in body temperature, heat exhaustion, and heat stroke.

Ecstasy and hyperthermia in rabbits

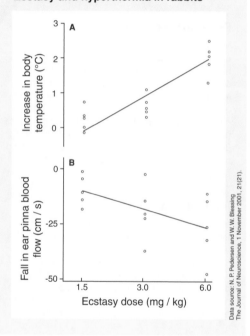

Data source: N. P. Pedersen and W. W. Blessing, The Journal of Neuroscience, 1 November 2001, 21(21).

1. (a) Describe the effects of ecstasy on body temperature in rabbits: _____

   _____

   (b) What conclusions can you draw about how ecstasy affects blood flow to the skin in rabbits? _____

   _____

   _____

2. Discuss how ecstasy can cause hyperthermia in humans: _____

   _____

   _____

   _____

   _____

   _____

29 Homeostasis in Newborns

Key Idea: Newborn babies need to rapidly switch from physiological processes supported by the mother to independently maintaining their own homeostatic state. Once delivered, the newborn must function independently of a placental connection. This requires a number of significant physiological changes associated with temperature regulation, blood glucose homeostasis, and fluid and electrolyte balance. Newborns require considerable help to maintain **homeostasis**, e.g. dressing them appropriately so they do not become too hot or too cold.

Thermoregulation in newborns

Newborn babies cannot fully thermoregulate until six months of age. They can become too cold or too hot very quickly.

Newborns cannot shiver to produce heat and have limited capacity to generate heat from large body movements because their ability to move is limited. Much of an infant's heat production comes from the metabolic activity of brown fat, a mitochondrial rich organ abundant in newborns. Heat is also generated by metabolic activity.

Newborns minimize heat loss by reducing the blood supply to the periphery (skin, hands, and feet). This helps to maintain the core body temperature. Increased brown fat activity and general metabolic activity generates heat. Newborns are often dressed in a hat to reduce heat loss from the head, and tightly wrapped to trap heat next to their bodies.

Newborns lower their temperature by increasing peripheral blood flow. This allows heat to be lost, cooling the core temperature. Newborns can also reduce their body temperature by sweating, although their sweat glands are not fully functional until four weeks after birth.

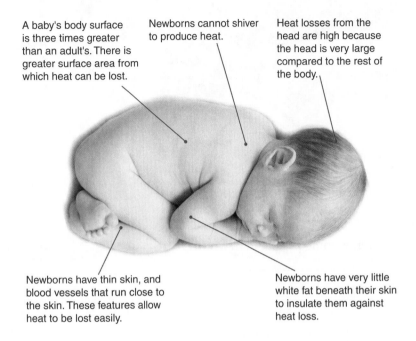

A baby's body surface is three times greater than an adult's. There is greater surface area from which heat can be lost.

Newborns cannot shiver to produce heat.

Heat losses from the head are high because the head is very large compared to the rest of the body.

Newborns have thin skin, and blood vessels that run close to the skin. These features allow heat to be lost easily.

Newborns have very little white fat beneath their skin to insulate them against heat loss.

Thermoregulation in premature newborns

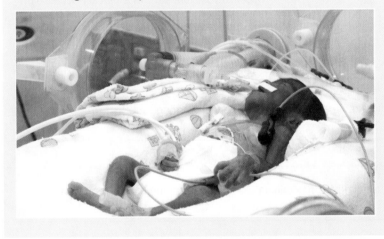

Premature babies have even less ability to thermoregulate than full-term newborns, and often have a very immature thermoregulatory system. Heat loss from evaporation when wet, conduction on cold surfaces, and convection in drafty rooms can lead to the premature newborn quickly becoming hypothermic. **Hypothermia** can then increase neonatal (newborn) mortality rates (28% per every 1°C below 36°C) and increase in sepsis/infection rates (11% per every 1°C below 36°C). Premature babies are placed in an enclosed temperature controlled incubator to help them maintain a stable temperature (left). Surfaces and fluids used are pre-warmed.

1. Describe the features of a newborn baby that make it susceptible to rapid heat loss: _____

_____

_____

_____

2. Describe how newborns can control body temperature by altering blood flow to the skin: _____

_____

_____

Glucose homeostasis in newborns

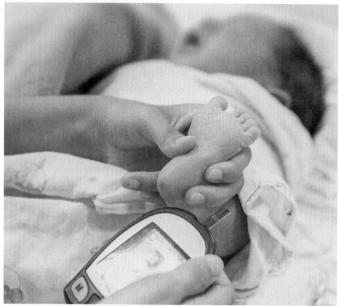

Newborn baby being checked for blood glucose levels

Prior to birth, most of the glucose supplied to a fetus/baby is provided continuously through the placenta from the mother. Once born, a newborn must rely on its own body glycogen stores, which release glucose, until sufficient volumes of milk are consumed. The hormones insulin and glucagon maintain glucose blood homeostasis and are present in the fetus from early gestation onwards. In the hours directly after birth, the ratio of these two hormones shifts rapidly in the newborn, moving from favoring glycogen storage in utero to an increase in glycogen breakdown to supply the now independent baby.

Premature babies are likely to have insufficient glycogen stores, as are some newborns who have metabolic mutations, or faced growth restriction in the uterus.

Excessive demands on glucose can be due to hypothermia, low oxygen levels, infection, or limited access to milk in the first week. Both lack of stores and increased utilization of glucose can lead to hypoglycemia (low blood glucose), and may lead to apnea (cessation of breathing), convulsions, and eventual death, if not treated. The blood glucose level of at-risk infants can be monitored using a meter (left) that extracts a small drop of blood from the newborn's heel.

Renal homeostasis in newborns

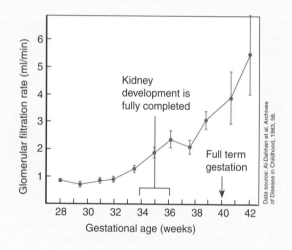

Newborn babies have inefficient kidneys. Ten days after birth, the filtration rate of the kidneys has increased significantly but is still half that of an adult. It takes one to two years for renal function to reach adult levels. The data (left) shows how kidney glomerular filtration rate, a measure of kidney efficiency, increases through gestation and after birth.

Low renal efficiency affects the ability of the newborn to maintain fluid and electrolyte balance. A newborn's kidneys are unable to concentrate urine very well, and absorption of some electrolytes (sodium and bicarbonate) is poor. Newborn babies have a greater risk of becoming dehydrated. This is partially because of their limited ability to concentrate urine, but also because their large surface area increases the rate of water loss through sweating and breathing.

3. (a) In which situations does blood glucose monitoring of newborns become especially important? _____

_____

_____

(b) Why is a ratio change of insulin to glucagon required for maintaining blood glucose homeostasis in a newborn?

_____

_____

_____

_____

_____

4. What are the consequences of newborns having a limited renal capacity? _____

_____

_____

_____

30 Chapter Summary

1. (a) Where is the temperature regulation center in humans located? _____

   (b) How does it carry out this role? _____

   _____

2. Describe the role of the following in maintaining a constant body temperature in humans:

   (a) The skin: _____

   _____

   (b) The muscles: _____

   _____

3. How is negative feedback involved in keeping body temperature within narrow limits? _____

   _____

   _____

   _____

4. (a) Why does infection result in an elevated core body temperature? _____

   _____

   (b) Explain why a prolonged fever can be fatal: _____

   _____

5. Summarize the features of a newborn that cause it to lose heat quickly: _____

   _____

   _____

6. Describe what types of medical imaging are commonly used in diagnostic medicine, giving examples: _____

   _____

   _____

7. Label the features in this cross-section of skin and describe their role in thermoregulation:

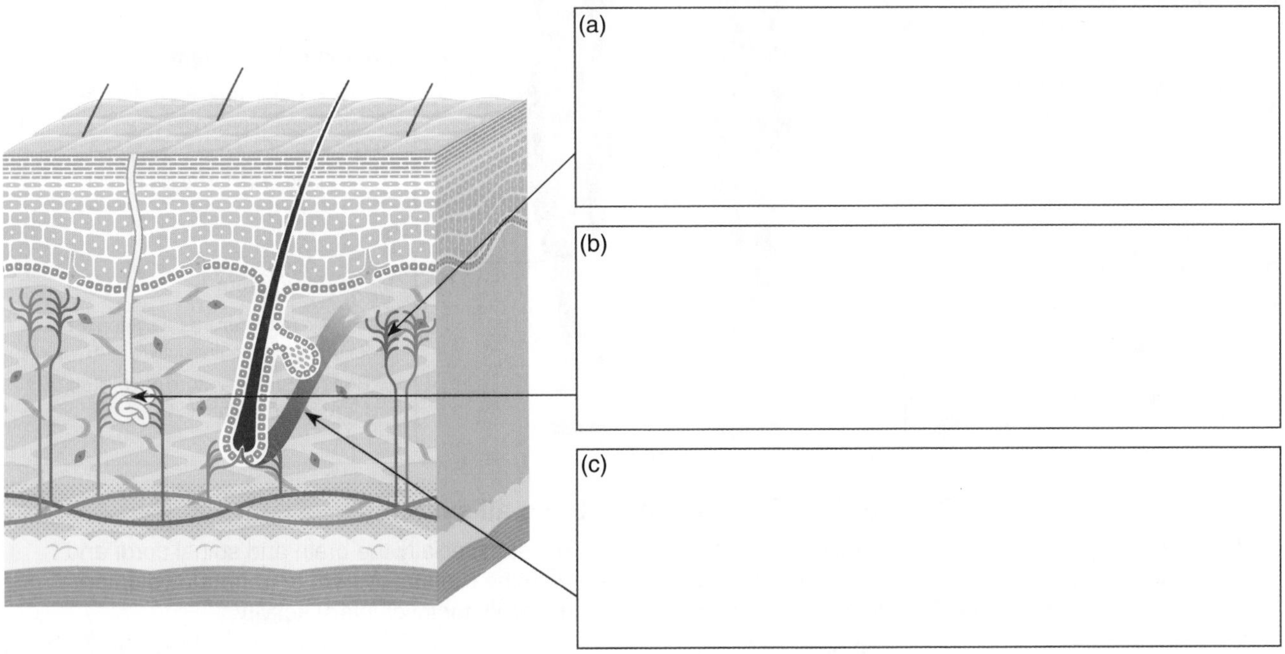

(a)

(b)

(c)

Muscular and Skeletal Systems

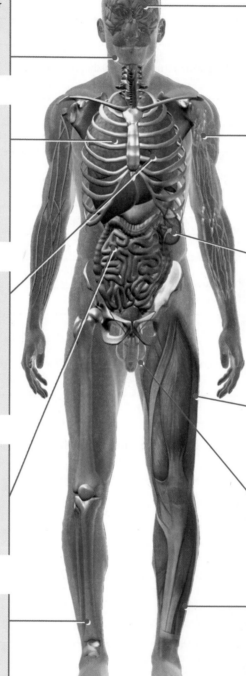

Endocrine system

- The skeleton protects the endocrine organs, especially in the pelvis, chest, and brain.
- Bone growth, remodeling, and repair occur in response to hormones.
- Androgens and growth hormone promote muscle strength and increase in mass.

Respiratory system

- Skeleton encloses and protects lungs.
- Flexible ribcage enables ventilation of the lungs for exchange of gases (O_2/CO_2).
- Diaphragm and intercostals produce volume changes in breathing.

Cardiovascular system

- Heart and blood vessels transport O_2, nutrients, and waste products to all the body.
- Bone marrow produces red blood cells.
- Bone matrix stores calcium, which is required for contraction of muscle in the heart and blood vessels.

Digestive system

- Skeleton provides some protection and support for the abdominal organs.
- Digestive system provides nutrients for growth, repair, and maintenance of muscle and connective tissues.

Skeletal system

- Muscular activity maintains bone strength and helps determine bone shape.
- Muscles pull on bones to create movement.

Nervous system

- The skeleton protects the CNS.
- Bone acts as a store of calcium ions required for nerve function.
- Innervation of bone and joint capsules provides sensation and positional awareness.
- Muscular activity is dependent on innervation.

Lymphatic system and immunity

- Stem cells in the bone marrow give rise to the lymphocytes involved in the immune response.

Urinary system

- The skeleton protects the pelvic organs.
- Final activation of vitamin D, which is involved in calcium and phosphorus metabolism, occurs in the kidneys.
- Urination is controlled by a voluntary sphincter in the urethra.

Integumentary system

- Skin absorbs and produces precursor of vitamin D, which is involved in calcium and phosphorus metabolism.
- Skin covers and protects the muscle tissue.

Reproductive system

- The skeleton protects the reproductive organs.
- Reproductive (sex) hormones influence skeletal development.

Muscular system

- The skeleton acts as a system of levers for muscular activity.
- Bone provides a store of calcium for muscle contraction.

General functions and effects on all systems

The skeletal system provides bony protection for the internal organs, especially the brain and spinal cord, and the lungs, heart, and pelvic organs. The muscular system acts with the skeletal system to generate voluntary movements. Smooth and cardiac muscle provide motility for involuntary activity.

| **Symptoms of disease** | • Pain (moderate to severe)
• Inflammation
• Limitations in function |

| **Diagnosis of disorders** | • Blood tests
• Bone scans
• Medical imaging techniques
• Athroscopy |

| **Disorders of the bones and joints** | • Growth disorders
• Trauma (fractures and sprains)
• Infection
• Tumors
• Degenerative diseases |

| **Treatment of injury** | • Surgery
• Physical and drug therapies
• Prosthetics and orthotics |

| **Diseases of the skeletal muscles** | • Inherited diseases
• Fibrosis (scarring)
• Strains, tears, and cramps
• Denervation and atrophy |

| **Treatment of inherited disorders** | • Surgery
• Radiotherapy (for cancers)
• Physical and drug therapies
• Prosthetics and orthotics
• Gene therapy |

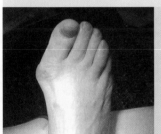

• Osteomalacia
• Osteoarthritis
• Osteoporosis
• Sarcomas
• Muscular dystrophy

• Joint replacement
• Grafts
• Genetic counselling
• X-rays
• MRI

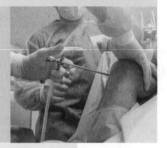

Support & Movement
The Musculoskeletal System

The musculoskeletal system can be affected by disease and undergoes changes associated with aging.

Medical technologies and exercise can be used to diagnose, treat, and delay the onset of musculoskeletal disorders.

• Osteoarthritis
• Osteoporosis
• Muscular atrophy

• Muscle fatigue
• Fast vs slow twitch
• Aerobic training
• Anaerobic training

| **Aging and the bones, joints, and muscles** | • Bone loss
• Loss of muscle mass
• Accumulated trauma
• Increased incidence of cancers |

| **Effects of exercise on bones, joints, and muscles** | • Increased bone density
• Increased lean muscle mass
• Changes in flexibility & joint mobility
• Changes in fiber type & recruitment
• Changes in oxidative capacity |

CHAPTER 3

The Skeletal System

KEY IDEAS

- The skeleton is the internal supporting structure of the body, composed of mineralized connective tissue.

- The skeleton, together with the body's system of muscles, enables movement of the body.

- Movement occurs at articulation in the skeleton, called joints. The amount of movement permitted depends on the joint type.

- Bone is dynamic tissue, undergoing growth, remodeling, and repair.

- Aging is associated with degenerative changes in the skeleton.

KEY TERMS

- Appendicular skeleton
- Axial skeleton
- Cartilaginous joint
- Fibrous joint
- Ossification
- Osteoarthritis
- Osteoblasts
- Osteocytes
- Osteoporosis
- Pectoral girdle
- Pelvic girdle
- Synovial joint

RESOURCE HUB

Scan the QR code to access:

- weblinks
- videos
- 3D models
- interactives

LEARNING OBJECTIVES

Activity number

☐ 1 Identify the two main divisions of the human skeleton as the axial and appendicular skeletons. Classify bones, according to their size and shape. Recognize long bones, short bones, flat bones, and irregular bones. Identify the bones that make up the skull and understand the difference between paired and single bones. **31**

☐ 2 Understand the structure of the spine, including the arrangement of vertebrae and the intervertebral disks. Describe ankylosing spondylitis as a disease that affects the spine. **32**

☐ 3 Describe the main bones that make up the pectoral girdle and explain the difference between the male and female pelvic girdle. **33**

☐ 4 Understand that bone is a living, dynamic substance that is continually remodeled and repaired. Use a diagram to describe the gross structure of a long bone, including the features that confer strength and shock absorption. Indicate the locations of the diaphysis, periosteum, and epiphysis, and associated cartilage. **34**

☐ 5 Describe ossification, explaining the role of osteoblasts and the process by which hyaline cartilage is replaced with hard bone. Explain the roles of parathyroid hormone and calcitonin in hormonal regulation of blood calcium levels. **34**

☐ 6 Describe the ultrastructure of compact bone. Identify the periosteum, osteoblasts, osteocytes, matrix, lacunae, and Haversian canals. **35**

☐ 7 Explain the differences between cartilaginous, synovial, and fibrous joints and name examples and locations of each of these joint types. Describe the structure of a synovial joint, explaining the role of synovial fluid. Explain why this type of joint is prone to injury. Explain the role of ligaments in the knee joint. **36**

☐ 8 Describe the degenerative changes in the skeleton that occur with increasing age, including reduction in the rate of bone remodeling, accelerated areas of bone loss, and osteoporosis and osteoarthritis. **38**

Background: Bone internal structure

31 The Human Skeleton

Key Idea: The human skeleton consists of two main divisions: the axial skeleton (made up of the skull, rib cage, and spine) and the appendicular skeleton (made up of the limbs and the shoulder and pelvic girdles).

Bones are identified by their location and described by their shape, e.g. irregular, flat, long, or short, related to their functional position in the skeleton. Most of the bones of the upper and lower limbs are long bones. Bones also have features such as processes, holes (foramina), and depressions (fossae), associated with nerves, blood vessels, ligaments, and muscles. Understanding the basic organization of the skeleton, the particular features associated with its component bones, and the nature of skeletal articulations (joints) is essential to understanding how the movement of body parts is achieved. Babies are born with 450 bones, many of which fuse as they grow. Adults have 206 bones.

Word list:

phalanges, humerus, patella, scapula, tibia, clavicle, sternum, lumbar vertebra, femur, phalanges, cranium, sacrum, metacarpals, rib, ilium of hip bone, fibula, carpals, tarsals, metatarsals, facial bones

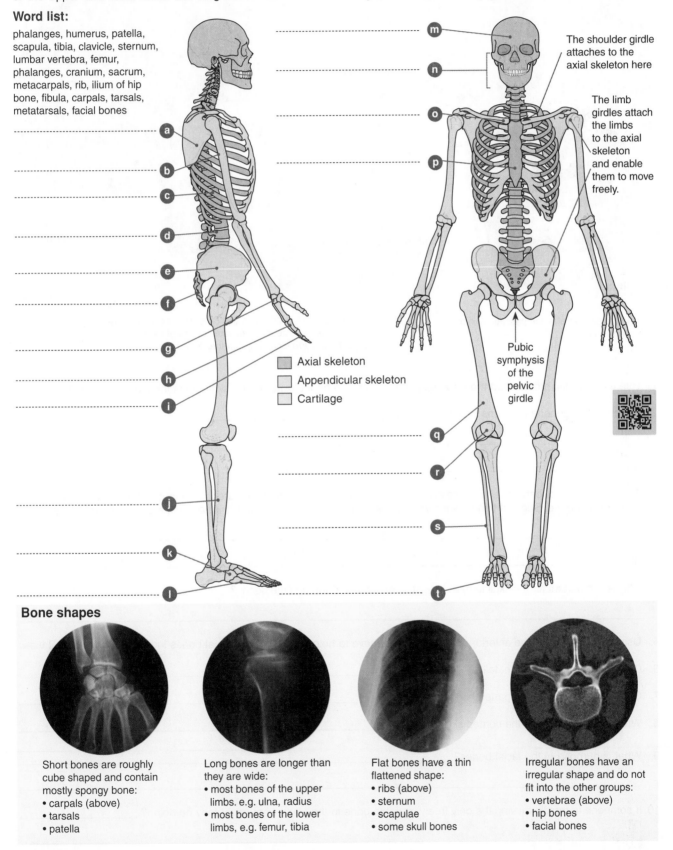

The shoulder girdle attaches to the axial skeleton here

The limb girdles attach the limbs to the axial skeleton and enable them to move freely.

Axial skeleton
Appendicular skeleton
Cartilage

Pubic symphysis of the pelvic girdle

Bone shapes

Short bones are roughly cube shaped and contain mostly spongy bone:
• carpals (above)
• tarsals
• patella

Long bones are longer than they are wide:
• most bones of the upper limbs. e.g. ulna, radius
• most bones of the lower limbs, e.g. femur, tibia

Flat bones have a thin flattened shape:
• ribs (above)
• sternum
• scapulae
• some skull bones

Irregular bones have an irregular shape and do not fit into the other groups:
• vertebrae (above)
• hip bones
• facial bones

Bones of the skull

The skull is formed from the cranial bones and the facial bones. The cranium is composed of eight large flat bones, and forms a protective dome enclosing the brain. The parietal and temporal bones are paired, but the rest of the cranial bones are single. The fourteen facial bones hold the eyes in position and enable attachment of the facial muscles. Twelve are paired and only the mandible and the small vomer bone in the nasal cavity are single. Of all the skull bones, only the mandible is freely movable. The rest are joined by sutures (immovable joints).

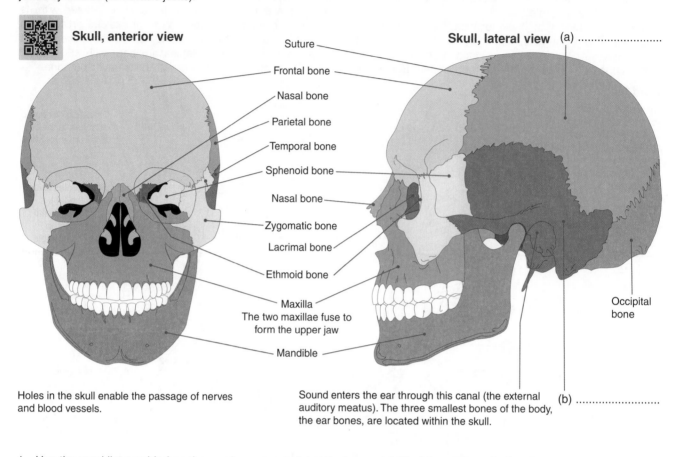

Skull, anterior view

Suture
Frontal bone
Nasal bone
Parietal bone
Temporal bone
Sphenoid bone
Nasal bone
Zygomatic bone
Lacrimal bone
Ethmoid bone
Maxilla
The two maxillae fuse to form the upper jaw
Mandible

Skull, lateral view (a) ....

Occipital bone

Holes in the skull enable the passage of nerves and blood vessels.

Sound enters the ear through this canal (the external auditory meatus). The three smallest bones of the body, the ear bones, are located within the skull.

(b) ....

1. Use the word list provided on the previous page to label the bones (a)-(t) of the skeleton in the diagram on p65:

2. Describe two general functions of the limb girdles: _____

    (a) _____

    (b) _____

3. The skull bones of babies at birth and early in infancy are not fused and some areas (the fontanelles) have still to be converted to bone. Suggest two reasons why the skull bones are not fused into sutures until around 2 years of age:

    (a) _____

    (b) _____

4. Why is it important for the skull to have holes (called foramina) through the bones? _____

    _____

5. Using the diagram of the anterior view of the skull above to help you label the cranial bones indicated on the lateral view:

6. Classify the shape of the patella: _____

7. Classify the shape of the parietal bone: _____

8. What is the purpose of the domed skull? _____

9. What is purpose of the facial bones? _____

    _____

10. If someone is rapidly moving the only freely movable bone in the skull, what might they be doing? _____

    _____

11. Label the human skull using the list of anatomical terms in the blue box below:

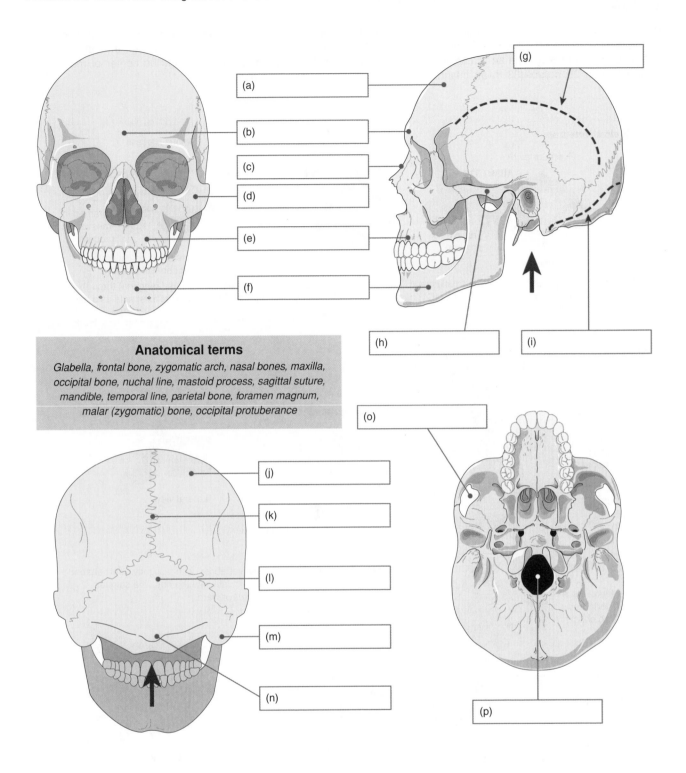

(a)

(b)

(c)

(d)

(e)

(f)

(g)

(h)

(i)

Anatomical terms

Glabella, frontal bone, zygomatic arch, nasal bones, maxilla, occipital bone, nuchal line, mastoid process, sagittal suture, mandible, temporal line, parietal bone, foramen magnum, malar (zygomatic) bone, occipital protuberance

(j)

(k)

(l)

(m)

(n)

(o)

(p)

12. Name three types of irregularly shaped bones and give their locations (you may have to research these):

(a) _____

(b) _____

(c) _____

13. Summarize the function of the human skeleton, in relation to movement: _____

_____

_____

©2023 **BIOZONE** International
ISBN: 978-1-99-101408-5
Photocopying Prohibited

32 The Bones of the Spine

Key Idea: The spine supports the skull and shoulder girdle and transmits the weight of the upper body to the lower limbs. It also forms a protective tube for the spinal cord. The spine is formed from 26 bones (33 in an infant, some of which later fuse), separated and connected by discs of cartilage called the intervertebral discs. Together, the vertebrae form an S-shaped bend which brings the center of mass to the mid-line of the body.

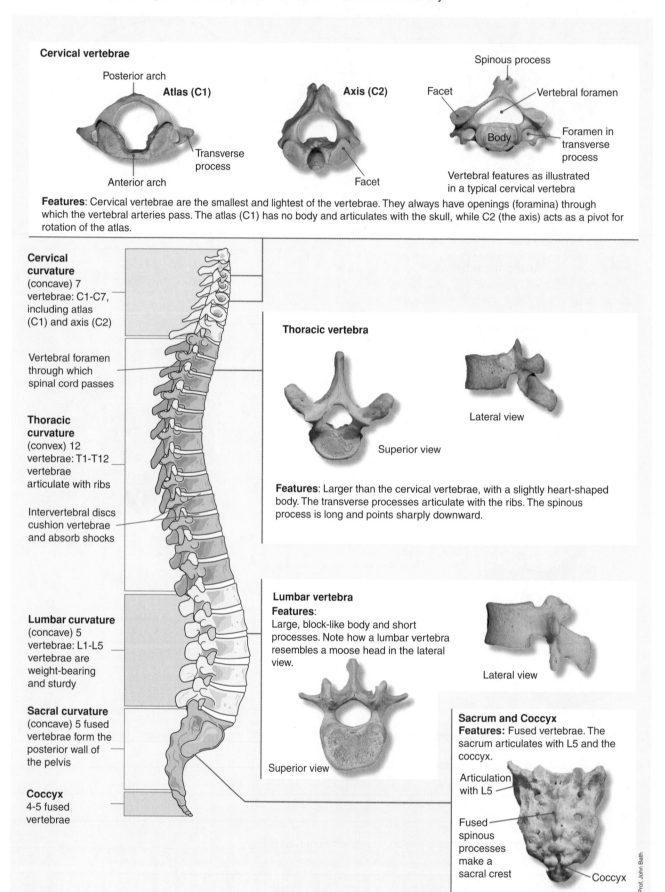

Cervical vertebrae

Atlas (C1)
- Posterior arch
- Transverse process
- Anterior arch

Axis (C2)
- Facet

- Spinous process
- Facet
- Vertebral foramen
- Body
- Foramen in transverse process

Vertebral features as illustrated in a typical cervical vertebra

Features: Cervical vertebrae are the smallest and lightest of the vertebrae. They always have openings (foramina) through which the vertebral arteries pass. The atlas (C1) has no body and articulates with the skull, while C2 (the axis) acts as a pivot for rotation of the atlas.

Cervical curvature
(concave) 7 vertebrae: C1-C7, including atlas (C1) and axis (C2)

Vertebral foramen through which spinal cord passes

Thoracic curvature
(convex) 12 vertebrae: T1-T12 vertebrae articulate with ribs

Intervertebral discs cushion vertebrae and absorb shocks

Lumbar curvature
(concave) 5 vertebrae: L1-L5 vertebrae are weight-bearing and sturdy

Sacral curvature
(concave) 5 fused vertebrae form the posterior wall of the pelvis

Coccyx
4-5 fused vertebrae

Thoracic vertebra

Lateral view

Superior view

Features: Larger than the cervical vertebrae, with a slightly heart-shaped body. The transverse processes articulate with the ribs. The spinous process is long and points sharply downward.

Lumbar vertebra
Features:
Large, block-like body and short processes. Note how a lumbar vertebra resembles a moose head in the lateral view.

Lateral view

Superior view

Sacrum and Coccyx
Features: Fused vertebrae. The sacrum articulates with L5 and the coccyx.

Articulation with L5

Fused spinous processes make a sacral crest

Coccyx

Prof. John Bath

©2023 **BIOZONE** International
ISBN: 978-1-99-101408-5
Photocopying Prohibited

Ankylosing spondylitis

Normal spine   **Ankylosing spondylitus**

Vertebra

Fusion

Inflammation

Disk

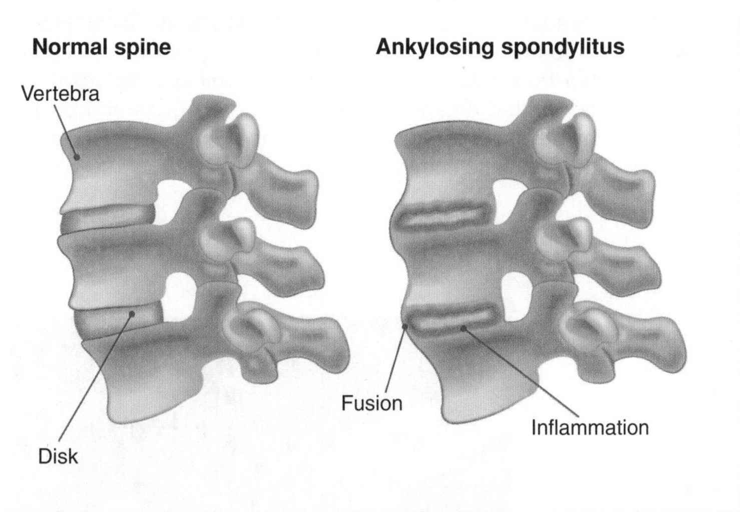

Healthy spine (left), and fused spine with ankylosing spondylitus (right).

Ankylosing spondylitis is a type of inflammatory arthritis that eventually results in the vertebral bones of the spine fusing together. The pain and swelling normally begins at the base of the spine, gradually moving up towards the neck region, and often creating a permanently bent posture.

The condition is most likely to begin in middle age, and is linked to a genetic mutation, although not all people with the defect develop the disease.

Other complications of the disease include weakened and breaking vertebrae, and the resulting spinal nerve damage. Eye damage, heart valve failure, and increased likelihood of bone, prostate, and colon cancer, are also linked to the disease.

1. Identify the vertebrae associated with each of the following features:

    (a) Functional role in bearing much of the spinal load: _____

    (b) Articulate with the ribs. Vertebral body is heart shaped (highlight this on the diagram): _____

    (c) Articulates with the skull and lacks a vertebral body: _____

    (d) Fused vestigial appendage: _____

    (e) Typically has a small body and foramina (openings) in the transverse processes: _____

    (f) Forms the posterior wall of the bony pelvis: _____

2. Suggest a function of the S-shape of the spine: _____

3. At birth, the spine consists of 33 bones, 9 more than an adult. What happens to these extra bones? _____

4. Referring to the diagram of the skeleton on page 65, what might the purpose of the sacrum be? _____

5. Scientists suggest that one or more gene mutations in the past could have been responsible for ape and human tail loss. A developing tail can be seen in human embryos from 5 weeks, but it disappears and fuses into the coccyx remnant by birth. What function might the coccyx provide in adults?

6. Why are the atlas and the axis vertebrae distinctly different from the remaining cervical, thoracic, and lumbar vertebrae?

33 The Limb Girdles

Key Idea: The pectoral (shoulder) and pelvic girdles attach the limbs to the axial skeleton and allow for the free and wide-ranging movement of the arms and legs.

The shoulder girdle, also called the pectoral girdle, consists of two scapulae (shoulder blades) and two clavicles (collar bones). The clavicles are joined (articulate) with the sternum (breastbone) so that the girdle forms an incomplete ring around the thorax. The pelvic (hip) girdle is formed of two hip bones (also called pelvic, innominate, or coxal bones) connected anteriorly at the pubic symphysis and posteriorly by the sacrum. Each hip bone arises by fusion of three bones: the ilium, ischium, and pubis.

The shoulder girdle

The scapula is attached to both the clavicle and the humerus. It is held in place by muscles.

The clavicle acts as a brace to keep the top of the arm away from the top of the thorax.

The sternoclavicular joint on each side joins the shoulder girdle and axial skeleton.

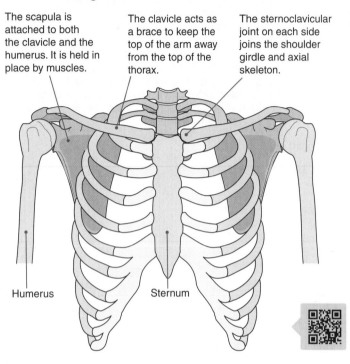

Humerus

Sternum

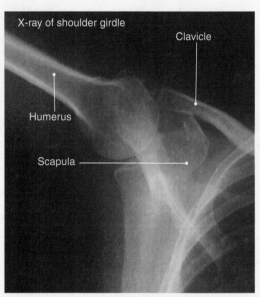

X-ray of shoulder girdle

Clavicle

Humerus

Scapula

Right side of shoulder girdle showing clavicle and scapula.

1. (a) What is the function of the shoulder girdle? _____

_____

(b) Identify the single point of attachment of shoulder girdle to the axial skeleton: _____

_____

2. What is the relationship between the range of movement of the arms and the shoulder girdle structure? _____

_____

_____

3. The clavicle is a commonly broken bone in shoulder impact injuries. Explain how an incorrectly healed clavicle bone could influence shoulder movement:

_____

_____

_____

4. The shoulder can become dislocated due to injury (right). Relate this injury to the shoulder girdle structure:

_____

_____

_____

_____

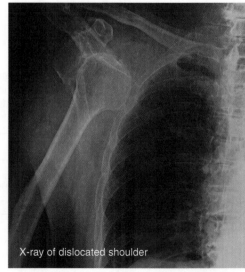

X-ray of dislocated shoulder

©2023 **BIOZONE** International
ISBN: 978-1-99-101408-5
Photocopying Prohibited

The pelvic girdle

Weight-bearing is the most important function of the pelvic girdle, so the bones are large and thick.

The bowl-shaped pelvic girdle also protects the reproductive organs, bladder, and the lower parts of the gut.

Fusion of bones provides rigidity

Femur

Pubic symphysis softens during childbirth to allow the pelvis to widen.

The angle between the pelvic bones is more acute in males than in females.

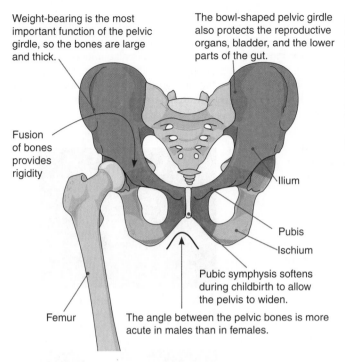

Ilium

Pubis

Ischium

The male and female pelves

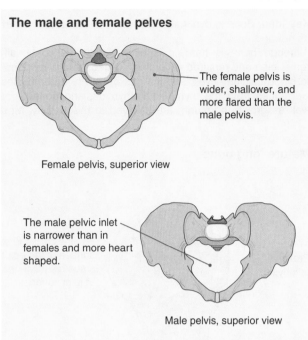

The female pelvis is wider, shallower, and more flared than the male pelvis.

Female pelvis, superior view

The male pelvic inlet is narrower than in females and more heart shaped.

Male pelvis, superior view

5. Relate the particular features of the pelvic girdle to its functional roles: _____

_____

_____

6. Explain how and why the male and female pelves (*sing.* pelvis) differ: _____

_____

_____

7. (a) What is the function of the shoulder girdle? _____

_____

(b) Identify the single point of attachment of shoulder girdle to the axial skeleton: _____

_____

8. What is the advantage of the pubic symphysis in women?

_____

_____

_____

_____

_____

_____

(a)

(b)

(c)

(d)

(e)

X-ray of the pelvis

9. On the X-ray (right), label femur, ilium, ischium, pubis, and pelvic inlet:

10. How could a pelvic X-ray indicate potential birthing issues in women?

_____

_____

_____

©2023 **BIOZONE** International
ISBN: 978-1-99-101408-5

34 Bone

Key Idea: Bone is dynamic and is remodelled and repaired, as needed.

Although bone is hard, it is dynamic and is continually remodeled and repaired according to needs and in response to blood calcium levels and the pull of gravity and muscles. Hormones from the thyroid, parathyroids, and gonads, as well as growth hormone, are involved in this activity. Most bones of the skeleton are formed from hyaline cartilage by a process of ossification (bone formation) and they grow by bone remodeling. Bone remodeling is also important in bone repair. Bones have a simple gross structure, as illustrated by a long bone such as the humerus (below). The hard (dense) bone surrounds spongy (cancellous) bone filled with red bone marrow.

Mature long bone

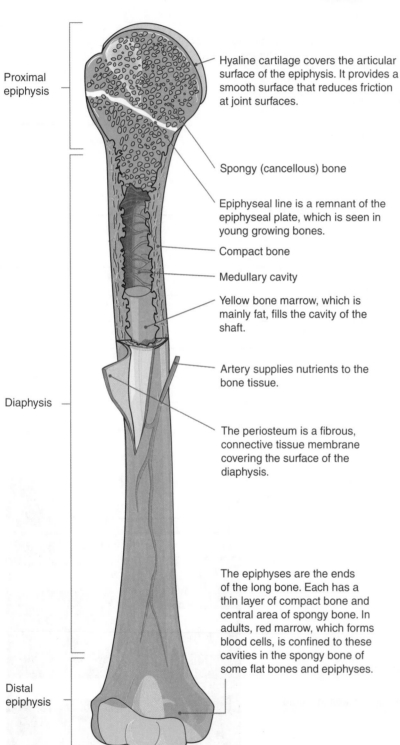

Proximal epiphysis

Hyaline cartilage covers the articular surface of the epiphysis. It provides a smooth surface that reduces friction at joint surfaces.

Spongy (cancellous) bone

Epiphyseal line is a remnant of the epiphyseal plate, which is seen in young growing bones.

Compact bone

Medullary cavity

Yellow bone marrow, which is mainly fat, fills the cavity of the shaft.

Artery supplies nutrients to the bone tissue.

Diaphysis

The periosteum is a fibrous, connective tissue membrane covering the surface of the diaphysis.

The epiphyses are the ends of the long bone. Each has a thin layer of compact bone and central area of spongy bone. In adults, red marrow, which forms blood cells, is confined to these cavities in the spongy bone of some flat bones and epiphyses.

Distal epiphysis

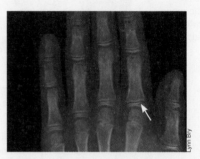

An X-ray shows the epiphyseal plates (growth plates) of a child's hand, seen as separate from the longer bones.

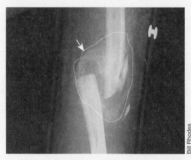

A fibrocartilage callus, or tissue mass, (indicated) begins the repair process on a fractured humerus. Cigarette smoking slows bone healing markedly.

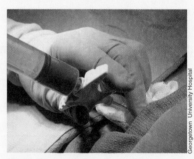

Red bone marrow is stored in the cavities of spongy bone. Here it is being extracted for transplant. Bone marrow is a source of stem cells.

A section of a femur head shows the compact bone surrounding inner spongy bone and marrow. Blood cells are formed in the red marrow.

©2023 **BIOZONE** International
ISBN: 978-1-99-101408-5

Ossification and bone growth

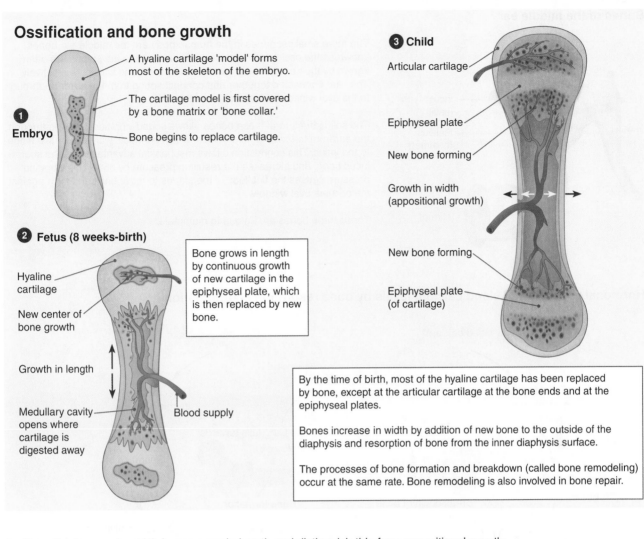

1 Embryo

A hyaline cartilage 'model' forms most of the skeleton of the embryo.

The cartilage model is first covered by a bone matrix or 'bone collar.'

Bone begins to replace cartilage.

2 Fetus (8 weeks-birth)

Hyaline cartilage

New center of bone growth

Growth in length

Medullary cavity opens where cartilage is digested away

Blood supply

Bone grows in length by continuous growth of new cartilage in the epiphyseal plate, which is then replaced by new bone.

3 Child

Articular cartilage

Epiphyseal plate

New bone forming

Growth in width (appositional growth)

New bone forming

Epiphyseal plate (of cartilage)

By the time of birth, most of the hyaline cartilage has been replaced by bone, except at the articular cartilage at the bone ends and at the epiphyseal plates.

Bones increase in width by addition of new bone to the outside of the diaphysis and resorption of bone from the inner diaphysis surface.

The processes of bone formation and breakdown (called bone remodeling) occur at the same rate. Bone remodeling is also involved in bone repair.

1. Describe the way in which bones grow in length and distinguish this from appositional growth: _____

_____

_____

_____

2. Describe how the skeleton fulfills each of the following functional roles:

(a) Support: _____

_____

(b) Protection: _____

_____

(c) Movement: _____

_____

(d) Blood cell production: _____

_____

(e) Mineral storage: _____

_____

3. Identify the feature described by each of the following definitions:

(a) A feature of bones that are still increasing in length: _____

(b) The long shaft of a mature bone: _____

Bones of the middle ear

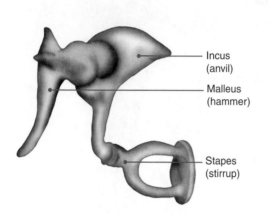

Incus
(anvil)

Malleus
(hammer)

Stapes
(stirrup)

The three smallest bones in the human body are the middle ear bones, known as the ossicles. The malleus, the incus, and the stapes are often known by their common names: hammer, anvil, and stirrup, respectively. They are connected together and conduct sound from the eardrum through to the oval window of the cochlea in the inner ear.

The solid structure of these bones allows sound vibrations moving through the eardrum to travel to the malleus, which connects with a lever-like hinge to the incus. This connection allows mechanical advantage due the shorter incus bone, and increases the resulting pressure by 35%. This vibrating pressure causes the flat 'foot' of the stapes to move back and forth against the cochlea oval window.

These three bones are unique to mammals.

Hormonal regulation of blood calcium levels by bone resorption and formation

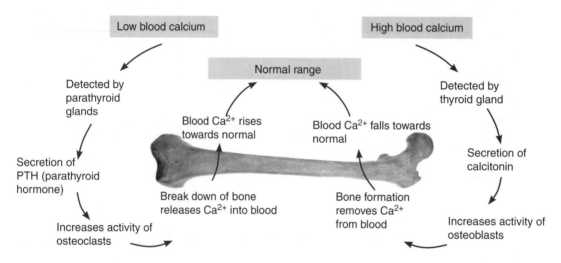

Low blood calcium

High blood calcium

Normal range

Detected by parathyroid glands

Detected by thyroid gland

Blood Ca^{2+} rises towards normal

Blood Ca^{2+} falls towards normal

Secretion of PTH (parathyroid hormone)

Secretion of calcitonin

Break down of bone releases Ca^{2+} into blood

Bone formation removes Ca^{2+} from blood

Increases activity of osteoclasts

Increases activity of osteoblasts

Bone stores calcium ions (Ca^{2+}) and phosphorus (in the form of phosphate ions, PO_4^{3-}). The levels of these minerals in the blood are maintained by adding to or removing them from stores in bone. Two hormones, PTH and calcitonin, regulate blood calcium levels through bone remodeling, which involves both the normal breakdown (resorption) and formation (ossification) of bone tissue. Remodeling allows bone to be reshaped and replaced after injury, as well as everyday wear and tear. Also, because bone remodeling occurs in response to the stress of weight-bearing activity, being physically active can help prevent bone loss, even into old age.

4. Why does the epiphysis of the bones become greatly reduced in adults? _____

_____

_____

_____

5. What is the advantage of the positioning of the ossicles (three small ear bones) in the ears of humans?

_____

_____

_____

6. Summarize how the fluctuations of calcium in the blood effect storage of calcium in the bones: _____

_____

_____

_____

_____

©2023 **BIOZONE** International
ISBN: 978-1-99-101408-5
Photocopying Prohibited

35 The Ultrastructure of Bone

Key Idea: Bones are composed of a number of different cell groups, each with their own role.

The cells that produce bone are called osteoblasts. They secrete the matrix of calcium phosphate and collagen fibers that forms the rigid bone. When they are mature, the bone cells are called osteocytes. They are trapped within the matrix but have many thin cytoplasmic extensions, which lie within small channels (called canaliculi). Dense bone has a very regular structure, composed of repeating units called osteons or Haversian systems, comprising canals and lamellae (after British physician Clopton Havers). Spongy bone is found inside dense bone. It has a much looser structure with irregular spaces filled with red bone marrow.

The structure of dense bone

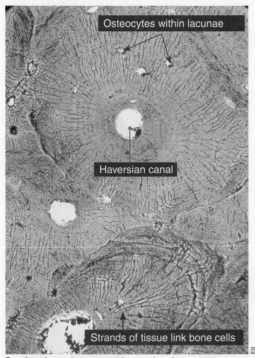

Osteocytes within lacunae

Haversian canal

Strands of tissue link bone cells

Section through compact bone showing osteons.

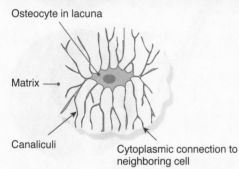

Osteocyte in lacuna

Matrix →

Canaliculi

Cytoplasmic connection to neighboring cell

Osteocyte (mature bone cell) embedded in a lacuna within the matrix. Osteocytes maintain the bone tissue (as opposed to osteoblasts, which form the bone).

Bone cross-section

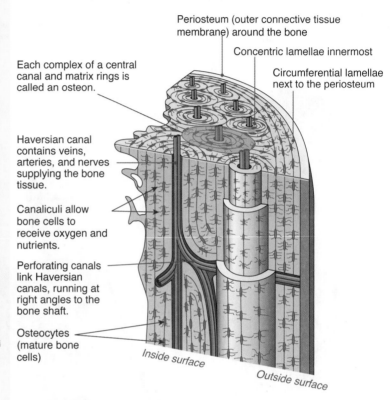

Periosteum (outer connective tissue membrane) around the bone

Concentric lamellae innermost

Circumferential lamellae next to the periosteum

Each complex of a central canal and matrix rings is called an osteon.

Haversian canal contains veins, arteries, and nerves supplying the bone tissue.

Canaliculi allow bone cells to receive oxygen and nutrients.

Perforating canals link Haversian canals, running at right angles to the bone shaft.

Osteocytes (mature bone cells)

Inside surface

Outside surface

Synonyms for bone types

You may come across several terms for the same thing:

Bone type	Also called	Features
Dense bone	Hard bone Cortical bone Compact bone	• Haversian canals surrounded by a regular arrangement of osteocytes. • A single Haversian system is called an osteon.
Spongy bone	Cancellate bone Cancellous bone Trabecular bone	• Less dense structure and higher surface area than dense bone. • Large irregular spaces containing red bone marrow.

1. Distinguish between the function of osteocytes and osteoblasts: _____

_____

2. What is the function of the Haversian canals in dense bone tissue? _____

_____

_____

3. Outline the differences between dense and spongy bone: _____

_____

_____

©2023 **BIOZONE** International
ISBN: 978-1-99-101408-5

36 Joints

Key Idea: All movements of the skeleton occur at joints: points of contact between bones, or between cartilage and bones.

Bones are too rigid to bend without damage. To allow movement, the skeletal system consists of many bones held together at joints by flexible connective tissues called ligaments. Joints may be classified structurally as fibrous, cartilaginous, or synovial, based on whether fibrous tissue, cartilage, or a joint cavity separates the bones of the joint. Each of these joint types allows a certain degree of movement. Bones move about a joint by the force of muscles acting upon them.

Cartilaginous joints

Here, the bone ends are connected by cartilage. Most allow limited movement, although some, e.g. between the first ribs and the sternum, are immovable.

Immovable fibrous joints

The bones are connected by fibrous tissue. In some, e.g. sutures of the skull, the bones are tightly bound by connective tissue fibers and there is no movement.

Synovial joints

These allow free movement in one or more planes. The articulating bone ends are separated by a joint cavity containing lubricating synovial fluid.

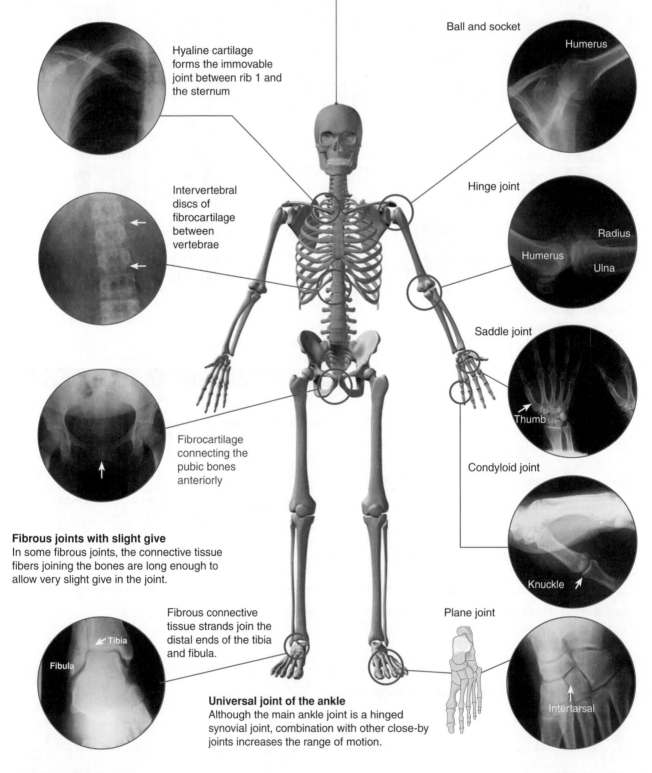

Hyaline cartilage forms the immovable joint between rib 1 and the sternum

Intervertebral discs of fibrocartilage between vertebrae

Fibrocartilage connecting the pubic bones anteriorly

Ball and socket

Humerus

Hinge joint

Radius

Humerus

Ulna

Saddle joint

Thumb

Condyloid joint

Knuckle

Plane joint

Intertarsal

Fibrous joints with slight give

In some fibrous joints, the connective tissue fibers joining the bones are long enough to allow very slight give in the joint.

Fibrous connective tissue strands join the distal ends of the tibia and fibula.

Tibia

Fibula

Universal joint of the ankle

Although the main ankle joint is a hinged synovial joint, combination with other close-by joints increases the range of motion.

©2023 **BIOZONE** International
ISBN: 978-1-99-101408-5
Photocopying Prohibited

Artificial joints

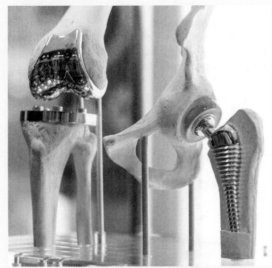

Artificial knee joint (left) and hip joint (right).

Some joints in the body can break down and become non-functional due to injury, old age, or disease, typically the shoulder, knee, and hip joints. Medical technology has enabled artificial replacement joints to be developed and surgically inserted in and around the bones, replicating the motion and function of the original joint.

Materials that are used to construct the joints need to be strong and resistant, yet still light. The stem that inserts into the bone is made from a metal alloy, usually titanium, with chromium or cobalt added for strength. The lining between the ball and socket of the artificial hip socket is a high density plastic, and ceramic components are usually present as well.

The first generation of artificial joints, developed in the 1960s and '70s had a life span of around 10-15 years. New innovations in how the joints work, and materials designed to closer mimic actual tissue, have prolonged the functionality of artificial joints currently being implanted.

1. Describe the basic function of joints: _____

_____

2. How are bones held together at joints? _____

_____

A   B   C   D   E

3. Classify each of the joint models (A-E) above, according to the descriptors below:

(a) Pivot: _____   (b) Hinge: _____   (c) Ball-and-socket: _____   (d) Saddle: _____   (e) Gliding: _____

4. Paraphrase the definition of the three groups of joints in the human body, giving examples:

(a) Cartilaginous joints: _____

_____

(b) Immovable fibrous joints: _____

_____

(c) Synovial joints: _____

_____

5. Link the structures and materials of an artificial hip joint to its functionality in replacing this joint: _____

_____

_____

_____

_____

_____

37 Synovial Joints

Key Idea: Synovial joints are distinguished from other joint types by the presence of a fluid-filled joint capsule surrounding the articulating surfaces of the bones.
Synovial joints are the most common and most movable joints in the body. They allow free movement of body parts in varying directions (one, two or three planes). The most freely movable synovial joints are also the least stable and the most prone to injury. Restricting the amount of movement gives less freedom, but also makes the joint more stable.

Structure of an elbow joint

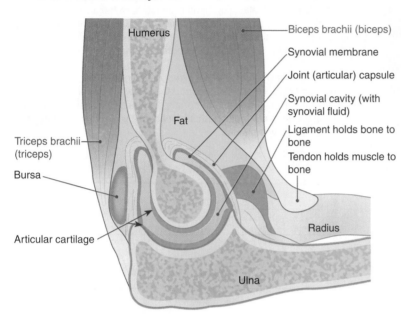

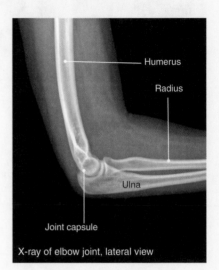

X-ray of elbow joint, lateral view

The elbow joint is a hinge joint and typical of a synovial joint. Like most synovial joints, it is reinforced by ligaments (not all shown). In the diagram (left), the brachialis muscle, which inserts into the ulna and is the prime mover for flexion of the elbow, has been omitted to show the joint structure. The X-ray above shows the position of this joint in the arm

Important definitions

A bursa is a fluid filled cavity lined with synovial membrane. It acts as a cushion, e.g. between tendon and bone, or between bones.
Cartilage is a flexible connective tissue. It protects a joint surface against wear, but has no blood supply (it is avascular).

1. (a) What features are common to most synovial joints? _____

    _____

    _____

    _____

    (b) Explain the role that synovial fluid and cartilage play in the structure and function of a synovial joint: _____

    _____

    _____

2. What purpose might the bursa and fat pads have in the synovial joint? _____

    _____

    _____

3. Joints contain baro-receptor sensory nerves that detect and respond to environmental changes, including temperature and pressure. These changes affect the amount, thickness, and pressure of fluid in the joint. How might lower temperatures and low barometric pressure affect synovial joint structure?

    _____

    _____

    _____

©2023 **BIOZONE** International
ISBN: 978-1-99-101408-5
Photocopying Prohibited

Structure of a knee joint

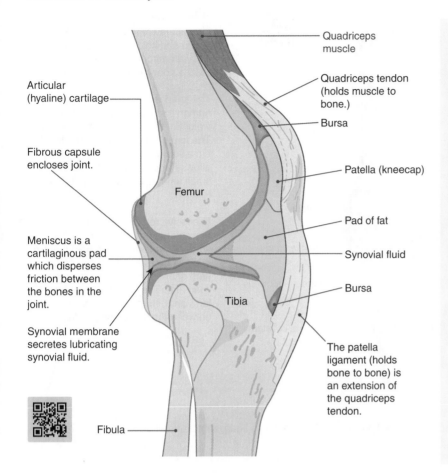

Quadriceps muscle

Quadriceps tendon (holds muscle to bone.)

Bursa

Articular (hyaline) cartilage

Patella (kneecap)

Fibrous capsule encloses joint.

Femur

Pad of fat

Synovial fluid

Meniscus is a cartilaginous pad which disperses friction between the bones in the joint.

Bursa

Tibia

Synovial membrane secretes lubricating synovial fluid.

The patella ligament (holds bone to bone) is an extension of the quadriceps tendon.

Fibula

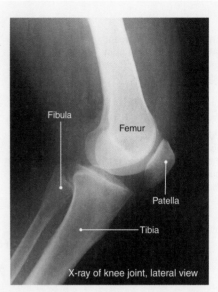

Fibula

Femur

Patella

Tibia

X-ray of knee joint, lateral view

Structurally, the knee joint is a condyloid joint, where a convex surface fits a concave surface. However, it functions as a hinge joint because the cartilage and the ligaments of the joint prevent any lateral (sideways) movement. Note that the patella ligament is the only ligament shown in the diagram (left), but other ligaments stabilize the joint (see next page).

4. (a) What specific type of synovial joint is the knee classified as, with reference to its movement: _____

_____

_____

(b) How does the movement of this joint compare to the movement of the shoulder joint? _____

_____

_____

5. Why is the knee joint so prone to becoming injured?_____

_____

_____

_____

6. Bursa can be damaged due to constant repetitive movement of the knee, such as that experienced by professional cyclists. The pre-patella bursa, in front of the patella, is one such structure that can be affected, with holes 'worn' through the layers of membrane. Suggest some likely effects of this injury:

_____

_____

7. Knees have both bone and cartilage in them. What are key differences between these two types of tissue?

_____

_____

_____

_____

Ligaments of the knee joint

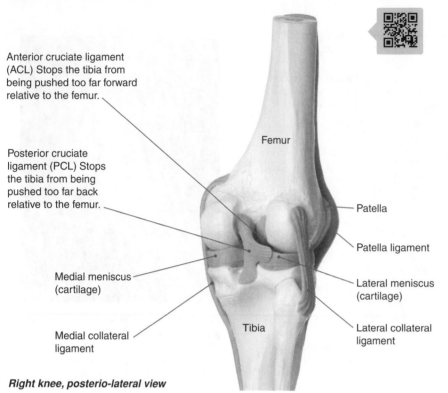

Anterior cruciate ligament (ACL) Stops the tibia from being pushed too far forward relative to the femur.

Posterior cruciate ligament (PCL) Stops the tibia from being pushed too far back relative to the femur.

Femur

Patella

Patella ligament

Medial meniscus (cartilage)

Lateral meniscus (cartilage)

Tibia

Lateral collateral ligament

Medial collateral ligament

Right knee, posterio-lateral view

About ligaments

Ligaments are made of connective tissue and hold the bones together. They are strong and flexible, but they have a poor blood supply.

The knee is the largest joint in the human body and bears most of the weight of the body during locomotion. The femur articulates with the tibia, but also with the patella. The joint allows flexion and extension and a small amount of medial and lateral rotation.

Excessive rotation and lateral movements are prevented by two sets of ligaments, which hold the joint in place and stabilize it. The diagram (left) shows the positions of these ligaments. The cruciate ligaments form an X shape through the center between the articulating surfaces.

8. The knee joint is reinforced and stabilized by several ligaments. How do these ligaments assist the joint function?

_____

_____

9. (a) Injuries to the knee's ligaments are quite common. Why do you think this is the case?

_____

_____

_____

_____

(b) Explain why torn ligaments are slow to heal:

_____

_____

_____

Ligament injuries

Tears to the ligaments of the knee are among the most common sporting injuries. The anterior cruciate ligament (ACL) is often injured by twisting and must be repaired.

X-ray of repair to the ACL of the right knee. Screws hold the ligament graft in correct place.

_____

10. Compare and contrast the structure and function of ligaments and tendons around the synovial joints: _____

_____

_____

_____

_____

_____

_____

_____

©2023 **BIOZONE** International
ISBN: 978-1-99-101408-5
Photocopying Prohibited

38 Aging and Diseases of the Bone

Key Idea: Aging refers to the degenerative changes that occur in the body, including the skeletal system, as a result of cell renewal rates slowing.

Aging affects all tissues, including bone and the other connective tissues that make up the skeleton. As people age, the rate of bone remodeling slows and bone resorption rates begin to exceed rates of deposition. As a result, the skeleton loses strength and there is an increased tendency for bones to fracture. The joints also tend to become less flexible. Some specific diseases of the skeleton (such as **osteoporosis**) are also more common in older people, although they are not exclusively associated with aging.

Bone density vs age

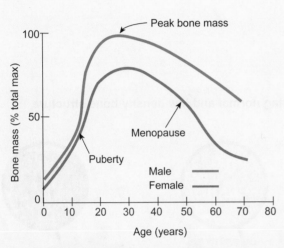

Bone density declines with age from a peak in the early to mid 20s. It is lower in females throughout life and more particularly so after menopause.

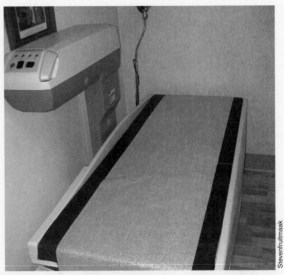

Osteoporosis is diagnosed by measuring bone mineral density (BMD). The most widely-used method is dual energy X-ray absorptiometry or DEXA (above). Two X-ray beams with different energy levels are aimed at the bone. BMD is determined from the bone's absorption of each beam.

1. Describe the main reason for age-related loss of bone mass: _____

_____

_____

2. Suggest why the weight-bearing joints of the body are most commonly affected by old age? _____

_____

3. Explain why loss of bone mineral density is associated with increased risk of bone fracture: _____

_____

_____

4. Approximately how much of peak bone mass will a be lost by age 70 in:

   (a) A male: _____ (b) A female: _____

5. Adequate dietary intake of calcium is very important for people in their first 20 years or so. Explain why:

_____

_____

6. A reduction of density in bones, leading to osteoporosis, or 'brittle bones', can be symptom-free and 'silent' until fractures begin. How does technology like the DEXA scan diagnose this condition more readily?

_____

_____

_____

Osteoporosis

Osteoporosis (OP), means 'porous bone', and is an age-related disorder where bone mass, structure, and density decrease, accompanied by a loss of height and an increased tendency for bones to fracture (break).

Women are at greater risk of developing the disease than men because their skeletons are lighter and their estrogen levels fall after menopause; estrogen provides some protection against bone loss. Around 25% of women over 65 will be diagnosed with some degree of osteoporosis. Younger women with low estrogen and/or low body weight are also affected.

Osteoporosis affects the whole skeleton, but especially the spine, hips, and legs. Sudden movement, such as coughing, or even small falls, can lead to unexpected fractures that are difficult to heal.

Although this disease cannot be cured, treatment, such as strengthening exercises, medication, dietary modification, and reduction or elimination of alcohol, smoking, and salt can alleviate the symptoms and slow down bone density loss.

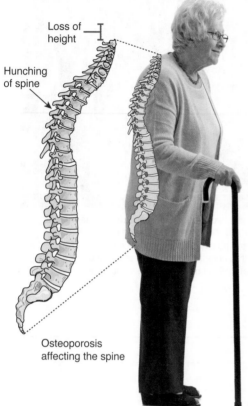

Loss of height

Hunching of spine

Osteoporosis affecting the spine

Comparing normal and low density bone structure

Normal density bone.

Low density bone from person suffering from osteoporosis.

7. Lack of physical activity increases the risk of osteoporosis. From what you know of bone remodeling, suggest why:

_____

_____

_____

8. What would suggest that bone density is affected by hormone levels? _____

_____

_____

9. Medications to treat osteoporosis include hormone replacement therapy (HRT), containing hormones such as estrogen, although this can lead to increased risk of breast cancer. Another treatment is synthetic calcitonin hormone. Suggest how this might work to increase bone density, and the advantages of this type of HRT:

_____

_____

_____

_____

_____

©2023 **BIOZONE** International
ISBN: 978-1-99-101408-5
Photocopying Prohibited

Osteoarthritis

Loss of lubricating fluid. Cartilage becomes rough and is gradually worn away.

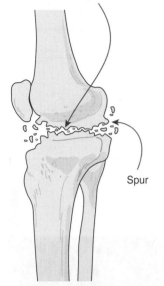

Spur

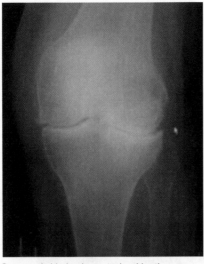

Osteoarthritis is characterized by the degeneration of cartilage and the formation of bony outgrowths (bone spurs or osteophytes) around the edges of the eroded cartilage.

Osteoarthritis (OA) a chronic, degenerative disease aggravated by mechanical stress on bone joints. This leads to pain, stiffness, inflammation, and full or partial loss of joint function. OA occurs in almost all people over the age of 60 and affects three times as many women as men. Weight bearing joints such as those in the knee, foot, hips, and spine are the most commonly affected. Although there is no cure, the symptoms can be greatly relieved by painkillers, anti-inflammatory drugs, and exercises to maintain joint mobility.

In severe osteoarthritis, the cartilage can become so thin that it no longer covers the bone. The bone ends touch, rub against each other, and start to wear away, as shown in this x-ray of an osteoarthritic knee (left).

Diagnosis of osteoarthritis

X-rays are one of the commonly used diagnostic methods for osteoarthritis as the features associated with the disease often show up clearly.

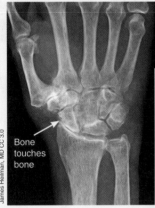

Bone touches bone

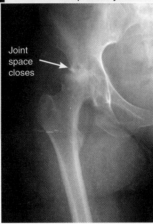

Joint space closes

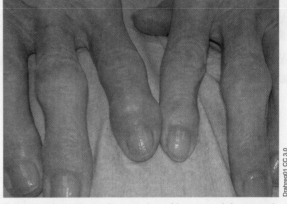

The loss of cartilage, the wearing of bone, and the growth of spurs all combine to change the shape of joints affected by osteoarthritis. This forces the bones out of their normal positions and causes deformity, as seen in the fingers of this elderly patient. Finger joint changes in particular are more common in women and may be hereditary.

10. Explain why joint injury and jobs involving repetitive actions (such as typing) can increase the risk of developing OA?

_____

_____

11. How do the structural changes in an osteoarthritic joint relate to the following symptoms of the disease:

(a) Loss of function: _____

_____

(b) Pain: _____

_____

(c) Deformity: _____

_____

39 Chapter Summary

1. What features indicate that bone is comprised of living cells? _____
   _____
   _____

2. Summarize the key functions of the human skeleton: _____
   _____
   _____

3. Label the bones and joint type, and define the joint type, in the X-ray below

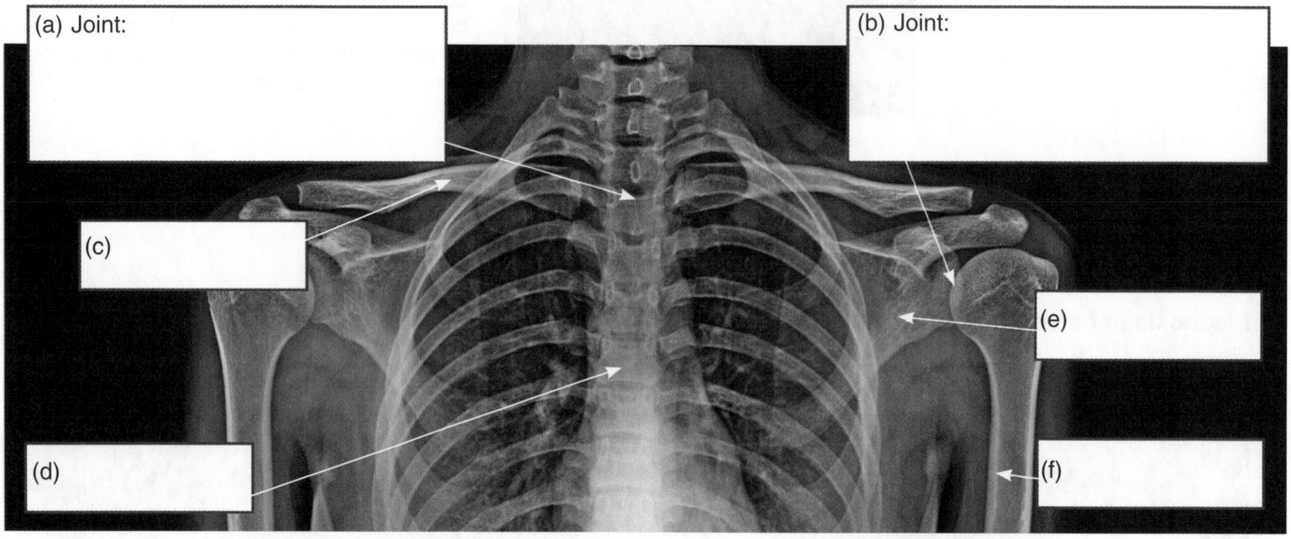

(a) Joint:

(b) Joint:

(c)

(d)

(e)

(f)

4. Summarize the key differences between the infant and adult skeleton and bones: _____
   _____
   _____
   _____
   _____

5. Compare and contrast between osteoporosis and osteoarthritis: _____
   _____
   _____
   _____
   _____

6. Discuss how medical practitioners use imaging technology to diagnose and correct skeleton injury and disease, providing several examples:
   _____
   _____
   _____
   _____
   _____
   _____   _____
   _____

©2023 **BIOZONE** International
ISBN: 978-1-99-101408-5
Photocopying Prohibited

The Muscular System

KEY IDEAS

- The muscular system is organized into discrete muscles, which work as antagonistic pairs.

- Skeletal muscle tissue acts with the bones of the skeleton to produce movements.

- In muscle, contraction results from the movement of actin filaments against myosin filaments.

- ATP is required for muscle contraction.

KEY TERMS

- Abduction
- Actin
- Adduction
- Antagonistic muscles
- Cardiac muscle
- Fast twitch
- Myosin
- Neuromuscular junction
- Oxygen debt
- Sarcomere
- Skeletal muscle
- Sliding filament theory
- Slow twitch
- Smooth muscle
- VO_2 max

RESOURCE HUB

Scan the QR code to access:

- weblinks
- videos
- 3D models
- interactives

LEARNING OBJECTIVES

Activity number

- [ ] 1 Understand that muscles in the body can be placed into broad groups. Explain what muscle fascicles are and give examples of different arrangements of fascicles and their locations in the body. — 41

- [ ] 2 Describe the ultrastructure of skeletal muscle, including organization of muscle into bundles of fibers, organization of fibers into myofibrils, and composition and arrangement of filaments within each myofibril. Understand the banding pattern of myofibrils and how these patterns change with muscle contraction. — 42

- [ ] 3 Describe the structure and function of the neuromuscular junction and understand the importance of action potential in the release of acetylcholine, resulting in contraction. Explain what is meant by the 'all or none' law of muscle contraction. Explain the mechanism of the sliding filament theory and understand the roles of Ca^{2+} and ATP, and the troponin-tropmomyosin complex. — 43-44

- [ ] 4 Understand the difference between short lived and longer term injuries to muscles and give some examples of these. Explain the role of dystrophin and the effect on muscles of the genetic disorder, muscular dystrophy. — 45

- [ ] 5 Explain what is meant by the terms muscle tone and core muscles. Understand the role of the muscle spindle organ. — 46

- [ ] 6 Understand the action of antagonistic muscles and give examples. Explain the terms prime mover, antagonist, and synergist. Understand how the muscular system acts to move the bones of the body at the joints. — 47

- [ ] 7 Identify sources of ATP for muscle contraction and compare aerobic and anaerobic pathways as sources of ATP for muscle contraction. Understand the principle of oxygen debt. Define VO_2 max and how it varies between age groups, sexes, and sports. — 48

- [ ] 8 Explain what is meant by muscle fatigue and that it is the result of a number of complex causes including lactate levels, pH, and phosphate (Pi) accumulation. Carry out an investigation into muscle fatigue. — 49-50

- [ ] 9 Understand that aerobic training can affect muscle physiology. Explain the difference between fast twitch and slow twitch muscle fibers, and know that the proportions of these in the body are genetically determined. — 51

Background: Muscle tissue

40 Types of Muscle

Key Idea: There are three types of muscle tissue: skeletal, cardiac (heart), and smooth.

Recall that mammalian muscles fall into one of three categories: skeletal, cardiac, or smooth. The muscles used for posture and locomotion are **skeletal muscles** and are largely under conscious (voluntary) control. Cardiac (heart) and involuntary (smooth) muscle are not under conscious control (involuntary). **Cardiac muscle** is located in the heart. **Smooth muscle** lines hollow organs such as blood vessels, the bladder, and gut. Each muscle type has a distinct structure.

Skeletal muscle

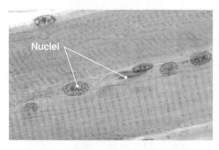

Nuclei

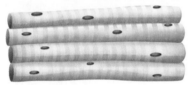

▶ Skeletal muscle is also called striated or voluntary muscle.

▶ It is involved in maintaining posture and in movement, e.g. walking.

▶ It is called voluntary muscle because it is under conscious control.

▶ It has a striated (striped or banded) appearance and the fibers (cells) contain many nuclei located at the edges.

▶ The muscle fibers are long and tubular.

Cardiac muscle

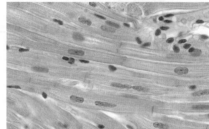

▶ Cardiac muscle is also sometimes called heart muscle.

▶ Cardiac muscle is striated and does not fatigue because the muscle has a built in rest period after each contraction.

▶ It is found only in the heart.

▶ It is an involuntary muscle and is not under conscious control.

▶ The muscle fibers are branching and uninucleate (have only one nucleus).

Smooth muscle

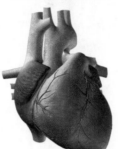

▶ Smooth muscle is not under conscious control.

▶ It lines the walls of hollow organs, e.g. blood vessels or digestive tract, enabling them to respond to stimuli, e.g. to create gut movements, or expand and contract blood vessels.

▶ The fibers are spindle shaped with one nucleus. They lack striations.

▶ They are irregularly arranged so the contraction is not in one direction.

1. Compare the structure and function of skeletal muscle, cardiac muscle, and smooth muscle: _____

_____

_____

_____

_____

_____

_____

2. In terms of its control, how does skeletal muscle differ from cardiac and smooth muscle? _____

_____

_____

©2023 **BIOZONE** International
ISBN: 978-1-99-101408-5
Photocopying Prohibited

41 Muscles of the Human Body

Key Idea: The muscles of the human body can be placed into specific groups.

The muscles of the human body occur as groups which work together to achieve an outcome. For example, the raising of the forearm is achieved by the contraction of the biceps brachii and the brachialis. This muscle group is sometimes referred to simply as the biceps. Similarly, 'abdominals' is used to refer to the muscle layers covering the body's anterior midsection. Muscle groups are divided between the head, trunk, upper and lower arms, thorax and midsection, and upper and lower legs, each with anterior and posterior muscles. Some common muscle groupings are illustrated below.

Muscle groups

Word list:
Facial muscles, pectorals, obliques (abdominal group), rectus abdominis (abdominal group), trapezius, latissimus dorsi, deltoid, biceps, triceps, gluteals, quadriceps, hamstrings, gastrocnemius

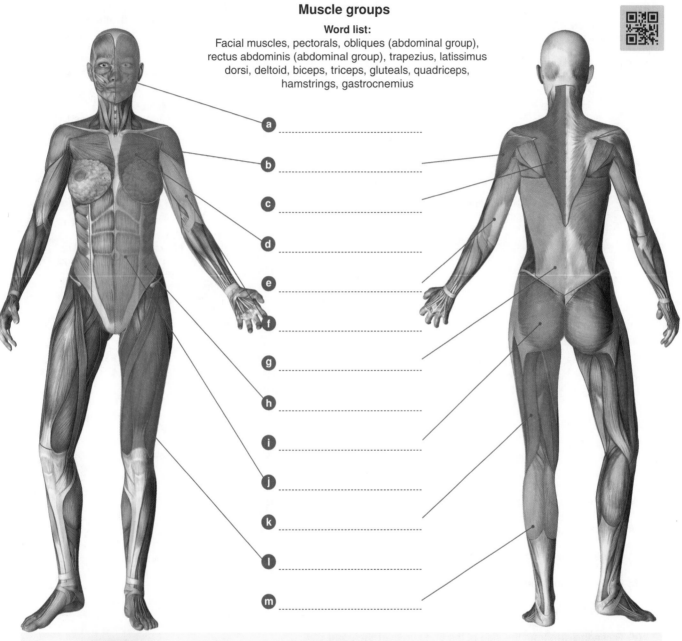

a ....

b ....

c ....

d ....

e ....

f ....

g ....

h ....

i ....

j ....

k ....

l ....

m ....

Head muscles

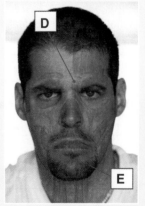

Head muscles are divided into the facial muscles, which make expressions, and the chewing muscles. Facial muscles are inserted into soft tissues, e.g. skin, and enable a range of facial expressions.

Smiling involves about 12 muscles. Major muscles involved include:
- Zygomaticus major (A) raises the corners of the mouth and produces the cheek dimples.
- Zygomaticus minor (B) raises the upper edges of the lips.
- Levator anguli oris (C) raises the upper lip to show the canine teeth.

Frowning involves about 11 muscles. Muscles involved include:
- Procerus (D) pulls the skin between the eyebrows down towards the nose producing the "fighters fold".
- Depressor anguli oris (E) pulls the corners of the mouth down to form the lips into an inverted U.

Muscle fascicles and muscle structure

Skeletal muscles consist of fascicles, i.e. bundles of muscle fibers surrounded by connective tissue layer. The arrangement of fascicles varies, producing a variety of muscle structures.

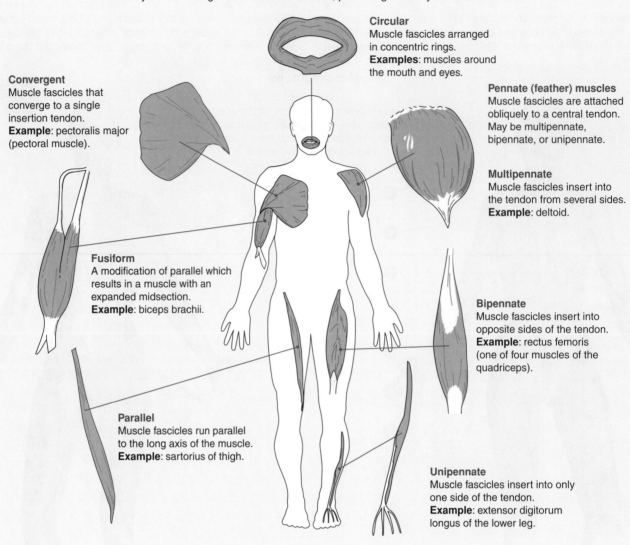

Circular
Muscle fascicles arranged in concentric rings.
Examples: muscles around the mouth and eyes.

Convergent
Muscle fascicles that converge to a single insertion tendon.
Example: pectoralis major (pectoral muscle).

Pennate (feather) muscles
Muscle fascicles are attached obliquely to a central tendon. May be multipennate, bipennate, or unipennate.

Multipennate
Muscle fascicles insert into the tendon from several sides.
Example: deltoid.

Fusiform
A modification of parallel which results in a muscle with an expanded midsection.
Example: biceps brachii.

Bipennate
Muscle fascicles insert into opposite sides of the tendon.
Example: rectus femoris (one of four muscles of the quadriceps).

Parallel
Muscle fascicles run parallel to the long axis of the muscle.
Example: sartorius of thigh.

Unipennate
Muscle fascicles insert into only one side of the tendon.
Example: extensor digitorum longus of the lower leg.

1. On the previous page, use the word list to label the muscle groups on the figure:

2. Which major muscles / group(s) would be used to carry out the following movements:

    (a) Raise the lower leg (i.e. tibia and fibula) towards the buttocks: _____

    (b) Bring the upper leg forward (i.e. the femur) as in taking a step: _____

    (c) Rotate the wrist: _____

    (d) Raise the arm from the side of the body up over the head: _____

3. What is the unusual feature of facial muscles? _____
   _____
   _____

4. Describe the difference between parallel and fusiform muscle structure: _____
   _____
   _____
   _____
   _____

©2023 **BIOZONE** International
ISBN: 978-1-99-101408-5
Photocopying Prohibited

42 Skeletal Muscle Structure and Function

Key Idea: Skeletal muscle is organized into bundles of muscle cells or fibers. The muscle fibers are made up of repeating contractile units called sarcomeres.

Skeletal muscle is organized into bundles of muscle cells or fibers. Each fiber is a single cell with many nuclei and each fiber is itself a bundle of smaller myofibrils arranged lengthwise. Each myofibril is, in turn, composed of two kinds of myofilaments (thick and thin), which overlap to form light and dark bands. It is the orderly alternation of these light and dark bands which gives skeletal muscle its striated or striped appearance. The **sarcomere**, bounded by dark Z lines, forms one complete contractile unit.

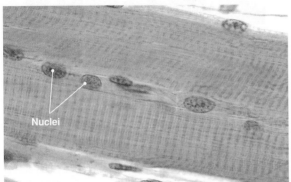

Nuclei

When viewed under a microscope (above), skeletal muscle has a banded appearance. The cells are large with many nuclei (multinucleate).

Skeletal muscles require a conscious action to control them. Physical actions, such as running, writing, and speaking require the contraction of skeletal muscles to occur.

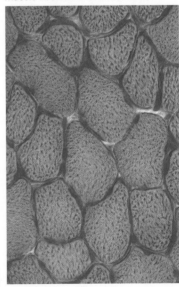

Structure of muscle

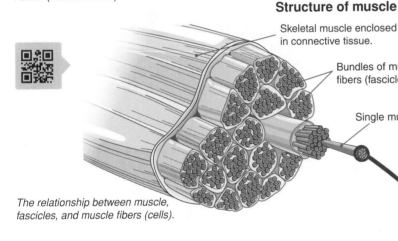

Skeletal muscle enclosed in connective tissue.

Bundles of muscle fibers (fascicles).

Single muscle fiber.

The relationship between muscle, fascicles, and muscle fibers (cells).

Structure of a muscle fiber (cell)

A single contractile unit of a muscle fiber (a sarcomere) is highlighted in this translucent blue section.

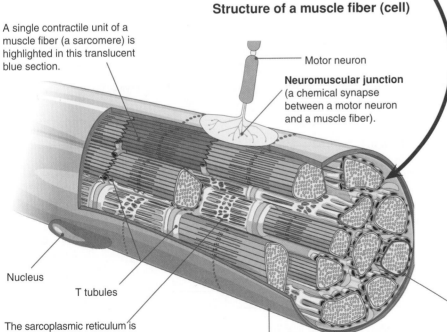

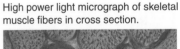
Motor neuron

Neuromuscular junction (a chemical synapse between a motor neuron and a muscle fiber).

High power light micrograph of skeletal muscle fibers in cross section.

Nucleus

T tubules

The sarcoplasmic reticulum is a specialized type of smooth endoplasmic reticulum. It is associated with the T tubules and forms a network containing a store of calcium ions.

The sarcolemma is the plasma membrane of the muscle cell and encloses the sarcoplasm (cytoplasm).

A myofibril (blue outline) with myofilaments in cross section.

©2023 **BIOZONE** International
ISBN: 978-1-99-101408-5

The banding pattern of myofibrils

Within a myofibril, the thin filaments, held together by the Z lines, project in both directions. The arrival of an action potential sets in motion a series of events that cause the thick and thin filaments to slide past each other. This is called contraction and it results in shortening of the muscle fiber. It is accompanied by a visible change in the appearance of the myofibril: the I band and the sarcomere shorten and H zone shortens or disappears (below).

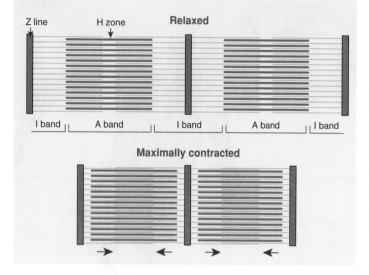

The response of a single muscle fiber to stimulation is to contract maximally or not at all; its response is referred to as the all-or-none law of muscle contraction. If the stimulus is not strong enough to produce an action potential, the muscle fiber will not respond. However, skeletal muscles as a whole are able to produce varying levels of contractile force. These are called graded responses.

Longitudinal section of a sarcomere

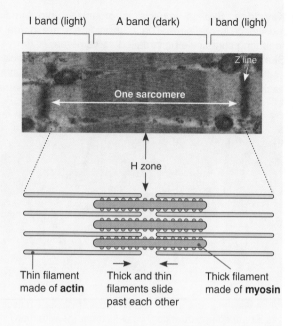

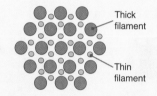

Cross section through a region of overlap between thick and thin filaments.

The photograph of a sarcomere (above) shows the banding pattern arising as a result of the highly organized arrangement of thin and thick filaments. It is represented schematically in longitudinal section and cross section.

1. (a) Explain the cause of the banding pattern visible in striated muscle: _____

_____

_____

(b) Explain the change in appearance of a myofibril during contraction with reference to the following:

The I band: _____

The H zone: _____

The sarcomere: _____

2. Study the electron micrograph of the sarcomere (top, right).

(a) Is it in a contracted or relaxed state (use the diagram, top left, to help you decide)? _____

(b) Explain your answer: _____

_____

_____

3. Explain what is meant by the all-or-none response of a muscle fiber: _____

_____

_____

©2023 **BIOZONE** International
ISBN: 978-1-99-101408-5
Photocopying Prohibited

43 The Neuromuscular Junction

Key Idea: The neuromuscular junction is the specialized synapse between a motor neuron and a muscle fiber. Arrival of an action potential at the neuromuscular junction results in contraction of the muscle fiber.

For a muscle fiber to contract, it must receive a threshold stimulus in the form of an action potential. Action potentials are carried by motor neurons from the central nervous system to the muscle fibers they supply. A motor neuron communicates with a muscle fiber across a specialized synapse called the **neuromuscular junction**. The arrival of an action potential at the neuromuscular junction results in release of the neurotransmitter acetylcholine and contraction of the fiber. The response of a single muscle fiber is all-or-none, meaning it contracts maximally or not at all.

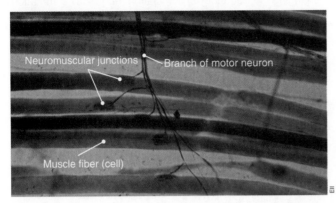

Axon terminals of a motor neuron supplying a muscle. Axon branches end on the sarcolemma (plasma membrane) of a muscle fiber at regions called neuromuscular junctions. Each fiber receives a branch of an axon, but one axon may supply many muscle fibers.

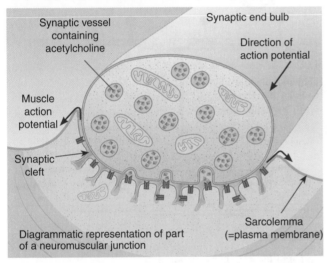

Diagrammatic representation of part of a neuromuscular junction

When an action potential arrives at the neuromuscular junction, it causes release of acetylcholine, which diffuses across the synaptic cleft to stimulate an action potential in the sarcolemma. The action potential is propagated throughout the muscle fiber via the system of T tubules and causes a release of stored calcium ions from the sarcoplasmic reticulum (endoplasmic reticulum of the muscle fiber).

Muscles have graded responses

Muscle fibers respond to an action potential by contracting maximally or not at all. This response is called the all or none law of muscle contraction. However, skeletal muscles can produce contractions of varying force. This is achieved by changing the frequency of stimulation (more rapid arrival of action potentials) and by changing the number of fibers active at any one time. A stronger muscle contraction is produced when a large number of muscle fibers is recruited (below left), whereas less strenuous movements, such as picking up a pen, require fewer active fibers (below right).

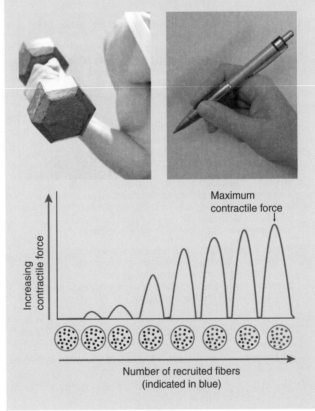

1. (a) Describe the structure of the neuromuscular junction: _____

_____

_____

(b) What neurotransmitter transmits the signal to the muscle fiber? _____

(c) What events happen as a result of this? _____

_____

_____

2. How does a muscle, as a whole, produce contractions of varying force? _____

_____

44 The Sliding Filament Theory

Key Idea: Muscles contract when thick and thin filaments slide past each other.

Recall that muscle contraction is achieved by the thick and thin muscle filaments sliding past one another. This sliding is possible because of the structure and arrangement of the thick and thin filaments. The ends of the thick myosin filaments are studded with heads or cross bridges that can link to the thin filaments next to them. The thin filaments contain the protein **actin**, but also a regulatory protein complex. When the cross bridges of the thick filaments connect to the thin filaments, a shape change moves one filament past the other. Two things are necessary for cross bridge formation: calcium ions, which are released from the sarcoplasmic reticulum

when the muscle receives an action potential, and ATP, which is hydrolyzed by ATPase enzymes on the **myosin**. When cross bridges attach and detach in sarcomeres throughout the muscle cell, the cell shortens. Although a muscle fiber responds to an action potential by contracting maximally, skeletal muscles, as a whole, can produce varying levels of contractile force. These graded responses are achieved by changing the frequency of stimulation (frequency summation) and by changing the number and size of motor units recruited (multiple fiber summation). Maximal contractions of a muscle are achieved when nerve impulses arrive at the muscle at a rapid rate and a large number of motor units are active at once.

The sliding filament theory

Muscle contraction requires calcium ions (Ca^{2+}) and energy (in the form of ATP) in order for the thick and thin filaments to slide past each other. The steps are:

1. The binding sites on the actin molecule, to which myosin 'heads' will locate, are blocked by a complex of two protein molecules: tropomyosin and troponin.

2. Prior to muscle contraction, ATP binds to the heads of the myosin molecules, priming them in an erect, high energy state. Arrival of an action potential causes a release of Ca^{2+} from the sarcoplasmic reticulum. The Ca^{2+} binds to the troponin and causes the blocking complex to move so that the myosin binding sites on the actin filament become exposed.

3. The heads of the cross-bridging myosin molecules attach to the binding sites on the actin filament. Release of energy from the hydrolysis of ATP accompanies the cross bridge formation.

4. The energy released from ATP hydrolysis causes a change in shape of the myosin cross bridge, resulting in a bending action (*the power stroke*). This causes the actin filaments to slide past the myosin filaments towards the centre of the **sarcomere**.

5. (Not illustrated). Fresh ATP attaches to the myosin molecules, releasing them from the binding sites and repriming them for a repeat movement. They become attached further along the actin chain as long as ATP and Ca^{2+} are available.

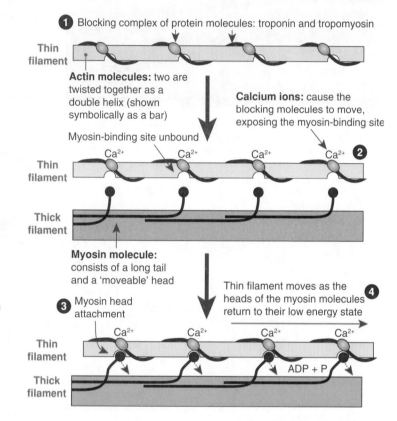

① Blocking complex of protein molecules: troponin and tropomyosin

Thin filament

Actin molecules: two are twisted together as a double helix (shown symbolically as a bar)

Calcium ions: cause the blocking molecules to move, exposing the myosin-binding site

Myosin-binding site unbound

Ca^{2+} Ca^{2+} Ca^{2+} Ca^{2+} ②

Thin filament

Thick filament

Myosin molecule: consists of a long tail and a 'moveable' head

③ Myosin head attachment

Thin filament moves as the heads of the myosin molecules return to their low energy state ④

Ca^{2+} Ca^{2+} Ca^{2+} Ca^{2+}

Thin filament

Thick filament

ADP + P

1. Match the following chemicals (a) to (e) with their functional role (1) to (5) in muscle movement:

   (a) Myosin   (1) Bind to the actin molecule in a way that prevents myosin head from forming a cross bridge

   (b) Actin   (2) Supplies energy for the flexing of the myosin 'head' (power stroke)

   (c) Calcium ions   (3) Has a moveable head that provides a power stroke when activated

   (d) Troponin-tropomyosin   (4) Two protein molecules twisted in a helix shape that form the thin filament of a myofibril

   (e) ATP   (5) Bind to the blocking molecules, causing them to move and expose the myosin binding site

   (a) _____ (b) _____ (c) _____ (d) _____ (e) _____

2. Describe the two ways in which a muscle, as a whole, can produce contractions of varying force:

   (a) _____

   _____

   (b) _____

   _____

3. Identify the two things necessary for cross bridge formation: _____

©2023 **BIOZONE** International
ISBN: 978-1-99-101408-5
Photocopying Prohibited

45 Muscle Disorders

Key Idea: Disorders and injuries of the muscles can make it very difficult for affected people to move about and severely impact their quality of life.

Injuries of the muscles can include short lived effects, such as cramp, which may take minutes for recovery, or severe trauma, such as muscle tears, which can take weeks to heal. Genetic disorders, such as muscular dystrophy, can be chronic and severe, resulting in the loss of muscle function.

Injuries

Skeletal muscle injuries are one of the most common sports injuries, especially in sports requiring intense bursts of speed (causing a muscle to suddenly tear) or require physical contact between opponents (causing impact trauma).

▶ Strains result from a muscle being over stretched, overused, or used improperly, e.g. the limb is moved in an unexpected way. Strains result in microscopic tears in the muscle fibers and can cause sore and stiff muscles. Strains commonly occur in the hamstrings, lower back, neck, and shoulders.

▶ Muscle tears are a more severe form of a strain. In this case the muscle tissue and blood vessels are torn due to excessive force. This can happen during maximal exertion, such as from a sprint start, or the sudden lifting of a heavy object. Tears happen in the same areas as strains.

▶ Contusions, or bruising, result from bleeding in the muscle tissue due to severe impact or trauma that does not cause the skin to break.

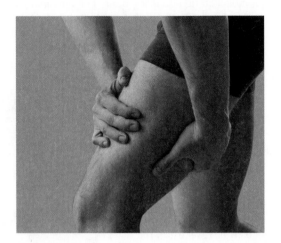

Muscular dystrophy

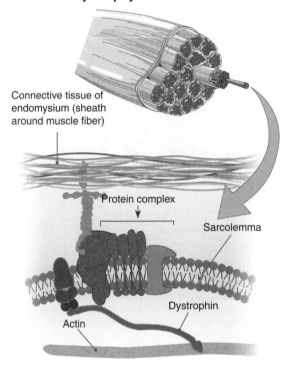

Connective tissue of endomysium (sheath around muscle fiber)

Protein complex

Sarcolemma

Dystrophin

Actin

▶ Duchenne's muscular dystrophy is an X-linked disorder caused by a mutation in the gene DMD, which codes for the protein dystrophin. The disease causes a rapid deterioration of muscle, eventually leading to loss of function and death. It is the most prevalent type of muscular dystrophy and generally, only affects males.

▶ Dystrophin is an important structural component within muscle tissue and it connects muscles fibers to the extracellular matrix through a protein complex on the sarcolemma. The absence of dystrophin allows excess calcium to penetrate the sarcolemma (the fiber's plasma membrane). This damages the sarcolemma, and eventually results in the death of the cell. Muscle fibers die and are replaced with adipose and connective tissue.

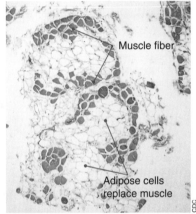

Muscle fiber

Adipose cells replace muscle

1. Describe the difference between a muscle strain and a muscle tear: _____

_____

_____

2. Why do muscle strain and tears generally occur during maximal effort? _____

_____

_____

3. Explain why the inability to produce dystrophin leads to a loss of muscle function: _____

_____

_____

46 Muscle Tone and Posture

Key Idea: Some muscle fibers are always active, giving muscles tone and maintaining posture.

Even when we consciously relax a muscle, a few of its fibers at any one time will be involuntarily active. This continuous and passive partial contraction of the muscles is responsible for muscle tone and is important in maintaining posture. The contractions are not visible but they are responsible for the healthy, firm appearance of muscle. The amount of muscle contraction is monitored by sensory receptors in the muscle called muscle spindle organs. These provide the sensory information necessary to adjust movement as required. We don't normally notice this constant use of muscles when standing still, unless we do it for a long time. Abnormally low muscle tone (hypotonia) can arise as a result of traumatic or degenerative nerve damage, so that the muscle no longer receives the innervation it needs to contract. The principal treatment for these disorders is physical therapy to help the person compensate for the neuromuscular disability.

We are usually not aware of the skeletal muscles that maintain posture, although they work almost continuously, making fine adjustments to maintain body position. Both posture and functional movements of the body are highly dependent on the strength of the body's core (the muscles in the pelvic floor, belly, and mid and lower back). The core muscles stabilize the thorax and the pelvis and lack of core strength is a major contributor to postural problems and muscle imbalances.

Physical therapy is a branch of health care concerned with maintaining or restoring functional movement throughout life. Loss of muscle tone and strength can develop as a result of aging, disease, or trauma. As a result of not being used, muscles will atrophy, losing both mass and strength. Although the type of physical therapy depends on the problem, it usually includes therapeutic exercise to help restore mobility and strength, and prevent or slow down the loss of muscle tissue.

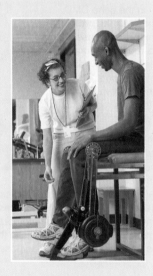

The role of the muscle spindle

Changes in length of a muscle are monitored by the muscle spindle organ, a stretch receptor located within **skeletal muscle**, parallel to the muscle fibers themselves. The muscle spindle is stimulated in response to sustained or sudden stretch on the central region of its specialized intrafusal fibers. Sensory information from the muscle spindle is relayed to the spinal cord. The motor response brings about adjustments to the degree of stretch in the muscle. These adjustments help in the coordination and efficiency of muscle contraction. Muscle spindles are important in the maintenance of muscle tone, postural reflexes, and movement control, and are concentrated in muscles that exert fine control over movement. They alert the brain to prevent muscles being overstretched.

Motor nerves send impulses to adjust the degree of contraction in the intrafusal and extrafusal fibers.

Sensory nerves monitor stretch in the non-contractile region of the spindle and send impulses to the spinal cord.

Striated appearance of contractile elements

Nucleus of muscle fiber

The muscle spindle organ comprises special intrafusal fibers which lie parallel to the muscle fibers within a lymph-filled capsule. Only the regions near the end can contract.

The spindle is surrounded by the muscle fibers of the skeletal muscle.

1. (a) Explain what is meant by muscle tone: _____

_____

(b) Explain how this is achieved: _____

_____

2. What is the purpose of the core muscles? _____

_____

_____

3. Explain the role of the muscle spindle organ: _____

_____

_____

©2023 **BIOZONE** International
ISBN: 978-1-99-101408-5
Photocopying Prohibited

Core muscles and posture

▶ The core muscles include the muscles around the spine, hips, and abdomen. These keep the body upright and the bones of the spine, hips, and neck correctly aligned. Incorrect alignment of these bones can lead to sore and stiff joints and long term postural and movement problems.

▶ Although definitions of core muscles vary, they broadly include the muscles of the torso, including the multifidus and erector spinae (the group of muscles running along the spine to the hips), the diaphragm, pelvic floor muscles, internal and external obliques, transverse abdominis, and the rectus abdominis.

▶ Maintaining a relatively active lifestyle is an important part of keeping the core muscles active and strong. Sedentary lifestyles, such as many office jobs, do not work the core muscles enough, and this can lead to back-ache and poor posture.

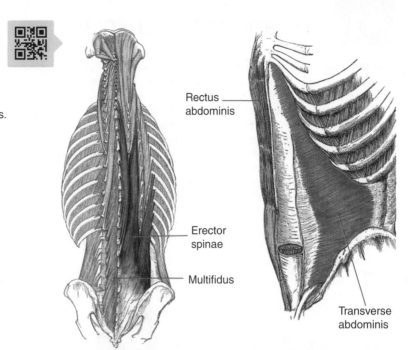

Rectus abdominis

Erector spinae

Multifidus

Transverse abdominis

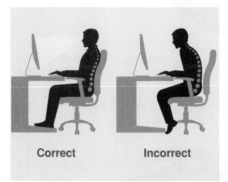

Correct   Incorrect

Many less active jobs involve sitting for long periods of time. It is important to have a correct working arrangement to maintain good posture.

Loss of strength and engagement in the core muscles can typically lead to a curving of the spine, with shoulders rolling forward and a concave abdomen.

Exercises such as planks are a good way of engaging and strengthening the core muscles. Strengthening both front and back muscles is important for posture.

4. With reference to the following, describe how the structure of the muscle spindle organ is related to its function:

(a) Intrafusal fibers lie parallel to the extrafusal fibers: _____

_____

_____

(b) Sensory neurons are located in the non-contractile region of the organ: _____

_____

_____

(c) Motor neurons synapse in the extrafusal fibers and the contractile region of the intrafusal fibers: _____

_____

_____

5. What can cause the loss of good posture, and how might good posture be retained or recovered? _____

_____

_____

_____

_____

©2023 **BIOZONE** International
ISBN: 978-1-99-101408-5
Photocopying Prohibited

47 Antagonistic Muscles

Key Idea: Antagonistic muscles are muscle pairs that have opposite actions to each other. Together, their opposing actions bring about movement of body parts.

Muscles provide the contractile force to move body parts. Muscles create movement of body parts when they contract across joints. Because muscles can only pull and not push, most body movements are achieved through the action of opposing sets of muscles called **antagonistic muscles**. Antagonistic muscles function by producing opposite movements, as one muscle contracts (shortens), the other relaxes (lengthens). Skeletal muscles are attached to the skeleton by tough connective tissue structures: tendons in vertebrates, such as humans. They always have at least two attachments: an origin and an insertion. Body parts move when a muscle contracts across a joint. The type and degree of movement depends on how much movement the joint allows and where the muscle is located in relation to the joint.

Muscles of the upper arm

When they contract, muscles pull on a bone. They cannot push, therefore they must work in opposing pairs.

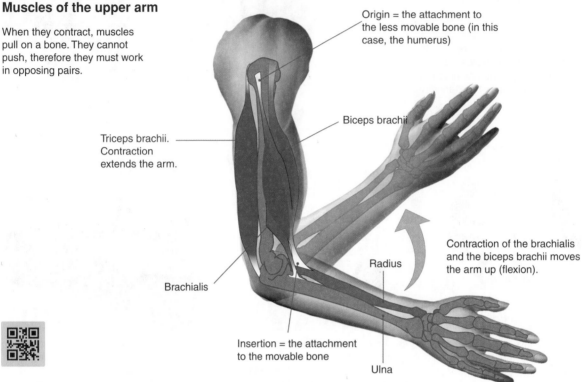

Origin = the attachment to the less movable bone (in this case, the humerus)

Biceps brachii

Triceps brachii. Contraction extends the arm.

Contraction of the brachialis and the biceps brachii moves the arm up (flexion).

Radius

Brachialis

Insertion = the attachment to the movable bone

Ulna

Opposing movements require opposing muscles

▶ The flexion (bending) and extension (unbending) of limbs is caused by the action of antagonistic muscles. Antagonistic muscles work in pairs and their actions oppose each other. During movement of a limb, muscles other than those primarily responsible for the movement may be involved to fine tune the movement.

▶ Every coordinated movement in the body requires the application of muscle force. This is accomplished by the action of agonists, antagonists, and synergists. The opposing action of agonists and antagonists (working constantly at a low level) also produces muscle tone. Note that either muscle in an antagonistic pair can act as the agonist or prime mover, depending on the particular movement (for example, flexion, or extension).

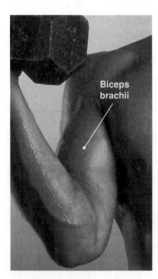

Biceps brachii

Agonists or prime movers are primarily responsible for the movement and produce most of the force required.

Antagonists oppose the prime mover. They may also play a protective role by preventing over-stretching of the prime mover.

Synergists assist the prime movers and may be involved in fine-tuning the direction of movement. During flexion of the forearm (left) the brachialis muscle acts as the prime mover and the biceps brachii is the synergist. The antagonist, the triceps brachii at the back of the arm, is relaxed. During extension, their roles are reversed.

Quadriceps

Hamstrings

Movement of the upper leg is achieved through the action of several large groups of muscles, collectively called the quadriceps and the hamstrings.

The hamstrings are actually a collection of three muscles, which act together to flex the leg.

The quadriceps are four large muscles at the front of the thigh that oppose the motion of the hamstrings and extend the leg.

When the prime mover contracts forcefully, the antagonist also contracts very slightly. This stops over-stretching and allows greater control over thigh movement.

©2023 **BIOZONE** International
ISBN: 978-1-99-101408-5
Photocopying Prohibited

Types of body movement

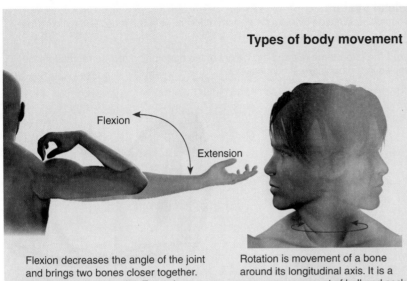

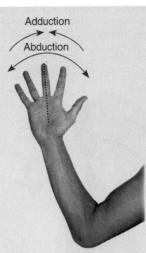

Adduction

Abduction

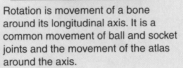

Flexion

Extension

Flexion decreases the angle of the joint and brings two bones closer together. Extension is its opposite. Extension more than 180° is called hyperextension.

Rotation is movement of a bone around its longitudinal axis. It is a common movement of ball and socket joints and the movement of the atlas around the axis.

Abduction is a movement away from the midline, whereas **adduction** describes movement towards the midline. The terms also apply to opening and closing the fingers.

1. Describe the role of each of the following muscles in moving a limb:

   (a) Prime mover: _____

   (b) Antagonist: _____

   (c) Synergist: _____

2. Explain why the muscles that cause movement of body parts tend to operate as antagonistic pairs:

   _____

   _____

   _____

3. Describe the relationship between muscles and joints. Using appropriate terminology, explain how antagonistic muscles act together to raise and lower a limb:

   _____

   _____

   _____

   _____

   _____

4. Explain the role of joints in the movement of body parts: _____

   _____

   _____

   _____

   _____

5. (a) Identify the insertion for the biceps brachii during flexion of the forearm: _____

   (b) Identify the insertion of the brachialis muscle during flexion of the forearm: _____

   (c) Identify the antagonist during flexion of the forearm: _____

   (d) Given its insertion, describe the forearm movement during which the biceps brachii is the prime mover:

   _____

The muscular system works with the skeletal system

▶ Skeletal muscles move the flexible joints of the body. The skeleton works as a system of levers, with the muscles providing the force required to move these levers.

▶ The joint acts as the fulcrum (F), the muscles exert the effort force (E) and the weight of the bone being moved represents the load (L). There are three classes of levers, examples in the body are shown below:

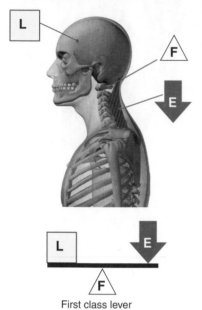

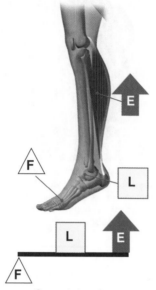

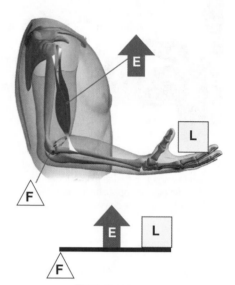

First class lever

Head nod. Head is the load and neck is the fulcrum. Neck muscles provide effort.

Second class lever

Standing on tiptoe. Load is body weight, centered between fulcrum and effort. Ball of foot is fulcrum. Effort is from calf muscle

Third class lever

Biceps curl. Load is forearm and any weight held by hand. Fulcrum is elbow joint. Effort is provided by contracting biceps.

Movement at joints

The synovial joints of the skeleton allow free movement in one or more planes. The articulating bone ends are separated by a joint cavity containing lubricating synovial fluid. Two types of synovial joint, the shoulder ball and socket joint and the hinge joint of the elbow, are illustrated (right).

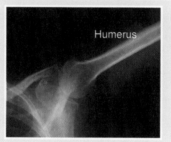

Ball and socket

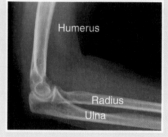

Hinge joint

6. (a) Describe a forearm movement in which the brachialis is the antagonist: _____

(b) Identify the prime mover in this movement: _____

7. (a) Describe the actions that take place in the neck when you nod your head up and down as if saying "yes":

_____

(b) Describe the action being performed when a person gives a thumbs up signal: _____

8. Explain the role of joints in the movement of body parts: _____

_____

_____

_____

_____

9. What class of lever is involved during flexion of the knee joint (raising the heel towards the buttocks)? _____

_____

10. What class of lever is involved during extension of the knee joint, e.g. raising the foot while seated? _____

_____

©2023 **BIOZONE** International
ISBN: 978-1-99-101408-5
Photocopying Prohibited

48 Energy for Muscle Contraction

Key Idea: Three energy systems supply energy (ATP) to carry out muscle contraction: the ATP-CP system, the glycolytic system, and the oxidative system.

During exercise, the metabolic rate of the muscles increases by up to 20 times and the body's systems must respond appropriately to maintain homeostasis. In order to continue to contract during exercise, energy in the form of ATP must be supplied. There are three energy systems to do this: the ATP-CP system, the glycolytic system, and the oxidative system. The ultimate sources of energy for ATP generation in muscle via these systems are glucose, and stores of glycogen and triglycerides. Prolonged exercise utilizes the oxidative system and relies on a constant supply of oxygen to the tissues.

The ATP-CP system

The simplest of the energy systems is the ATP-CP system. CP or creatine phosphate is a high energy compound that stores energy sufficient for brief periods of muscular effort. Energy released from the breakdown of CP is not used directly to accomplish cellular work. Instead, it rebuilds ATP to maintain a relatively constant supply. This process is anaerobic, occurs very rapidly, and is accomplished without any special structures in the cell.

CP levels decline steadily as it is used to replenish depleted ATP levels. The ATP-CP system maintains energy levels for 3-15 seconds. Beyond this, the muscle must rely on other processes for ATP generation.

CP provides enough energy to fuel about 10 s of maximum effort, e.g. a 100 m race.

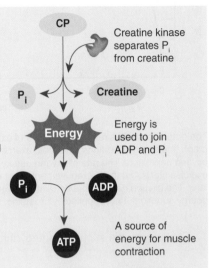

Creatine kinase separates P_i from creatine

Energy is used to join ADP and P_i

A source of energy for muscle contraction

The glycolytic system

ATP can also be provided by glycolysis. The yield of ATP from glycolysis is low, only giving 2 ATP per molecule of glucose, but it is produced rapidly and does not require oxygen. The fuel for the glycolytic system is glucose in the blood, or glycogen, which is stored in the muscle or liver and broken down to glucose-6-phosphate. Pyruvate is reduced to lactate, regenerating NAD^+ and allowing further glycolysis.

Glycolysis provides ATP for exercise for just a few minutes. Its main limitation is that it causes an accumulation of H^+, because protons are not being removed via mitochondrial respiration, and lactate ($C_3H_5O_3$) in the tissues. These changes lead to impairment of muscle function.

Soccer and other field sports demand brief intense efforts with recovery in-between.

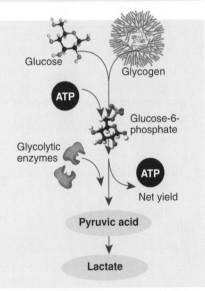

Glucose
Glycogen
ATP
Glucose-6-phosphate
Glycolytic enzymes
ATP
Net yield
Pyruvic acid
Lactate

The oxidative system

In the oxidative system, glucose is completely broken down to yield around 32 molecules of ATP. This process uses oxygen and occurs in the mitochondria. Aerobic metabolism has a high energy yield and is the primary method of energy production during sustained high activity. It relies on a continued supply of oxygen and therefore on the body's ability to deliver oxygen to the muscles. The fuels for aerobic respiration are glucose, stored glycogen, or stored triglycerides. Triglycerides provide free fatty acids, which are oxidized in the mitochondria by the successive removal of two-carbon fragments in a process called beta-oxidation. These two carbon units enter the Krebs cycle as acetyl coenzyme A (acetyl CoA).

Prolonged aerobic effort (e.g. distance running) requires a sustained ATP supply.

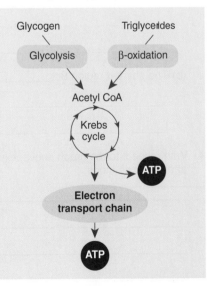

Glycogen
Triglycerides
Glycolysis
β-oxidation
Acetyl CoA
Krebs cycle
ATP
Electron transport chain
ATP

©2023 **BIOZONE** International
ISBN: 978-1-99-101408-5

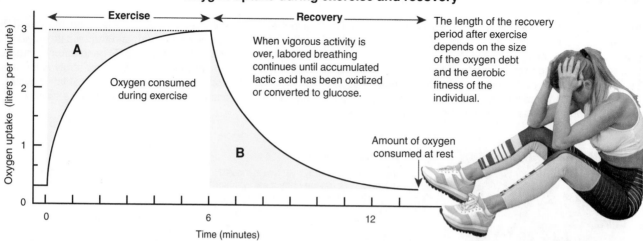

Oxygen uptake during exercise and recovery

The graph above illustrates the principle of **oxygen debt**. In the graph, the energy demands of aerobic exercise require 3 L of oxygen per minute. The rate of oxygen uptake increases immediately exercise starts, but the full requirement is not met until six minutes later. The oxygen deficit is the amount of oxygen needed (for aerobic energy supply) but not supplied by breathing. During the first six minutes, energy is supplied largely from anaerobic pathways: the ATP-CP and glycolytic systems. After exercise, oxygen uptake per minute does not drop immediately to resting level. The extra oxygen that is taken in despite the drop in energy demand is the oxygen debt. The oxygen debt is used to replace oxygen reserves, restore creatine phosphate, and oxidize the lactate or convert it to glucose.

1. Explain why the supply of energy through the glycolytic system is limited: _____

   _____

   _____

2. Summarize the features of the three energy systems in the table below:

	ATP-CP system	Glycolytic system	Oxidative system
ATP supplied by:			
Duration of ATP supply:			

3. Study the graph and explanatory paragraph above, then identify and describe what is represented by:

   (a) The shaded region A: _____

   _____

   _____

   (b) The shaded region B: _____

   _____

   _____

4. With respect to the graph above, explain why the rate of oxygen uptake does not immediately return to its resting level after exercise stops:

   _____

   _____

   _____

   _____

©2023 **BIOZONE** International
ISBN: 978-1-99-101408-5

VO₂ max

- The VO_2 is the amount of oxygen used by muscles during a specified interval for cell metabolism and energy production. It is expressed in milliliters of oxygen used per kilogram of body mass per min. VO_2 max is the maximum volume of oxygen that can be delivered to the body and used per minute and therefore represents an individual's upper limit of aerobic metabolism.

- VO_2 max is high in trained athletes. At some percentage of VO_2 max the body is unable to meet its energy demands aerobically and lactate begins to accumulate in the blood, contributing to muscle fatigue. This point is called anaerobic threshold (AT).

- Highly trained athletes have high ATs. The percentage of VO_2 max at which AT occurs is a good measure of an athlete's ability to maintain maximal exercise over a long distance or period of time.

- VO_2 max varies between ages and sexes and between sports, as shown in the tables below.

For athletes with the same VO_2 max, the percentage at which the aerobic threshold occurs will determine their ability to maintain performance.

VO₂ max (ml/kg/min) for age groups

Age	Males	Females
10-19	47-56	36-46
20-29	43-52	33-42
30-39	39-48	30-38
40-49	36-44	26-35
50-59	34-41	24-33
60-69	31-38	22-30
70-79	28-35	20-27

VO₂ max (ml/kg/min) for athletes

Sport	Age of competitors	Males	Females
Cycling	18-26	62-74	47-57
Rowing	20-35	60-72	58-65
Alpine skiing	18-30	57-68	50-55
Swimming	10-25	50-70	40-60
Running	18-39	60-85	50-75

5. The rate of oxygen uptake increases immediately exercise starts. Explain how the oxygen supply from outside the body to the cells is increased during exercise:

_____

_____

_____

_____

6. Lactic acid levels in the blood continue to rise for a time after exercise has stopped. Explain why this occurs:

_____

_____

_____

7. (a) What is VO_2 max? _____

_____

_____

   (b) Why is VO_2 max not necessarily the best indicator of an athlete's endurance ability? _____

_____

_____

_____

_____

8. At which age in males and females does VO_2 max peak? _____

_____

©2023 **BIOZONE** International
ISBN: 978-1-99-101408-5
Photocopying Prohibited

49 Muscle Fatigue

Key Idea: Muscle fatigue refers to the decline in a muscle's ability to generate force in a prolonged or repeated contraction. Long or intense periods of vigorous activity can result in muscle fatigue, i.e. the decline in a muscle's ability to contract efficiently and generate force. It is a normal result of vigorous exercise but the reasons for it are complex. Muscles can fatigue because of shortage of fuel or because of the accumulation of metabolites which interfere with the activity of calcium in the muscle. Contrary to older thinking, muscle fatigue is not caused by the toxic effects of lactic acid accumulation in oxygen-starved muscle. In fact, lactate formed during exercise is an important source of fuel, through conversion to glucose, and delays fatigue and metabolic acidosis during moderate activity by acting as a buffer. However, during sustained exhausting exercise, more of the muscle's energy needs must be met by glycolysis, and this leads to the metabolic changes that contribute to fatigue, including accumulation of lactate and phosphate. Accumulated lactate is metabolized within the muscle itself or transported to the liver and converted back into glucose.

At rest

▶ Muscles produce a surplus of ATP.

▶ This extra energy is stored in CP (creatine phosphate) and glycogen.

During moderate activity

▶ ATP requirements are met by the aerobic metabolism of glycogen and lipids.

▶ There is no proton accumulation in the cell.

During peak activity

▶ Effort is limited by ATP. ATP production is ultimately limited by availability of oxygen.

▶ During short-term, intense activity, more of the muscle's ATP needs must be met by glycolysis. This leads to an increase in H^+.

▶ Removal of H^+ is slow because mitochondrial respiration is hampered. Lactate may accumulate and coincides with metabolic acidosis but is not the cause of it.

▶ Muscle contraction is impaired (fatigue).

The complex causes of muscle fatigue

During intense exercise, oxygen is limited and more of the muscle's energy needs must be met through anaerobic metabolism. The effects of this are:

▶ An increase in H^+ (acidosis) because protons are not being removed via the mitochondrial electron transport system.

▶ Lactate accumulates faster than it can be oxidized.

▶ Accumulation of phosphate (P_i) from breakdown of ATP and creatine phosphate.

These metabolic changes lead to a fall in ATP and impaired calcium release from the sarcoplasmic reticulum (SR), both of which contribute to muscle fatigue.

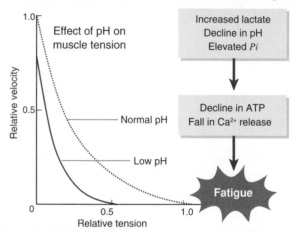

Effect of pH on muscle tension

Increased lactate
Decline in pH
Elevated P_i

Decline in ATP
Fall in Ca^{2+} release

Fatigue

Short term maximal exertion (sprint)

▶ Lactic acid build-up lowers pH.

▶ Depletion of creatine phosphate.

▶ Buildup of phosphate (P_i) affects the sensitivity of the muscle to Ca^{2+}

Mixed aerobic and anaerobic (5 km race)

▶ Lactate accumulation in the muscle.

▶ Build-up of ADP and P_i

▶ Decline in Ca^{2+} release affects the ability of the muscle to contract.

Extended sub-maximal effort (marathon)

▶ Depletion of all energy stores (glycogen, lipids, amino acids) leads to a failure of Ca^{2+} release.

▶ Repetitive overuse damages muscle fibers.

1. Explain the mechanism by which lactate accumulation is associated with muscle fatigue: _____

_____

2. Identify the two physiological changes in the muscle that ultimately result in a decline in muscle performance:

(a) _____ (b) _____

3. Suggest why the reasons for fatigue in a long distance race are different from those in a 100 m sprint: _____

_____

_____

©2023 **BIOZONE** International
ISBN: 978-1-99-101408-5
Photocopying Prohibited

50 Investigating Muscle Fatigue

Key Idea: A simple experiment can be used to show how muscles fatigue in response to prolonged work.

When **skeletal muscle** undergoes prolonged or repetitive work, it becomes fatigued, meaning it loses its ability to produce contractile force. Muscle fatigue can be measured electronically by recording the force of the contraction over time, or can be studied more simply by measuring the number of repetitive contractions that can take place over a set time. In the activity below, you will work in a group of three to test the effect of muscle fatigue in your fingers.

In this practical, you will demonstrate the effects of muscle fatigue in fingers by opening and closing a spring-loaded peg over ten 10 second intervals. You will need to work in a group of three for this experiment.

Test subject: The person who opens and closes the peg.
Time keeper: Calls out the time in 10 second intervals.
Recorder: Records the number of times the peg is opened in each 10 second interval.

The test subject holds the clothes peg comfortably with the thumb and forefinger of their dominant hand (the hand they write with). They should practice opening and closing the peg fully several times before beginning the experiment.

When the timekeeper says go, the test subject opens and closes the peg fully as many times as possible for the duration of the experiment. The timekeeper calls out each 10 second interval so that the recorder can accurately record the data in the chart right.
Switch roles until everyone in your group has completed the experiment.

	Student 1	Student 2	Student 3
1st 10 sec			
2nd 10 sec			
3rd 10 sec			
4th 10 sec			
5th 10 sec			
6th 10 sec			
7th 10 sec			
8th 10 sec			
9th 10 sec			
10th 10 sec			

1. (a) On the grid (right) plot the data for all three individuals:

   (b) Describe the results: _____

   _____

   _____

   _____

   _____

   _____

   _____

   (c) Are these results what you expected? Why or why not?

   _____

   _____

   _____

   _____

   (d) Predict what would happen if the experiment was repeated using the non-dominant hand:

   _____

   _____

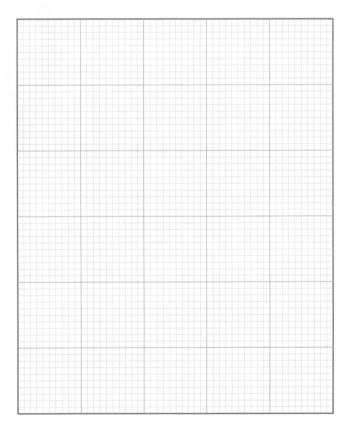

51 Muscle Physiology and Performance

Key Idea: The overall effect of aerobic training on muscle is improved oxidative function and better endurance.

Regardless of the type of training, some of our ability to perform different types of activity depends on our genetic make-up. This is particularly true of aspects of muscle physiology, such as the relative proportions of different fiber types in the skeletal muscles. Muscle fibers are primarily of two types: **fast twitch** (FT) or **slow twitch** (ST). Fast twitch fibers predominate during anaerobic, explosive activity, whereas slow twitch fibers predominate during endurance activity. In the table below, note the difference in the degree to which the two fiber types show fatigue. Training can increase fiber size and, to some extent, the makeup of the fiber, but not the proportion of ST to FT, which is genetically determined.

The effects of aerobic training on muscle physiology

Improved oxidation of glycogen. Training increases the capacity of **skeletal muscle** to generate ATP aerobically.

An increased capacity of the muscle to oxidize fats. This allows muscle and liver glycogen to be used at a slower rate. The body also becomes more efficient at mobilizing free fatty acids from adipose tissue for use as fuel.

Increased myoglobin content. Myoglobin stores oxygen in the muscle cells and aids oxygen delivery to the mitochondria. Endurance training increases muscle myoglobin by 75%-80%.

Increase in lean muscle mass and decrease in body fat. Trained endurance athletes typically have body fat levels of 15-19% (women) or 6-18% (men), compared with 26% (women) and 15% (men) for non-athletes.

The size of slow twitch fibers increases. This change in size is associated with increased aerobic capacity.

An increase in the size and density of mitochondria in the skeletal muscles and an increase in the activity and concentration of Krebs cycle enzymes.

An increase in the number of capillaries surrounding each muscle fiber. Endurance trained men have 5%-10% more capillaries in their muscles than sedentary men.

Fast vs slow twitch muscle

Feature	Fast twitch	Slow twitch
Color	White	Red
Diameter	Large	Small
Contraction rate	Fast	Slow
ATP production	Fast	Slow
Metabolism	Anaerobic	Aerobic
Rate of fatigue	Fast	Slow
Power	High	Low

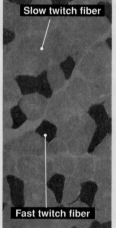

Slow twitch fiber

Fast twitch fiber

Slow twitch fibers appear light colored when stained with a myofibrillar ATPase stain.

Type II fast twitch fibers are classified further according to their metabolism:
- Type IIa (intermediate) =some oxidative capacity
- Type IIb =fast glycolytic only

There are two basic types of muscle fibers: slow twitch (type I) and fast twitch (type II). Both fiber types generally produce the same force per contraction but fast twitch fibers produce that force at a higher rate. Slow twitch fibers contain more mitochondria and myoglobin than fast twitch fibers so they are more efficient at using oxygen to generate ATP without lactate build up. In this way, they can fuel repeated muscle contractions, such as those required for endurance events.

1. Explain the following changes that occur due to aerobic training:

(a) Slow twitch fibers increase in size: _____

_____

_____

(b) Improved oxidation of glycogen: _____

_____

_____

(c) Increase in lean muscle mass and decrease in body fat: _____

_____

_____

©2023 **BIOZONE** International
ISBN: 978-1-99-101408-5
Photocopying Prohibited

52 Chapter Summary

1. (a) Put these in order from largest to smallest: myofibril, muscle tissue, myofilament, muscle fiber, fascicles.

_____

(b) Identify the structural unit shown below: _____

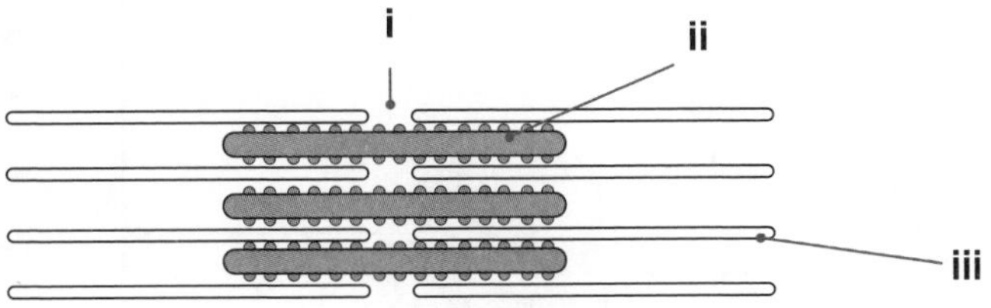

(c) On the diagram above, Identify the structures labelled i, ii, and iii:

i: _____

ii: _____

iiii: _____

(d) What happens to the H zone when the muscle is fully contracted? _____

2. Contrast the properties of fast and slow twitch skeletal muscle fibers, identifying how these properties contribute to their performance in different conditions:

_____

_____

_____

_____

_____

_____

3. (a) Study the graph (right). Describe the change in a person's muscle mass over their lifetime:

_____

_____

_____

Muscle loss due to aging

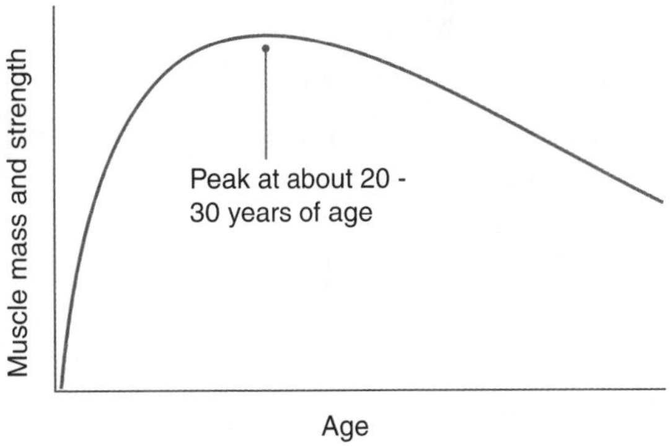

Peak at about 20 - 30 years of age

Muscle mass and strength

Age

(b) Why is there a peak in muscle mass around 20-30 years of age?

_____

_____

_____

(c) How might a person reduce the effects of aging on muscle mass after the age of 30? _____

_____

_____

4. Explain why sprinters tend to have much larger leg and arm muscles compared to marathon runners: _____

_____

_____

_____

Nervous and Endocrine Systems

Endocrine system

- The hypothalamus controls the activity of the anterior pituitary gland.
- Sympathetic nervous system stimulates release of "fight or flight" hormones from the adrenal medulla.

Cardiovascular system

- Autonomic nervous system (ANS) regulates heart rate and blood pressure.
- Cardiovascular system supplies nervous and endocrine tissues with O_2 and removes wastes.
- Hormones influence blood volume and pressure, and heart activity.

Respiratory system

- Nervous system regulates breathing.
- Epinephrine (adrenaline) dilates bronchioles and increases the rate and depth of breathing.
- Respiratory system enables gas exchange, providing O_2 and removing CO_2
- Angiotensin II, which increases blood pressure, is activated in the lung capillaries.

Skeletal system

- Nerves supply bones.
- The skeleton protects the nervous and endocrine systems and provides Ca^{2+} for nerve function.
- Parathyroid hormone regulates blood calcium.
- Growth hormone, and thyroid and sex hormones regulate skeletal growth and development.

Muscular system

- Somatic NS controls skeletal muscle activity.
- Muscular activity promotes release of catecholamine hormones from the adrenal medulla.
- Growth hormone is required for normal muscle development.
- Thyroid hormones and catecholamines influence muscle metabolism.

Nervous system

- Hormones, e.g. growth hormone, thyroid hormones, and sex hormones, influence the growth, development, and activity of the nervous system.

Lymphatic system and immunity

- Glucocorticoids, e.g. cortisol, depress the immune response.
- Maturation of lymphocytes occurs in response to hormones from the thymus.
- Nervous system innervates and regulates immune system function.

Urinary system

- Final activation of vitamin D occurs in the kidneys (bioactive vitamin D is classed as a steroid hormone).
- Bladder emptying is regulated by both the autonomic NS and voluntary activity (control of the urethral sphincter).
- Autonomic NS regulates renal blood pressure.

Digestive system

- Digestion is regulated by the autonomic NS, by gastrointestinal hormones, and by adrenal hormones, e.g. epinephrine.
- Bioactive vitamin D is needed to absorb calcium from the diet.

Reproductive system

- Autonomic NS activity regulates erectile tissue in males and females and ejaculation in males.
- Testosterone underlies sexual drive.
- Hormones from the hypothalamus, gonads, and pituitary regulate the development and functioning of the reproductive system.

Integumentary system

- Sebaceous glands are influenced by sex hormones.
- Sympathetic NS activity regulates sweat glands and blood vessels in the skin (thermoregulation).

General functions and effects on all systems

The nervous system regulates all the visceral and motor functions of the body, integrating with the endocrine system to provide both short term and longer term responses to stimuli. The endocrine system produces hormones that activate and regulate homeostatic functions, growth, and development.

Disease

Symptoms of disease
- Loss of function or control
- Loss of voluntary control
- Failure to develop normally

Diseases of the nervous system
- Inherited, e.g. Huntington's disease
- Infection, e.g. meningitis
- Autoimmune (multiple sclerosis)
- Tumors
- Degenerative diseases

Diseases of the endocrine system
- Inherited disease (e.g. congenital adrenal hyperplasia)
- Cancers (e.g. thyroid cancer)
- Autoimmune damage
- Dietary related diseases

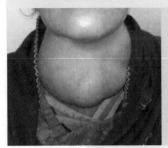

- Multiple sclerosis
- Type 1 & 2 diabetes
- Goiter (left)
- GH deficiency

Medicine and Technology

Diagnosis of disorders
- Multiple sclerosis
- Type 1 & 2 diabetes
- Goiter
- GH deficiency

Treatment of injury
- Surgery
- Physical therapies
- Drug therapies

Treatment of inherited disorders
- Dietary management
- Physical and drug therapies
- Radiotherapy (for cancers)
- Stem cell therapy and transplants
- Gene therapy, e.g. for Huntington's

- Brain scans (right)
- Genetic counselling
- Dietary modification
- Transplants
- Cell therapy

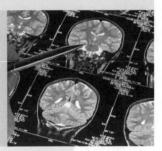

Integration & Control
Nervous & Endocrine Systems

The endocrine and nervous systems are closely linked. They can be affected by disease and undergo marked changes associated with aging.

Nervous and endocrine disorders may respond to exercise and medical treatment.

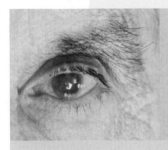

- Alzheimer's disease
- Hearing loss
- Changes in vision
- Menopause

Effects of aging on nervous and endocrine function
- Sensory impairment
- Loss of neurons (Alzheimer's)
- Increased risks of falls
- Increased risks of cancers
- Decreased levels of some hormones

The Effects of Aging

- Control of diabetes
- Improved cognitive function (brain)
- Improved autonomic NS function

Effects of exercise on nervous and endocrine function
- Improved coordination
- Reduced risk of memory loss
- Improved blood glucose management
- Reduced risk of type 2 diabetes

Exercise

The Nervous System

KEY IDEAS

- The nervous system regulates activity by sensing and responding to stimuli.

- The central nervous system is the integration center for sensing and responding.

- Neurons are electrically excitable cells capable of transmitting impulses over a considerable distance.

- Action potentials are discrete, all-or-nothing impulses. They are transmitted across chemical synapses by diffusion of a neurotransmitter.

- Sensory receptors act as biological transducers.

KEY TERMS

- Autonomic nervous system (ANS)

- Axon

- Central nervous system (CNS)

- Cerebellum

- Cerebrum

- Nerve impulse

- Neuroglia

- Neuron

- Neurotransmitter

- Peripheral nervous system (PNS)

- Sensory receptors

- Synapse

RESOURCE HUB

Scan the QR code to access:

- weblinks
- videos
- 3D models
- interactives

LEARNING OBJECTIVES

		Activity number
☐ 1	Understand that the nervous and endocrine systems work together to maintain homeostasis. Describe the roles of the central and peripheral nervous systems and their locations in the body. Understand that the autonomic nervous system is responsible for involuntary actions such as reflexes. Know that the sympathetic and parasympathetic divisions of the system release different neurotransmitters and that their effect on the body lasts for differing time spans.	53-55
☐ 2	Describe the primary structure of the brain with reference to the four main regions: the cerebrum, diencephalon, brainstem, and cerebellum. Understand that the cerebrum is divided into two hemispheres, divided by a deep fissure, and that the surface area of the cerebrum is increased through a system of folds and grooves. Know the location of the grey and white matter. Know the locations of the main functional regions of the cerebrum. Explain the difference between the primary somatosensory cortex and primary motor cortex.	56-57
☐ 3	Describe the structure of neurons and the functions of axons, soma, and dendrites. Explain the role of myelin and the difference between myelinated and non-myelinated neurons. Describe the function of glial cells, giving examples.	58
☐ 4	Know what is meant by a reflex and explain the differences between monosynaptic and polysynaptic reflexes, giving examples of each.	60
☐ 5	Understand the sodium potassium pump's role in maintaining the resting potential of the neuron. Describe a nerve impulse in terms of electrical activity and explain the role of voltage-gated ion channels. Explain the role of neurotransmitters and understand the difference between excitatory and inhibitory neurotransmitters, giving examples of each.	61-62
☐ 6	Understand the role of the synapse in transmitting nerve impulses. Describe how drugs can interact with neurotransmitters to increase or decrease their effect at synapses, giving examples. Describe how neurotransmitter disruption can result in brain disorders, giving examples.	63-66
☐ 7	Describe the roles of sensory receptors in detecting and responding to stimuli such as pressure, temperature, chemical changes, and light. Understand the signal transduction pathway.	67-69
☐ 8	Understand the structure of the eyes and the physiology of vision. Explain, using diagrams, how myopia and hypermetropia may be corrected using corrective lenses and other means. Understand the role of the receptors for pain, touch, temperature, and pressure in the skin.	70-73
☐ 9	Describe, using diagrams, the anatomy of the ear and explain the ear's role in balance. Describe the causes of hearing loss and give examples of ways in which hearing disorders can be corrected. Describe the receptor cells responsible for our sense of taste and smell. Describe the effects of aging on the nervous system, giving examples.	74-78

Background: Veins (abstract)

53 Nervous Regulatory Systems

Key Idea: The nervous and endocrine systems work together to maintain homeostasis. Neurons of the nervous system transmit information as nerve impulses to the central nervous system, which coordinates appropriate responses to stimuli. In humans, the nervous and endocrine (hormonal) systems work together to regulate the internal environment and maintain homeostasis in a fluctuating external environment.

The nervous system includes cells called **neurons** (nerve cells) which are specialized to transmit information in the form of electrochemical impulses (action potentials). The nervous system is a signaling network with branches carrying information directly to and from specific target tissues. Impulses can be transmitted over considerable distances and the response is very precise and rapid.

Coordination by the nervous system

The nervous system consists of the **central nervous system** (brain and spinal cord), and the **peripheral nervous system** (nerves and receptors outside of the CNS). Sensory input to receptors comes via stimuli. Information about the effect of a response is provided by feedback mechanisms so that the system can be readjusted. The basic organization of the nervous system can be simplified into a few key components: the **sensory receptors**, a central nervous system processing point, and the effectors, which bring about the response.

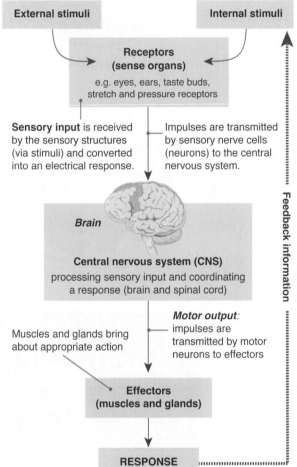

External stimuli → **Receptors (sense organs)** ← **Internal stimuli**
e.g. eyes, ears, taste buds, stretch and pressure receptors

Sensory input is received by the sensory structures (via stimuli) and converted into an electrical response.

Impulses are transmitted by sensory nerve cells (neurons) to the central nervous system.

Brain

Central nervous system (CNS)
processing sensory input and coordinating a response (brain and spinal cord)

Muscles and glands bring about appropriate action

Motor output: impulses are transmitted by motor neurons to effectors

Effectors (muscles and glands)

RESPONSE

Feedback information

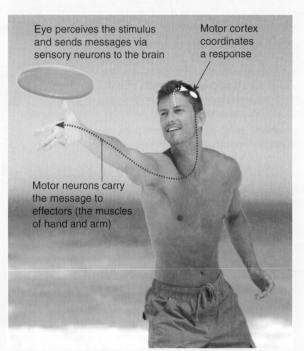

Eye perceives the stimulus and sends messages via sensory neurons to the brain

Motor cortex coordinates a response

Motor neurons carry the message to effectors (the muscles of hand and arm)

In the example above, the frisbee's approach is perceived by the eye. The motor cortex of the brain integrates the sensory message. Coordination of hand and body orientation is brought about through motor neurons to the muscles.

Comparison of nervous and hormonal control

	Nervous control	Hormonal control
Communication	Impulses across **synapses**	Hormones in the blood
Speed	Very rapid (within a few milliseconds)	Relatively slow (over minutes, hours, or longer)
Duration	Short term and reversible	Longer lasting effects
Target pathway	Specific (through nerves) to specific cells	Hormones broadcast to target cells everywhere
Action	Causes glands to secrete or muscles to contract	Causes changes in metabolic activity

1. Identify the three basic components of a nervous system and describe their role:

   (a) _____

   (b) _____

   (c) _____

2. Comment on the significance of the differences between the speed and duration of nervous and hormonal controls:

   _____

   _____

   _____

54 The Nervous System

Key Idea: The human nervous system consists of the central and peripheral nervous systems. The peripheral nervous system comprises sensory and motor pathways. Motor pathways control the voluntary and autonomic responses of the body to sensory information.

The nervous system is the body's control and communication center. Its roles are to detect stimuli, interpret them, and coordinate appropriate responses, even those that occur unconsciously. These roles are performed by the central and **peripheral nervous systems** (below).

The human nervous system

The nervous system has two major divisions: the **central nervous system** (CNS) and the peripheral nervous system (PNS).

The central nervous system comprises the brain and spinal cord. The spinal cord is a cylinder of nervous tissue extending from the base of the brain down the back, protected by the spinal column. It transmits messages to and from the brain, and controls spinal reflexes.

The peripheral nervous system comprises all the nerves and **sensory receptors** outside the central nervous system.

Below: *cross sections through the spinal cord to show entry and exit of* **neurons**.

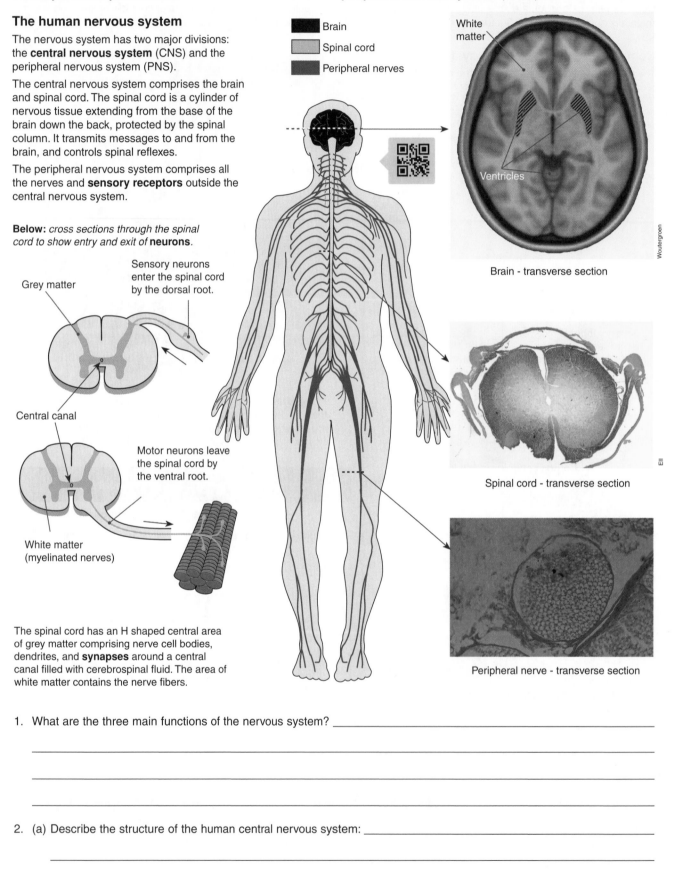

- Brain
- Spinal cord
- Peripheral nerves

White matter

Ventricles

Brain - transverse section

Grey matter

Sensory neurons enter the spinal cord by the dorsal root.

Central canal

Motor neurons leave the spinal cord by the ventral root.

White matter (myelinated nerves)

Spinal cord - transverse section

Peripheral nerve - transverse section

The spinal cord has an H shaped central area of grey matter comprising nerve cell bodies, dendrites, and **synapses** around a central canal filled with cerebrospinal fluid. The area of white matter contains the nerve fibers.

1. What are the three main functions of the nervous system? _____

_____

_____

_____

2. (a) Describe the structure of the human central nervous system: _____

_____

_____

©2023 **BIOZONE** International
ISBN: 978-1-99-101408-5
Photocopying Prohibited

The divisions of the nervous system

```
                    ┌─────────────────────┐
                    │  The nervous system │
                    └─────────────────────┘
              ┌──────────────┴───────────────┐
    ┌──────────────────┐           ┌──────────────────┐
    │  Central nervous │           │    Peripheral    │
    │     system       │           │  nervous system  │
    └──────────────────┘           └──────────────────┘
        ┌────┴────┐                   ┌────┴──────┐
   ┌────────┐ ┌────────┐        ┌──────────┐ ┌──────────┐
   │ Brain  │ │ Spinal │        │  Motor   │ │ Sensory  │
   │        │ │  cord  │        │ pathways │ │ pathways │
   └────────┘ └────────┘        └──────────┘ └──────────┘
```

Somatic (voluntary) nervous system	Autonomic nervous system

Sympathetic division Prepares the body for emergencies or strenuous activity (fight or flight)	**Parasympathetic division** Maintains involuntary processes and conserves energy (rest and digest)

The peripheral nervous system (PNS)

The PNS comprises sensory and motor divisions. Peripheral nerves all enter or leave the CNS, either from the spinal cord (the spinal nerves) or the brain (cranial nerves). They can be sensory (from sensory receptors), motor (running to a muscle or gland), or mixed (containing sensory and motor neurons). Cranial nerves are numbered in roman numerals, I-XII. They include the vagus (X), a mixed nerve with an important role in regulating bodily functions, including heart rate and digestion.

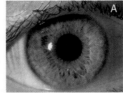

David Fankhauser

Sensory Division
Sensory nerves arise from sensory receptors and carry messages to the central nervous system for processing.

The sensory system keeps the central nervous system aware of the external and internal environments. This division includes the familiar sense organs such as ears, eyes (A), and taste buds, as well as internal receptors that monitor pressure (B), thirst, hunger, body position, movement and pain.

Motor Division
Motor nerves carry impulses from the CNS to effectors: muscles and glands. The motor division comprises two parts:

Somatic nervous system: the neurons that carry impulses to voluntary (skeletal) muscles (C).

Autonomic nervous system: regulates visceral functions over which there is generally no conscious control, e.g. heart rate, gut peristalsis involving smooth muscle (D), pupil reflex, and sweating.

---

2. (b) Describe the function of the human central nervous system: _____

_____

_____

3. (a) Describe the structure of the peripheral nervous system: _____

_____

_____

(b) Describe the function of the peripheral nervous system: _____

_____

_____

4. Explain the significance of the separation of the motor division of the PNS into somatic and autonomic divisions:

_____

_____

_____

5. Describe the two different functions of the sympathetic and parasympathetic divisions of the autonomic nervous system:

_____

_____

_____

55 The Autonomic Nervous System

Key Idea: The autonomic system is an involuntary reflex system.

The **autonomic nervous system** (ANS) regulates involuntary visceral functions through reflexes. Although most autonomic nervous system activity is beyond our conscious control, voluntary control over some basic reflexes, such as bladder emptying, can be learned. Most visceral effectors have dual innervation, receiving fibers from both branches of the ANS. These two branches, the parasympathetic and sympathetic divisions, have broadly opposing actions on the organs they control (excitatory or inhibitory). Nerves in the parasympathetic division release acetylcholine. This **neurotransmitter** is rapidly deactivated at the **synapse** and its effects are short lived and localized. Most sympathetic postganglionic nerves release norepinephrine (noradrenaline), which enters the bloodstream and is deactivated slowly. Hence, sympathetic stimulation tends to have more widespread and long lasting effects than parasympathetic stimulation. Aspects of ANS structure and function are illustrated below. The arrows indicate nerves to organs or ganglia, which are concentrations of nerve cell bodies.

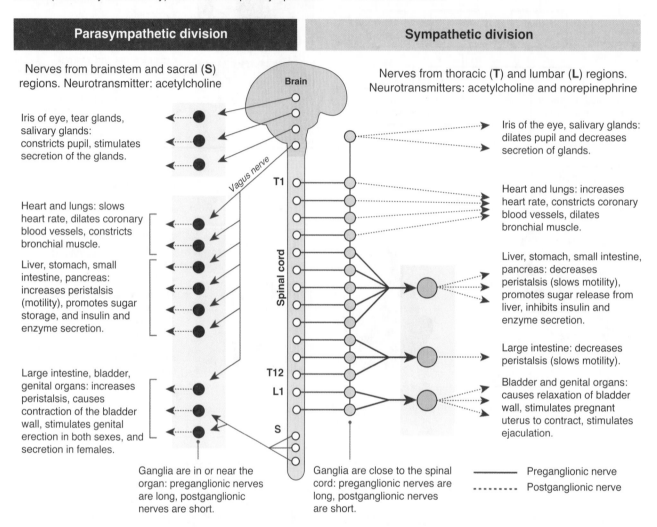

Parasympathetic division	Sympathetic division

Parasympathetic division

Nerves from brainstem and sacral (**S**) regions. Neurotransmitter: acetylcholine

Iris of eye, tear glands, salivary glands: constricts pupil, stimulates secretion of the glands.

Heart and lungs: slows heart rate, dilates coronary blood vessels, constricts bronchial muscle.

Liver, stomach, small intestine, pancreas: increases peristalsis (motility), promotes sugar storage, and insulin and enzyme secretion.

Large intestine, bladder, genital organs: increases peristalsis, causes contraction of the bladder wall, stimulates genital erection in both sexes, and secretion in females.

Ganglia are in or near the organ: preganglionic nerves are long, postganglionic nerves are short.

Brain

Vagus nerve

Spinal cord

T1

T12

L1

S

Sympathetic division

Nerves from thoracic (**T**) and lumbar (**L**) regions. Neurotransmitters: acetylcholine and norepinephrine

Iris of the eye, salivary glands: dilates pupil and decreases secretion of glands.

Heart and lungs: increases heart rate, constricts coronary blood vessels, dilates bronchial muscle.

Liver, stomach, small intestine, pancreas: decreases peristalsis (slows motility), promotes sugar release from liver, inhibits insulin and enzyme secretion.

Large intestine: decreases peristalsis (slows motility).

Bladder and genital organs: causes relaxation of bladder wall, stimulates pregnant uterus to contract, stimulates ejaculation.

Ganglia are close to the spinal cord: preganglionic nerves are long, postganglionic nerves are short.

——— Preganglionic nerve

- - - - - Postganglionic nerve

The effects of the autonomic nervous system on the body

When a person is fearful, their pupils enlarge as a consequence of sympathetic nervous system activity, i.e. the fight or flight response. The same response occurs during sexual arousal. Sympathetic stimulation also decreases secretion of the lacrimal (tear) glands.

Parasympathetic stimulation is responsible for bladder emptying through contraction of the bladder wall and relaxation of the urethral sphincter. This reflex activity can be inhibited by conscious control, but this ability does not develop until 2-4 years of age.

As part of the fight or flight response, the sympathetic nervous system dilates arteries and increases the rate and force at which the heart contracts. Heart rate is increased when increased blood flow to the heart causes reflex stimulation of the accelerator center.

The enteric nervous system (ENS) is an interdependent part of the ANS. The ENS regulates itself but is influenced by sympathetic and parasympathetic nerves which are connected to it. The ENS innervates the gut, pancreas, and gall bladder.

©2023 **BIOZONE** International
ISBN: 978-1-99-101408-5
Photocopying Prohibited

1. Explain the structure and role of each of the following divisions of the autonomic nervous system:

   (a) The sympathetic nervous system: _____

   _____

   _____

   (b) The parasympathetic nervous system: _____

   _____

   _____

   _____

2. (a) Explain why the sympathetic and parasympathetic divisions of the ANS are often described as being opposing or antagonistic in function:

   _____

   _____

   _____

   _____

   (b) Explain why sympathetic stimulation tends to have more widespread and longer lasting effects than parasympathetic stimulation:

   _____

   _____

   _____

3. Using the example of the control of heart rate, describe the role of reflexes in autonomic nervous system function:

   _____

   _____

   _____

   _____

   _____

4. With reference to the emptying of the bladder, explain how conscious control can modify a reflex activity:

   _____

   _____

   _____

   _____

   _____

5. Predict how the sympathetic reflexes controlling blood vessels would respond to a sudden decrease in blood pressure:

   _____

   _____

   _____

6. Asthma can be treated by inhaling a drug that mimics the action of norepinephrine (noradrenaline) on the sympathetic NS. Describe how this drug could be used to target the patient's respiratory system:

   _____

   _____

56 | The Human Brain

Key Idea: The brain is the body's control center. It comprises several distinct but communicating regions, each with a specialized role in physiology or behaviour.

The brain is constantly receiving, processing, and prioritizing information and coordinating appropriate responses to stimuli. The human brain consists of four main regions: the **cerebrum**, diencephalon (thalamus and hypothalamus), brainstem (midbrain, pons, and medulla oblongata), and **cerebellum**. The cerebrum is divided into two hemispheres, each of which has four lobes. The cerebrum is responsible for higher thought processes, whereas reflex activity is mainly the job of the cerebellum and medulla.

Primary structural regions of the brain

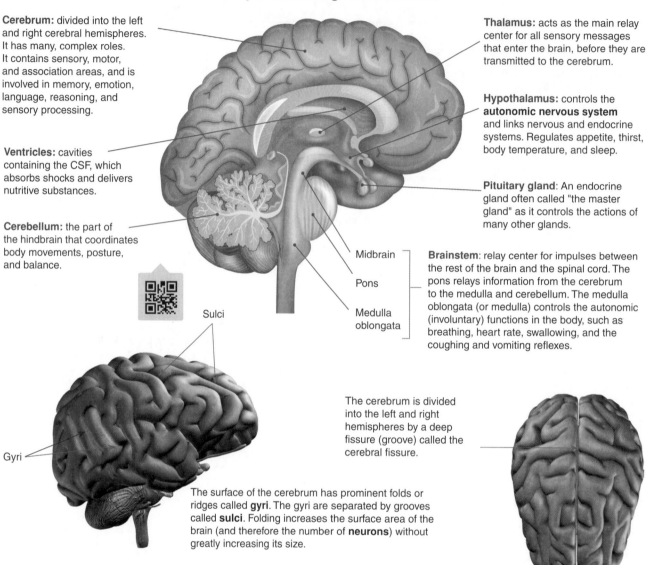

Cerebrum: divided into the left and right cerebral hemispheres. It has many, complex roles. It contains sensory, motor, and association areas, and is involved in memory, emotion, language, reasoning, and sensory processing.

Ventricles: cavities containing the CSF, which absorbs shocks and delivers nutritive substances.

Cerebellum: the part of the hindbrain that coordinates body movements, posture, and balance.

Sulci

Gyri

Thalamus: acts as the main relay center for all sensory messages that enter the brain, before they are transmitted to the cerebrum.

Hypothalamus: controls the **autonomic nervous system** and links nervous and endocrine systems. Regulates appetite, thirst, body temperature, and sleep.

Pituitary gland: An endocrine gland often called "the master gland" as it controls the actions of many other glands.

Midbrain

Pons

Medulla oblongata

Brainstem: relay center for impulses between the rest of the brain and the spinal cord. The pons relays information from the cerebrum to the medulla and cerebellum. The medulla oblongata (or medulla) controls the autonomic (involuntary) functions in the body, such as breathing, heart rate, swallowing, and the coughing and vomiting reflexes.

The cerebrum is divided into the left and right hemispheres by a deep fissure (groove) called the cerebral fissure.

The surface of the cerebrum has prominent folds or ridges called **gyri**. The gyri are separated by grooves called **sulci**. Folding increases the surface area of the brain (and therefore the number of **neurons**) without greatly increasing its size.

1. Identify the regions labeled on the diagram of the human brain (bottom right) and state their function:

   A: _____

   _____

   B: _____

   _____

   C: _____

   _____

   D: _____

   _____

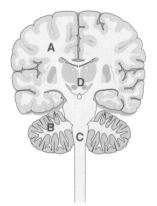

©2023 **BIOZONE** International
ISBN: 978-1-99-101408-5
Photocopying Prohibited

Pathways for the somatosensory system

The somatosensory (somatic-sensory) system is a system of sensory neurons and pathways that monitor and respond to changes within or at the surface of the body. Messages are relayed to the cerebral cortex, where specific areas are responsible for specific senses.

The brain is divided into left and right hemispheres. Any sensory system going to the cerebral cortex must cross over at some point because the cerebral cortex operates on a contralateral (opposite side) basis. Nerve fibers in the left or right halves of the spinal cord therefore cross over in the medulla (lower brain stem) so that signals from sensory neurons on the body's left hand side are processed by the right hand side of the brain and vice versa (right).

Note that voluntary nerves are controlled in the cerebral cortex and pass through the cerebellum. The cerebellum receives information from higher brain centers about what muscles *should* be doing and from the **peripheral nervous system** about what the muscles *are* doing. It has a critical role in providing corrective feedback to minimize any discrepancies and ensure smooth motor activity.

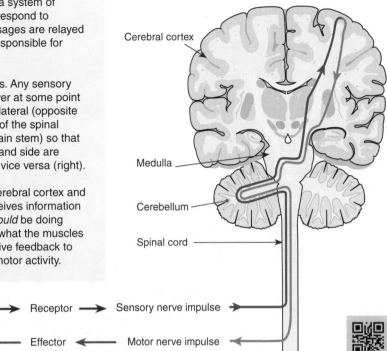

Cerebral cortex

Medulla

Cerebellum

Spinal cord

Stimulus → Receptor → Sensory nerve impulse →

Response ← Effector ← Motor nerve impulse ←

2. What is the main function of the brain? _____

_____

_____

3. Why does the brain use so much of the body's energy supply? _____

_____

4. Explain how the brain is protected against physical damage: _____

_____

_____

5. Suggest why damage to the brainstem could cause serious impairment or even death: _____

_____

_____

_____

6. (a) Describe the general stimulus-response pathway in the somatosensory system: _____

_____

_____

_____

(b) Explain why nerve impulses for muscle control travel through the cerebellum: _____

_____

_____

7. Suggest which region of the brain is important in the perfection of motor skills, and why? _____

_____

_____

©2023 **BIOZONE** International
ISBN: 978-1-99-101408-5
Photocopying Prohibited

57 Functions of the Cerebrum

Key Idea: The cerebrum is the largest region in the brain. It is involved in the control of voluntary actions.

The human brain has a large, well developed **cerebrum** divided into two hemispheres. It has prominent folds (gyri) and grooves (sulci). Each cerebral hemisphere has an outer region of grey matter and an inner region of white matter, and is divided into four lobes by deep sulci or fissures. These lobes are the temporal, frontal, occipital, and parietal lobes. The cerebrum provides us with the ability to write, speak, calculate, plan, and produce new ideas.

Functional regions in the cerebrum

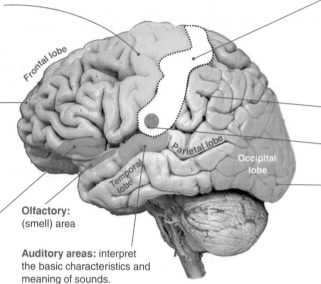

Primary motor area: controls voluntary muscle movement. Stimulation of a point one side of the motor area results in muscular contraction on the opposite side of the body.

Frontal lobe: includes the primary motor cortex but is also responsible for emotion, abstract thought, problem solving, and memory.

Language areas: the motor speech area (Broca's area) is concerned with speech production. The sensory speech area (Wernicke's area) is concerned with speech recognition and coherence.

Olfactory: (smell) area

Auditory areas: interpret the basic characteristics and meaning of sounds.

Primary somatosensory area: receives sensations from receptors in the skin, muscles and viscera, allowing recognition of pain, temperature, or touch. The size of the sensory region for different body parts depends on the number of receptors in that particular body part.

Sensory association area: gives meaning to the sensations.

Primary gustatory area: interprets sensations related to taste.

Visual areas: within the occipital lobe, these receive, interpret, and evaluate visual stimuli. In vision, each eye views both sides of the visual field but the brain receives impulses from left and right visual fields separately. The visual cortex combines the images into a single impression or perception of the image.

Touch is interpreted in the primary somatosensory area. The fingertips and the lips have a relatively large amount of area devoted to them.

Humans rely heavily on vision. The importance of this special sense in humans is indicated by the large occipital region of the brain.

The olfactory tract connects the olfactory bulb (innervated from the nasal epithelium) with the cerebral hemispheres where olfactory information is interpreted.

1. What is the function of the primary somatosensory area? _____

_____

_____

2. What is the function of the primary motor area? _____

_____

_____

3. For each of the following body functions, identify the region(s) of the brain involved in its control:

(a) Visual processing: _____

(b) Taste: _____

(c) Language: _____

(d) Memory: _____

The cerebral cortex

▸ The surface area of the cerebral cortex is increased by the gyri and sulci.

▸ The outer part of the cerebrum is the cerebral cortex, comprising a layer of grey matter around 3-4 mm thick.

▸ Most of the brain's neural activity occurs in the cerebral cortex. It also contains 10% of the brain's **neurons**.

▸ The cerebral cortex has three primary activities: sensory, motor, and associative. The associative area of the cerebral cortex is the site of higher mental functions. In humans, it makes up 95% of the cerebral cortex.

Motor and sensory cortex

The primary somatosensory cortex and primary motor cortex (below) are regions of the cerebral cortex involved in sensing and responding, respectively. Different parts of these areas receive signals from and control different areas of the body. Parts of the body with many nerve endings, e.g. the hands, take up greater areas of these regions in the brain than parts of the body with only a few nerve endings.

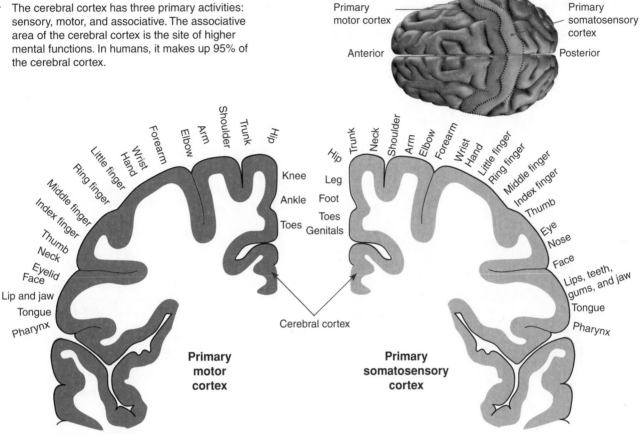

4. How is the area of the cerebral cortex enlarged without increasing the volume of the brain? _____

_____

_____

_____

5. (a) What are the three primary activities of the cerebral cortex? _____

_____

(b) Suggest why the associative area of the brain is so large in humans: _____

_____

_____

_____

6. (a) Why do you think the occipital lobe in a human brain is so large? _____

_____

_____

(b) Contrast (6a) with the size of the olfactory lobe and suggest a reason for the size difference: _____

_____

_____

58 Neuron Structure

Key Idea: Neurons transmit nerve impulses.
Nervous tissue is made up of two main cell types: **neurons** (nerve cells), which are specialized to transmit **nerve impulses**, and supporting cells, which are collectively called **neuroglia**. Neurons have a recognizable structure with a cell body (soma) and long processes (dendrites and axons).

Most long neurons in the **PNS** are also supported by a fatty insulating sheath of myelin. Information, in the form of electrochemical impulses, is transmitted along neurons from receptors to effectors. The speed of impulse conduction depends primarily on the **axon** diameter and whether or not the axon is myelinated.

Sensory (afferent) neuron

Transmits impulses from **sensory receptors** to the brain or spinal cord.

Two axonal branches, one central (to the **CNS**) and one peripheral (to the **sensory receptor**). The axons of sensory neurons tend to be short.

Axon terminal

Myelin sheath

Dendrites are usually associated with sensory receptors. Dendrites are long, compared with other neurons.

Sense organ (pressure receptor) in the skin.

Cell body or soma containing the organelles to keep the neuron alive and functioning.

Relay neuron

Links sensory and motor neurons in the CNS (as in reflexes).

Axon terminal

Axon is short within the CNS. Neurons have only one axon.

Dendrites are thin processes from the cell body that receive stimuli.

Dendrites are short. Neurons have many dendrites.

Soma of a motor neuron is located in the CNS. Dark staining Nissl bodies are the site of protein synthesis.

Motor (efferent) neuron

Transmits impulses from the CNS to effectors (muscles or glands).

The axon is an extension of the cell that transmits the nerve impulse to another neuron or to an effector (e.g. muscle). The axons of motor neurons may be very long.

Axon terminal with synaptic knob.

Node of Ranvier

Dendrites are short

Axon hillock is a specialized part of the soma where the axon begins and action potentials are generated.

1. (a) Describe a structural difference between a motor and a sensory neuron:

    _____

    _____

    _____

    _____

    _____

    (b) Describe a functional difference between a motor and a sensory neuron:

    _____

    _____

    _____

    _____

2. (a) Describe a structural difference between a motor and a relay neuron:

    _____

    _____

    _____

    _____

    (b) Describe a functional difference between a motor and a relay neuron:

    _____

    _____

    _____

    _____

    _____

3. Explain why the axons of relay neurons are short, whereas those of motor neurons may be very long:

    _____

    _____

    _____

    _____

    _____

    _____

©2023 **BIOZONE** International
ISBN: 978-1-99-101408-5
Photocopying Prohibited

Myelinated neurons

Where conduction speed is important, the axons of neurons are sheathed within a lipid-rich substance called myelin. Outside the CNS, in the peripheral nervous system, myelin is produced by specialized cells called Schwann cells. At intervals along myelinated axons, there are gaps between neighboring Schwann cells and their sheaths, called nodes of Ranvier. Myelin acts as an insulator, increasing the speed at which nerve impulses travel because it forces the impulse to "jump" from one uninsulated region to the next.

Diameter: 1-25 μm
Conduction speed: 6-120 m/s

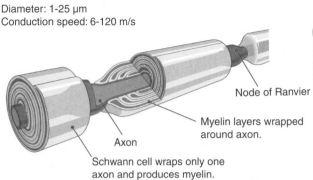

Node of Ranvier

Myelin layers wrapped around axon.

Axon

Schwann cell wraps only one axon and produces myelin.

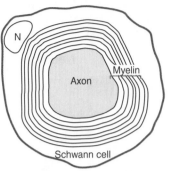

N

Axon

Myelin

Schwann cell

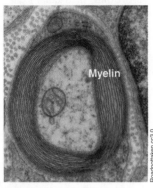

Myelin

Drawing (above left) and TEM cross section (above right) through a myelinated axon. N = nucleus of Schwann cell.

Non-myelinated neurons

Non-myelinated axons are more common in the CNS where the distances traveled are less than in the peripheral nervous system. Here, the axons are protected by Schwann cells, but there is no myelin produced. Impulses travel more slowly because the nerve impulse is propagated along the entire axon membrane, rather than jumping from node to node as in myelinated neurons.

Diameter: <1 μm
Conduction speed: 0.2-0.5 m/s

Cytoplasmic extensions

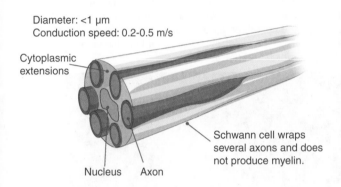

Schwann cell wraps several axons and does not produce myelin.

Nucleus   Axon

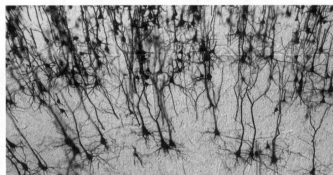

Unmyelinated pyramidal neurons in the cerebral cortex of the brain.

4. (a) What is the function of myelination in neurons? _____

_____

(b) What cell type is responsible for myelination in the CNS? _____

(c) What cell type is responsible for myelination in the PNS? _____

(d) Explain why many of the neurons in the peripheral nervous system are myelinated, whereas those in the central nervous system are often not:

_____

_____

_____

5. (a) Explain how an action potential travels in a myelinated neuron: _____

_____

(b) How does this differ from its travel in a non-myelinated neuron? _____

_____

(c) Describe the adaptive advantage of faster conduction of nerve impulses: _____

_____

6. Identify two types of effectors innervated by motor neurons: _____

_____

59 Neuroglia

Key Idea: Neuroglia support and protect neurons. Their roles include supplying nutrients, insulating, and protecting neurons. **Neuroglia**, also called glial cells, are the cells that support and protect **neurons**. Neuroglia have a range of functions. These include holding **neurons** in place, insulating them, supplying them with nutrients and oxygen, destroying pathogens, and removing dead neurons. There are two main types of neuroglia in the **PNS**, Schwann cells and satellite cells. The neuroglia of the **CNS** include astrocytes, microglia, ependymal cells, and oligodendrocytes. Each has a different function in supporting the neurons of the CNS. The structure and function of the CNS neuroglia are described below.

Neuroglia of the CNS

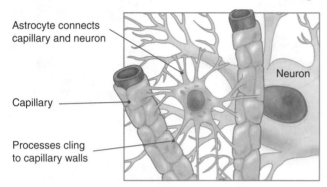

Astrocyte connects capillary and neuron

Neuron

Capillary

Processes cling to capillary walls

Astrocytes are the most abundant supportive cells in nervous tissue. They anchor **neurons** to capillaries and support the blood-brain barrier by restricting the passage of certain substances. They are also important in the repair of the brain and spinal cord following injury.

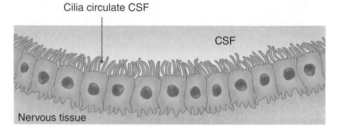

Cilia circulate CSF

CSF

Nervous tissue

Ependymal cells are epithelial cells lining the ventricles in the brain and the central canal of the spinal cord. The surfaces of these cuboidal cells are covered in cilia and microvilli, which circulate and absorb cerebrospinal fluid (CSF). Specialized ependymal cells and capillaries together form the choroid plexuses, which produce the CSF.

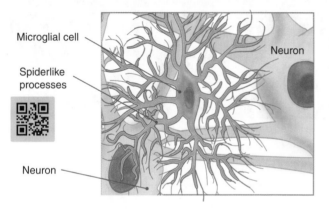

Microglial cell

Neuron

Spiderlike processes

Neuron

Microglia are the defense cells of nervous tissue. Antibodies are too large to cross the blood-brain barrier, so the phagocytic microglia must be able to recognize and dispose of foreign material and debris.

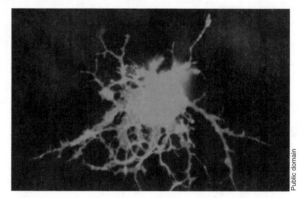

Public domain

Oligodendrocytes produce insulating myelin sheaths around the axons of neurons in the CNS. A single oligodendrocyte can extend to wrap around up to 50 axons. The image above shows an oligodendrocyte genetically altered to fluoresce.

1. What are neuroglia? _____

_____

2. Describe the functional role of each of the following neuroglia, with reference to the features associated with that role:

(a) Astrocytes: _____

_____

(b) Ependymal cells: _____

_____

(c) Microglia: _____

_____

(d) Oligodendrocytes: _____

_____

©2023 **BIOZONE** International
ISBN: 978-1-99-101408-5
Photocopying Prohibited

60 Reflexes

Key Idea: A reflex is an involuntary response to a stimulus.
A reflex is an automatic response to a stimulus involving a small number of **neurons** and a **central nervous system** (CNS) processing point (usually the spinal cord, but sometimes the brain stem). This type of circuit is called a reflex arc. Reflexes permit rapid responses to stimuli. They are classified according to the number of CNS **synapses** involved. Monosynaptic reflexes involve only one CNS synapse, e.g. knee jerk reflex, whereas polysynaptic reflexes involve two or more, e.g. pain withdrawal reflex. Both are spinal reflexes. The pupil reflex (opening and closure of the pupil) is an example of a cranial reflex.

Pain withdrawal: A polysynaptic reflex arc

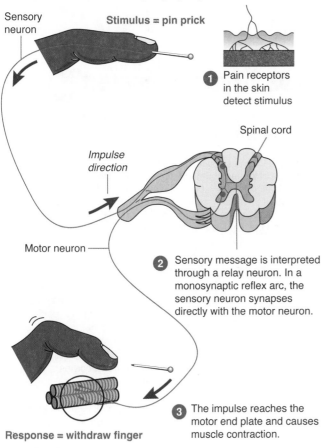

Sensory neuron

Stimulus = pin prick

1 Pain receptors in the skin detect stimulus

Spinal cord

Impulse direction

Motor neuron

2 Sensory message is interpreted through a relay neuron. In a monosynaptic reflex arc, the sensory neuron synapses directly with the motor neuron.

3 The impulse reaches the motor end plate and causes muscle contraction.

Response = withdraw finger

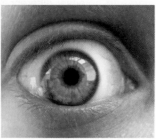

The patella (knee jerk) reflex is a simple deep tendon reflex used to test the function of the femoral nerve and spinal cord segments L2-L4. It helps to maintain posture and balance when walking.

The pupillary light reflex refers to the rapid expansion or contraction of the pupils in response to the intensity of light falling on the retina. It is a polysynaptic cranial reflex and can be used to test for brain death.

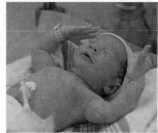

Normal newborns exhibit a number of primitive reflexes in response to particular stimuli. These reflexes disappear within a few months of birth as the child develops. Primitive reflexes include the grasp reflex (above left) and the startle or Moro reflex (above right) in which a sudden noise will cause the infant to throw out its arms, extend the legs and head, and cry. The rooting and sucking reflexes are further examples of primitive reflexes.

1. Reflexes do not require conscious thought to occur. How does this provide a survival advantage? _____

_____

_____

2. (a) Describe the difference between a monosynaptic and a polysynaptic reflex arc: _____

_____

_____

_____

(b) Which would produce the most rapid response, given similar length sensory and motor pathways? Explain: _____

_____

3. What might be the survival advantage of primitive reflexes in newborns? _____

_____

_____

_____

_____

©2023 **BIOZONE** International
ISBN: 978-1-99-101408-5
Photocopying Prohibited

61 The Nerve Impulse

Key Idea: A nerve impulse occurs in response to a stimulus and involves the transmission of a membrane depolarization along the axon of a neuron.

The plasma membrane of cells, including **neurons**, contain sodium-potassium ion pumps that actively pump sodium ions (Na^+) out of the cell and potassium ions (K^+) into the cell. The action of these ion pumps in neurons creates a separation of charge (a potential difference or voltage) either side of the membrane and makes the cells electrically excitable. It is this property that enables neurons to transmit electrical impulses. The resting state of a neuron, with a net negative charge inside, is maintained by the sodium-potassium pumps, which actively move two K^+ into the neuron for every three Na^+ moved out (below left). When a nerve is stimulated, a brief increase in membrane permeability to Na^+ temporarily reverses the membrane polarity (a depolarization). After the **nerve impulse** passes, the sodium-potassium pump restores the resting potential.

The resting neuron

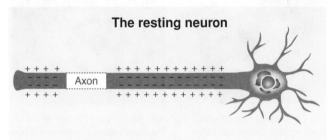

When a neuron is not transmitting an impulse, the inside of the cell is negatively charged relative to the outside and the cell is said to be electrically polarized. The potential difference (voltage) across the membrane is called the resting potential. For most nerve cells, this is about -70 mV. Nerve transmission is possible because this membrane potential exists.

The nerve impulse

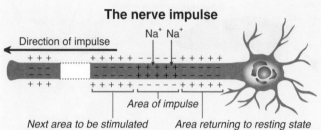

When a neuron is stimulated, the distribution of charges on each side of the membrane briefly reverses. This process of depolarization causes a burst of electrical activity to pass along the **axon** of the neuron as an action potential. As the charge reversal reaches one region, local currents depolarize the next region and the impulse spreads along the axon.

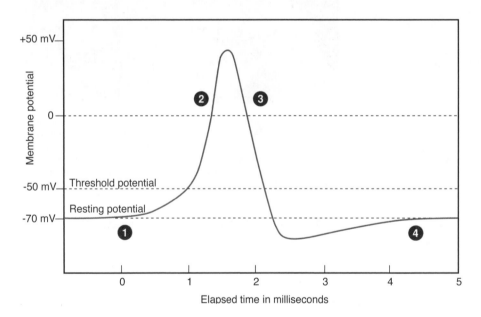

The depolarization in an axon can be shown as a change in membrane potential (in millivolts). A stimulus must be strong enough to reach the threshold potential before an action potential is generated. This is the voltage at which the depolarization of the membrane becomes unstoppable.

The action potential is all or nothing in its generation and because of this, impulses (once generated) always reach threshold and move along the axon without weakening. The resting potential is restored by the movement of potassium ions (K^+) out of the cell. During this refractory period, the nerve cannot respond, so nerve impulses are discrete.

Voltage-gated ion channels and the course of an action potential

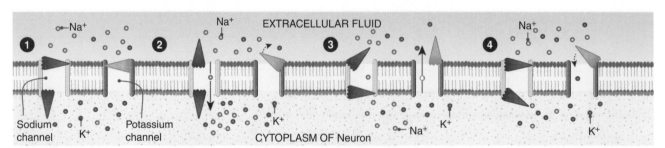

Resting state:
Voltage activated Na^+ and K^+ channels are closed. Negative interior is maintained by the Na^+/K^+ pump.

Depolarization:
Voltage activated Na^+ channels open and there is a rapid influx of Na^+ ions. The interior of the neuron becomes positive relative to the outside.

Repolarization:
Voltage activated Na^+ channels close and the K^+ channels open; K^+ moves out of the cell, restoring the negative charge to the cell interior.

Returning to resting state:
Voltage activated Na^+ and K^+ channels close and the Na^+/K^+ pump restores the original balance of ions, returning the neuron to its resting state (3Na^+ out for 2K^+ in).

©2023 **BIOZONE** International
ISBN: 978-1-99-101408-5
Photocopying Prohibited

Axon myelination is a feature of vertebrate nervous systems and it enables them to achieve very rapid speeds of nerve conduction.

In a myelinated neuron, action potentials are generated only at the nodes, which is where the voltage-gated channels occur. The axon is insulated so the action potential at one node is sufficient to trigger an action potential in the next node and the impulse 'jumps' along the axon (called saltatory conduction). This contrasts with a non-myelinated neuron in which voltage-gated channels occur along the entire length of the axon.

As well as increasing the speed of conduction, the myelin sheath reduces energy expenditure because the area over which depolarization occurs is less. The number of sodium and potassium ions that need to be pumped to restore resting potential is, therefore, also less.

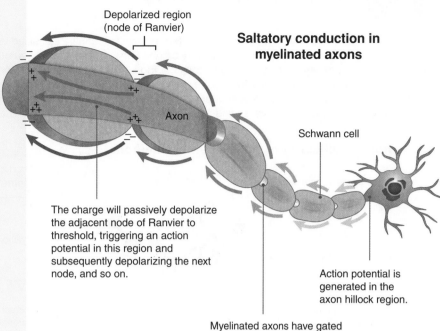

Saltatory conduction in myelinated axons

Depolarized region (node of Ranvier)

Axon

Schwann cell

The charge will passively depolarize the adjacent node of Ranvier to threshold, triggering an action potential in this region and subsequently depolarizing the next node, and so on.

Action potential is generated in the axon hillock region.

Myelinated axons have gated channels only at their nodes.

1. What is an action potential? _____

_____

2. Describe the movement of voltage-gated channels and ions associated with:

   (a) Depolarization of the neuron: _____

   (b) Repolarization of the neuron: _____

3. Summarize the sequence of events in a neuron when it receives a stimulus sufficient to reach threshold:

   (i): _____

   _____

   (ii): _____

   _____

   (iii): _____

   _____

   (iv): _____

   _____

4. (a) Explain why the nerve impulse in a myelinated neuron jumps along the axon from node to node:

   _____

   _____

   (b) How does myelination reduce the energetic costs of impulse conduction? _____

   _____

   _____

5. How is the resting potential restored in a neuron after an action potential has passed? _____

_____

6. Explain how the refractory period influences the direction in which an impulse will travel: _____

_____

62 Neurotransmitters

Key Idea: Neurotransmitters are chemicals that transmit signals between neurons. They can be excitatory or inhibitory. **Neurotransmitters** are found in the **axon** endings of **neurons** and are released into the space between one neuron and the next (the synaptic cleft) after a depolarization or hyperpolarization of the nerve ending. Neurotransmitters can be classified into amino acids, peptides, or monoamines. The many neurotransmitters produce various responses, depending on their location in the body. They can be excitatory (likely to cause an action potential in the receiving neuron) or inhibitory (causing hyperpolarization), depending on the receptor they activate.

Neurotransmitters carry signals between neurons

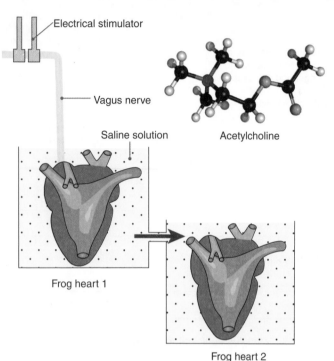

Electrical stimulator

Vagus nerve

Saline solution

Acetylcholine

Frog heart 1

Frog heart 2

Chemical signaling between neurons was first demonstrated in 1921 by Otto Loewi. In his experiment, the still-beating hearts of two frogs were placed in connected flasks filled with saline solution. The vagus nerve (parasympathetic) of the first heart was still attached and was stimulated by electricity to reduce its rate of beating. After a delay, the rate of beating in the second heart also slowed. Increasing the beating rate in the first heart caused an increase in the beating rate in the second heart, showing electrical stimulus of the first heart caused it to release a chemical into the saline solution that then affected the heartbeat of the second heart. The chemical was found to be acetylcholine.

Neurotransmitters

Name	Postsynaptic effect	
Acetylcholine	Excitatory/ inhibitory	Responsible for the stimulation of muscles. Found in sensory neurons and the **autonomic nervous system**.
Norepinephrine (noradrenaline)	Excitatory	Brings the nervous system into high alert. Increases heart rate and blood pressure.
Dopamine	Excitatory/ inhibitory	Associated with reward mechanisms in the brain. Produces the "feel good" feeling.
Gamma amino butyric acid (GABA)	Inhibitory	Inhibits excitatory neurotransmitters that can cause anxiety.
Glutamate	Excitatory	Found in the **central nervous system** and concentrated in the brain.
Serotonin	Inhibitory	Serotonin is strongly involved in regulation of mood and perception.
Endorphin	Excitatory	Involved in pain reduction and pleasure.

1. Describe the purpose of a neurotransmitter: _____

_____

2 (a) Explain why stimulating the first frog heart with electricity caused it to change its beating rate: _____

_____

_____

(b) Explain why the second heart in the experiment reduced its beating rate after a delay: _____

_____

_____

3. Why can some neurotransmitters be both excitatory and inhibitory? _____

_____

_____

_____

©2023 **BIOZONE** International
ISBN: 978-1-99-101408-5
Photocopying Prohibited

63 Chemical Synapses

Key Idea: Synapses are junctions between neurons, or between neurons and receptor or effector cells. **Nerve impulses** are transmitted across synapses.

Action potentials are transmitted across junctions called **synapses**. Almost all synapses in vertebrates are chemical synapses, which involve the diffusion of a signal molecule or **neurotransmitter** from one cell to another. Chemical synapses can occur between two **neurons**, between a receptor cell and a neuron, or between a neuron and an effector (e.g. muscle fiber or gland cell). The synapse consists of the **axon** terminal (synaptic knob), a gap called

the synaptic cleft, and the membrane of the post-synaptic (receiving) cell. Arrival of an action potential at the axon terminal causes release of the neurotransmitter, which diffuses across the cleft and produces an electrical response in the post-synaptic cell (an example of signal transduction). Cholinergic synapses are named for the neurotransmitter they release, acetylcholine (ACh). In the example pictured below, ACh results in depolarization (excitation) of the post-synaptic neuron. Unlike electrical synapses, in which transmission can occur in either direction, transmission at chemical synapses is always in one direction (unidirectional).

The structure of a cholinergic synapse

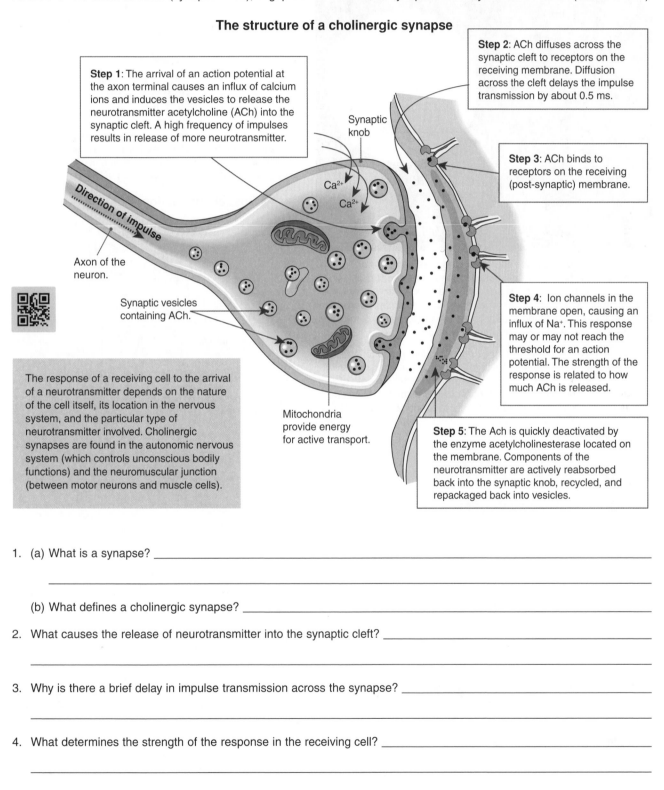

Step 1: The arrival of an action potential at the axon terminal causes an influx of calcium ions and induces the vesicles to release the neurotransmitter acetylcholine (ACh) into the synaptic cleft. A high frequency of impulses results in release of more neurotransmitter.

Step 2: ACh diffuses across the synaptic cleft to receptors on the receiving membrane. Diffusion across the cleft delays the impulse transmission by about 0.5 ms.

Step 3: ACh binds to receptors on the receiving (post-synaptic) membrane.

Step 4: Ion channels in the membrane open, causing an influx of Na$^+$. This response may or may not reach the threshold for an action potential. The strength of the response is related to how much ACh is released.

Step 5: The Ach is quickly deactivated by the enzyme acetylcholinesterase located on the membrane. Components of the neurotransmitter are actively reabsorbed back into the synaptic knob, recycled, and repackaged back into vesicles.

Synaptic knob

Ca^{2+}

Ca^{2+}

Direction of impulse

Axon of the neuron.

Synaptic vesicles containing ACh.

Mitochondria provide energy for active transport.

The response of a receiving cell to the arrival of a neurotransmitter depends on the nature of the cell itself, its location in the nervous system, and the particular type of neurotransmitter involved. Cholinergic synapses are found in the autonomic nervous system (which controls unconscious bodily functions) and the neuromuscular junction (between motor neurons and muscle cells).

1. (a) What is a synapse? _____

   _____

   (b) What defines a cholinergic synapse? _____

2. What causes the release of neurotransmitter into the synaptic cleft? _____

   _____

3. Why is there a brief delay in impulse transmission across the synapse? _____

   _____

4. What determines the strength of the response in the receiving cell? _____

   _____

   _____

64 Integration at Synapses

Key Idea: Synapses play a pivotal role in the ability of the nervous system to respond appropriately to stimulation and to adapt to change by integrating all inputs.

The nature of synaptic transmission in the nervous system allows the integration (interpretation and coordination) of inputs from many sources. These inputs can be excitatory (causing depolarization) or inhibitory (making an action potential less likely). It is the sum of all excitatory and inhibitory inputs that leads to the final response in a post-synaptic cell. Synaptic integration is behind all the various responses we have to stimuli. It is also the most probable mechanism by which learning and memory are achieved.

Summation at synapses

Graded postsynaptic responses may sum to produce an action potential.

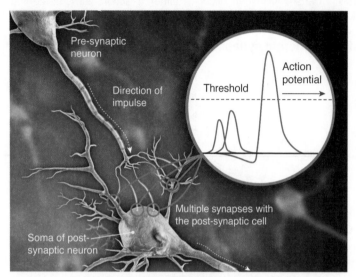

Impulse transmission across chemical **synapses** has several advantages, despite the delay caused by **neurotransmitter** diffusion. Chemical synapses transmit impulses in one direction to a precise location and, because they rely on a limited supply of neurotransmitter, they are subject to fatigue (inability to respond to repeated stimulation). This protects the system against overstimulation.

Synapses allow inputs from many sources to be integrated. The response of a post-synaptic cell is often not strong enough on its own to generate an action potential. However, because the strength of the response is related to the amount of neurotransmitter released, subthreshold responses can sum together to produce a response in the post-synaptic cell. This additive effect is called summation. Summation can be temporal or spatial (right).

❶ Temporal summation

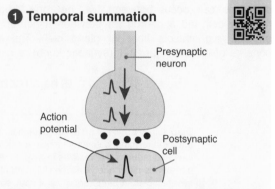

Several impulses may arrive at the **synapse** in quick succession from a single **axon**. The individual responses are so close in time that they sum to reach threshold and produce an action potential in the post-synaptic neuron.

❷ Spatial summation

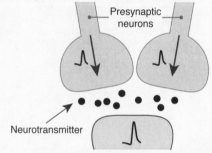

Impulses from spatially separated axon terminals may arrive simultaneously at different regions of the same post-synaptic **neuron**. The responses from the different places sum to produce an action potential.

1. Explain the purpose of nervous system integration: _____

_____

_____

2. Describe two advantages of chemical synapses:

   (a) _____

   _____

   (b) _____

   _____

3. (a) Explain what is meant by summation: _____

   _____

   (b) In simple terms, distinguish between temporal and spatial summation: _____

   _____

   _____

©2023 **BIOZONE** International
ISBN: 978-1-99-101408-5
Photocopying Prohibited

65 Drugs at Synapses

Key Idea: Drugs may increase or decrease the effect of neurotransmitters at synapses.

Drugs may act at **synapses,** either mimicking or blocking the usual effect of a **neurotransmitter**, whether it be excitatory or inhibitory. Drugs that increase the usual effect of a neurotransmitter are called agonists, while those that decrease their effect are called antagonists. Many recreational and therapeutic drugs work through their action at synapses, controlling the response of the receiving cell to incoming action potentials.

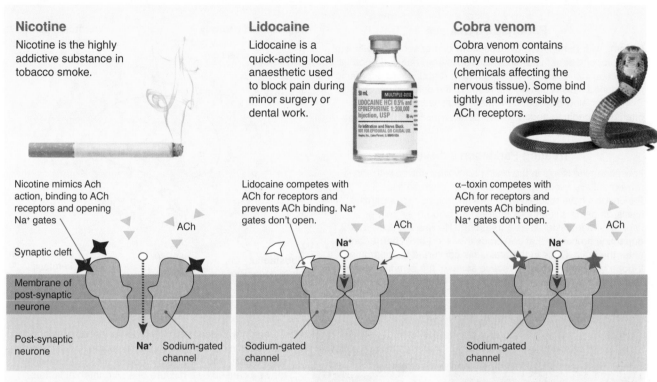

Nicotine

Nicotine is the highly addictive substance in tobacco smoke.

Nicotine mimics Ach action, binding to ACh receptors and opening Na⁺ gates

ACh

Synaptic cleft

Membrane of post-synaptic neurone

Post-synaptic neurone

Na⁺   Sodium-gated channel

Effect: Agonistic
Result: Action potential generation.
Nicotine acts as an agonist at nicotinic synapses (autonomic ganglia and the motor end plate). It binds to and activates ACh receptors on the postsynaptic membrane, e.g. of a muscle cell. This opens sodium gates, leading to a sodium influx and membrane depolarization.

Lidocaine

Lidocaine is a quick-acting local anaesthetic used to block pain during minor surgery or dental work.

Lidocaine competes with ACh for receptors and prevents ACh binding. Na⁺ gates don't open.

Na⁺

ACh

Sodium-gated channel

Effect: Antagonistic
Result: Sensory inhibition.
Lidocaine binds to the ACh receptors on sensory **neurons** and prevents ACh binding. No depolarization occurs, so no action potential is generated on the post-synaptic neuron. Pain signals are not generated.

Cobra venom

Cobra venom contains many neurotoxins (chemicals affecting the nervous tissue). Some bind tightly and irreversibly to ACh receptors.

α–toxin competes with ACh for receptors and prevents ACh binding. Na⁺ gates don't open.

Na⁺

ACh

Sodium-gated channel

Effect: Antagonistic
Result: Muscular paralysis.
Toxins in cobra venom bind to ACh receptors and prevent ACh binding to receptors on the plasma membrane of muscle cells. As a result, sodium channels remain closed and no action potentials are produced. They can cause muscular paralysis, respiratory failure, and death.

1. Explain the difference between an agonistic and antagonistic drug: _____

_____

_____

2. Nicotine and cobra venom both bind to acetylcholine receptors. Explain why their effects are different: _____

_____

_____

_____

_____

3. Explain why lidocaine is used as a local anaesthetic: _____

_____

_____

_____

66 Chemical Imbalances in the Brain

Key Idea: Brain disorders result from disruptions of the natural levels of specific neurotransmitters. These can result in changes in behaviour and control of the body.

The brain uses chemicals (**neurotransmitters**) to transmit messages between nerve cells. Neurotransmitters are released from presynaptic **neurons** and diffuse across the synaptic cleft to postsynaptic neurons to cause a specific effect. Many brain disorders result from disturbances to natural levels of specific neurotransmitters, and can lead to the failure of specific neural pathways. Sometimes the pathways can be restored using drugs that either replace or boost levels of specific neurotransmitters.

Parkinson's disease

Patients with Parkinson's disease show decreased stimulation in the motor cortex of the brain. This results from reduced dopamine production in the substantia nigra region (right) where dopamine is produced. This is usually the result of the death of nerve cells. Symptoms: slow physical movement and spasmodic tremors often don't begin to appear until a person has lost 70% of their dopamine-producing cells.

Treating Parkinson's disease

Low dopamine levels in the brain pathways involved with movement are a feature of this disease. Treatments for Parkinson's have focused on increasing the body's dopamine levels. Dopamine is unable to cross the blood-brain barrier, so cannot be administered as a treatment. However, L-dopa is a dopamine precursor that can cross the blood-brain barrier and enter the brain. Once in the brain, it is converted to dopamine. L-dopa has been shown to reduce some of the symptoms of Parkinson's disease.

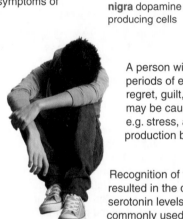

Nigrostriatal pathway dopamine deficiency causes Parkinson's disease

Serotonin pathways serotonin deficiency causes depression

Substantia nigra dopamine producing cells

Raphe nuclei serotonin producing cells

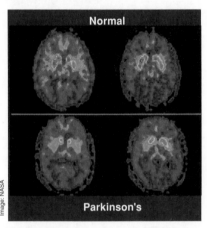

Normal

Parkinson's

Image: NASA

Positron emission tomography (PET) measures the activity of dopamine neurons in the substantia nigra area of the brain. Parkinson's patients (lower panel) show reduced activity in the dopamine neurons compared with normal patients.

Depression

A person with depression (left) experiences prolonged periods of extremely low mood, including low self esteem, regret, guilt, and feelings of hopelessness. Depression may be caused by a mixture of environmental factors, e.g. stress, and biological factors, e.g. low serotonin production by the raphe nuclei in the brain, above.

Treating depression

Recognition of the link between serotonin and depression has resulted in the development of antidepressant drugs that alter serotonin levels. Monoamine oxidase inhibitors (MAOI) are commonly used antidepressants that increase serotonin levels by preventing its breakdown in the brain.

Newer drugs, called Selective Serotonin Re-uptake Inhibitors (SSRIs), stop serotonin re-uptake by presynaptic cells. This increases the levels of extracellular serotonin, making more available to bind to the postsynaptic cells, and stabilizing serotonin levels in the brain. SSRIs have fewer side effects than other antidepressants because they specifically target serotonin and no other neurotransmitters.

1. Describe the function of a neurotransmitter: _____

_____

_____

_____

2. Describe the pharmacological cause of the following diseases and identify the major symptom of each:

(a) Parkinson's disease: _____

_____

_____

(b) Depression: _____

_____

_____

©2023 **BIOZONE** International
ISBN: 978-1-99-101408-5
Photocopying Prohibited

67 Detecting Changing States

Key Idea: Sensory receptors allow the body to respond to a range of stimuli in the internal and external environments. A stimulus is any physical or chemical change in the environment capable of provoking a response in an organism. Organisms respond to stimuli in order to survive. This response is adaptive and acts to maintain the organism's state of homeostasis. Stimuli may be either external (outside the organism) or internal (within its body). Some of the stimuli to which humans respond are described below, together with the sense organs that detect and respond to these stimuli. **Sensory receptors** respond to specific stimuli, so the sense organs we possess determine how we perceive the world.

Photoreceptor cells in the eyes detect color, intensity, and movement of light.

Hair cells in the vestibule of the inner ear respond to gravity by detecting the rate of change and direction of the head and body. Other hair cells in the cochlea of the inner ear detect sound waves. The sound is directed and amplified by specialized regions of the outer and middle ear (pinna, canal, middle ear bones).

Chemoreceptors in certain blood vessels, e.g. carotid arteries, monitor carbon dioxide levels (and therefore pH) of the blood. Breathing and heart rate increase or decrease, as appropriate, to adjust blood composition.

Proprioceptors (stretch receptors) in the muscles, tendons, and joints monitor limb position, stretch, and tension. The muscle spindle is a stretch receptor that monitors the state of muscle contraction and enables muscle to maintain its length.

Olfactory receptors in the nose detect airborne chemicals. The human nose has about 5 million of these receptors, a bloodhound nose has more than 200 million. The taste buds of the tongue detect dissolved chemicals (gustation). Tastes are combinations of five basic sensations: sweet, salt, sour, bitter, and savory (umami receptor).

Pressure deforms the skin surface and stimulates sensory receptors in the dermis. These receptors are especially abundant on the lips and fingertips.

Baroreceptors in the walls of some arteries, e.g. aorta, monitor blood pressure. Heart rate and blood vessel diameter are adjusted accordingly.

Pain and temperature are detected by simple nerve endings in the skin. Deep tissue injury is sometimes felt on the skin as referred pain.

Humans rely heavily on their hearing when learning to communicate. Without it, speech and language development are more difficult.

Breathing and heart rates are regulated in response to sensory input from chemoreceptors.

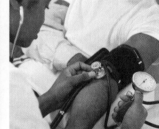

Baroreceptors and osmoreceptors act together to keep blood pressure and volume within narrow limits.

1. Provide a concise definition of a stimulus: _____

   _____

2. Using humans as an example, discuss the need for communication systems to respond to changes in the environment:

   _____

   _____

   _____

   _____

3. What is the purpose of chemoreceptors in blood vessels?_____

   _____

68 The Basis of Sensory Reception

Key Idea: Sensory receptors act as transducers, detecting stimuli and converting them to an electrochemical signal.

Sensory receptors are specialized to detect stimuli and respond by producing an electrical or chemical discharge. In this way they act as biological transducers, converting the energy from a stimulus into an electrochemical signal. They can do this because the stimulus opens (or closes) ion channels and leads to localized changes in membrane potential called receptor potentials. Receptor potentials are graded and not self-propagating, but sense cells can amplify them, generating action potentials directly or inducing the release of a **neurotransmitter**. The stimulus is transduced into action potentials whose frequency is dependent on stimulus strength. This happens whether the sensory cell itself fires action potentials or not. The simplest sensory receptors consist of a single sensory neuron, e.g. nerve endings. More complex sense cells form **synapses** with their sensory **neurons**, e.g. taste buds. Sensory receptors are classified according to the stimuli to which they respond, e.g. photoreceptors respond to light.

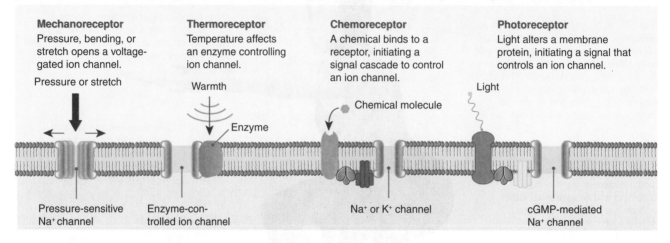

Mechanoreceptor
Pressure, bending, or stretch opens a voltage-gated ion channel.

Pressure or stretch

Pressure-sensitive
Na⁺ channel

Thermoreceptor
Temperature affects an enzyme controlling ion channel.

Warmth

Enzyme

Enzyme-controlled ion channel

Chemoreceptor
A chemical binds to a receptor, initiating a signal cascade to control an ion channel.

Chemical molecule

Na⁺ or K⁺ channel

Photoreceptor
Light alters a membrane protein, initiating a signal that controls an ion channel.

Light

cGMP-mediated
Na⁺ channel

Signal transduction

Sensory cells convert one type of stimulus energy, e.g. pressure, into an electrical signal by altering the flow of ions across the plasma membrane and generating receptor potentials. In many cases, as in the Pacinian corpuscle, this leads directly to action potentials which are generated in the voltage-gated region of the sensory cell.

In some receptor cells, the receptor potential leads to neurotransmitter release, which then directly or indirectly leads to action potentials in a post-synaptic cell.

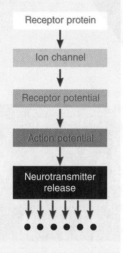

Receptor protein
↓
Ion channel
↓
Receptor potential
↓
Action potential
↓
Neurotransmitter release
↓↓↓↓↓
● ● ● ● ● ●

The Pacinian corpuscle

Pacinian corpuscles are pressure receptors in deep tissues of the body. They are relatively large but structurally simple, consisting of a sensory nerve ending (dendrite) surrounded by a capsule of connective tissue layers. Pressure deforms the capsule, stretching the nerve ending and leading to a localized depolarization called a receptor potential. Receptor potentials are graded and do not spread far, although they may sum together and increase in amplitude.

The sense cell converts the receptor potentials to action potentials at the start of the **axon**, where there are voltage-gated channels. The action potential is then propagated along the axon.

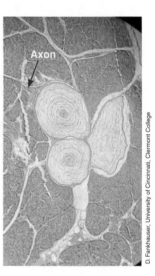

Axon

D. Frankhauser, University of Cincinnati, Clermont College

1. Explain why sensory receptors are termed 'biological transducers': _____

_____

_____

2. Identify one feature that all sensory receptors have in common: _____

_____

3. Explain how a stimulus received by a sensory receptor is converted into an electrical response: _____

_____

_____

4. Describe the properties of receptor potentials: _____

_____

_____

©2023 **BIOZONE** International
ISBN: 978-1-99-101408-5
Photocopying Prohibited

69 Encoding Information

Key Idea: A sensory receptor communicates information about stimulus strength in the frequency of action potentials.

A receptor must do more than simply record a stimulus. It is important that it also provides information about the stimulus strength. Action potentials obey the 'all or none law' and are always the same size, so stimulus strength cannot be encoded by varying the amplitude of the action potentials. Instead, the frequency of impulses conveys information about the stimulus intensity: the higher the frequency of

impulses, the stronger the stimulus. This encoding method is termed frequency modulation, and it is the way that receptors inform the brain about stimulus strength. In the Pacinian corpuscle (below) frequency modulation is possible because a stronger pressure produces larger receptor potentials, which depolarize the first node of Ranvier to threshold more rapidly and results in a more rapid volley of action potentials. **Sensory receptors** also show sensory adaptation and will cease responding to a stimulus of the same intensity.

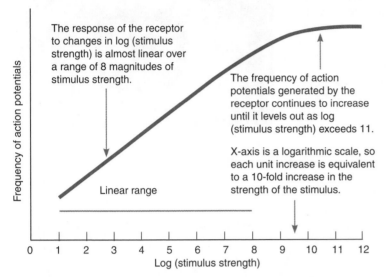

The response of the receptor to changes in log (stimulus strength) is almost linear over a range of 8 magnitudes of stimulus strength.

The frequency of action potentials generated by the receptor continues to increase until it levels out as log (stimulus strength) exceeds 11.

X-axis is a logarithmic scale, so each unit increase is equivalent to a 10-fold increase in the strength of the stimulus.

Linear range

Y-axis: Frequency of action potentials
X-axis: Log (stimulus strength) — 0 1 2 3 4 5 6 7 8 9 10 11 12

Receptors can use variation in action potential frequency to encode stimulus strengths that vary by nearly 11 orders of magnitude.

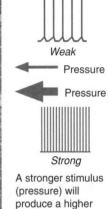

Layers of connective tissue deformed by pressure.

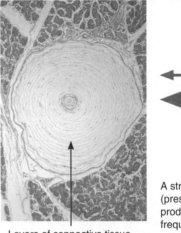

Weak

Pressure

Pressure

Strong

A stronger stimulus (pressure) will produce a higher frequency of action potentials than a weaker stimulus.

A Pacinian corpuscle (above), illustrating the many layers of connective tissue. Pacinian corpuscles are rapidly adapting receptors; they fire at the beginning and end of a stimulus, but do not respond to unchanging pressure.

1

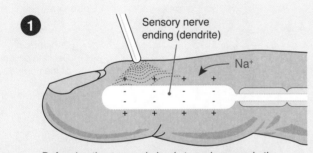

Sensory nerve ending (dendrite)

Na⁺

Deforming the corpuscle leads to an increase in the permeability of the nerve to sodium. Na$^+$ diffuses into the nerve ending creating a localized depolarization. This depolarization is called a receptor potential.

2

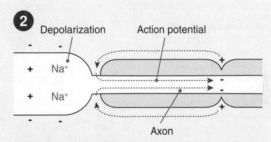

Depolarization   Action potential

Na$^+$

Na$^+$

Axon

The receptor potential spreads to the first node of Ranvier, which is the first region with voltage-gated Na$^+$ channels. It depolarizes the node to threshold and generates an action potential, which propagates along the **axon**.

1. (a) Explain how the strength of a stimulus is encoded by the nervous system: _____

_____

(b) Explain the significance of encoding information in this way: _____

_____

_____

2. Using the example of the Pacinian corpuscle, explain how stimulus strength is linked to frequency of action potentials:

_____

_____

3. Why is sensory adaptation important? _____

_____

70 The Structure of the Eye

Key Idea: Light entering the eye is focused by the lens onto the retina the layer contain the light detecting cells.

The eye is a complex and highly sophisticated sense organ, specialized to detect light. The adult eyeball is about 25 mm in diameter. Only the anterior one-sixth of its total surface area is exposed; the rest lies recessed and protected by the orbit into which it fits. The eyeball is protected and given shape by a fibrous coat. The posterior part of this structure is the sclera (the white of the eye), while the anterior transparent portion is the cornea, which covers the colored iris.

Forming a visual image

Before light can reach the photoreceptor cells of the retina, it must pass through the cornea, aqueous humor, pupil, lens, and vitreous humor. For vision to occur, light reaching the photoreceptor cells must form an image on the retina. This requires refraction of the incoming light, accommodation (shape adjustment) of the lens, and constriction of the pupil.

The anterior of the eye is concerned mainly with refracting (bending) the incoming light rays so that they focus on the retina. Most refraction occurs at the cornea. The lens adjusts the degree of refraction to produce a sharp image. Accommodation adjusts the eye for near or far objects. Constriction of the pupil narrows the diameter of the hole through which light enters the eye, preventing light rays entering from the periphery.

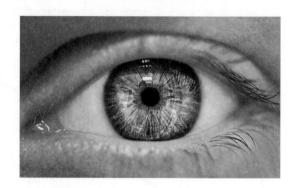

The structure and function of the mammalian eye

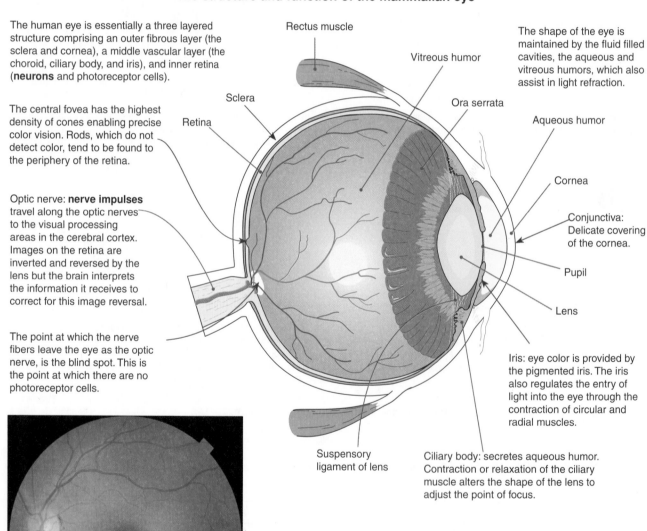

The human eye is essentially a three layered structure comprising an outer fibrous layer (the sclera and cornea), a middle vascular layer (the choroid, ciliary body, and iris), and inner retina (**neurons** and photoreceptor cells).

The central fovea has the highest density of cones enabling precise color vision. Rods, which do not detect color, tend to be found to the periphery of the retina.

Optic nerve: **nerve impulses** travel along the optic nerves to the visual processing areas in the cerebral cortex. Images on the retina are inverted and reversed by the lens but the brain interprets the information it receives to correct for this image reversal.

The point at which the nerve fibers leave the eye as the optic nerve, is the blind spot. This is the point at which there are no photoreceptor cells.

Rectus muscle

Vitreous humor

Sclera

Ora serrata

Retina

The shape of the eye is maintained by the fluid filled cavities, the aqueous and vitreous humors, which also assist in light refraction.

Aqueous humor

Cornea

Conjunctiva: Delicate covering of the cornea.

Pupil

Lens

Iris: eye color is provided by the pigmented iris. The iris also regulates the entry of light into the eye through the contraction of circular and radial muscles.

Suspensory ligament of lens

Ciliary body: secretes aqueous humor. Contraction or relaxation of the ciliary muscle alters the shape of the lens to adjust the point of focus.

Mikael Häggström· Wiki PD

Photograph, through the eye, of a normal retina. The blind spot, where the ganglion cell axons exit the eye to form the optic nerve, is seen as the bright area to the left of the image. The central fovea, where cone density is highest, is in the darker region at the center of the image. Note the rich blood supply.

©2023 **BIOZONE** International
ISBN: 978-1-99-101408-5
Photocopying Prohibited

▶ The lens of the eye has two convex surfaces (biconvex). When light enters the eye, the lens bends the incoming rays towards each other so that they intersect at the focal point on the central fovea of the retina. By altering the curvature of the lens, the focusing power of the eye can be adjusted. This adjustment of the eye for near or far vision is called accommodation and it is possible because of the elasticity of the lens.

Normal vision

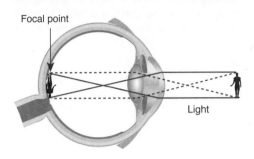

Accommodation for near and distant vision

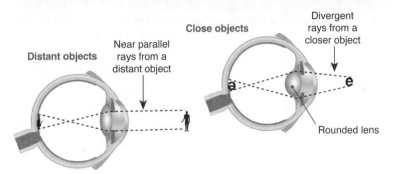

In normal vision, light rays from an object are bent sufficiently by the cornea and lens, and converge on the central fovea. A clear image is formed. Images are focused upside down and mirror reversed on the retina. The brain automatically interprets the image as the right way up.

The degree of refraction occurring at each surface of the eye is precise. The light rays reflected from an object 6 m or more away are nearly parallel to one another. Those reflected from near objects are divergent. The light rays must be refracted differently in each case so that they fall exactly on the central fovea. This is achieved through adjustment of the shape of the lens (accommodation). Accommodation from distant to close objects occurs by rounding the lens to shorten its focal length, since the image distance to the object is essentially fixed.

1. Identify the function of each of the structures of the eye listed below:

   (a) Cornea: _____

   _____

   (b) Ciliary body: _____

   _____

   (c) Iris: _____

   _____

2. (a) The first stage of vision involves forming an image on the retina. In simple terms, explain what this involves:

   _____

   _____

   _____

   (b) Explain how accommodation is achieved: _____

   _____

   _____

   _____

   _____

   _____

3. (a) Describe the function of the pupil: _____

   (b) Suggest why control of pupil diameter would be under reflex control: _____

   _____

   _____

   _____

71 The Physiology of Vision

Key Idea: Pigments in photoreceptors cells of the retina absorb light and change shape, creating a nerve impulse.

The eye is a sensory organ that converts light into **nerve impulses**, resulting in the formation of a visual image. In the mammalian eye, this is achieved by focusing the light through a lens to form an image on the retina (the back of the eye). When light reaches the retina, it is absorbed by the photosensitive pigments associated with the membranes of the photoreceptor cells (the rods and cones). The pigment molecules are altered by the absorption of light in such a way as to lead to the generation of nerve impulses. The electrical signals are transmitted from the eye via the optic nerve, along the visual pathway to the visual cortex of the brain, where the information is interpreted. The retina is not uniform. The area called the central fovea is where there is a high density of cones and virtually no rods. It is the region of highest acuity.

Structure and function of the retina

Optic nerve fibers

Ganglion cells generate the nerve impulse.

Amacrine cell enhances information about light level.

Bipolar neuron has two processes, one receives and one transmits.

Horizontal cell enhances information about contrast.

Many rods synapse with one bipolar cell. This increases sensitivity (e.g. for vision in dim light).

Only one cone synapses with one bipolar cell. This increases acuity (sharpness of vision).

Membranes with photosensitive pigments.

Pigmented epithelium absorbs excess light.

Light passes through the neuron layer to reach the rods and cones.

Light

4 The ganglion cells respond with depolarizations and initiate nerve impulses which pass through the optic chiasma and eventually to the visual areas of the cerebral cortex.

3 The bipolar neurons transmit the potentials to the ganglion cells.

2 The graded hyperpolarizations spread through the photoreceptor cells and are transmitted to the bipolar neurons.

1 Light induces structural changes in the photochemical pigments of the photoreceptor (rod and cone) membranes. These structural changes result in a graded hyperpolarization (the electrical response).

1. Describe the role of each of the following in human vision:

(a) Retina: _____

_____

_____

_____

(b) Optic nerve: _____

_____

_____

(c) Central fovea: _____

_____

_____

_____

©2023 **BIOZONE** International
ISBN: 978-1-99-101408-5
Photocopying Prohibited

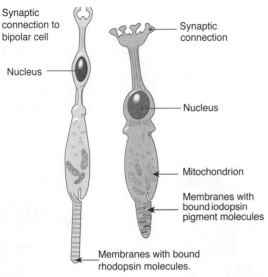

Synaptic connection to bipolar cell

Nucleus

Synaptic connection

Nucleus

Mitochondrion

Membranes with bound iodopsin pigment molecules

Membranes with bound rhodopsin molecules.

Structure of rod (left) and cone (right) photoreceptor cells

The basis of trichromatic vision.

There are three classes of cones, each with a maximal response in either short (blue), intermediate (green) or long (yellow-green) wavelength light (below). The yellow-green cone is also sensitive to the red part of the spectrum and is often called the red cone. The differential responses of the cones to light of different wavelengths provides the basis of trichromatic color vision.

Cone response to light wavelengths

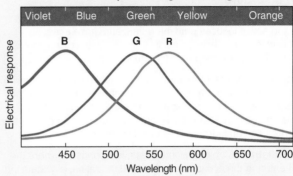

Color blindness is the term commonly used to describe the condition when a person is unable to detect certain wavelengths of light. The most common is the condition known as red-green color blindness. This can be divided into an insensitivity to red light (protanomaly) and an insensitivity to green light (deuteranomaly), which is the most common form of color blindness.

2. Complete the table below, comparing the features of rod and cone cells:

Feature	Rod cells	Cone cells
Visual pigment(s):	_____	_____
Visual acuity:	_____	_____
Overall function:	_____	_____

3. Identify the three major types of neuron making up the retina and describe their basic function:

   (a) _____

   (b) _____

   (c) _____

4. Identify two types of accessory neurons in the retina and describe their basic function:

   (a) _____

   (b) _____

5. Account for the differences in acuity and sensitivity between rod and cone cells: _____

   _____

   _____

6. (a) What is meant by the term photochemical pigment (photopigment)? _____

   _____

   _____

   (b) Identify two photopigments and their location: _____

7. In your own words, explain how light is able to produce a nerve impulse in the ganglion cells: _____

   _____

   _____

   _____

©2023 **BIOZONE** International
ISBN: 978-1-99-101408-5
Photocopying Prohibited

72 Correcting Vision Disorders

Key Idea: Vision disorders can be inherited, or can arise from environmental damage. They affect a range of structures and their functions in the eye.

In the eye, a multitude of different structures work together to process light energy into coherent electrochemical signals which are sent to the visual cortex of the brain. Total blindness from birth can be due to many factors, including an inherited genetic disorder, premature birth, and nutritional deficiency in the uterus. Sight disorders, such as color-blindness, are also inherited. Many other disorders, such as long or short sightedness, and cataracts, become more pronounced as a person ages.

Vision disorders

Types of vision loss can be divided into those affecting the entry of light and how it focuses onto the retina, and those affecting light conversion into electrochemical signals. Glasses and contact lenses (right) can correct problems with focusing.

▸ **Myopia**, or short-sightedness, is often caused by a cornea with high curvature (more rounded), which refracts (bends) the light entering the eye and causes it to focus before reaching the retina. Images are blurred. This disorder can be both genetically inherited and arise from excessive eye strain.

▸ **Hypermetropia**, or long-sightedness, is a condition where the light entering the eye is focused behind the retina, also causing blurred images. This disorder is often the result of reduced curvature of either the cornea or the lens, or a misshapen eyeball.

▸ **Cataracts** scatter light due to a 'cloudy' lens. Proteins in the eye build up and block the straight passage of light through the lens. This condition is common as a person ages but can also be caused by conditions such as diabetes, nutritional deficiency, or environmental exposure to bright sunlight.

Glasses

Contact lenses

An elderly man with cataracts

Corrective glasses for myopia and hypermetropia

▸ The degree of refraction occurring at each surface of the eye is precise. Light rays reflected from an object 6m or more away are nearly parallel to one another; those reflected from near objects are divergent. The light rays must be refracted differently in each case so that they fall exactly on the central fovea of the retina. This is achieved by adjustment of the shape of the eye lens by the surrounding ciliary muscle and is known as accommodation. If the lens is unable to change shape correctly, or the eyeball shape is incorrect, corrective lenses can be used to restore normal vision.

Short sightedness (myopia)

▸ Myopia results from an elongated eyeball or a thickened lens. Left uncorrected, distant objects have a point of focus in front of the retina and appear blurred.

▸ To correct myopia, concave (negative) lenses are used to move the point of focus backward to the retinal fovea.

Long sightedness (hypermetropia)

▸ Long sightedness results from a shortened eyeball or from a lens that is too thin. Left uncorrected, light is focused at a point that would be behind the retina and near objects appear blurred.

▸ Mild or moderate hypermetropia, which occurs naturally in young children, may be overcome by accommodation. In more severe cases, corrective lenses are used to bring the point of focus forward to produce a clear image. This is achieved using a convex (positive) lens.

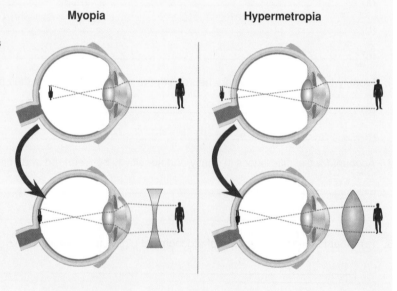
Myopia **Hypermetropia**

1. With respect to formation of the image, describe what is happening in:

   (a) Short sighted people: _____

   _____

   (b) Long sighted people: _____

   _____

©2023 **BIOZONE** International
ISBN: 978-1-99-101408-5
Photocopying Prohibited

Cell therapy - Stem cells for Stargardt's disease

Stargardt's disease is an inherited form of juvenile macular degeneration, which is loss of the central visual field of the eye. The disease is associated with a number of mutations and results in dysfunction of the retinal pigment epithelium (RPE) cells, which nourish the retinal rod and cone cells and protect the retina from excess light. Damaged RPE causes a deterioration of the photoreceptor (rod and cone) cells in the central portion of the retina, and progressive loss of central vision. This often begins between ages 6 and 12 and continues until a person is legally blind. Trials using stem cells have obtained promising results in treating the disease.

1. Human embryonic stem cells (hESC) are cultured in the lab to develop into retinal pigment epithelium (RPE) cells.

2. The RPE cells are injected just below the retina of the eye and above the choroid, i.e. the layer containing the blood vessels.

3. The RPE cells develop and replace the patient's damaged RPE cells, restoring vision.

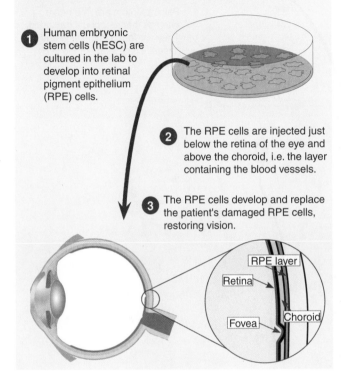

RPE layer
Retina
Fovea
Choroid

Laser eye surgery

A large part of the focal power of the eye comes from the cornea, the outer transparent part of the eye, rather than the lens. Reshaping the cornea can improve how the eye focuses light and can compensate for a lens that is not focusing correcting. Reshaping can be done using LASIK (Laser-Assisted In Situ Keratomileusis).

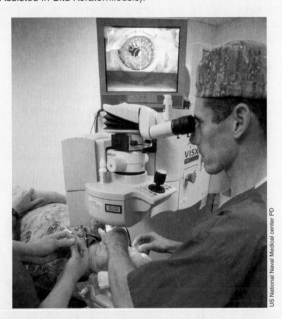

US National Naval Medical center PD

The patient is given anesthetic eye drops. A laser is used to cut a flap on the cornea. The flap is folded out of the way and the laser then reshapes the cornea. Once reshaping is complete, the flap is repositioned and will heal over time.

Laser eye surgery produces satisfactory results in more than 90% of patients.

2. In general terms, describe how the use of lenses corrects the following problems associated with vision:

(a) Myopia: _____

_____

(b) Hypermetropia: _____

_____

3. LASIK eye surgery permanently changes the shape of the cornea. What are the key differences of this technology in comparison to wearing corrective lenses?

_____

_____

_____

4. Why would LASIK eye surgery or corrective lenses **not** be useful to a person with Stargardt's disease?

_____

_____

5. Embryonic stem cells, used in the cell therapy for Stargardt's disease are **pluripotent.** Research and define this word:

_____

_____

_____

73 Skin Senses

Key Idea: The skin is an important sensory organ, with receptors for pain, pressure, touch, and temperature.

While some receptors in the skin are specialized receptor structures, many are simple unmyelinated nerves. Tactile (touch) and pressure receptors are mechanoreceptors and are stimulated by mechanical distortion. In the Pacinian corpuscle, the layers of tissue comprising the sensory structure are pushed together with pressure, stimulating the **axon**. Human skin structure is illustrated below. Human skin is fairly uniform in its basic structure, but the density and distribution of glands, hairs, and receptors varies according to the region of the body. Meissner's corpuscles, for example, are concentrated in areas sensitive to light touch and, in hairy skin, tactile receptors are clustered into specialized epithelial structures called touch domes or hair disks.

Tactile receptors
Meissner's corpuscles are rapidly adapting nerve endings providing information on light touch. Other more slowly adapting receptors provide information on texture. Both are in the superficial layers of the skin.

Hair

Pain receptors are free nerve endings that respond if damaged. They are found in the skin and in almost every tissue of the body.

Skin surface

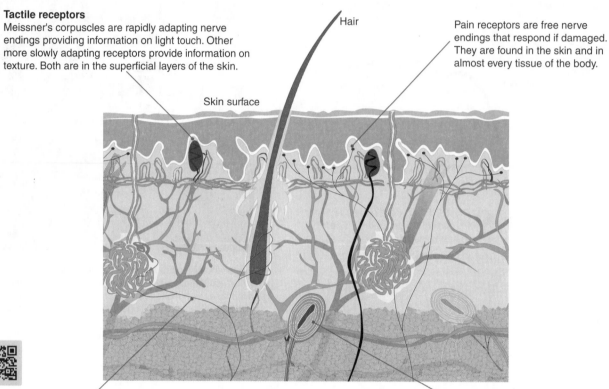

Temperature receptors are thought to be free nerve ending associated with the hair follicles.

Pressure receptors, such as Pacinian corpuscles and Ruffini's endings, are located deep in the skin and register mechanical deformation.

Merkel cells are oval shaped mechano-receptors located in the epidermis, and detect light touch. They are abundant in highly sensitive areas, such as the finger tips, and help with activities such reading Braille.

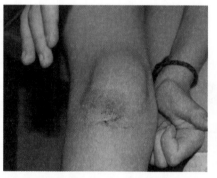

Nociceptors are free nerve endings found in the dermis. They respond to damaging stimuli by sending pain signals to the brain. A graze or burn is painful because they trigger many of these receptors.

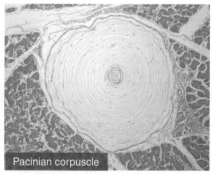

Pacinian corpuscle

Pacinian corpuscles are a mechanoreceptor that responds to pressure, e.g. from grasping an object. They are located deep within the dermis.

1. What is the purpose of the following:

(a) Nociceptors: _____

(b) Meissener's corpuscles: _____

(c) Merkel cells: _____

©2023 **BIOZONE** International
ISBN: **978-1-99-101408-5**
Photocopying Prohibited

Testing the distribution of touch receptors

The receptors in the skin are more concentrated in some parts of the body than in others. The distribution of receptors can be tested by using the two point touch test. This involves finding the smallest distance at which someone can correctly distinguish two point stimuli.

Method

▶ Repeatedly touch your lab partner's skin lightly with either one or two blunt needles or the point of a set of tweezers. Your partner's eyes should be closed. At each touch, they should report the sensation as "one" or "two", depending on whether they perceive one or two touches.

▶ Begin with the touching points far apart and gradually reduce the separation until only about 8 in 10 reports are correct.

▶ This separation distance (in mm) is called the two point threshold. When the test subject can feel only one receptor (when there are two) it means that only one receptor is being stimulated. A large two point threshold indicates a low receptor density, a low one indicates a high receptor density.

▶ Repeat this exercise for: the forearm, the back of the hand, the palm of the hand, and the fingertip, and then complete the table provide below:

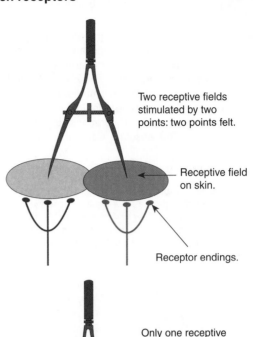

Two receptive fields stimulated by two points: two points felt.

Receptive field on skin.

Receptor endings.

Only one receptive field stimulated by two points: one point is felt.

Receptive field on skin.

Receptor endings.

Area of skin	Two point threshold (in mm)
Forearm	
Back of hand	
Palm of hand	
Fingertip	

2. Name the region with the greatest number of touch receptors: _____

3. Name the region with the least number of touch receptors: _____

4. Explain why there is a difference between these two regions: _____

_____

_____

_____

5. (a) Many skin receptors are adaptive; their response reduces over time when repeatedly stimulated. Explain the purpose of this:

_____

_____

_____

(b) Nociceptors do not adapt to repeated stimulation, i.e. their response is not reduced over time. Explain the purpose of this:

_____

_____

6. Why are the touch receptors in the fingertips close together? _____

_____

74 Hearing and Balance

Key Idea: The ear is involved in both hearing and balance. Most animals respond to sound and have receptors for the detection of sound waves. In mammals, these receptors are organized into hearing organs called ears. Sound is produced by the vibration of particles in a medium and it travels in waves that can pass through solids, liquids, or gases. The distance between wave 'crests' determines the frequency (pitch) of the sound. The absolute size (amplitude) of the waves determines the intensity or loudness of the sound. Sound reception in mammals is the role of mechanoreceptors: tiny hair cells in the cochlea of the inner ear. The hair cells are very sensitive and are easily damaged by prolonged exposure to high intensity sounds. Gradual hearing loss with age is often caused by the cumulative loss of sensory hair cell function, especially at the higher frequencies. Such hearing loss is called perceptive deafness.

The anatomy of the ear

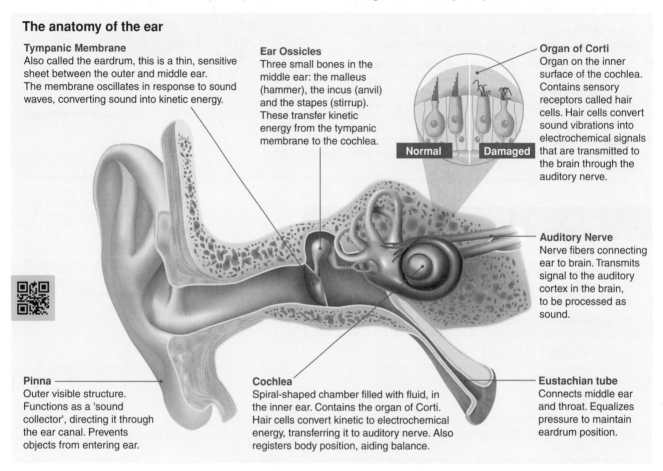

Tympanic Membrane
Also called the eardrum, this is a thin, sensitive sheet between the outer and middle ear. The membrane oscillates in response to sound waves, converting sound into kinetic energy.

Ear Ossicles
Three small bones in the middle ear: the malleus (hammer), the incus (anvil) and the stapes (stirrup). These transfer kinetic energy from the tympanic membrane to the cochlea.

Organ of Corti
Organ on the inner surface of the cochlea. Contains sensory receptors called hair cells. Hair cells convert sound vibrations into electrochemical signals that are transmitted to the brain through the auditory nerve.

Normal   Damaged

Auditory Nerve
Nerve fibers connecting ear to brain. Transmits signal to the auditory cortex in the brain, to be processed as sound.

Pinna
Outer visible structure. Functions as a 'sound collector', directing it through the ear canal. Prevents objects from entering ear.

Cochlea
Spiral-shaped chamber filled with fluid, in the inner ear. Contains the organ of Corti. Hair cells convert kinetic to electrochemical energy, transferring it to auditory nerve. Also registers body position, aiding balance.

Eustachian tube
Connects middle ear and throat. Equalizes pressure to maintain eardrum position.

Schematic of ear and perception of sound

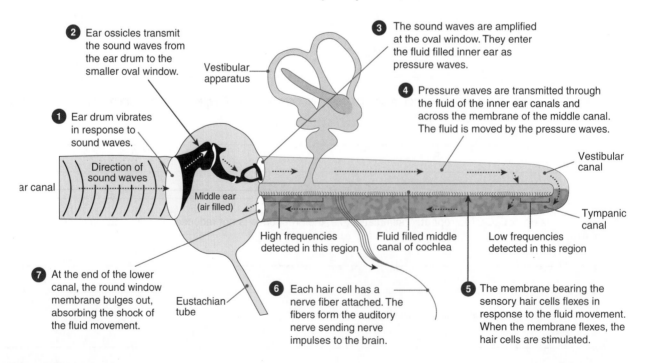

2 Ear ossicles transmit the sound waves from the ear drum to the smaller oval window.

Vestibular apparatus

3 The sound waves are amplified at the oval window. They enter the fluid filled inner ear as pressure waves.

4 Pressure waves are transmitted through the fluid of the inner ear canals and across the membrane of the middle canal. The fluid is moved by the pressure waves.

1 Ear drum vibrates in response to sound waves.

Direction of sound waves

ar canal

Middle ear (air filled)

Vestibular canal

Tympanic canal

High frequencies detected in this region

Fluid filled middle canal of cochlea

Low frequencies detected in this region

7 At the end of the lower canal, the round window membrane bulges out, absorbing the shock of the fluid movement.

Eustachian tube

6 Each hair cell has a nerve fiber attached. The fibers form the auditory nerve sending nerve impulses to the brain.

5 The membrane bearing the sensory hair cells flexes in response to the fluid movement. When the membrane flexes, the hair cells are stimulated.

©2023 **BIOZONE** International
ISBN: 978-1-99-101408-5

Balance

Balance requires the input of several different sensory organs, including the ear. More specifically, the part of the ear that helps sense balance is the vestibular apparatus, comprising the vestibule and the semicircular canals. Within these, are sensitive hair cells which sense the movement of fluid in the vestibule of semicircular canal. The vestibule is concerned mainly with the position of the head relative to the direction of gravity while the canals react to the direction and speed of movement of the head, e.g. turning the head.

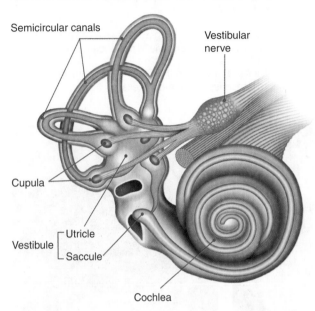

Semicircular canals

Vestibular nerve

Cupula

Vestibule
- Utricle
- Saccule

Cochlea

Vestibule

Each of the vestibule's two parts have a patch of hair cells called the macula. The tips of the cells extend into a membrane covered with mineral crystals. When the head tilts the hair cells detect the movement of the crystals. When the head is level the macula in the utricle is horizontal, while the macula in the saccule is vertical.

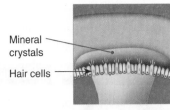

Mineral crystals

Hair cells

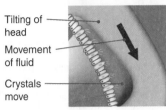

Tilting of head

Movement of fluid

Crystals move

Canals

One end of the semicircular canals ends in bulges called the ampulla. The ampulla contain a mound of hair cells on which is situated a structure called the cupula. When the head turns, fluid in the canals swirls past the cupula and makes it bend. The bending is detected by the hair cells, which trigger a **nerve impulse**.

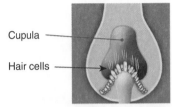

Cupula

Hair cells

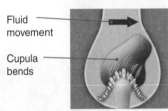

Fluid movement

Cupula bends

1. In a short sentence, outline the role of each of the following in the reception and response to sound:

    (a) The ear drum: _____

    (b) The ear ossicles: _____

    (c) The oval window: _____

    (d) The sensory hair cells: _____

    (e) The auditory nerve: _____

2. Explain the significance of the inner ear being fluid filled: _____

3. (a) Explain how the head position relative to a level surface is detected: _____

    (b) Explain how the direction of the head's turning is detected in the ear: _____

Hearing loss

Types of hearing loss are divided into conductive, involving sound wave interference between outer and middle ear; and sensorineural, concerning issues of the inner ear or auditory nerve.

Causes of conductive hearing loss	Causes of sensorineural hearing loss
• Ear infections in outer and middle ear. • Glue ear. • Excessive ear wax and foreign bodies in ear canal. • Mis-shaped structures in outer and middle ear. • Otosclerosis - a genetic disorder that hardens the stapes bone due to extra growth.	• Progressive damage to cochlear hair cells in the organ of Corti due to old age, after a lifetime of noise. • Excessive or repeated loud nose exposure, causing damage to hair cells. • Excessive loud noise, damaging auditory nerve such that sound is not transmitted correctly to the auditory cortex. • Genetic disorders, including the CABPP2 gene mutation, that affects transmission from hair cells.

Prolonged loud sounds or sudden bursts of very loud sound can cause long term hearing loss by damaging the cells of the inner ear. Musicians playing large concerts often experience some form of hearing loss.

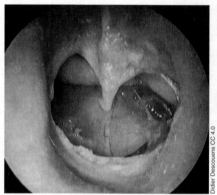

The eardrum is a thin membrane at the end of the ear canal. Loud sounds, and infections can cause serious damage to it, or even cause perforations, i.e.a burst eardrum, (above). Burst ear drums can heal over time but major damage may require surgery.

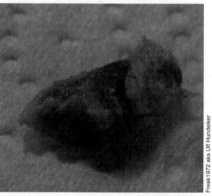

Earwax is a waxy substance secreted in the ear canal. It assists in protecting and cleaning the ear canal, but excessive build up can cause a loss of hearing from pressing against the ear drum or blocking the ear canal.

4. Explain why the a person remains dizzy for a few moments after a ride on a roundabout or merry-go-round:

_____

_____

_____

5. As people get older, the membranes in the cochlea may stiffen. How does this affect hearing? _____

_____

_____

_____

6. List the predominant energy form present in each structure during the process of hearing:

(a) Ear canal: _____ (b) Ear ossicles: _____ (c) Auditory nerve: _____

7. Explain how persistent loud noise can cause hearing damage, linking to specific structures in the ear:

_____

_____

8. (a) What is the purpose of earwax? _____

(b) How can it cause hearing loss? _____

_____

_____

©2023 **BIOZONE** International
ISBN: 978-1-99-101408-5
Photocopying Prohibited

75 Correcting Hearing Disorders

Key Idea: Hearing loss can be corrected by medical technology, including external devices or implants.
Technology can be used as a treatment for a number of disorders. Hearing loss can be improved with external hearing aids, surgically embedded cochlear implants, and bone conduction implants. External hearing aids amplify sounds and can be designed for many different situations, and be shaped to fit individuals. External hearing aids are only useful if the inner ear is still functional. Implants can bypass the damaged sections of ear to restore hearing.

Cochlear implant

While a hearing aid can be used to amplify sound waves if the cochlear hair cell receptors are partially damaged, it will not work at all if the hair cells are completely non-functioning. The cochlear implant is surgically inserted and completely bypasses the hair cells. It transmits information received from sound waves directly to the auditory nerve that connects to the brain. This technology, while expensive, can restore hearing to certain groups of people that would otherwise be deaf.

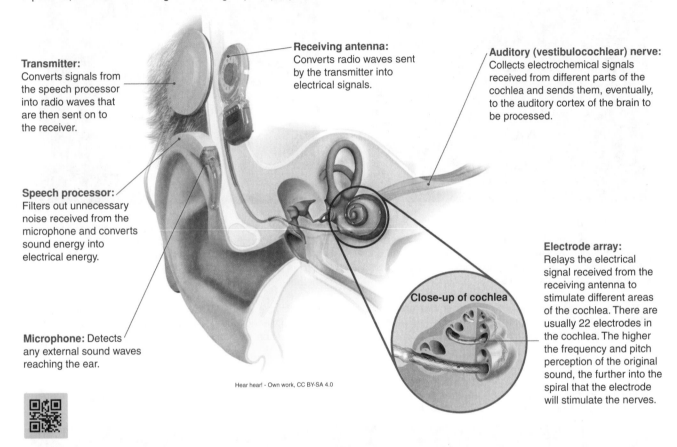

Transmitter:
Converts signals from the speech processor into radio waves that are then sent on to the receiver.

Receiving antenna:
Converts radio waves sent by the transmitter into electrical signals.

Auditory (vestibulocochlear) nerve:
Collects electrochemical signals received from different parts of the cochlea and sends them, eventually, to the auditory cortex of the brain to be processed.

Speech processor:
Filters out unnecessary noise received from the microphone and converts sound energy into electrical energy.

Electrode array:
Relays the electrical signal received from the receiving antenna to stimulate different areas of the cochlea. There are usually 22 electrodes in the cochlea. The higher the frequency and pitch perception of the original sound, the further into the spiral that the electrode will stimulate the nerves.

Microphone: Detects any external sound waves reaching the ear.

Close-up of cochlea

Hear hear! - Own work, CC BY-SA 4.0

1. Cochlear implants combine a number of pieces of technology. In the boxes below, state the energy transformations (if there are any) carried out by the specific part of the cochlear implant as it processes sound and transmits it to the auditory cortex of the brain, e.g. sound to electrical energy.

1. Microphone	2. Speech processor	3. Transmitter	4. Receiving antenna	5. Electrode array
(a)	(b)	(c)	(d)	(e)

2. What structure and function in the ear does the electrode array replace, and explain, in detail, how it achieves that?

_____

_____

_____

_____

_____

Corrective technology for hearing loss

Hearing aids

Hearing aids are small, battery-powered devices that fit inside the ear canal and amplify sounds. A microphone detects sound waves, which are converted to a digital signal. These signals are then amplified and sent to the ear through a speaker.

Hearing aids are useful when the hair cells still have some partial function, as the amplified signals boost the threshold for being stimulated by sound level.

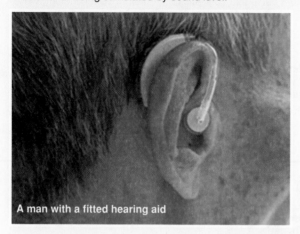

A man with a fitted hearing aid

Hearing aids are relatively inexpensive in comparison to more invasive surgical technologies, such as cochlear and bone conduction implants. However, they must constantly have batteries charged or replaced, and can be easily lost or damaged when out of the ear.

Once the hair cells cease to function, either through aging, damage due to loud noise, or through an inherited genetic disorder, the hearing aids become ineffective.

Bone conduction implant

Sound waves normally travel through to the cochlea via the ear canal, tympanic membrane, and ear ossicles. If any of these are damaged or non-functional, they can be bypassed with a bone conduction implant.

These devices are surgically implanted in the bone of the skull behind the ear and receive sound vibrations that are detected by an external microphone. They transfer sound by bone vibration directly to the cochlea.

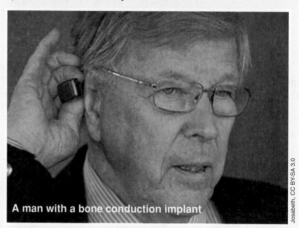

A man with a bone conduction implant

Josabeth, CC BY-SA 3.0

Bone conduction implants are permanently attached to the body. However, they do require some functionality of the hair cells in order to improve hearing. Because of this, they are not a suitable technology if all function has been lost in the hair cells.

A detachable version of this device is also available, and offers similar advantages and disadvantages to hearing aids as a non-surgical option.

3. Hearing aids, cochlear implants, and bone conduction implants all assist in correcting hearing loss. The selection of suitable technology depends on the area of damage or dysfunction in the ear. Complete the chart below to show which area, and the extent of damage if appropriate, that is compensated for by each device:

Technology	Associated area of ear damaged
Hearing aids	(a)
Bone conduction implant	(b)
Cochlear implant	(c)

4. Describe the advantages and disadvantages of using external hearing aids: _____

_____

_____

_____

_____

©2023 **BIOZONE** International
ISBN: 978-1-99-101408-5
Photocopying Prohibited

76 Taste and Smell

Key Idea: Chemosensory receptors are responsible for our sense of smell (olfaction) and taste (gustation).

The receptors for smell and taste both respond to chemicals (chemoreceptors), either carried in the air (smell) or dissolved in a fluid (taste). In humans and other mammals, these are located in the nose and tongue respectively. Each receptor type is basically similar: they are collections of receptor cells equipped with chemosensory microvilli or cilia. When chemicals stimulate their membranes, the cells respond by producing **nerve impulses** that are transmitted to the appropriate region of the cerebral cortex for interpretation.

Taste (gustation)

The organs of taste are the taste buds of the tongue. Most of the taste buds on the tongue are located on raised protrusions of the tongue surface called papillae. Each bud is flask-like in shape, with a pore opening to the surface of the tongue, enabling molecules and ions dissolved in saliva to reach the receptor cells inside. Each taste bud is an assembly of 50-150 taste cells. These connect with nerves that send messages to the gustatory region of the brain. There are five basic taste sensations. Salty and sour operate through ion channels, while sweet, bitter, and umami (savory) operate through membrane signaling proteins. These taste sensations are found on all areas of the tongue, although some regions are more sensitive than others.

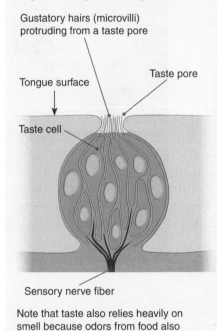

Gustatory hairs (microvilli) protruding from a taste pore

Tongue surface

Taste pore

Taste cell

Sensory nerve fiber

Note that taste also relies heavily on smell because odors from food also stimulate olfactory receptors.

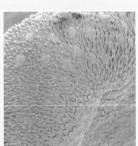
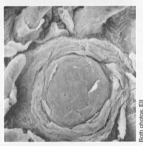

Above: SEMs of the surface of the tongue (top) and close up of one of the papillae (below).

Smell (olfaction)

In humans, the receptors for smell are located at the top of the nasal cavity. The receptors are specialized hair cells that detect airborne molecules and respond by sending nerve impulses to the olfactory center of the brain. Unlike taste receptors, olfactory receptors can detect many different odors. However, they quickly adapt to the same smell and will cease to respond to it. This phenomenon is called sensory adaptation.

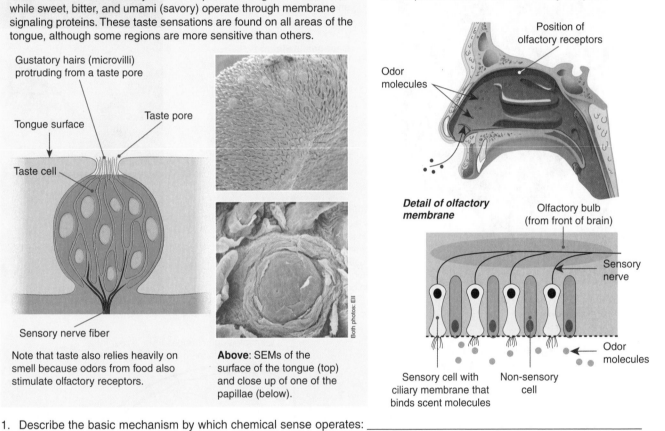

Position of olfactory receptors

Odor molecules

Detail of olfactory membrane

Olfactory bulb (from front of brain)

Sensory nerve

Odor molecules

Sensory cell with ciliary membrane that binds scent molecules

Non-sensory cell

1. Describe the basic mechanism by which chemical sense operates: _____

_____

_____

_____

2. Take a deep breath of a non-toxic, pungent substance such as perfume. Take a sniff of the substance at 10 second intervals for about 1 minute. Make a record of how strongly you perceived the smell to be at each time interval. Use a scale of 1 to 6: **1.** *Very strong;* **2.** *Quite strong;* **3.** *Noticeable;* **4.** *Weak;* **5.** *Very faint;* **6.** *Could not detect.*

Time	Strength	Time	Strength	Time	Strength
10 s	_____	30 s	_____	50 s	_____
20 s	_____	40 s	_____	1 min	_____

3. (a) Explain what happened to your sense of smell over the time period: _____

   (b) Explain why this happens: _____

   _____

77 Aging and the Nervous System

Key Idea: The aging process affects all body systems, including the nervous system.

Neuron loss begins around age 30, and accumulates over time, which is why the changes are often more obvious in the elderly. Common changes include impaired (diminished) hearing and vision, short term memory loss, slower reaction times, and loss of fine motor skills. Performing mental and physical exercise slows down the loss of **neurons** in the areas of the brain associated with memory, and helps the remaining neurons to function properly. Lack of mental and physical stimulation, a poor diet, and the consumption of two or more alcoholic drinks a day can increase the rate of neuron loss in the brain.

The effects of aging on the nervous system

Loss of neurons
Brain size reduces with age as neurons are lost, but this does not lead to dementia. Dementia disorders, such as Alzheimer's and vascular dementia, severely reduce the number of neurons in the brain and retard its functioning.

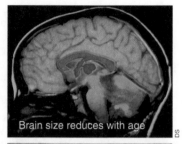
Brain size reduces with age

Changes in vision
Visual acuity diminishes with age. The lens becomes less flexible and cannot focus light on to the retina correctly. The lens also becomes more opaque, reducing the amount of light falling on the retina. Cataracts (clouding of the lens) obstruct the passage of light and are common in the elderly.

An elderly man with cataracts

Sensory impairment
Neuron loss leads to a decrease in sensory perception. Hearing loss is often the most obvious sensory impairment in elderly people and usually begins with inability to hear high pitched sounds. Hearing aids are often worn to correct the problem.

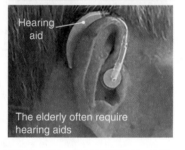
Hearing aid

The elderly often require hearing aids

How age affects cognitive ability

▸ The Seattle longitudinal study began in 1956 with the purpose of determining how cognitive (mental) ability and intelligence change with age. Every seven years, additional subjects were added to the study, and all participants undertook a series of cognitive tests and psychological questioning. Approximately 6,000 people have been tested.

▸ The graph (right) summarizes some of the results to date. Some cognitive abilities (perceptual speed and numeric ability) begin to decrease from early maturity, while others, such as verbal memory, do not begin to deteriorate until much later in life (60 years old). The study also showed that training (use of specific mental techniques) could slow the decline in cognitive ability.

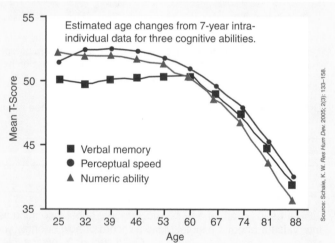

Estimated age changes from 7-year intra-individual data for three cognitive abilities.

Mean T-Score vs Age

■ Verbal memory
● Perceptual speed
▲ Numeric ability

Source: Schaie, K. W. *Res Hum Dev.* 2005; 2(3): 133–158.

1. (a) Why do many cognitive abilities diminish with age? _____

_____

_____

(b) What steps can be taken to reduce the rate of cognitive decline? _____

_____

_____

©2023 **BIOZONE** International
ISBN: 978-1-99-101408-5
Photocopying Prohibited

78 Alzheimer's and the Brain

Key Idea: Alzheimer's disease is a neuro-degenerative disorder, causing dementia.

Alzheimer's disease is a disabling neurological disorder affecting about 5% of the population over 65. Although its causes are largely unknown, people with a family history of Alzheimer's have a greater risk, implying that a genetic factor is involved. Some of the cases of Alzheimer's with a familial (inherited) pattern involve a mutation of the gene for amyloid precursor protein (APP), found on chromosome 21, and nearly all people with Down syndrome who live into their 40s develop the disease. The gene for the protein apoE, which has an important role in lipid transport, degeneration and regulation in nervous tissue, is also a risk factor that may be involved in modifying the age of onset. Alzheimer's sufferers have trouble remembering recent events and they become confused and forgetful. In the later stages of the disease, people with Alzheimer's become very disorientated, lose past memories, and may become paranoid and moody. Dementia and loss of reason occur at the end stages of the disease. The effects of the disease are irreversible and it has no cure.

The malfunctioning brain: The effects of Alzheimer's disease

Alzheimer's is associated with accelerated loss of **neurons**, particularly in regions of the brain that are important for memory and intellectual processing, such as the cerebral cortex and hippocampus. The disease has been linked to abnormal accumulations of protein-rich amyloid plaques and tangles, which invade the brain tissue and interfere with synaptic transmission.

Cerebral cortex: Conscious thought, reasoning, and language. Alzheimer's sufferers show considerable loss of function from this region.

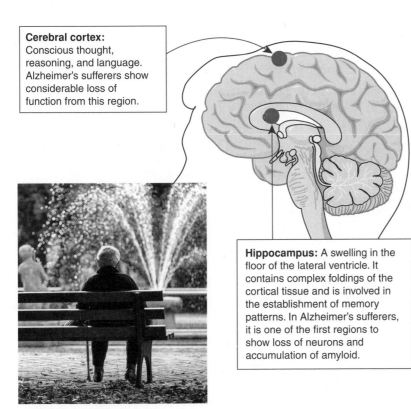

Hippocampus: A swelling in the floor of the lateral ventricle. It contains complex foldings of the cortical tissue and is involved in the establishment of memory patterns. In Alzheimer's sufferers, it is one of the first regions to show loss of neurons and accumulation of amyloid.

It is not uncommon for Alzheimer's sufferers to wander and become lost and disorientated.

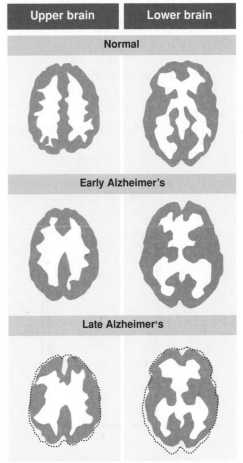

Upper brain	Lower brain
Normal	
Early Alzheimer's	
Late Alzheimer's	

The brain scans above show diminishing brain function in certain areas of the brain in Alzheimer's sufferers. Note, particularly in the two lower scans, how much the brain has shrunk (original size indicated by the dotted line). Light areas indicate brain activity.

1. Describe the biological basis behind the degenerative changes associated with Alzheimer's disease:

_____

_____

2. Describe the evidence for Alzheimer's disease having a genetic component in some cases: _____

_____

_____

3. Some loss of neuronal function occurs normally as a result of aging. Identify the features distinguishing Alzheimer's disease from normal age related loss of neuronal function:

_____

_____

79 Chapter Summary

1. (a) Label the components of the neuron pictured on the right:

A: ______________________

B: ______________________

C: ______________________

D: ______________________

E: ______________________

F: ______________________

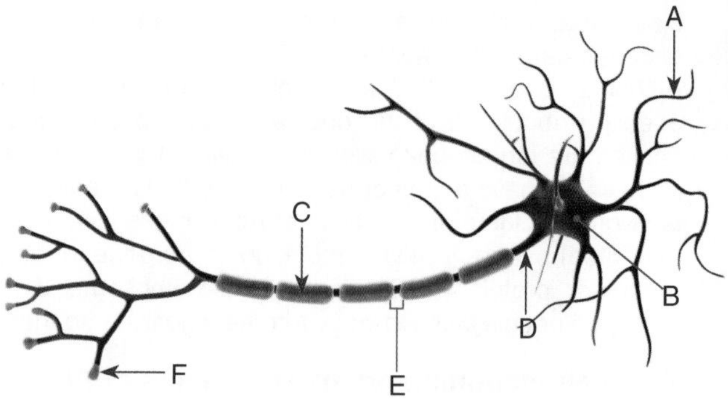
A
C
B
D
F
E

(b) Is this neuron myelinated or unmyelinated? ______________________

(c) Explain your answer: ______________________

(d) In what form do electrical signals travel in this cell? ______________________

2. (a) The graph below shows a recording of the changes in membrane potential in an axon during transmission of an action potential. Match each stage (A-E) to the correct summary provided below.

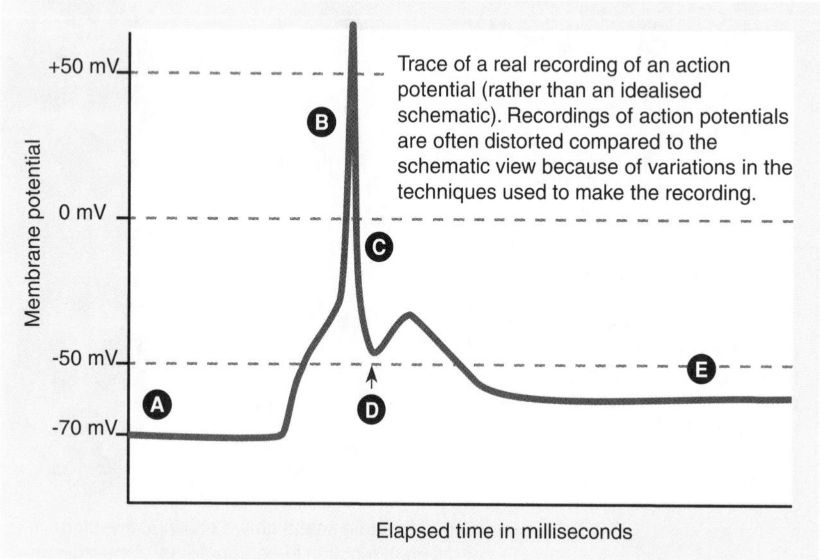
+50 mV
0 mV
-50 mV
-70 mV
Membrane potential
Elapsed time in milliseconds
A
B
C
D
E
Trace of a real recording of an action potential (rather than an idealised schematic). Recordings of action potentials are often distorted compared to the schematic view because of variations in the techniques used to make the recording.

- ☐ Membrane depolarization (due to rapid Na^+ entry across the axon membrane).
- ☐ Hyperpolarization (an overshoot caused by the delay in closing of the K^+ channels).
- ☐ Return to resting potential after the stimulus has passed.
- ☐ Repolarization as the Na^+ channels close and slower K^+ channels begin to open.
- ☐ The membrane's resting potential.

(b) What is the resting potential of the axon? ______________________

(c) What is the maximum voltage reached by the action potential? ______________________

3. Explain why in the dark it is easier to see an object by looking slightly to the left or right of it, rather than directly at it:

____

4. Multiple sclerosis (MS) is a disease involving progressive destruction of the myelin sheaths around axons. Why does MS impair nervous system function even though the axons are still intact?

____

ISBN: 978-1-99-101408-5

The Endocrine System

KEY IDEAS

- Endocrine glands produce hormones that are carried in the blood to affect target cells and tissues.

- Endocrine regulation is slower and longer lasting that nervous regulation.

- Endocrine secretions are regulated primarily by negative feedback mechanisms.

- Disruption to normal endocrine regulation can result in disease.

KEY TERMS

- Adrenal gland
- Cell signaling
- Diabetes mellitus
- Endocrine gland
- Exocrine gland
- Glucagon
- Hormone
- Hypothalamus
- Insulin
- Pancreas
- Pituitary
- Signal transduction
- Thermoregulation

LEARNING OBJECTIVES

Activity number

☐ 1   Understand that the endocrine system is made up of a number of glands distributed throughout the body. Know that these glands secrete hormones, carried in the blood, that can influence cells some distance from the gland itself. Describe the location, structure, and function of the adrenal glands and the hormones they produce. Understand what is meant by antagonistic hormone and give examples.   80-81

☐ 2   Know the location of the pituitary gland and the hormones it releases, and understand the functions of these hormones in the body. Know the location and role of the hypothalamus and its role in linking the nervous system to the endocrine system. Understand that the pancreas acts as both an exocrine and endocrine gland and describe these differences in function.   82-84

☐ 3   Explain the role of ligands and receptors and give examples of different types of cell signaling. Understand the steps involved in signal transduction, and what is meant by a signal cascade. Explain how signal transduction results in the uptake of glucose into cells. Describe the difference between hydrophilic and hydrophobic signal molecules.   85-87

☐ 4   Understand the role of the hypothalamus and the hormones that are responsible for thermoregulation.   88

☐ 5   Describe the role of the liver in metabolizing carbohydrates, and understand the functions of insulin, glucagon, epinephrine, and glucocorticoids, e.g. cortisol. Describe, using a labelled diagram, how blood glucose is regulated using negative feedback.   89-90

☐ 6   Explain how type 1 diabetes mellitus arises. Describe its effects on the body and how regular insulin injections help to stabilize blood glucose levels. Explain the difference between type 1 and type 2 diabetes. Describe the risk factors for type 2 diabetes and how the disease can be managed. Explain how blood glucose regulation can be affected by alcohol and nicotine.   91-93

☐ 7   Understand how interactions between the hypothalamus, pituitary, and adrenal glands contribute to the body's ability to cope with both short and long term stressors.   94

☐ 8   Describe how aging affects the endocrine system, with particular reference to menopause.   95

RESOURCE HUB

Scan the QR code to access:

- weblinks
- videos
- 3D models
- interactives

80 | The Endocrine System

Key Idea: The endocrine system is made up of ductless glands, which secrete hormones into the blood. These participate in feedback loops and regulate internal functions. **Endocrine glands** are scattered widely throughout the body and their positioning does not necessarily reflect the location of their influence. Unlike **exocrine glands**, e.g. salivary glands, endocrine glands lack ducts and secrete hormones directly into the blood. **Hormones** are chemical messengers that are produced at one endocrine site and carried in the blood to influence target cells that may be quite distant.

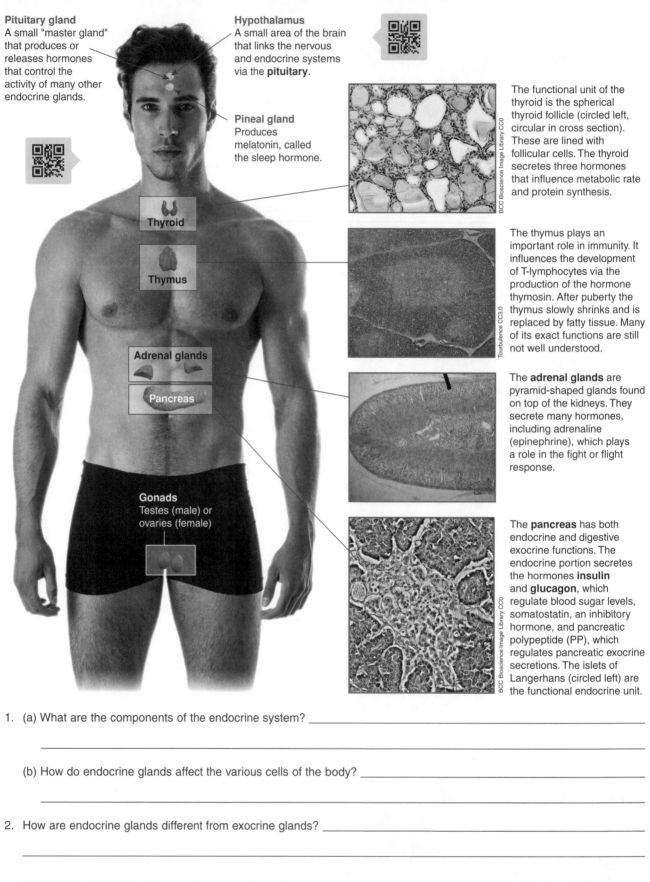

Pituitary gland
A small "master gland" that produces or releases hormones that control the activity of many other endocrine glands.

Hypothalamus
A small area of the brain that links the nervous and endocrine systems via the **pituitary**.

Pineal gland
Produces melatonin, called the sleep hormone.

Thyroid

Thymus

Adrenal glands

Pancreas

Gonads
Testes (male) or ovaries (female)

The functional unit of the thyroid is the spherical thyroid follicle (circled left, circular in cross section). These are lined with follicular cells. The thyroid secretes three hormones that influence metabolic rate and protein synthesis.

BCC Bioscience Image Library CC0

The thymus plays an important role in immunity. It influences the development of T-lymphocytes via the production of the hormone thymosin. After puberty the thymus slowly shrinks and is replaced by fatty tissue. Many of its exact functions are still not well understood.

Tourbulence CC3.0

The **adrenal glands** are pyramid-shaped glands found on top of the kidneys. They secrete many hormones, including adrenaline (epinephrine), which plays a role in the fight or flight response.

The **pancreas** has both endocrine and digestive exocrine functions. The endocrine portion secretes the hormones **insulin** and **glucagon**, which regulate blood sugar levels, somatostatin, an inhibitory hormone, and pancreatic polypeptide (PP), which regulates pancreatic exocrine secretions. The islets of Langerhans (circled left) are the functional endocrine unit.

BCC Bioscience Image Library CC0

1. (a) What are the components of the endocrine system? _____

_____

(b) How do endocrine glands affect the various cells of the body? _____

_____

2. How are endocrine glands different from exocrine glands? _____

_____

_____

©2023 **BIOZONE** International
ISBN: 978-1-99-101408-5
Photocopying Prohibited

The adrenal glands

▶ The adrenal glands are endocrine glands that produce a variety of hormones with roles in carbohydrate metabolism, ion regulation, and response to stress.

▶ One adrenal sits above each kidney. They are surrounded by a fatty capsule and have two functionally and structurally distinct regions: an outer cortex and an inner medulla (below right).

▶ The inner adrenal medulla produces the catecholamine hormones, adrenaline and noradrenaline. These are responsible for the 'fight or flight' response, which includes increased breathing and heart rates, and paling of skin.

▶ The outer adrenal cortex produces a number of corticosteroid hormones.

▶ Glucocorticoids, e.g. cortisol, have effects on carbohydrate metabolism, and are also secreted in response to long term stress.

▶ Mineralocorticoids, (principally aldosterone) are involved in blood pressure and ion (particularly sodium) regulation.

▶ The release of hormones from the adrenal cortex is controlled by the hormone ACTH from the anterior pituitary gland.

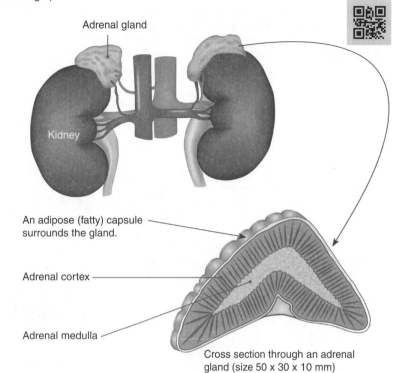

Adrenal gland

Kidney

An adipose (fatty) capsule surrounds the gland.

Adrenal cortex

Adrenal medulla

Cross section through an adrenal gland (size 50 x 30 x 10 mm)

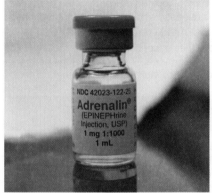

Adrenaline (epinephrine) is a stress related hormone involved in the fight or flight response. Medically, it is used as a treatment for heart attacks and anaphylaxis (severe allergic reaction).

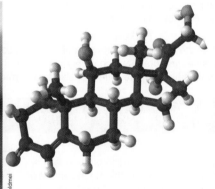

Cortisol is released by the adrenal cortex in response to stress and low blood glucose. It activates the formation of glucose from glycogen in the liver, and suppresses the inflammatory response.

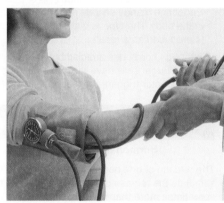

Aldosterone is involved in regulating blood pressure and ion balance. It acts on the distal convoluted tubule and collecting duct of the kidneys to stimulate reabsorption of sodium and secretion of potassium.

3. (a) Describe the structure of the adrenal gland: _____

    _____

   (b) What is the role of each distinct region of the adrenal gland? _____

    _____

    _____

4. (a) What is the effect of adrenaline on the body? _____

    _____

   (b) What is a medical use of adrenaline? _____

    _____

81 Hormonal Regulation

Key Idea: The endocrine system is an internal coordination system that uses hormones to provide a pathway from stimulus to response.

In humans, the two main internal coordination systems that maintain homeostasis are the endocrine system and the nervous system, that act either independently or together. The two systems are quite different in their modes of action,

the responses they elicit, and the duration of action. The endocrine system produces a slower, more long-lasting response through blood-borne chemicals called **hormones**. The hormonal pathway starts with endocrine cells or glands secreting a hormone directly into the bloodstream in response to a particular stimulus. It ends when target cells receive the hormone and respond.

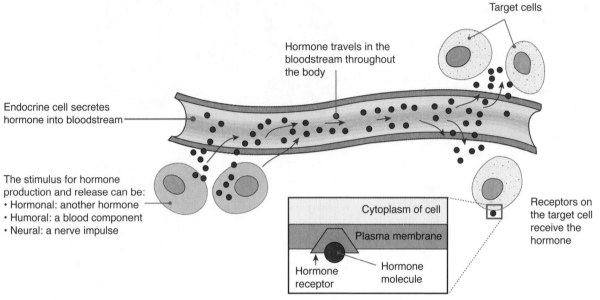

Target cells

Hormone travels in the bloodstream throughout the body

Endocrine cell secretes hormone into bloodstream

The stimulus for hormone production and release can be:
• Hormonal: another hormone
• Humoral: a blood component
• Neural: a nerve impulse

Receptors on the target cell receive the hormone

Cytoplasm of cell

Plasma membrane

Hormone receptor

Hormone molecule

How hormones work

▶ The endocrine system is made up of endocrine cells (organized into **endocrine glands**) and the hormones they produce. Endocrine glands secrete hormones directly into the bloodstream, targeting specific receptors located on certain cells or tissues in the body. The type and strength of the stimulus determines which specific hormone is released and, therefore, what response is produced as a result.

▶ Although hormones are distributed throughout the body via the network of blood vessels, they affect only specific target cells. These target cells have receptors on the plasma membrane which recognise and bind the hormone. The binding of the hormone and receptor triggers the response in the target cell. Cells are unresponsive to a hormone if they lack the appropriate receptors.

Types of stimulus for hormone production		
Hormonal stimuli	**Humoral stimuli**	**Neural stimuli**
The release of one hormone can stimulate the release of another, with sometimes more than two steps involved in the process. The **pituitary** gland and **hypothalamus** often play a role in these types of stimuli.	Changes in the concentration of a substance or ion in the blood can act as a stimulus in some negative feedback loops.	Hormone producing glands can be directly stimulated by a neural impulse. Stress and 'fight-or-flight' responses are common examples of this type of stimulus.

1. (a) What is a hormone? _____

_____

_____

(b) Why can a hormone only influence specific target cells even though all cells may be exposed to the hormone?

_____

_____

(c) What is the stimulus for the release of insulin (see right): humoral, hormonal, or neural? _____

2. The endocrine system consists of glands, yet the sweat glands are not considered part of the endocrine system. What two features are required for a gland to be classified as part of the endocrine system?

_____

©2023 **BIOZONE** International
ISBN: 978-1-99-101408-5
Photocopying Prohibited

Hormonal pathways in an endocrine system

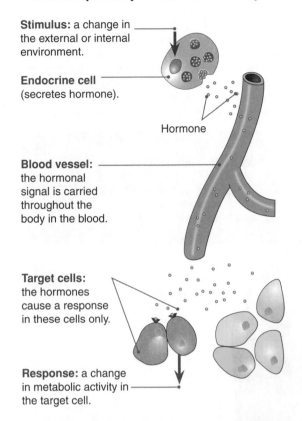

Stimulus: a change in the external or internal environment.

Endocrine cell (secretes hormone).

Hormone

Blood vessel: the hormonal signal is carried throughout the body in the blood.

Target cells: the hormones cause a response in these cells only.

Response: a change in metabolic activity in the target cell.

How hormones work	
Communication	Hormones in the blood.
Speed	Relatively slow (over minutes, hours, or longer).
Duration	Longer lasting effects.
Target pathway	Hormones broadcast to target cells everywhere.
Action	Causes changes in metabolic activity.

Antagonistic hormones in blood glucose control

A pair of hormonal pathways can operate together to maintain homeostasis, with the feedback mechanism used to adjust the balance. The effects of one hormone are often counteracted by an opposing hormone. They are therefore referred to as antagonistic pairs.

Example: Insulin acts to decrease blood glucose and **glucagon** acts to raise it.

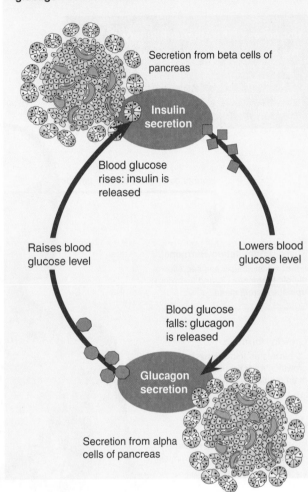

Secretion from beta cells of pancreas

Insulin secretion

Blood glucose rises: insulin is released

Raises blood glucose level

Lowers blood glucose level

Blood glucose falls: glucagon is released

Glucagon secretion

Secretion from alpha cells of pancreas

---

3. Complete the flowchart, summarizing key steps in a hormonal pathway during a homeostasis response:

Key step: (a)	Key step: (b)	Key step: (c)

4. Explain how antagonistic hormones act to maintain homeostasis: _____

_____

5. What function do the following organs have in the hormonal regulation of blood glucose control?

   (a) The pancreas: _____

   _____

   (b) The liver: _____

   _____

82 Hormones of the Pituitary

Key idea: The pituitary gland (or hypophysis) is a tiny **endocrine gland**, about the size of a pea, hanging from the inferior surface of the hypothalamus.

The **pituitary** gland has two regions or lobes, each with a different structure and origin. The posterior pituitary is neural (nervous) in origin and is essentially an extension of the **hypothalamus** (see next activity). Its neurosecretory cells have their cell bodies in the hypothalamus, and release oxytocin and ADH directly into the bloodstream in response to nerve impulses. The anterior pituitary is connected to the hypothalamus by blood vessels and receives releasing and inhibiting hormones (factors) from the hypothalamus via a capillary network. These releasing **hormones** regulate the further secretion of the anterior pituitary's hormones.

Hormones of the Anterior Pituitary

The anterior pituitary releases at least seven peptide hormones (below) into the blood from simple secretory cells. The release of these hormones is regulated by releasing and inhibiting hormones from the hypothalamus.

Hormones of the Posterior Pituitary

The posterior pituitary develops as an extension of the hypothalamus. The release of its two hormones, oxytocin and antidiuretic hormone (ADH), occurs directly as a result of nervous input to the hypothalamus.

Hypothalamus

Hormones from the anterior pituitary

Hormones from the posterior pituitary

Thyroid Stimulating Hormone

Increases synthesis and secretion of thyroid hormones (T_3 and thyroxine) from the thyroid gland.

Growth Hormone

Stimulates protein synthesis and growth in most tissues; one of the main regulators of metabolism.

Prolactin

Stimulates growth of the mammary glands and synthesis of milk protein.

Oxytocin

Acts on the mammary glands to stimulate milk ejection (let down) and on the uterus to stimulate contraction during labor.

Adrenocorticotrophic Hormone

Usually abbreviated to ACTH, this hormone increases synthesis and secretion of hormones (aldosterone and cortisol) from the adrenal cortex.

Antidiuretic Hormone

Acts on the kidney to increase water reabsorption from the filtrate (urine).

Follicle Stimulating Hormone

In <u>females</u>: Stimulates maturation of the ovarian follicles.
In <u>males</u>: Increases the production of sperm in the seminiferous tubules.

Luteinizing Hormone

In <u>females</u>: Stimulates secretion of ovarian hormones, ovulation, and formation of the corpus luteum.
In <u>males</u>: Stimulates synthesis and secretion of testosterone.

Melanophore Stimulating Hormone

Increases melanin synthesis and dispersal in the skin's melanocytes.

©2023 **BIOZONE** International
ISBN: **978-1-99-101408-5**
Photocopying Prohibited

Effects of growth hormone

▶ Growth hormone (GH) is released in response to GHRH (growth hormone releasing hormone) from the hypothalamus. GH acts directly and indirectly to affect metabolic activities associated with growth.

▶ GH directly stimulates metabolism of fat, but its major role is to stimulate the liver and other tissues to secrete IGF-I (Insulin-like Growth Factor) and through this, stimulate bone and muscle growth. GH secretion is regulated via negative feedback:

▶ High levels of IGF-1 suppress GHRH secretion from the hypothalamus.

▶ High levels of IGF-1 also stimulate release of somatostatin from the hypothalamus, which also suppresses GH secretion (not shown).

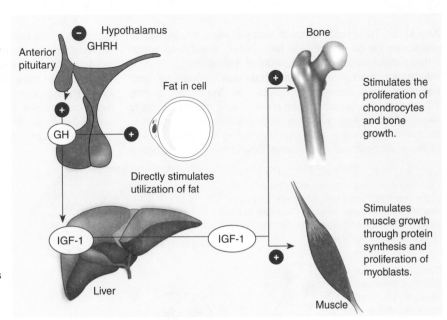

1. (a) What are the effects of growth hormone (GH)? _____

_____

_____

   (b) Predict the effect of chronic GH deficiency in infancy: _____

_____

_____

   (c) Predict the effect of chronic GH hypersecretion in infancy: _____

_____

_____

   (d) Describe the two main mechanisms through which the secretion of growth hormone is regulated: _____

_____

_____

_____

2. "The pituitary releases a number of hormones that regulate the secretion of hormones from other glands". Discuss this statement with reference to growth hormone (GH) and thyroid stimulating hormone (TSH):

_____

_____

_____

_____

3. Using the example of TSH and its target tissue (the thyroid), explain how the release of anterior pituitary hormones is regulated. Include reference to the role of negative feedback mechanisms in the process:

_____

_____

_____

_____

83 The Role of the Hypothalamus

Key Idea: The hypothalamus is located below the thalamus, just above the brain stem and the pituitary gland, with which it has a close structural and functional relationship.

Information comes to the **hypothalamus** through sensory pathways from sensory receptors. On the basis of this information, the hypothalamus controls and integrates many basic physiological activities, e.g. temperature regulation, food and fluid intake, and sleep, including the reflex activity of the autonomic nervous system. One of the most important functions of the hypothalamus is to link the nervous system to the endocrine system (via the **pituitary**). The hypothalamus contains neurosecretory cells. These are specialized secretory neurons, which are both nerve cells and endocrine cells. They produce **hormones** (usually peptides) in the cell body, which are packaged into droplets and transported along the axon. At the axon terminal, the neurohormone is released into the blood in response to nerve impulses.

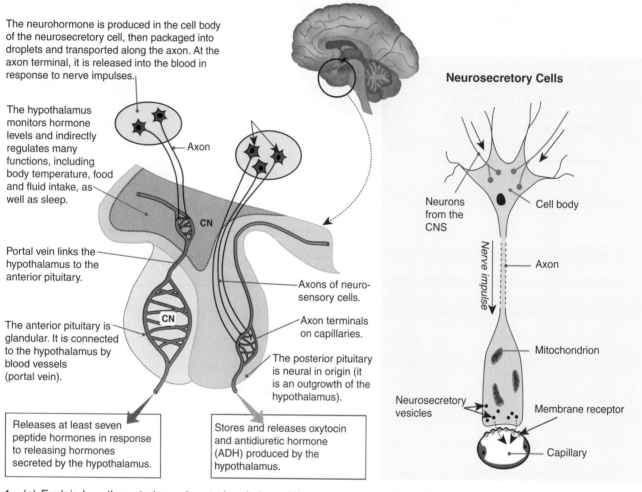

The neurohormone is produced in the cell body of the neurosecretory cell, then packaged into droplets and transported along the axon. At the axon terminal, it is released into the blood in response to nerve impulses.

The hypothalamus monitors hormone levels and indirectly regulates many functions, including body temperature, food and fluid intake, as well as sleep.

Axon

Portal vein links the hypothalamus to the anterior pituitary.

The anterior pituitary is glandular. It is connected to the hypothalamus by blood vessels (portal vein).

Axons of neuro-sensory cells.

Axon terminals on capillaries.

The posterior pituitary is neural in origin (it is an outgrowth of the hypothalamus).

Releases at least seven peptide hormones in response to releasing hormones secreted by the hypothalamus.

Stores and releases oxytocin and antidiuretic hormone (ADH) produced by the hypothalamus.

Neurosecretory Cells

Neurons from the CNS

Nerve impulse

Cell body

Axon

Mitochondrion

Neurosecretory vesicles

Membrane receptor

Capillary

1. (a) Explain how the anterior and posterior pituitary differ with respect to their relationship to the hypothalamus: _____

_____

_____

_____

(b) Explain how these differences relate to the nature of the hormonal secretions for each region: _____

_____

_____

2. Describe the neurohormones released by the hypothalamus: _____

_____

_____

3. Explain why the adrenal and thyroid glands atrophy if the pituitary gland ceases to function: _____

_____

_____

©2023 **BIOZONE** International
ISBN: 978-1-99-101408-5
Photocopying Prohibited

84 The Role of the Pancreas

Key Idea: The pancreas has dual exocrine and endocrine roles.

The **pancreas** is a diffuse organ, located alongside the stomach. It is both an **exocrine gland**, producing digestive secretions, and an **endocrine gland**, producing **hormones** from ductless cell clusters within the pancreatic tissue. This endocrine tissue is called the islets of Langerhans, after its discoverer and two of the hormones produced, **insulin** and **glucagon**, regulate blood glucose levels. The histology of the pancreas, and the functions of its endocrine and exocrine regions are described below.

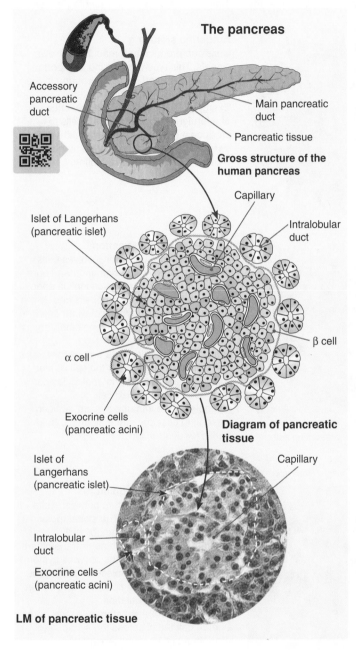

The pancreas

Accessory pancreatic duct

Main pancreatic duct

Pancreatic tissue

Gross structure of the human pancreas

Capillary

Islet of Langerhans (pancreatic islet)

Intralobular duct

β cell

α cell

Exocrine cells (pancreatic acini)

Diagram of pancreatic tissue

Islet of Langerhans (pancreatic islet)

Capillary

Intralobular duct

Exocrine cells (pancreatic acini)

LM of pancreatic tissue

Endocrine function

The islets of Langerhans are distinctive areas containing the endocrine cells of the pancreas. They make up 1-2% of the total mass of the pancreas. Islet cells are not readily distinguishable by routine staining techniques. Special stains are required to differentiate them. There are five types of endocrine cells. The alpha (α) cells and beta (β) cells make up the majority of the islet cell mass (15% and 65% of the total, respectively). The main homeostatic role of the pancreas is to regulate blood sugar levels.

▸ The α cells secrete **glucagon**, which elevates blood glucose levels if they become too low.

▸ The β cells secrete **insulin**, which lowers blood glucose by promoting its cellular uptake. The two hormones work together to maintain blood glucose at a constant level.

▸ The remaining endocrine cells have the following roles:

▸ Delta (δ) cells: produce the hormone somatostatin, which affects neurotransmission and cell proliferation.

▸ PP-cells: control self regulation of pancreatic secretions.

▸ Epsilon (ε) cells: produce ghrelin, an appetite stimulant.

Exocrine function

The bulk of the pancreas is composed of pancreatic exocrine cells, which are arranged in clusters called acini (singular acinus). The cells contain bicarbonate ions and precursor digestive enzymes which are secreted into the duodenal region of the small intestine to aid digestion of food. Secretion from the acini is via a series of small intralobular ducts which drain into the major pancreatic duct, and from there into the duodenum.

The enzymes (in their active form) are as follows:
▸ Trypsin and chymotrypsin: digestion of protein

▸ Pancreatic lipase: digestion of lipid (fats)

▸ Pancreatic amylase: digestion of carbohydrates

The role of the bicarbonate ions is to neutralise the acidic chyme entering the small intestine from the stomach. The increase in pH allows the digestive enzymes of the small intestine to function.

1. (a) Which part of the pancreas has an endocrine function? _____

(b) What is the endocrine function of the pancreas? _____

_____

_____

2. How would you distinguish the endocrine from the exocrine tissue in a stained section of the pancreas? _____

_____

_____

_____

85 Cell Signaling

Key Idea: Cells use chemical messengers to communicate and to gather information about, and respond to, changes in their cellular environment.

Cell signaling allows cells to communicate and respond to changes in their environment by sending, receiving, and processing signals. Most signals are chemicals (signal molecules or ligands). To alter cellular behavior, a ligand must be able to interact with the cell and initiate a cellular response. This interaction occurs via receptors, either on the cell's plasma membrane or inside the cell itself. Cells with the receptors to bind a particular ligand are the target cells for that specific ligand. If a cell does not have the 'right' receptor, it is unaffected by the signal. Signal molecules may act over varying distances, having localized or far reaching effects.

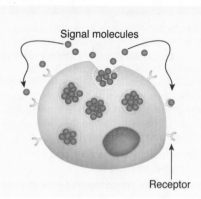
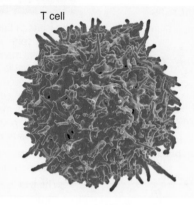

Signal molecules

T cell

Receptor

Autocrine signaling
Cells can produce and react to their own signals. This type of signaling is important during growth and development and in the functioning of the immune system.
<u>Example</u>: In vertebrates, the presence of a foreign antibody causes T-cells to produce a growth factor to stimulate their own production. The increased number of T-cells helps to fight the infection.

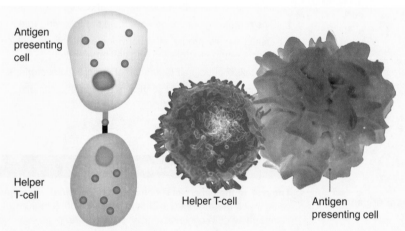

Antigen presenting cell

Helper T-cell

Helper T-cell

Antigen presenting cell

Cell-to-cell communication
Cell-to-cell communication involves cells interacting directly with one another. There are two forms: 1) communication via special channels between adjacent cells and 2) two cells bind to and communicate with each other because they have complementary proteins on their surfaces.
<u>Example</u>: Plasmodesmata are microscopic channels that run through the cell wall of adjacent plant cells. Signal molecules can pass through to the next cell.
<u>Example</u>: In the immune system, antigen presenting cells present antigens to helper T-cells for destruction.

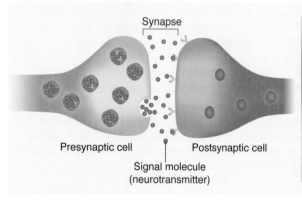

Synapse

Presynaptic cell

Postsynaptic cell

Signal molecule (neurotransmitter)

Synapse

Signaling by local regulators
Some cell signaling occurs between cells that are close together. The signal molecule binds to receptors on a nearby cell, causing a response. Both neurotransmitters (signaling molecules in the nervous system) and cytokines (small molecules produced by a range of different cells) are involved in this type of local regulation.
<u>Example</u>: Neurotransmitters released from a nerve cell travel across the synapse (gap) to another cell to cause a response.

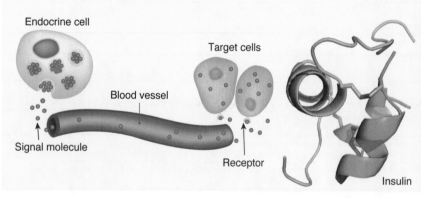

Endocrine cell

Target cells

Blood vessel

Signal molecule

Receptor

Insulin

Endocrine signaling
A signal is carried in the bloodstream to target cells, often some distance away. Endocrine signaling may involve **hormones** (released from the cells of **endocrine glands**) or cytokines as the signaling molecule although cytokines are also important in local regulation and circulate in more variable concentrations than hormones.
<u>Example</u>: **Insulin** from the pancreas stimulates the cellular uptake of glucose.

©2023 **BIOZONE** International
ISBN: 978-1-99-101408-5
Photocopying Prohibited

What is a receptor?

Chemical signals must be received by a cell in order to exert their effect. Reception of signal molecules (ligands) is the job of proteins called receptors, which bind ligands and link them to a biochemical pathway to cause a cellular response. The specificity of receptors to their particular signal molecule increases the efficiency of cellular responses and saves energy. The binding sites of cell receptors are specific only to certain ligands. This stops them reacting to every signal the cell encounters. Receptors generally fall into two main categories:

Intracellular receptors

Intracellular (cytoplasmic) receptors are located within the cell's cytoplasm and bind ligands that can cross the cell membrane.

Extracellular receptors

Extracellular (transmembrane) receptors span the cell membrane with regions both inside and outside the cell. They bind ligands that cannot cross the cell membrane (right).

Extracellular (transmembrane) receptor

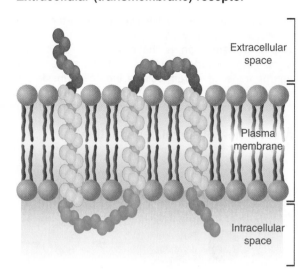

Extracellular space

Plasma membrane

Intracellular space

1. Describe the following types of cell signaling:

    (a) Autocrine signaling: _____

    _____

    _____

    (b) Cell-to-cell communication: _____

    _____

    _____

    (c) Local regulation: _____

    _____

    _____

    (d) Endocrine signaling: _____

    _____

    _____

2. Explain the features shared by all types of communication that use signaling: _____

    _____

    _____

    _____

3. Explain how cells are able to communicate over varying distances using different types of signaling: _____

    _____

    _____

    _____

    _____

    _____

4. Cytokines and hormones are both involved in endocrine signaling. Explain how they differ: _____

    _____

    _____

©2023 **BIOZONE** International
ISBN: 978-1-99-101408-5
Photocopying Prohibited

86 Signals and Signal Transduction

Key Idea: Signal transduction converts an external signal into a functional change within the cell.

Signal transduction is the process by which molecular signals are converted from one form to another so that they can be transmitted from outside the cell to inside and bring about a response. The transduction involves an external signal molecule binding to a receptor and triggering a series of biochemical reactions. The series of biochemical reactions is often called a cascade and usually involves phosphorylation of a number of molecules in a sequence. The type of cellular response varies and may include activation of a metabolic pathway, gene expression to produce a specific protein, or membrane permeability to allow entry of specific molecules. The process is outlined in simple form below.

An overview of signal transduction

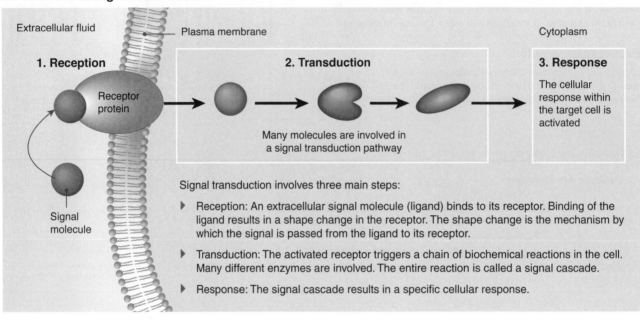

Signal transduction involves three main steps:

▶ Reception: An extracellular signal molecule (ligand) binds to its receptor. Binding of the ligand results in a shape change in the receptor. The shape change is the mechanism by which the signal is passed from the ligand to its receptor.

▶ Transduction: The activated receptor triggers a chain of biochemical reactions in the cell. Many different enzymes are involved. The entire reaction is called a signal cascade.

▶ Response: The signal cascade results in a specific cellular response.

1. Describe the three stages of signal transduction:

(a) _____

_____

(b) _____

_____

_____

(c) _____

_____

2. (a) Why doesn't every cell respond to a particular signal molecule? _____

_____

(b) Why is this important? _____

_____

3. The images below show a signaling pathway but the steps are out of order. Assign each image a number (1-4) to indicate its correct position in the sequence:

(a) _____   (b) _____   (c) _____   (d) _____

 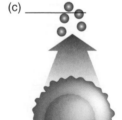   

How signal transduction generates a cellular response

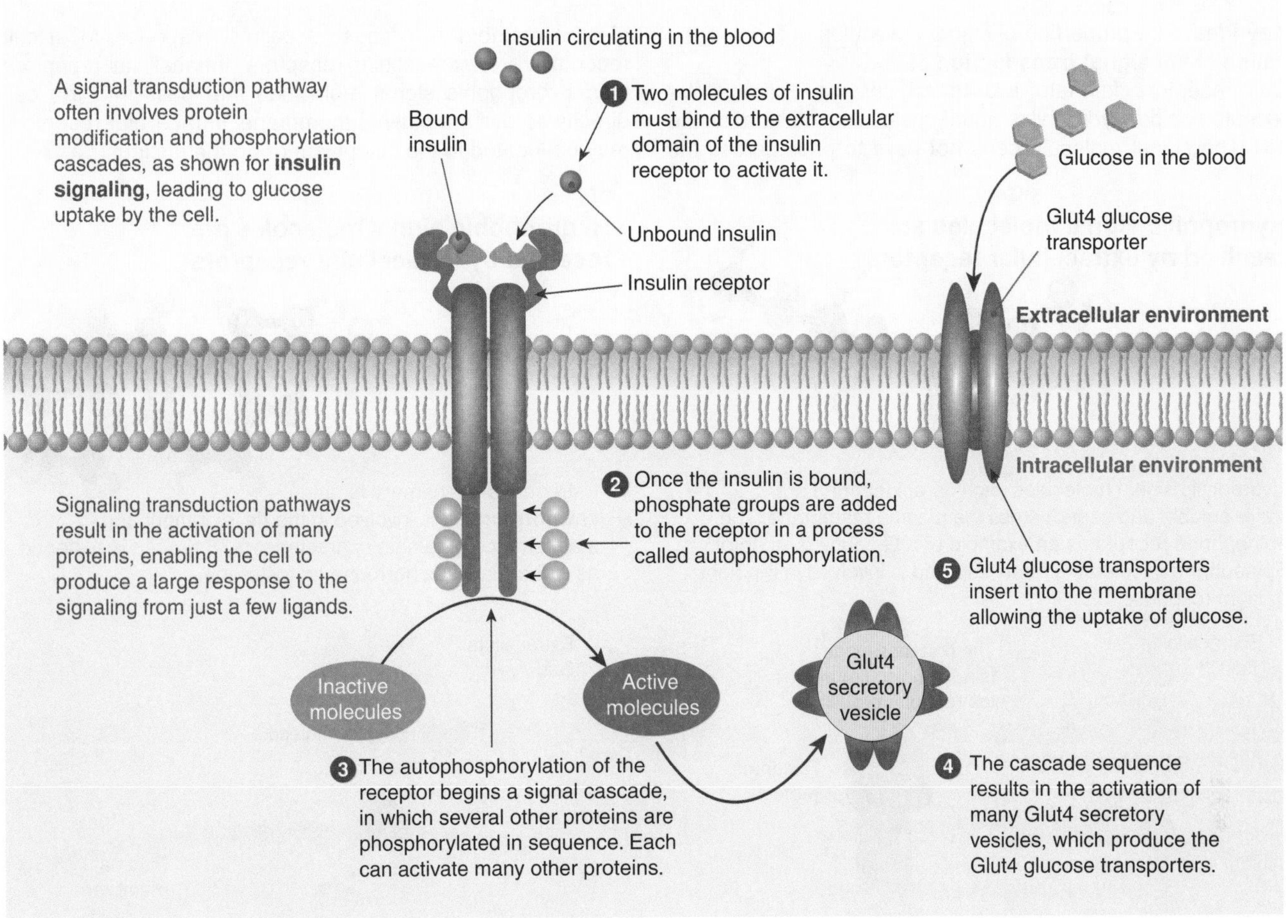

A signal transduction pathway often involves protein modification and phosphorylation cascades, as shown for **insulin signaling**, leading to glucose uptake by the cell.

Insulin circulating in the blood

Bound insulin

1 Two molecules of insulin must bind to the extracellular domain of the insulin receptor to activate it.

Unbound insulin

Insulin receptor

Glucose in the blood

Glut4 glucose transporter

Extracellular environment

Intracellular environment

2 Once the insulin is bound, phosphate groups are added to the receptor in a process called autophosphorylation.

Signaling transduction pathways result in the activation of many proteins, enabling the cell to produce a large response to the signaling from just a few ligands.

Inactive molecules

Active molecules

Glut4 secretory vesicle

5 Glut4 glucose transporters insert into the membrane allowing the uptake of glucose.

3 The autophosphorylation of the receptor begins a signal cascade, in which several other proteins are phosphorylated in sequence. Each can activate many other proteins.

4 The cascade sequence results in the activation of many Glut4 secretory vesicles, which produce the Glut4 glucose transporters.

4. (a) What type of signaling does the example above, of insulin, represent? _____

(b) Explain your answer: _____

_____

5. Why must blood glucose levels be tightly regulated? _____

_____

_____

6. Describe the process by which insulin signaling causes the uptake of glucose into cells: _____

_____

_____

_____

_____

_____

7. How does the signal cascade increase the response of the insulin receptor? _____

_____

_____

_____

8. In terms of cell communication, what is important about signal transduction pathways? _____

_____

_____

©2023 **BIOZONE** International
ISBN: 978-1-99-101408-5
Photocopying Prohibited

87 Types of Signal Transduction

Key Idea: The properties of signal molecules determine the nature of the **signal transduction** pathway.

Cell receptors fall into two broad classes. Extracellular receptors bind hydrophilic signal molecules outside of the cell. The signal molecule does not have to pass across the plasma membrane to cause a cellular response. Most cell receptors are extracellular receptors. Intracellular receptors bind hydrophobic signal molecules that pass into the cell directly across the plasma membrane. Intracellular receptors may be located in the cytoplasm or on the nucleus.

Hydrophilic signal molecules are received by extracellular receptors

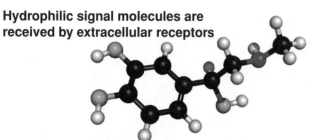

Hydrophilic signal molecules such as epinephrine are water soluble and cannot cross the plasma membrane. The epinephrine receptor is an example of a G-coupled receptor. Epinephrine accelerates heart rate and is involved in the fight or flight response.

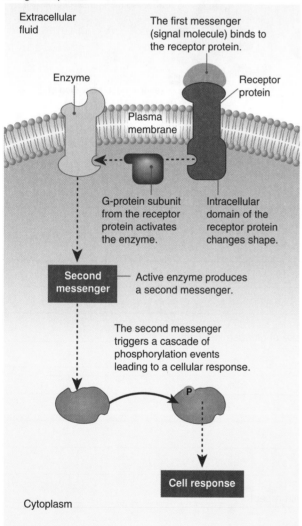

Hydrophilic signal molecules cannot cross the plasma membrane and must exert their effect by interacting with an extracellular receptor. Hydrophilic signals include water soluble **hormones** such as epinephrine and **insulin**. The signal molecule is the first messenger. When it binds, the extracellular receptor changes shape, triggering a sequence of biochemical reactions, including activation of a second messenger. As a consequence, the original signal is amplified, bringing about a cellular response. This pathway is given in more detail in the next activity.

Hydrophobic signal molecules are received by intracellular receptors

Estrogen is the primary female sex **hormone**. It is involved in the development and maintenance of female characteristics. Estrogen is a steroid, as is the male sex hormone testosterone.

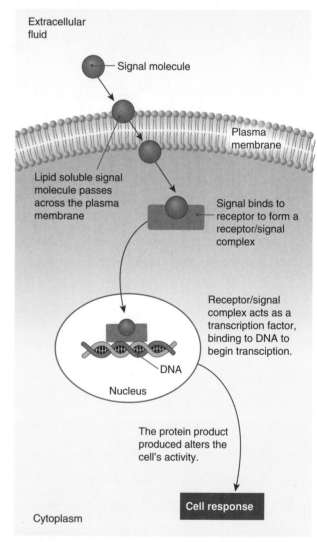

Hydrophobic hormones, such as steroids, e.g. estrogen, diffuse freely across the plasma membrane and into the cytoplasm of target cells. Once inside the cell, they bind to intracellular receptors in the cytoplasm to form a receptor-signal complex. The complex moves to the cell nucleus where it binds directly to the DNA and acts as a transcription factor, resulting in the transcription of one or more specific genes. Concentrations of the different gene products (proteins) change as a result (a phenotypic change).

©2023 **BIOZONE** International
ISBN: 978-1-99-101408-5
Photocopying Prohibited

1. Describe the differences between an intracellular receptor and an extracellular receptor: _____

    _____

    _____

    _____

2. What must a signal molecule do in order to activate a receptor? _____

    _____

3. In terms of their ability to cross the plasma membrane, describe the difference between a hydrophobic signal molecule and a hydrophilic signal molecule:

    _____

    _____

    _____

4. (a) Describe the process of signal transduction via an extracellular receptor: _____

    _____

    _____

    _____

    _____

    (b) Describe the differences between a first messenger and a second messenger: _____

    _____

    _____

    _____

5. Describe the process of signal transduction via an intracellular receptor: _____

    _____

    _____

    _____

    _____

6. The diagram on the right represents a cell signaling process.

    (a) Does this diagram represent an extracellular or intracellular signaling process? Explain your answer:

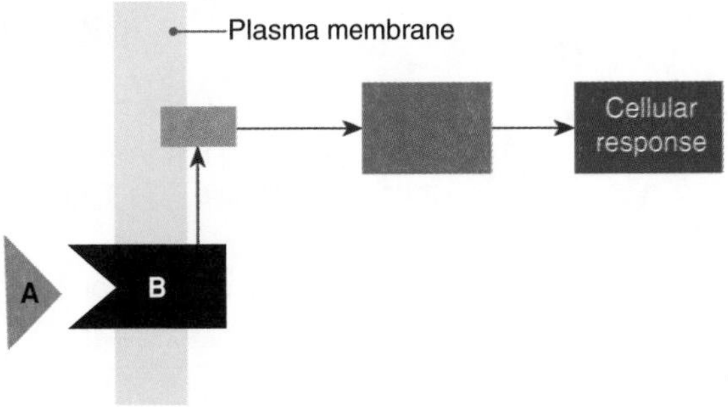

    _____

    _____

    _____

    (b) What type of receptor is B? _____

    (c) What does A represent? _____

    (d) Would A be hydrophobic or hydrophilic? Explain your answer: _____

    _____

    _____

    _____

    _____

88 Hormonal Mechanisms for Thermoregulation

Key Idea: The hypothalamus, located on the underside of the brain, functions as a link between the endocrine and nervous internal coordination systems to maintain thermoregulation.

The **hypothalamus** acts as a control system for **hormone** release by other glands throughout the body. When the nervous system registers a decrease in core body temperature, a signal is sent to the hypothalamus. This initiates a chain of hormone releases, via the **pituitary** gland, to reach the thyroid gland, situated under the larynx. Thyroxine, produced by the thyroid gland, is an important hormone in **thermoregulation** and causes an increase in internal heat by boosting metabolism. **Insulin** has also been shown to exert a thermoregulatory role and can have a direct effect on core body temperature.

Hormonal thermoregulation

Thyroxine (T_4) production is controlled by a negative feedback loop (shown below). This mechanism involves two parts of the brain, the hypothalamus and the pituitary gland.

1. Low body temperature →
2. stimulates the hypothalamus to secrete thyrotropin releasing hormone (TRH) →
3. which in turn stimulates cells in the anterior pituitary to secrete thyroid stimulating hormone (TSH) →
4. TSH acts on the thyroid gland, causing it to produce thyroid hormones, including T_4 (thyroxine). T_4 binds to target cells, increasing their metabolic activity and producing heat. →
5. High levels of circulating thyroid hormones inhibit production of TRH and TSH. As a result, thyroid secretion is reduced.

The thyroid gland

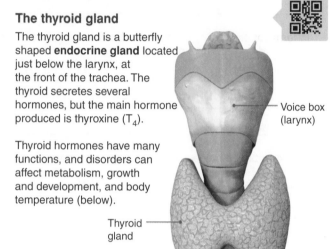

The thyroid gland is a butterfly shaped **endocrine gland** located just below the larynx, at the front of the trachea. The thyroid secretes several hormones, but the main hormone produced is thyroxine (T_4).

Thyroid hormones have many functions, and disorders can affect metabolism, growth and development, and body temperature (below).

Voice box (larynx)

Thyroid gland

Wind pipe (trachea)

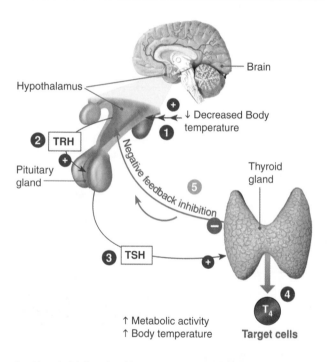

Brain

Hypothalamus

↓ Decreased Body temperature

2 TRH

Pituitary gland

Negative feedback inhibition

5

Thyroid gland

3 TSH

4

T_4

↑ Metabolic activity
↑ Body temperature

Target cells

Graves' disease

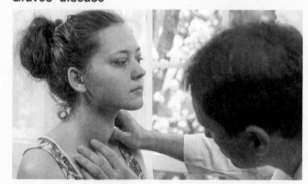

The most common cause of hyperthyroidism is Graves' disease, characterized by an enlarged thyroid (goitre) and bulging eyes. In Graves' disease, the negative feedback loop is bypassed because a protein called thyroid stimulating immunoglobulin (TSI) binds directly to the thyroid and stimulates T_4 production. Because T_4 production is independent of TSH production, the usual regulatory mechanisms are ineffective in its control.

1. How is T_4 involved in temperature regulation? _____

_____

_____

2. Explain how T_4 production is regulated by negative feedback: _____

_____

_____

_____

_____

©2023 **BIOZONE** International
ISBN: 978-1-99-101408-5
Photocopying Prohibited

Insulin and thermoregulation

▶ **Insulin** is a hormone that is usually associated with regulation of blood glucose, signaling cells to take up glucose from the blood. The cells then use this glucose to produce ATP for use in metabolic processes. However, research has also shown that insulin can directly affect core body temperature.

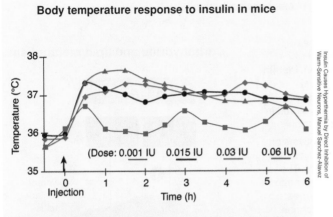

Body temperature response to insulin in mice

Insulin Causes Hyperthermia by Direct Inhibition of Warm-Sensitive Neurons, Manuel Sanchez-Alavez

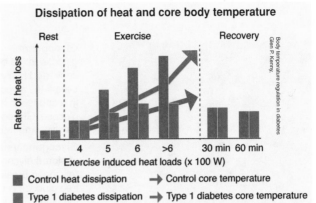

Dissipation of heat and core body temperature

Body temperature regulation in diabetes Glen P. Kenny.

Experiments have shown that, when insulin is injected into the preoptic area of the hypothalamus, there is a rapid, hyperthermic (increased temperature) response, caused by the stimulation of thermogenesis in brown fat. This may help to explain why people with **diabetes**, whose cells do not produce insulin or do not respond to insulin, often have difficulty with thermoregulation.

Insulin also indirectly affects thermoregulation. People with type 1 diabetes (a lack of insulin production) and type 2 diabetes (insulin resistance) often suffer from thermoregulation problems. In particular, type 2 diabetes results in impaired vasodilation, affecting the ability to dissipate heat. Diabetes is also associated with impaired sweat production, also affecting the ability to dissipate heat.

3. Why do high levels of T_4 not inhibit its production from the thyroid gland in a person with Graves' disease?

_____

_____

_____

_____

4. (a) Would you expect someone with an overactive thyroid gland to feel hot or cold? _____

   (b) Would you expect someone with an underactive thyroid gland to feel hot or cold? _____

5. What was the effect of injecting insulin into the preoptic area of the hypothalamus in the study described above?

_____

_____

6. (a) Describe the relationship between exercise-induced heat loads and core body temperature: _____

_____

_____

   (b) How does this differ between people with type 1 diabetes and without (control)? _____

_____

_____

_____

7. Why does impaired vasodilation affect thermoregulation in people with type 2 diabetes? _____

_____

_____

_____

©2023 **BIOZONE** International
ISBN: 978-1-99-101408-5

89 Carbohydrate Metabolism in the Liver

Key idea: Carbohydrate is stored or made available to cells as required and is regulated by hormones, principally insulin and glucagon, but also epinephrine and glucocorticoids.

The liver has a central role in carbohydrate metabolism, specifically the production of glucose from non-carbohydrate sources, and the interconversion of glucose and glycogen (a glucose polysaccharide).

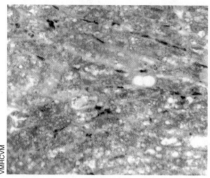

Glycogen is stored within the liver cells. Glucagon stimulates its conversion to glucose.

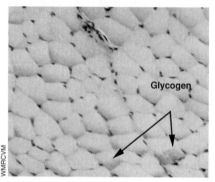

Glycogen is also stored in muscle, where it is squeezed out to the periphery of the cells.

▶ **Glycogenesis:** Excess glucose in the blood is converted to glycogen. **Insulin** stimulates glycogenesis in response to high blood glucose. Glycogen is stored in the liver and muscle tissue.

▶ **Glycogenolysis:** Conversion of stored glycogen to glucose (glycogen breakdown). The free glucose is released into the blood. The **hormones glucagon** and epinephrine stimulate glycogenolysis in response to low blood glucose.

▶ **Gluconeogenesis:** Production of glucose from non-carbohydrate sources, e.g. glycerol, pyruvate, lactate, and amino acids. Epinephrine and glucocorticoid hormones, e.g. cortisol, stimulate gluconeogenesis in response to fasting, starvation, or prolonged periods of exercise when glycogen stores are exhausted. It is also part of the general adaptation syndrome in response to stress.

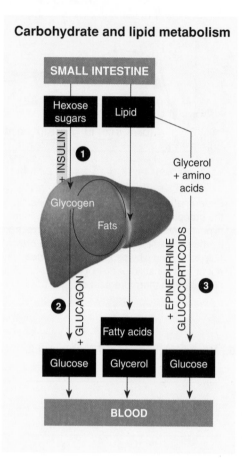

Carbohydrate and lipid metabolism

1. Explain the three important processes of carbohydrate metabolism in the liver, including how these are regulated:

(a) _____

_____

(b) _____

_____

(c) _____

_____

2. Identify the processes occurring at each numbered stage on the diagram above, right:

(a) Process occurring at point 1: _____

(b) Process occurring at point 2: _____

(c) Process occurring at point 3: _____

3. Explain why it is important that the body can readily convert and produce different forms of carbohydrates:

_____

_____

_____

_____

©2023 **BIOZONE** International
ISBN: 978-1-99-101408-5
Photocopying Prohibited

90 Control of Blood Glucose

Key Idea: The endocrine portion of the pancreas produces two hormones, insulin and glucagon, which maintain blood glucose at a steady state through negative feedback.

Blood glucose levels are controlled by negative feedback involving two hormones: **insulin** and **glucagon**. These **hormones** are produced by the islet cells of the **pancreas**, and act in opposition to control blood glucose levels. Insulin lowers blood glucose by promoting the uptake of glucose by the body's cells and the conversion of glucose into the storage molecule glycogen in the liver. Glucagon increases blood glucose by stimulating the breakdown of stored glycogen and the synthesis of glucose from amino acids. Negative feedback stops hormone secretion when normal blood glucose levels are restored. Blood glucose homeostasis allows energy to be available to cells as required. The liver has a central role in these carbohydrate conversions.

The importance of blood glucose

▸ Glucose is the body's main energy source. It is chemically broken down during cellular respiration to generate ATP, which is used to power metabolism. Glucose is the main sugar circulating in blood, so it is often called blood sugar. Blood glucose levels are regulated by negative feedback involving two hormones, insulin and glucagon.

▸ Blood glucose levels are tightly controlled because cells must receive an adequate and regular supply of fuel. Prolonged high or low blood glucose causes serious physiological problems and even death. Normal activities, such as eating and exercise, alter blood glucose levels, but the body's control mechanisms regulate levels so that fluctuations are minimized and generally occur within a physiologically acceptable range. For humans, this is 60-110 mg/dL, indicated by the shaded area in the graph (p168).

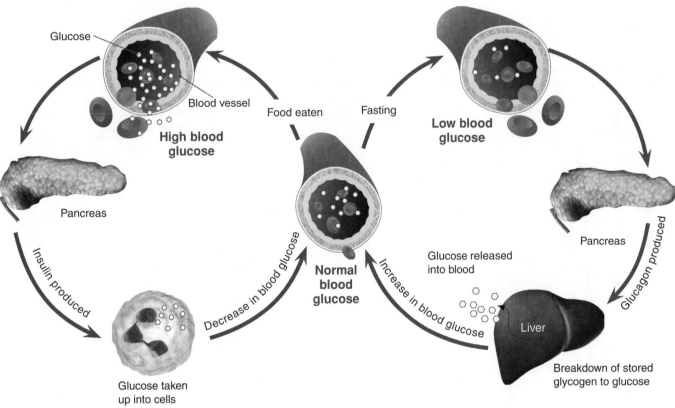

1. For the following two scenarios, describe how normal blood glucose level is restored:

   (a) Low blood glucose: _____

   _____

   (b) High blood glucose: _____

   _____

2. What is the role of the liver in blood glucose homeostasis? _____

   _____

3. In what way are the actions of the hormones insulin and glucagon antagonistic? _____

   _____

   _____

Negative feedback in blood glucose regulation

Blood glucose can be tested using a finger prick test. The glucose in the blood reacts with an enzyme electrode, generating an electric charge proportional to the glucose concentration. This is displayed as a digital readout.

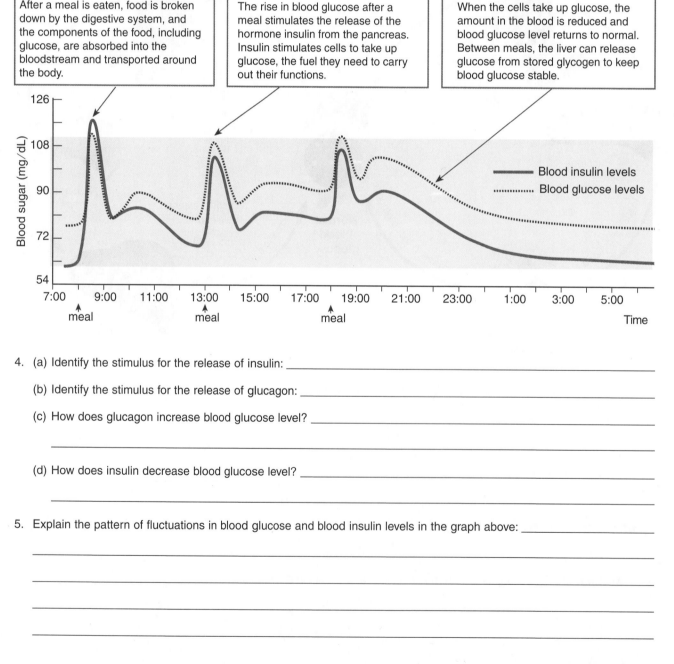

beta cells
Stimulates β cells to secrete insulin

alpha cells
Stimulates α cells to secrete glucagon

Uptake of glucose by cells. Glucose converted to glycogen or fat in the liver.

Rise in BG

Normal blood glucose (BG) level 3.9-5.6 mmol /L

Fall in BG

Breakdown of glycogen to glucose in the liver.

Decreases blood glucose.

Release of glucose into the blood.

Blood sugar fluctuations

After a meal is eaten, food is broken down by the digestive system, and the components of the food, including glucose, are absorbed into the bloodstream and transported around the body.

The rise in blood glucose after a meal stimulates the release of the hormone insulin from the pancreas. Insulin stimulates cells to take up glucose, the fuel they need to carry out their functions.

When the cells take up glucose, the amount in the blood is reduced and blood glucose level returns to normal. Between meals, the liver can release glucose from stored glycogen to keep blood glucose stable.

Blood insulin levels
Blood glucose levels

Blood sugar (mg/dL): 54, 72, 90, 108, 126

Time: 7:00, 9:00, 11:00, 13:00, 15:00, 17:00, 19:00, 21:00, 23:00, 1:00, 3:00, 5:00

meal (8:00), meal (13:00), meal (18:00)

Time

4. (a) Identify the stimulus for the release of insulin: _____

(b) Identify the stimulus for the release of glucagon: _____

(c) How does glucagon increase blood glucose level? _____

_____

(d) How does insulin decrease blood glucose level? _____

_____

5. Explain the pattern of fluctuations in blood glucose and blood insulin levels in the graph above: _____

_____

_____

_____

_____

©2023 **BIOZONE** International
ISBN: 978-1-99-101408-5
Photocopying Prohibited

91 Type 1 Diabetes Mellitus

Key Idea: Diabetes mellitus is a condition in which blood glucose levels are too high and glucose appears in the urine. In type 1 diabetes, the insulin-producing cells of the pancreas are destroyed and insulin is not produced.

Diabetes mellitus is characterized by large volumes (diabetes) of sweet (mellitus) urine and extreme thirst. Type 1 diabetes is an inherited condition. The **insulin** producing beta cells of the **pancreas** are destroyed by the body's immune system, so no insulin is produced. Patients must have regular insulin injections to stabilise blood glucose levels.

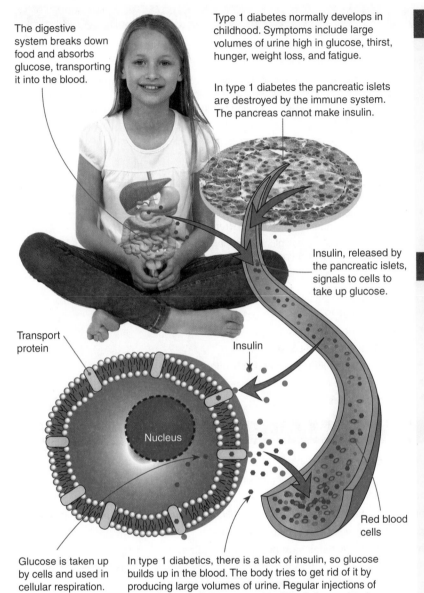

The digestive system breaks down food and absorbs glucose, transporting it into the blood.

Type 1 diabetes normally develops in childhood. Symptoms include large volumes of urine high in glucose, thirst, hunger, weight loss, and fatigue.

In type 1 diabetes the pancreatic islets are destroyed by the immune system. The pancreas cannot make insulin.

Insulin, released by the pancreatic islets, signals to cells to take up glucose.

Transport protein

Insulin

Nucleus

Red blood cells

Glucose is taken up by cells and used in cellular respiration.

In type 1 diabetics, there is a lack of insulin, so glucose builds up in the blood. The body tries to get rid of it by producing large volumes of urine. Regular injections of insulin allow diabetics to regulate blood glucose levels.

Short term effects

Low blood sugar *(hypoglycaemia)*: Blood glucose levels below normal (<4 mmol/L) can result in clumsiness, confusion, and seizures. It can result from too much insulin, usually after injection if glucose levels are already low.

High blood sugar *(hyperglycaemia)*: High blood glucose levels (> 6 mmol/L) occur when glucose fails to enter the cells. Effects include frequent urination, fatigue, thirst, and blurred vision

Ketoacidosis: A lack of insulin can result in a build up of molecules called ketones caused by metabolism of fats for fuel. Ketones are acidic and can lead to metabolic acidosis (fall in tissue pH), which can quite quickly be fatal.

Long term effects

General circulation: Over time, high blood glucose damages the lining of small blood vessels, making them prone to developing plaques and become narrow and clogged. The result of this is increased blood pressure.

Heart disease: Nearly 3 in 4 people with type 1 diabetes will suffer some form of heart disease. Causes may be from autoimmune responses and high blood glucose and blood pressure.

Kidney disease: Damage to the small blood vessels of the kidney causes kidney function to decline and produces many associated health problems. Glucose in the urine can also result in fungal infections in the bladder.

Eye problems: Damage to the blood vessels in the eyes leads to cataracts and retinal damage.

Nerve damage: High blood glucose levels cause nerve damage indirectly through blood vessel damage. Symptoms include tingling and weakness in the limbs. Numbness can lead to unnoticed and hard to treat infections and ulcers.

1. (a) What is type 1 diabetes? _____

(b) Explain how the usual mechanisms for blood glucose homeostasis are disrupted in a person with type 1 diabetes. How does this disruption result in the symptoms observed?

_____

_____

_____

_____

2. How do regular insulin injections help a person with type 1 diabetes to maintain their blood glucose homeostasis?

_____

_____

92 Type 2 Diabetes Mellitus

Key idea: Type 2 diabetes mellitus is characterized by a resistance to insulin's effects and relative (rather than absolute) insulin deficiency.

The **pancreas** produces **insulin**, but the body's cells cease to respond to it and glucose levels in the blood remain high.

Type 2 **diabetes** is a chronic, progressive disease, usually caused by lifestyle choices, and becomes worse with time if not managed. Its long-term effects include heart disease, strokes, blindness, and kidney failure. However, ketoacidosis (a feature of type 1 diabetes), is uncommon.

Symptoms of type 2 diabetes mellitus

a

Symptoms may be mild at first.

▶ The body's cells do not respond appropriately to the insulin present and blood glucose levels become elevated. Normal blood glucose level is 3.3-6.1 mmol/L (60-110 mg/dL). In diabetics, fasting blood glucose level is 7 mmol/L (126 mg/dL) or higher.

b

Symptoms occur with varying degrees of severity:

▶ Cells are starved of fuel. This can lead to increased appetite and overeating and may contribute to an existing obesity problem.

▶ Urine production increases to rid the body of the excess glucose. Glucose is present in the urine and patients are frequently very thirsty.

▶ The body's inability to use glucose properly leads to muscle weakness and fatigue, irritability, frequent infections, and poor wound healing.

c

Uncontrolled, elevated blood glucose eventually results in damage to the blood vessels and leads to:

▶ coronary artery disease
▶ peripheral vascular disease
▶ retinal damage, blurred vision and blindness
▶ kidney damage and renal failure
▶ persistent ulcers and gangrene

Risk factors

▶ Obesity: BMI greater than 27. Distribution of weight is also important.
▶ Age: Risk increases with age, although the incidence of type 2 diabetes is increasingly being reported in obese children.
▶ Sedentary lifestyle: Inactivity increases risk through its effects on body weight.
▶ Family history: There is a strong genetic link for type 2 diabetes. Those with a family history of the disease are at greater risk.
▶ Ethnicity: Certain ethnic groups are at higher risk of developing of type 2 diabetes.
▶ High blood pressure: Up to 60% of people with undiagnosed diabetes have high blood pressure.
▶ High blood lipids: More than 40% of people with diabetes have abnormally high levels of cholesterol and similar lipids in the blood.

1. Type 2 diabetes is a non-infectious disease that interferes with the homeostatic control of blood glucose in the body.

(a) Describe the type 2 diabetes disease and the common symptoms experienced by an individual: _____

_____

_____

_____

(b) Describe the risk factors that increase the chance of developing type 2 diabetes: _____

_____

(c) Explain how ONE current treatment of type 2 diabetes controls or eliminates the disease: _____

_____

_____

©2023 **BIOZONE** International
ISBN: 978-1-99-101408-5
Photocopying Prohibited

Treating type 2 diabetes

- Diabetes is not curable but can be managed to minimize the health effects:
- Regularly check blood glucose level
- Manage diet to reduce fluctuations in blood glucose level
- Take regular exercise
- Reduce weight
- Reduce blood pressure
- Reduce or stop smoking
- Take prescribed anti-diabetic drugs
- In time, insulin therapy may be required

Insulin

Glucose

Fat cell

Blood vessel

Insulin

▸ The beta cells of the pancreatic islets (above) produce insulin, the **hormone** responsible for the cellular uptake of glucose.

▸ In type 2 diabetes, the body's cells do not use the insulin properly. Cellular uptake of glucose is impaired and glucose remains in the blood.

▸ Type 2 diabetes is also called insulin resistance.

2. How does type 2 diabetes differ from type 1 diabetes with respect to:

(a) Cause: _____

_____

_____

(b) Symptoms: _____

_____

_____

(c) Treatment: _____

_____

_____

3. Antidiabetic drugs can work in several ways. For each of the statements below, state how the drug would help restore blood glucose homeostasis:

(a) Drug increases sensitivity of cells to insulin: _____

_____

(b) Drug increases pancreatic secretion of insulin: _____

_____

4. Explain what dietary advice you would give to a person diagnosed with type 2 diabetes: _____

_____

_____

5. Explain why the increase in type 2 diabetes is considered epidemic in the developed world: _____

_____

_____

93 Alcohol, Nicotine, and Blood Glucose

Key Idea: The amount of glucose in the blood (the blood glucose level) is tightly regulated by negative feedback, but can be affected by alcohol and nicotine.

Nicotine is the highly addictive component of tobacco, and a potent carcinogen (cancer causing agent). It is also responsible for depression of appetite in smokers, partly through its effect on blood glucose. The alcohol in alcoholic beverages acts as a preservative and adds to its flavor. Alcohol is toxic and its metabolism reduces the body's capacity to regulate blood glucose levels.

Alcohol

The liver metabolizes alcohol, so while there is alcohol in the blood, it has less capacity to regulate blood glucose. Alcohol lowers blood glucose levels by stimulating **insulin** production. Low to moderate alcohol intakes don't affect the body's response to insulin. However, long-term alcohol abuse damages the liver and interferes with many aspects of metabolism, including metabolism of glucose.

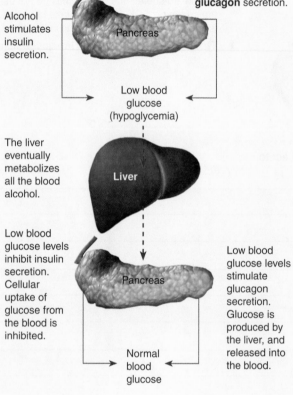

Alcohol inhibits **glucagon** secretion.

Alcohol stimulates insulin secretion.

Pancreas

Low blood glucose (hypoglycemia)

The liver eventually metabolizes all the blood alcohol.

Liver

Low blood glucose levels inhibit insulin secretion. Cellular uptake of glucose from the blood is inhibited.

Pancreas

Low blood glucose levels stimulate glucagon secretion. Glucose is produced by the liver, and released into the blood.

Normal blood glucose

Nicotine

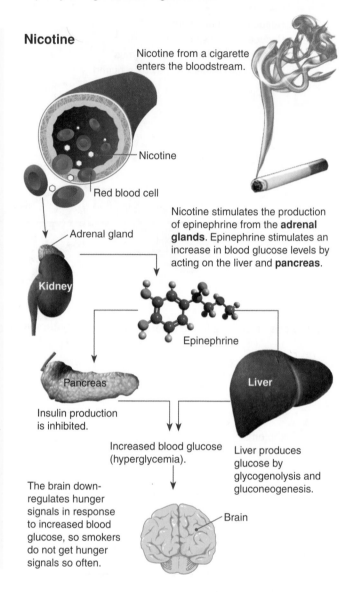

Nicotine from a cigarette enters the bloodstream.

Nicotine

Red blood cell

Adrenal gland

Kidney

Nicotine stimulates the production of epinephrine from the **adrenal glands**. Epinephrine stimulates an increase in blood glucose levels by acting on the liver and **pancreas**.

Epinephrine

Pancreas

Insulin production is inhibited.

Liver

Increased blood glucose (hyperglycemia).

Liver produces glucose by glycogenolysis and gluconeogenesis.

The brain down-regulates hunger signals in response to increased blood glucose, so smokers do not get hunger signals so often.

Brain

---

1. (a) How does drinking alcohol result in low blood glucose? _____

_____

_____

   (b) The liver prioritizes the metabolism of alcohol before restoring blood glucose. Suggest why this is the case: _____

_____

2. (a) Explain how nicotine reduces appetite: _____

_____

_____

   (b) Explain why people who stop smoking often put on weight: _____

_____

_____

©2023 **BIOZONE** International
ISBN: 978-1-99-101408-5
Photocopying Prohibited

94 Stress and the Endocrine System

Key Idea: The stress response is triggered through sympathetic stimulation of the central medulla region of the adrenal glands, in what is popularly know as the fight or flight syndrome.

The interactions of the **hypothalamus**, **pituitary**, and **adrenal glands** together constitute the hypothalamic-pituitary-adrenal axis, which is responsible for controlling the body's reactions to stress and regulating many of the body's processes, including digestion, immune function, mood, sexuality, and energy storage and expenditure. This stimulation causes the release of catecholamines (epinephrine and norepinephrine). These **hormones** help to prepare the body to cope with short-term stressful situations. Continued stress results in release of glucocorticoids (especially cortisol) from the outer cortex of the adrenals. These hormones help the body to resist longer term stress. Their secretion is a normal part of what is called the general adaptation syndrome, but continued, unrelieved stress can be damaging, or even fatal.

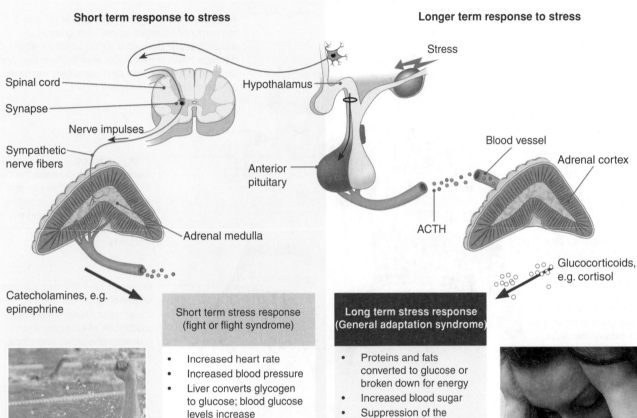

Short term response to stress

- Spinal cord
- Synapse
- Nerve impulses
- Sympathetic nerve fibers
- Adrenal medulla
- Catecholamines, e.g. epinephrine

Longer term response to stress

- Stress
- Hypothalamus
- Anterior pituitary
- Blood vessel
- Adrenal cortex
- ACTH
- Glucocorticoids, e.g. cortisol

Short term stress response (fight or flight syndrome)

- Increased heart rate
- Increased blood pressure
- Liver converts glycogen to glucose; blood glucose levels increase
- Dilation of bronchioles
- Blood flow to gut and kidney reduced
- Blood flow to muscles and brain increased
- Increased metabolic rate

The physiological changes occurring as part of the short term stress response help us to operate at peak efficiency when endangered, competing, or whenever a high level of performance is required.

Long term stress response (General adaptation syndrome)

- Proteins and fats converted to glucose or broken down for energy
- Increased blood sugar
- Suppression of the immune system

A state of long term unrelieved stress is not normal. The body responds to prolonged periods of stress by making physiological changes to resist the stress, e.g. conserving energy during periods of starvation. If the stress continues unrelieved, the body enters a phase of exhaustion, where its resistance to stress is eroded, and the immune system fails and loses its ability to fight disease.

1. Explain how the body's short term response to stress is adaptive: _____

_____

_____

2. Describe features of the long term stress response that help to maintain activity through the period of the stress:

_____

_____

_____

95 Aging and the Endocrine System

Key Idea: Aging influences the physiology of the endocrine system.

Despite age-related changes, the endocrine system functions well in most older people. However, some endocrine changes do occur because of normal cellular damage accumulating as a result of the aging process and genetically programmed cellular changes. Aging produces changes in **hormone** production and secretion, hormone metabolism (how quickly excess hormones are broken down and leave the body, for example, through urination), levels of circulating hormones, target tissue response to hormones, and biological rhythms, such as sleep and the menstrual cycle.

Melatonin secretion from the pineal declines in the elderly, leading to a disruption in the normal sleep patterns. Melatonin supplements are used to relieve some of the symptoms associated with menopause (in women).

The **pituitary** gland shrinks and becomes more fibrous in old age. Production and secretion of growth hormone declines markedly, and this is related to a decrease in lean muscle mass, an increase in fat mass, and a decrease in bone density.

Cardiovascular and renal problems become more common in old age. The liver and kidneys are primarily responsible for clearing hormones from the bloodstream. Several clearance processes become altered or slowed in individuals with chronic heart, liver, or kidney disorders.

Age-related thinning and loss of hair is related to hormonal changes as circulating levels of a testosterone derivative (DHT) increase and damage the hair follicles. In women, hair loss and thinning is the result of DHT sensitivity increasing as estrogen levels decline.

In post-menopausal women, low estrogen levels increase the risk of cardiovascular disease and accelerate bone loss, resulting in osteoporosis, hunching of the spine, and increased risk of fractures.

In menopause, the ovaries stop responding to FSH and LH from the anterior pituitary. Ovarian production of estrogen and progesterone slows and stops, and the menstrual cycle stops.

Increasing age is correlated with increased rates of type 2 **diabetes** and associated problems such as poor peripheral circulation. With aging, the target cell response time becomes slower, especially in people who might be at risk for this disorder.

Aging is associated with an increase in the number of aberrant cells and an increased incidence of cancers as cellular damage accumulates. Tumors of the endocrine organs are more common in old age.

1. Describe two consequences of declining output of growth hormone in old age:

    (a) _____

    (b) _____

2. Explain why the levels of LH and FSH increase in post-menopausal women: _____
_____
_____

3. Identify one process that accelerates in elderly women as a result of loss of estrogen: _____
_____

©2023 **BIOZONE** International
ISBN: 978-1-99-101408-5
Photocopying Prohibited

96 | Chapter Summary

1. Use information from the diagram to summarize how the endocrine system functions to regulate blood glucose homeostasis in the human body:

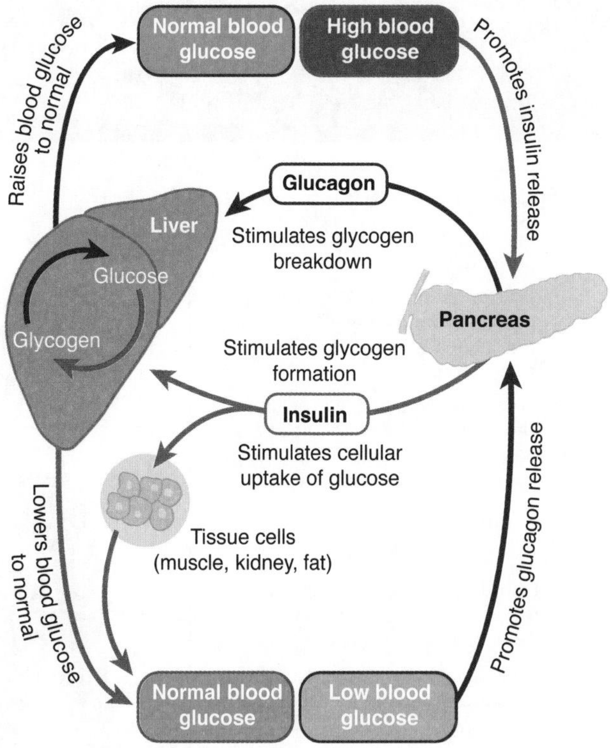

_____

_____

_____

_____

_____

_____

_____

_____

_____

_____

_____

_____

_____

Normal blood glucose **High blood glucose**

Raises blood glucose to normal

Promotes insulin release

Glucagon
Stimulates glycogen breakdown

Liver
Glucose
Glycogen

Pancreas

Stimulates glycogen formation

Insulin
Stimulates cellular uptake of glucose

Lowers blood glucose to normal

Tissue cells (muscle, kidney, fat)

Promotes glucagon release

Normal blood glucose **Low blood glucose**

2. Compare and contrast type 1 and type 2 diabetes, linked to dysfunction of the endocrine system: _____

_____

_____

_____

_____

_____

_____

3. Discuss why the pituitary gland is known as the "master gland", and describe its key role in the endocrine system:

_____

_____

_____

_____

4. Explain how endocrine signaling differs from other types of cell signaling: _____

_____

_____

_____

5. Compare and contrast the endocrine system response to short-term and long-term stress: _____

_____

_____

_____

_____

Cardiovascular and Lymphatic System

Endocrine system

- Lymph and blood distribute hormones.
- Endocrine function produces hormones for the development of the lymphatic organs and T cell maturation.
- Blood pressure and fluid volume are regulated via the renin-angiotensin-aldosterone system.

Cardiovascular system

- Lymphatic vessels pick up leaked tissue fluid and proteins and return them to general circulation.
- Spleen destroys RBCs, removes cellular debris from the blood, and stores iron.
- Blood is the source of lymph and circulates antibodies and immune system cells.

Digestive system

- Products of digestion are transported in the blood and lymph.
- Lymphoid nodules in the intestinal wall protect against invasion by pathogens.
- Gastric acidity destroys pathogens.

Skeletal system

- Bones are the site of blood cell production (hematopoiesis) for both cardiovascular and lymphatic systems.
- Bones protect cardiovascular and lymphatic organs and provide a store of calcium, which is needed for regulating blood volume.

Integumentary system

- Blood vessels in the skin provide a reservoir of blood and are a site of heat loss.
- Skin provides a physical and chemical barrier to pathogens.

Nervous system

- The nervous system innervates lymphatic organs and vessels. The brain helps to regulate the immune response.
- The autonomic ANS regulates cardiac output; the sympathetic division regulates blood pressure and distribution.

Lymphatic system and immunity

- The lymphatic system returns tissue fluid and proteins to the cardiovascular system.
- Lymph forms from blood. Blood and lymph transport antibodies and immune cells.

Respiratory system

- The lymphatic system returns tissue fluid and proteins to the cardiovascular system.
- Lymph forms from blood. Blood and lymph transport antibodies and immune cells.

Urinary system

- Urinary system eliminates wastes transported in the blood and maintains water, electrolyte, and acid-base balance.
- The urinary system helps to regulate blood pressure and volume by altering urine output.

Reproductive system

- Lightly acidic vaginal secretions in women prevent the growth of bacteria and fungi.
- Estrogen maintains cardiovascular health in women (and in men as a result of conversion from testosterone).

Muscular system

- Activity of skeletal muscles aids return of blood and lymph to the heart.
- Muscles protect superficial lymph nodes.
- Aerobic activity improves cardiovascular health and efficiency.

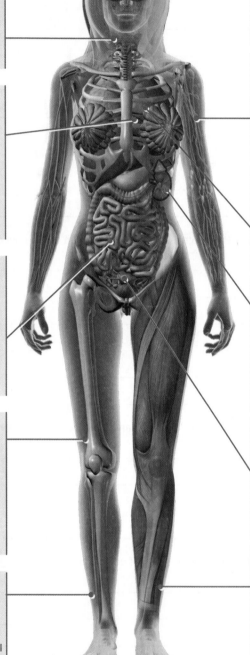

General functions and effects on all systems

The cardiovascular system delivers oxygen and nutrients to organs and tissues and removes carbon dioxide and other waste products of metabolism. Lymphatic vessels pick up leaked tissue fluid and proteins and return them to general circulation. The immune system protects the body's tissues and organs against pathogens.

Symptoms of disease
- Pain (moderate to severe)
- Loss of function, e.g. cardiac arrest
- Swelling and immunodeficiency
- Tissue loss and gangrene

Diagnosis of disorders
- Electrocardiography
- X-rays, MRI and CT scans
- Ultrasound
- Blood and DNA tests

Infectious of the heart and blood vessels
- Congenital heart disorders
- Atherosclerosis and heart disease
- Peripheral vascular disease & stroke
- Cancers, e.g. leukemia

Treatment of CVD
- Surgery
- Diet and lifestyle management
- Drug therapies

Lymphatic system disorders
- Cancers, e.g. lymphomas
- Infectious diseases, e.g. HIV
- Inherited disorders, e.g. SCID
- Autoimmune disorders

Treatment of immune disorders
- Surgery
- Radiotherapy (for cancers)
- Drug and physical therapies
- Immunotherapy (desensitization)
- Gene and cell therapy (SCID)

- Asthma
- Allergy
- Atherosclerosis
- Myocardial infarction
- HIV

- ECGs
- Coronary bypass
- Valve replacement
- Asthma treatment
- Organ transplants

Internal transport
The Cardiovascular and Lymphatic Systems

The cardiovascular and lymphatic systems are linked in a communication network extending throughout the body.

Exercise and medical therapies can alleviate the symptoms of some age and disease related changes to these systems.

- CVD risk factors
- Cardiac pacemakers
- Stroke
- Cancer
- Rheumatoid arthritis

Effects of exercise on:
- Stroke volume
- Cardiac output
- Pulse rate
- Blood pressure
- Venous return

Exercise can delay or reverse some age-related changes to cardiovascular function

Effects of aging on heart and immune function
- Higher rates of autoimmune disease
- Increased susceptibility to disease
- Decline in cardiovascular performance
- Higher risk of stroke and CVD
- Increased risk of hypertension

Effects of exercise on heart and immune function
- Improved immune function
- Improved cardiovascular performance
- Increase in cardiac output
- Reduced risk of CVD and stroke
- Lowered blood pressure

CHAPTER 7

The Cardiovascular System

KEY IDEAS

- The cardiovascular system transports blood to all parts of the body within closed vessels.

- Blood carries oxygen, nutrients, and waste products and has a defensive role in the body.

- The heart is a muscular pump with its own intrinsic rate of beating. This rate is influenced by the autonomic nervous system.

- Cardiovascular diseases affect the heart and blood vessels. Many are treatable.

KEY TERMS

- Aorta
- Artery
- Atrium
- Blood
- Capillary
- Cardiovascular cycle
- Cardiovascular disease
- Circulatory system
- Hematopoiesis
- Plasma
- Vein
- Ventricle

RESOURCE HUB

Scan the QR code to access:

- weblinks
- videos
- 3D models
- interactives

LEARNING OBJECTIVES

			Activity number

☐ 1 Understand that the circulatory system is a network of vessels that transports nutrients, respiratory gases, and wastes around the body. Distinguish between pulmonary circulation and systemic circulation.   **97**

☐ 2 Use annotated diagrams to describe the structure of arteries, veins, and capillaries, and explain the relationship between the structure and function of each of these blood vessels. Describe how water and solutes enter and leave capillaries and bathe tissue cells.   **98-102**

☐ 3 Distinguish between the cellular and non-cellular components of blood and give examples of the different roles of these components. Describe the process of hematopoiesis. Know that the rate of blood flow around the body increases during exercise.   **103-105**

☐ 4 Use an annotated diagram to understand the external and internal structure of the heart, including the chambers, blood vessels, and valves.   **106**

☐ 5 Understand what is meant by the cardiac cycle and that the heartbeat is a response to electrical impulses that can be recorded using an electrocardiogram (ECG). Analyze data showing pressure and volume changes during the cardiac cycle.   **107**

☐ 6 Compare an annotated diagram to a dissection (real, video, or photographs) of an animal heart.   **108**

☐ 7 Describe the intrinsic regulation of the heartbeat. Understand the role of the sinoatrial node, the atrioventricular node, and the atrioventricular bundle.   **109**

☐ 8 Describe the extrinsic control of heart rate and the factors that contribute to increase or decrease it. Understand the effect of stress on heart rate. Review the general structure of the heart and its role in circulation.   **110-112**

☐ 9 Understand what is meant by cardiovascular fitness and carry out an activity to analyze heart rate and blood pressure. Know that training through aerobic exercise has physiological effects on the body that allow it to meet the demands of exercise more efficiently.   **113-114**

☐ 10 Know that cardiovascular disease is a term that describes a wide range of diseases that affect the heart and blood vessels. Understand that these diseases can be inherited or arise in response to lifestyle choices and that some heart problems can be corrected through medical treatments.   **115-118**

Background: Tissue (abstract)

97 The Human Transport System

Key Idea: The circulatory system is responsible for the transport of nutrients, respiratory gases, and wastes in the blood, to and from the body's cells, via a network of vessels. The **circulatory system** comprises the heart, **arteries**, **veins**, **capillaries**, and **blood**. The blood transports oxygen and nutrients to the cells, carbon dioxide to the lungs, and metabolic wastes to the kidneys. It is also moves cells of the immune system (the white blood cells) around the body.

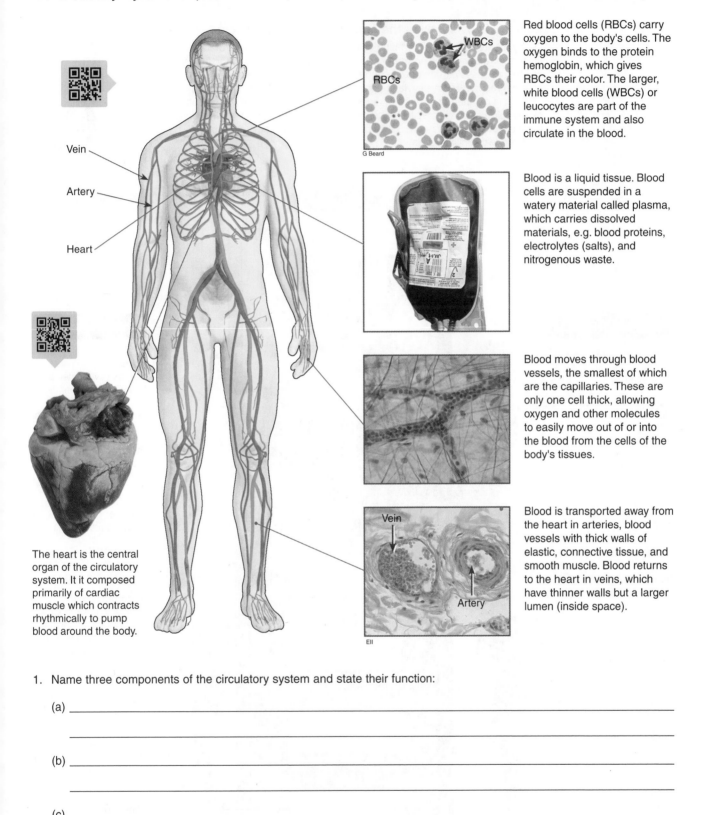

Red blood cells (RBCs) carry oxygen to the body's cells. The oxygen binds to the protein hemoglobin, which gives RBCs their color. The larger, white blood cells (WBCs) or leucocytes are part of the immune system and also circulate in the blood.

Blood is a liquid tissue. Blood cells are suspended in a watery material called plasma, which carries dissolved materials, e.g. blood proteins, electrolytes (salts), and nitrogenous waste.

Blood moves through blood vessels, the smallest of which are the capillaries. These are only one cell thick, allowing oxygen and other molecules to easily move out of or into the blood from the cells of the body's tissues.

Blood is transported away from the heart in arteries, blood vessels with thick walls of elastic, connective tissue, and smooth muscle. Blood returns to the heart in veins, which have thinner walls but a larger lumen (inside space).

The heart is the central organ of the circulatory system. It it composed primarily of cardiac muscle which contracts rhythmically to pump blood around the body.

1. Name three components of the circulatory system and state their function:

(a) _____

_____

(b) _____

_____

(c) _____

_____

2. (a) Which component of the blood carries oxygen to the body's cells? _____

(b) Which component of the blood carries metabolic waste to the kidneys? _____

The blood vessels of the circulatory system form a vast network of tubes that carry blood away from the heart, transport it to the tissues of the body, and then return it to the heart. The arteries, arterioles, capillaries, venules, and veins are organized into specific routes to circulate the blood throughout the body. The figure below shows a number of the basic circulatory routes through which the blood travels. Mammals have a double circulatory system: a pulmonary system (or circulation), which carries blood between the heart and lungs, and a systemic system (circulation), which carries blood between the heart and the rest of the body. The systemic circulation has many subdivisions. Two important subdivisions are the coronary (cardiac) circulation, which supplies the heart muscle itself, and the hepatic portal circulation, which runs from the gut to the liver.

Schematic overview of the human circulatory system

Deoxygenated blood (colored blue below) travels to the right side of the heart via the vena cavae. The heart pumps the deoxygenated blood to the lungs, where it releases carbon dioxide and receives oxygen. The oxygenated blood (colored red below) travels via the pulmonary vein back to the heart from where it is pumped to all parts of the body. The venous system (figure, left) returns blood from the capillaries to the heart. The arterial system (figure right) carries blood from the heart to the capillaries. Portal systems carry blood between two capillary beds.

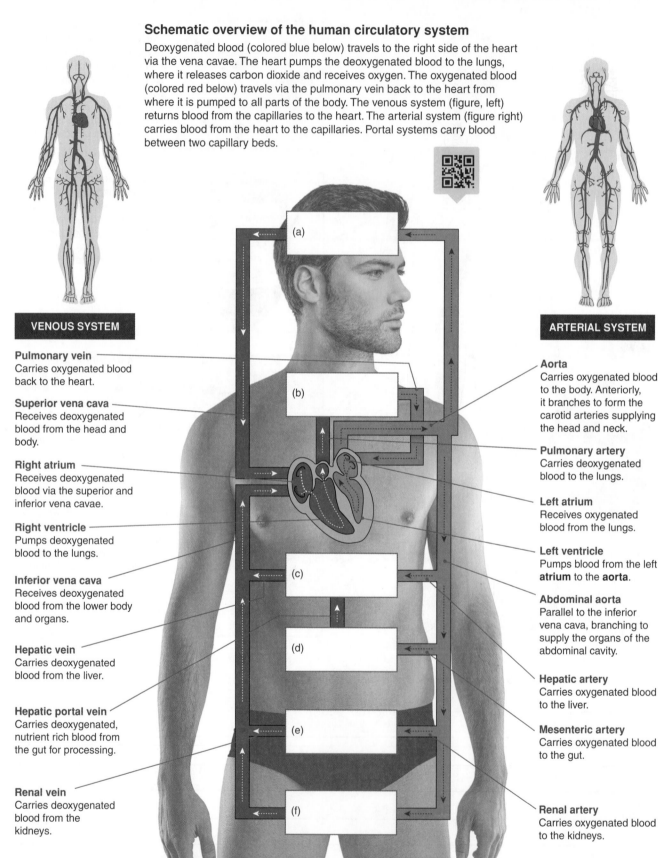

VENOUS SYSTEM

Pulmonary vein
Carries oxygenated blood back to the heart.

Superior vena cava
Receives deoxygenated blood from the head and body.

Right atrium
Receives deoxygenated blood via the superior and inferior vena cavae.

Right ventricle
Pumps deoxygenated blood to the lungs.

Inferior vena cava
Receives deoxygenated blood from the lower body and organs.

Hepatic vein
Carries deoxygenated blood from the liver.

Hepatic portal vein
Carries deoxygenated, nutrient rich blood from the gut for processing.

Renal vein
Carries deoxygenated blood from the kidneys.

ARTERIAL SYSTEM

Aorta
Carries oxygenated blood to the body. Anteriorly, it branches to form the carotid arteries supplying the head and neck.

Pulmonary artery
Carries deoxygenated blood to the lungs.

Left atrium
Receives oxygenated blood from the lungs.

Left ventricle
Pumps blood from the left **atrium** to the **aorta**.

Abdominal aorta
Parallel to the inferior vena cava, branching to supply the organs of the abdominal cavity.

Hepatic artery
Carries oxygenated blood to the liver.

Mesenteric artery
Carries oxygenated blood to the gut.

Renal artery
Carries oxygenated blood to the kidneys.

3. Complete the diagram above by labeling the boxes with the organs or structures they represent.

©2023 **BIOZONE** International
ISBN: 978-1-99-101408-5
Photocopying Prohibited

98 Arteries

Key Idea: Arteries are thick-walled blood vessels that carry blood away from the heart to the capillaries within the tissues. Large **arteries** leave the heart and divide into medium-sized (distributing) arteries. Within the tissues and organs, these distributing arteries branch to form arterioles, which deliver **blood** to **capillaries**. Arterioles lack the thick layers of arteries and consist only of an endothelial layer wrapped by a few smooth muscle fibers at intervals along their length. Blood flow to the tissues is altered by contraction (vasoconstriction) or relaxation (vasodilation) of the blood vessel walls. Vasoconstriction increases blood pressure, whereas vasodilation has the opposite effect.

Arteries

Arteries, regardless of size, can be recognized by their well-defined, rounded lumen (internal space) and the muscularity of the vessel wall. Arteries have an elastic, stretchy structure that gives them the ability to withstand the high pressure of blood being pumped from the heart. At the same time, they help to maintain pressure by having some contractile ability themselves (a feature of the central muscle layer). Arteries nearer the heart have more elastic tissue, giving greater resistance to the higher blood pressures of the blood leaving the left ventricle. Arteries further from the heart have more muscle to help them maintain blood pressure. Between heartbeats, the arteries undergo elastic recoil and contract. This tends to smooth out the flow of blood through the vessel. Arteries comprise three main regions (right):

1. A thin inner layer of epithelial cells called the tunica intima (endothelium) lines the artery.
2. A thick central layer (the tunica media) of elastic tissue and smooth muscle that can both stretch and contract.
3. An outer connective tissue layer (the tunica externa) has a lot of elastic tissue.

(a)

(b)

(c)

(d)

Structure of an artery

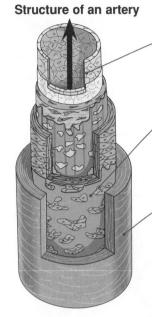

Tunica intima (endothelium)
Thin endothelial layer of squamous epithelium is in contact with the blood. Arrow indicates direction of blood flow.

Tunica media
Thick layer of elastic tissue and smooth muscle tissue allows for both stretch and contraction, maintaining blood flow without loss of pressure.

Tunica externa
Layer of elastic connective tissue (collagen and elastin) anchors the artery to other tissues and allows it to resist overexpansion. Relatively thinner in larger elastic arteries and thicker in muscular, distributing arteries.

Cross section through a large artery

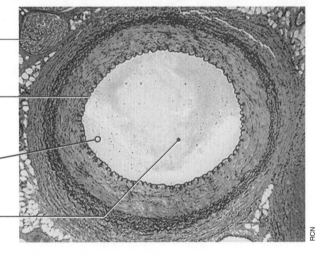

1. Using the information above to help you, label the photograph (a)-(d) of the cross section through an artery (above).

2. Why do the walls of arteries need to be thick with a lot of elastic tissue? _____

3. What is the purpose of the smooth muscle in the artery walls? _____

4. How do arteries contribute to the regulation of blood pressure? _____

99 Veins

Key Idea: Veins are blood vessels that return the blood from the tissues to the heart.

The smallest **veins** (venules) return blood from the **capillaries** to the veins. Veins and their branches contain about 59% of the blood in the body. The structural differences between veins and **arteries** are mainly in the relative thickness of the vessel layers, and the diameter of the lumen (veins have a large lumen). Both are related to the vessel's functional role.

Veins

When several capillaries unite, they form small veins called venules. The venules collect the blood from capillaries and drain it into veins. Veins are made up of the same three layers as arteries but they have less elastic and muscle tissue, a relatively thicker tunica externa, and a larger, less defined lumen. The venules closest to the capillaries consist of an endothelium and a tunica externa of connective tissue. As the venules approach the veins, they also contain the tunica media characteristic of veins (right). Although veins are less elastic than arteries, they can still expand enough to adapt to changes in the pressure and volume of the blood passing through them. Blood flowing in the veins has lost a lot of pressure because it has passed through the narrow capillary vessels. The low pressure in veins means that many veins, especially those in the limbs, need to have valves to prevent back-flow of the blood as it returns to the heart.

Structure of a vein

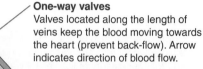

One-way valves
Valves located along the length of veins keep the blood moving towards the heart (prevent back-flow). Arrow indicates direction of blood flow.

Tunica intima (endothelium)
Thin endothelial layer of squamous epithelium lines the vein.

Tunica media
Layer of smooth muscle tissue with collagen fibres (connective tissue). The tunica media is much thinner relative to that of an artery and the smaller venules may lack this layer.

Direction of blood flow

Tunica externa
Layer of connective tissue (mostly collagen). Relatively thicker than in arteries and thicker than the tunica media.

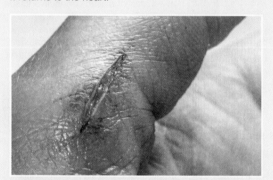

If a vein is cut, as is shown in this finger wound, the blood oozes out slowly in an even flow, and usually clots quickly as it leaves. In contrast, arterial blood spurts rapidly and requires pressure to slow the flow.

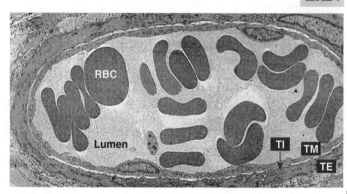

TEM of a vein showing red blood cells (RBC) in the lumen, and the tunica intima (TI), tunica media (TM), and tunica externa (TE).

1. Contrast the structure of veins and arteries for each of the following properties:

   (a) Thickness of muscle and elastic tissue: _____

   _____

   (b) Size of the lumen (inside of the vessel): _____

   _____

2. With respect to their functional roles, explain the differences you have described above: _____

   _____

   _____

   _____

3. What is the role of the valves in assisting the veins to return blood back to the heart? _____

   _____

4. Why does blood ooze from a venous wound rather than spurting, as it does from an arterial wound? _____

   _____

   _____

©2023 **BIOZONE** International
ISBN: 978-1-99-101408-5
Photocopying Prohibited

100 Capillaries

Key Idea: Capillaries are small, thin-walled vessels that allow the exchange of material between the blood and the tissues. **Capillaries** are very small vessels that connect arterial and venous circulation and allow efficient exchange of nutrients and wastes between the blood and tissues. Capillaries form networks or beds and are abundant where metabolic rates are high. Fluid that leaks out of the capillaries has an essential role in bathing the tissues.

Thin endothelium (one cell thick)

Basement membrane

Red blood cell

Nucleus of endothelial cell

Slow blood flow. (< 1 mm s^{-1})

Fluid leaks from capillaries to bathe the tissues.

CO_2 and wastes move from the tissues into the capillary

O_2 and nutrients move from the capillary into the cells of the tissues

Exchanges in capillaries

Blood passes from the arterioles into the capillaries where the exchange of materials between the body cells and the **blood** takes place. Capillaries are small blood vessels with a diameter of just 4-10 μm. The only tissue present is an endothelium of squamous epithelial cells. Capillaries are so numerous that no cell is more than 25 μm from any capillary.

Blood pressure causes fluid to leak from capillaries through small gaps where the endothelial cells join. This fluid bathes the tissues, supplying nutrients and oxygen, and removing wastes (left). The density of capillaries in a tissue is an indication of that tissue's metabolic activity. For example, cardiac muscle relies heavily on oxidative metabolism. It has a high demand for blood flow and is well supplied with capillaries. Smooth muscle is far less active than cardiac muscle, relies more on anaerobic metabolism, and does not require such an extensive blood supply.

Vein

Lymphatic vessel

Capillary

Body cells

Artery

The pressure at the arterial end of a capillary forces fluid from the blood through gaps between the capillary endothelial cells. This tissue fluid contains nutrients and oxygen. Some of it returns to the blood at the venous end of the capillary bed, but some is drained by lymph vessels to form lymph. Blood transports nutrients, wastes, and respiratory gases to and from the tissues. Tissue fluid helps transport these between the blood and the tissues. Lymph drains excess tissue fluid and returns it to the general circulation and it has a role in the immune system.

Comparing blood, tissue fluid, and lymph

	Blood	Tissue fluid	Lymph
Cells	Erythrocytes, leucocytes, platelets	Some leucocytes	Lymphocytes
Proteins	Hormones and plasma proteins	Some hormones and proteins	Few
Glucose	High	None	Low
Amino acids	High	Used by body cells	Low
Oxygen	High	Used by body cells	Low
Carbon dioxide	Low	Produced by body cells	High

1. What is the role of capillaries? _____

_____

2. Describe the structure of a capillary, contrasting it with the structure of a vein and an artery: _____

_____

_____

_____

_____

_____

3. Distinguish between blood, tissue fluid, and lymph: _____

_____

_____

_____

_____

101 Capillary Networks

Key Idea: Capillaries form branching networks where exchanges between the blood and tissues take place.

The flow of **blood** through a **capillary** bed is called microcirculation. In most parts of the body, there are two types of vessels in a capillary bed: the true capillaries, where exchanges take place, and a vessel called a vascular shunt, which connects the arteriole and venule at either end of the bed. The shunt diverts blood past the true capillaries when the metabolic demands of the tissue are low, e.g. vasoconstriction in the skin when conserving body heat. When tissue activity increases, then the entire network fills with blood.

1. Describe the structure of a capillary network:

_____

_____

_____

_____

_____

_____

_____

2. Explain the role of the smooth muscle sphincters and the vascular shunt in a capillary network:

_____

_____

_____

_____

_____

_____

_____

_____

3. (a) Describe a situation where the capillary bed would be in the condition labeled A:

_____

_____

_____

_____

_____

(b) Describe a situation where the capillary bed would be in the condition labeled B:

_____

_____

_____

_____

_____

_____

_____

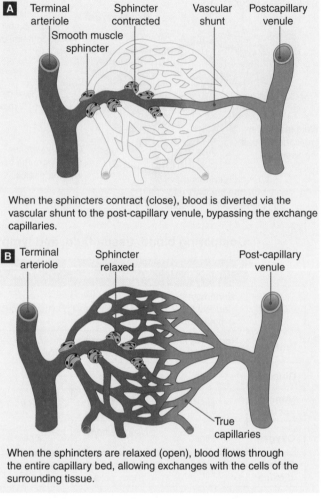

When the sphincters contract (close), blood is diverted via the vascular shunt to the post-capillary venule, bypassing the exchange capillaries.

When the sphincters are relaxed (open), blood flows through the entire capillary bed, allowing exchanges with the cells of the surrounding tissue.

Connecting capillary beds: portal venous systems

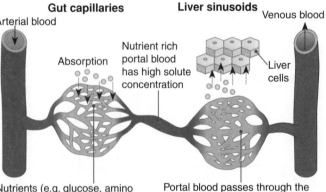

Nutrients (e.g. glucose, amino acids) and toxins are absorbed from the gut lumen into the capillaries.

Portal blood passes through the liver lobules where nutrients and toxins are absorbed, excreted, or converted.

A portal venous system occurs when a capillary bed drains into another capillary bed through veins, without first going through the heart. Portal systems are relatively uncommon; most capillary beds drain into veins which then drain into the heart, not into another capillary bed. The diagram above depicts the hepatic portal system, which includes both capillary beds and the blood vessels connecting them.

©2023 **BIOZONE** International
ISBN: 978-1-99-101408-5
Photocopying Prohibited

102 The Formation of Tissue Fluid

Key Idea: The network of capillaries supplying the body's tissues ensures that no substance has to diffuse far to enter or leave a cell.

As with all cells, substances can move into and out of the endothelial cells of the **capillary** walls in several ways: by diffusion, by cytosis, and through gaps where the membranes are not joined by tight junctions. Some capillaries are also more permeable than others. These specialized capillaries are important where absorption or filtration occurs, e.g. in the intestine or the kidney. Capillaries are leaky, so fluid flows across their plasma membranes. Whether fluid moves into or out of a capillary depends on the balance between the **blood (hydrostatic) pressure** and the concentration of solutes at each end of a capillary bed.

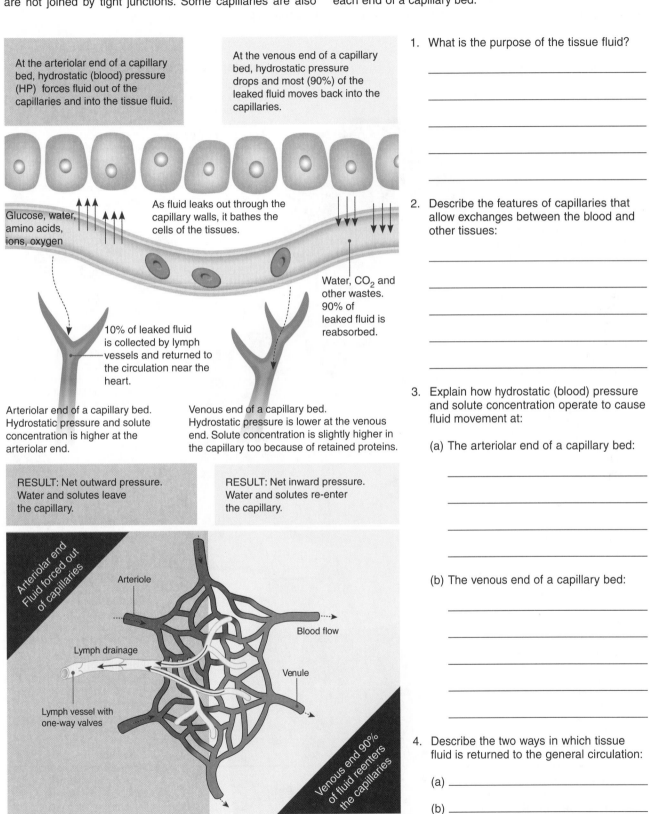

At the arteriolar end of a capillary bed, hydrostatic (blood) pressure (HP) forces fluid out of the capillaries and into the tissue fluid.

At the venous end of a capillary bed, hydrostatic pressure drops and most (90%) of the leaked fluid moves back into the capillaries.

Glucose, water, amino acids, ions, oxygen

As fluid leaks out through the capillary walls, it bathes the cells of the tissues.

Water, CO₂ and other wastes. 90% of leaked fluid is reabsorbed.

10% of leaked fluid is collected by lymph vessels and returned to the circulation near the heart.

Arteriolar end of a capillary bed. Hydrostatic pressure and solute concentration is higher at the arteriolar end.

Venous end of a capillary bed. Hydrostatic pressure is lower at the venous end. Solute concentration is slightly higher in the capillary too because of retained proteins.

RESULT: Net outward pressure. Water and solutes leave the capillary.

RESULT: Net inward pressure. Water and solutes re-enter the capillary.

Arteriolar end Fluid forced out of capillaries

Arteriole

Blood flow

Lymph drainage

Venule

Lymph vessel with one-way valves

Venous end 90% of fluid reenters the capillaries

1. What is the purpose of the tissue fluid?

_____

_____

_____

_____

_____

_____

2. Describe the features of capillaries that allow exchanges between the blood and other tissues:

_____

_____

_____

_____

_____

3. Explain how hydrostatic (blood) pressure and solute concentration operate to cause fluid movement at:

(a) The arteriolar end of a capillary bed:

_____

_____

_____

_____

(b) The venous end of a capillary bed:

_____

_____

_____

_____

_____

4. Describe the two ways in which tissue fluid is returned to the general circulation:

(a) _____

(b) _____

As described above, not all the fluid reenters the capillaries at the venous end of the capillary bed. This extra fluid is collected by the lymphatic vessels, a network of vessels alongside the blood vessels. Once the fluid enters the lymphatic vessels it is called lymph. The lymphatic vessels drain into the subclavian **vein** near the heart. Lymph is similar to tissue fluid but has more lymphocytes.

103 Blood

Key Idea: Blood is a complex liquid tissue comprising cellular components suspended in plasma, making up about 8% of body weight.

If a **blood** sample is taken, the cells can be separated from the plasma by centrifugation. The cells settle as a dense red pellet below the transparent, straw-colored **plasma**. Blood performs many functions: it transports nutrients, respiratory gases, hormones, and wastes and has a role in thermoregulation through the distribution of heat. Blood also defends against infection and its ability to clot protects against blood loss. The examination of blood is also useful in diagnosing disease. The cellular components of blood are normally present in particular specified ratios. A change in the morphology, type, or proportion of different blood cells can therefore be used to indicate a specific disorder or infection (see following page).

Non-cellular blood components

The non-cellular blood components form the plasma. Plasma is a watery matrix of ions and proteins and makes up 50-60% of the total blood volume.

Water
The main constituent of blood and lymph.
Role: Transports dissolved substances. Provides body cells with water. Distributes heat and has a central role in thermoregulation. Regulation of water content helps to regulate blood pressure and volume.

Mineral ions
Sodium, bicarbonate, magnesium, potassium, calcium, chloride.
Role: Osmotic balance, pH buffering, and regulation of membrane permeability. They also have a variety of other functions, e.g. Ca^{2+} is involved in blood clotting.

Plasma proteins
7-9% of the plasma volume.
Serum albumin
Role: Osmotic balance and pH buffering, Ca^{2+} transport.
Fibrinogen and prothrombin
Role: Take part in blood clotting.
Immunoglobulins
Role: Antibodies involved in the immune response.
α-globulins
Role: Bind/transport hormones, lipids, fat soluble vitamins.
β-globulins
Role: Bind/transport iron, cholesterol, fat soluble vitamins.
Enzymes
Role: Take part in and regulate metabolic activities.

Substances transported by non-cellular components
Products of digestion
Sugars, fatty acids, glycerol, and amino acids.
Excretory products
Urea.
Hormones and vitamins
Insulin, sex hormones.
Vitamins A and B12
These substances occur at varying levels in the blood. They are transported to and from the cells dissolved in the plasma or bound to plasma proteins.

Cellular blood components

The cellular components of the blood (also called the formed elements) float in the plasma and make up 40-50% of the total blood volume.

Erythrocytes (red blood cells or RBCs)
5-6 million per mm^3 blood; 38-48% of total blood volume.
Role: RBCs transport oxygen (O_2) and a small amount of carbon dioxide (CO_2). The oxygen is carried by being bound to hemoglobin (Hb) in the cells. Each Hb molecule can bind four molecules of oxygen.

7- 8 μm

Platelets
Small, membrane-bound cell fragments derived from bone marrow cells; about 1/4 the size of RBCs.
0.25 million per mm^3 blood.
Role: To start the blood clotting process.

2 μm

Lymphocytes
T and B cells.
24% of the white cell count.
Role: Antibody production and cell mediated immunity.

Neutrophils
Phagocytes.
70% of the white cell count.
Role: Engulf foreign material.

Eosinophils
Rare leukocytes; normally 1.5% of the white cell count.
Role: Mediate allergic responses, such as hayfever and asthma.

Basophils
Rare leukocytes; normally 0.5% of the white cell count.
Role: Produce heparin (an anti-clotting protein), and histamine. Involved in inflammation.

©2023 **BIOZONE** International
ISBN: 978-1-99-101408-5
Photocopying Prohibited

The examination of blood

Different types of microscopy give different information about blood. A SEM (right) shows the detailed, external morphology of the blood cells. A fixed smear of a blood sample viewed with a light microscope (far right) can be used to identify the different blood cell types present, and their ratio to each other. Determining the types and proportions of different white blood cells in blood is called a differential white blood cell count. Elevated counts of particular cell types indicate allergy or infection.

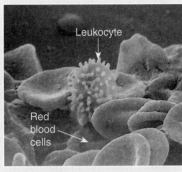

SEM of red blood cells and a leukocyte.

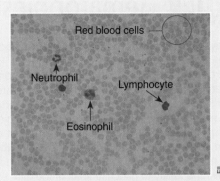

Light microscope view of a fixed blood smear.

1. For each of the following blood functions, identify the component (or components) of the blood responsible and state how the function is carried out (the mode of action). The first one is done for you:

   (a) Temperature regulation. Blood component: _Water component of the plasma_

   Mode of action: _Water absorbs heat and dissipates it from sites of production (i.e. organs)_

   (b) Protection against disease. Blood component: _____

   Mode of action: _____

   (c) Communication between cells, tissues, and organs. Blood component: _____

   Mode of action: _____

   (d) Oxygen transport. Blood component: _____

   Mode of action: _____

   (e) CO_2 transport. Blood component: _____

   Mode of action: _____

   (f) Nutrient supply. Blood component: _____

   Mode of action: _____

   (g) Tissue repair. Blood component: _____

   Mode of action: _____

   (h) Transport of hormones, lipids, and fat soluble vitamins. Blood component: _____

   Mode of action: _____

2. Identify a feature that distinguishes red and white blood cells: _____

   _____

   _____

3. Explain two physiological advantages of red blood cell structure (lacking nucleus and mitochondria):

   (a) _____

   (b) _____

4. Describe what each of the following results from a differential white blood cell count would suggest:

   (a) Elevated levels of eosinophils (above the normal range): _____

   (b) Elevated levels of neutrophils (above the normal range): _____

   (c) Elevated levels of basophils (above the normal range): _____

   (d) Elevated levels of lymphocytes (above the normal range): _____

104 Hematopoiesis

Key Idea: Hematopoiesis (also called hemopoiesis) refers to the formation of blood cells.

All cellular **blood** components are derived from hematopoietic stem cells (HSCs). In a healthy adult person, approximately 10^{11}-10^{12} new blood cells are produced every day in order to maintain homeostasis of the peripheral circulation. Before birth, **hematopoiesis** occurs in aggregates of blood cells in the yolk sac, then the liver, and eventually the bone marrow. In normal adults, HSCs reside in the red bone marrow and have the ability to give rise to all of the different mature blood cell types. Like all stem cells, HSCs can divide many times while remaining unspecialized and, when given the right signals, they can differentiate into other cell types. When they proliferate, some of the daughter cells remain as HSCs and some give rise to progenitor cells. The progenitor cells then each commit to any of the alternative differentiation pathways that lead to the production of one or more types of blood cells. Blood cells are divided into lineages. Erythroid cells are the oxygen carrying red blood cells. Lymphoid cells are the white blood cells of the adaptive immune system. They are derived from common lymphoid progenitors. Myeloid cells are derived from common myeloid progenitors, and are involved in many diverse roles within the body's defense system.

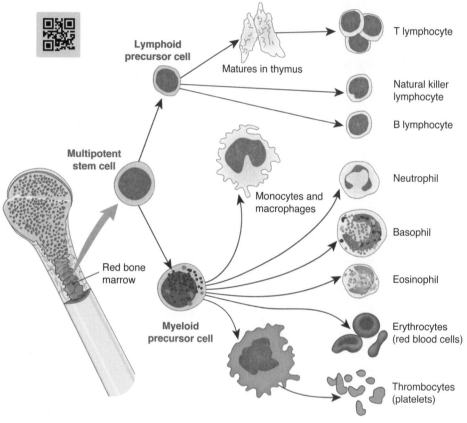

Stem cells and blood cell production

▶ New blood cells are produced in the red bone marrow, which becomes the main site of blood production after birth, taking over from the fetal liver.

▶ All types of blood cells develop from a single cell type called a multi-potent stem cell or hemocytoblast. These cells are capable of mitosis and of differentiation into 'committed' precursors of each of the main types of blood cell. Each of the different cell lines is controlled by a specific growth factor.

▶ When a stem cell divides, one of its daughters remains a stem cell, while the other becomes a precursor cell, either a lymphoid cell or myeloid cell. These cells continue to mature into the various type of blood cells, developing their specialized features and characteristic roles as they do so.

1. Where are new blood cells produced in the body:

   (a) Before birth? _____

   (b) After birth? _____

2. Identify the blood cell types arising from each of the progenitor cell types:

   (a) Myeloid progenitor cells: _____

   _____

   (b) Lymphoid progenitor cells: _____

   _____

3. (a) Using an example, explain the purpose of stem cells in an adult: _____

   _____

   _____

   (b) Identify where else in the body, apart from the red bone marrow, you might find stem cells: _____

   _____

 ©2023 **BIOZONE** International
ISBN: 978-1-99-101408-5
Photocopying Prohibited

105 Exercise and Blood Flow

Key Idea: Exercise promotes health by improving the rate of blood flow back to the heart (venous return).
A healthier and stronger heart is achieved by strengthening all types of muscle and by increasing the efficiency of the heart. During exercise, **blood** flow to different parts of the body changes in order to cope with the extra demands of the muscles, the heart, and the lungs.

1. The following table gives data for the rate of blood flow to various parts of the body at rest and during strenuous exercise. Calculate the percentage of the total blood flow that each organ or tissue receives under each different regime of activity. The first row has been completed for you:

Organ or tissue	At rest		Strenuous exercise	
	cm^3/min	% of total	cm^3/min	% of total
Brain	700	14	750	4.2
Heart	200		750	
Lung tissue	100		200	
Kidneys	1100		600	
Liver	1350		600	
Skeletal muscles	750		12 500	
Bone	250		250	
Skin	300		1900	
Thyroid gland	50		50	
Adrenal glands	25		25	
Other tissue	175		175	
TOTAL	5000	100	17 800	100

2. Explain how the body increases the rate of blood flow during exercise: _____
_____
_____

3. (a) State approximately how many times the total rate of blood flow increases between rest and exercise: _____

   (b) Explain why the increase is necessary: _____
   _____
   _____

4. (a) Identify which organs or tissues show no change in the rate of blood flow with exercise: _____
   _____

   (b) Explain why this is the case: _____
   _____
   _____

5. (a) Identify the organs or tissues that show the most change in the rate of blood flow with exercise: _____
   _____

   (b) Explain why this is the case: _____
   _____
   _____

©2023 **BIOZONE** International
ISBN: 978-1-99-101408-5
Photocopying Prohibited

106 Structure of the Mammalian Heart

Key Idea: Humans have a four chambered heart, divided into left and right halves, acting as a double pump.

The heart is the center of the human cardiovascular system. It is a hollow, muscular organ made up of four chambers (two atria and two ventricles) that alternately fill and empty with blood, acting as a double pump. The left side (systemic circuit) pumps blood to the body tissues and the right side (pulmonary circuit) pumps **blood** to the lungs. The heart lies between the lungs, to the left of the midline, and is surrounded by a double layered pericardium of connective tissue, which prevents over-distension of the heart and anchors it within the central compartment of the thoracic cavity.

Human heart structure

(sectioned, anterior view)

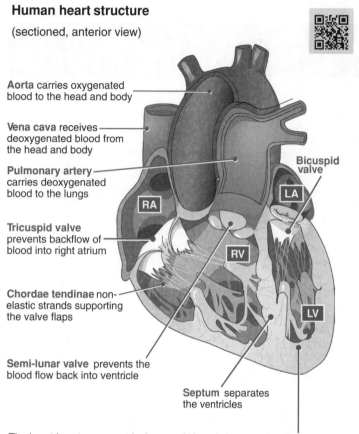

Aorta carries oxygenated blood to the head and body

Vena cava receives deoxygenated blood from the head and body

Pulmonary artery carries deoxygenated blood to the lungs

Tricuspid valve prevents backflow of blood into right atrium

Chordae tendinae non-elastic strands supporting the valve flaps

Semi-lunar valve prevents the blood flow back into ventricle

Bicuspid valve

RA

LA

RV

LV

Septum separates the ventricles

The heart is not a symmetrical organ. Although the quantity of blood pumped by each side is the same, the walls of the left ventricle are thicker and more muscular than those of the right ventricle. This difference affects the shape of the ventricular cavities, so the right ventricle is twisted over to the left.

RA	Right **atrium**: receives deoxygenated blood via the anterior and posterior vena cava.
RV	Right **ventricle**: pumps deoxygenated blood to the lungs via the pulmonary artery.
LA	Left atrium: receives blood returning to the heart from the lungs via the pulmonary veins.
LV	Left ventricle: pumps oxygenated blood to the head and body via the aorta.

Top view of a heart in section, showing valves

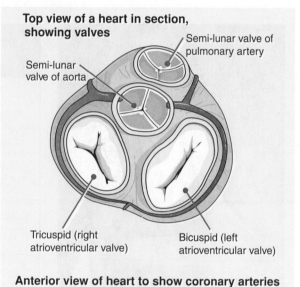

Semi-lunar valve of pulmonary artery

Semi-lunar valve of aorta

Tricuspid (right atrioventricular valve)

Bicuspid (left atrioventricular valve)

Anterior view of heart to show coronary arteries

Superior vena cava

Aorta

Pulmonary artery

Pulmonary veins

Right coronary artery

Pulmonary veins

Left coronary artery

Right cardiac vein

RV

LV

Inferior vena cava

Descending aorta

Left cardiac vein

Coronary arteries: the high oxygen demand of the heart muscle is met by a dense **capillary** network. Coronary **arteries** arise from the **aorta** and spread over the surface of the heart, supplying the cardiac muscle with oxygenated blood. Deoxygenated blood is collected by cardiac **veins** and returned to the right atrium via a large coronary sinus.

1. In the schematic diagram of the heart below, label the four chambers and the main vessels entering and leaving them. The arrows indicate the direction of blood flow.

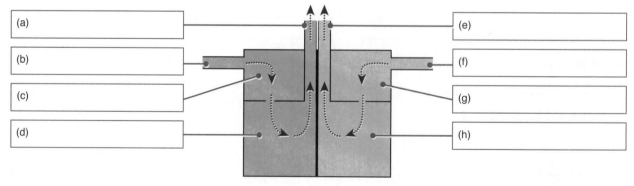

(a)
(b)
(c)
(d)
(e)
(f)
(g)
(h)

©2023 **BIOZONE** International
ISBN: 978-1-99-101408-5
Photocopying Prohibited

Pressure changes and the asymmetry of the heart

The heart is not a symmetrical organ. The left ventricle and its associated arteries are thicker and more muscular than the corresponding structures on the right side. This asymmetry is related to the necessary pressure differences between the pulmonary (lung) and systemic (body) circulations, not to the distance over which the blood is pumped. The graph below shows changes in blood pressure in each of the major blood vessel types in the systemic and pulmonary circuits (the horizontal distance is not to scale). The pulmonary circuit must operate at a much lower pressure than the systemic circuit to prevent fluid from accumulating in the alveoli of the lungs. The left side of the heart must develop enough "spare" pressure to enable increased blood flow to the muscles of the body and maintain kidney filtration rates without decreasing the blood supply to the brain.

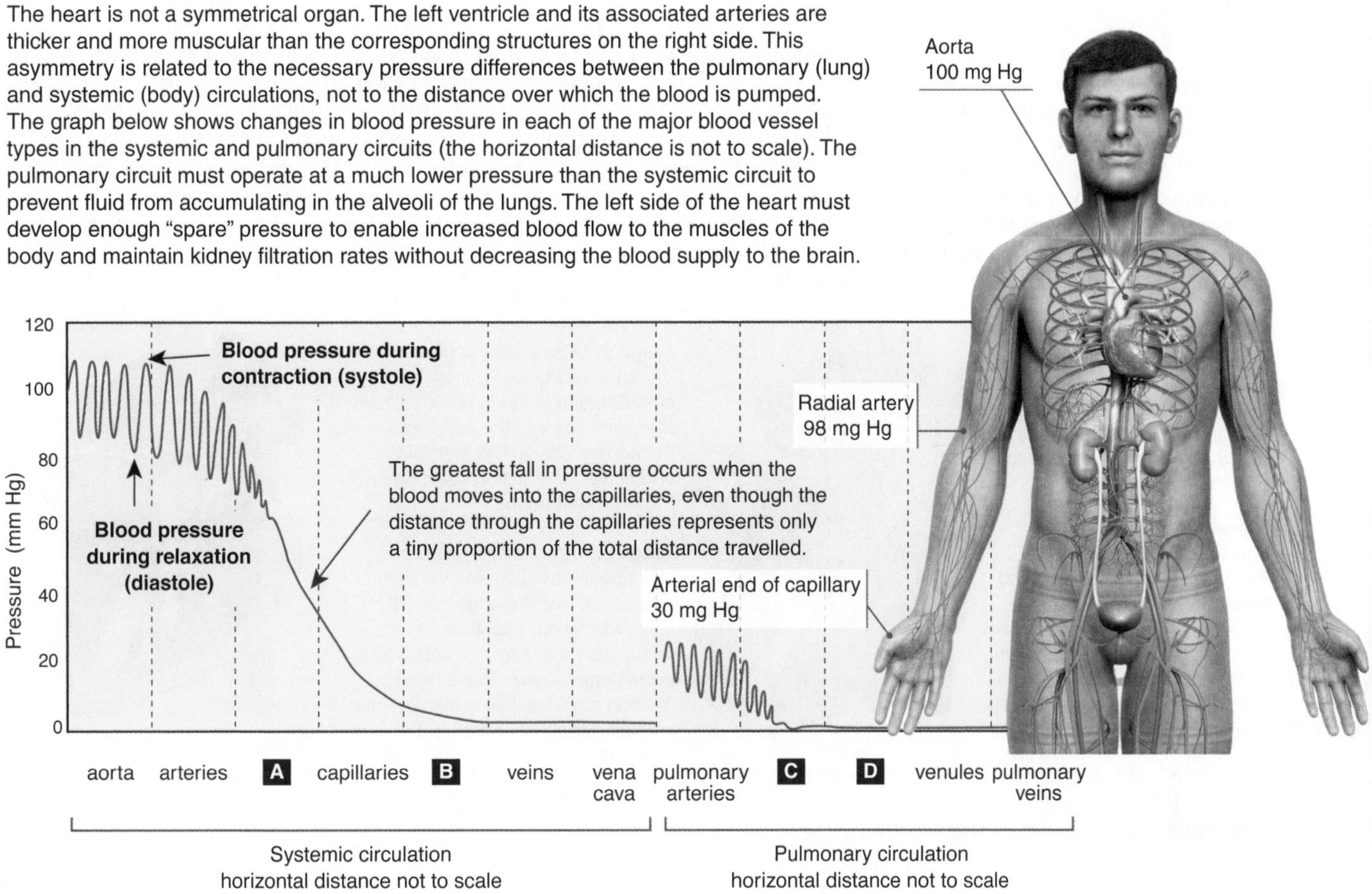

Aorta
100 mg Hg

Radial artery
98 mg Hg

Blood pressure during contraction (systole)

Blood pressure during relaxation (diastole)

The greatest fall in pressure occurs when the blood moves into the capillaries, even though the distance through the capillaries represents only a tiny proportion of the total distance travelled.

Arterial end of capillary
30 mg Hg

aorta   arteries   **A**   capillaries   **B**   veins   vena cava   pulmonary arteries   **C**   **D**   venules   pulmonary veins

Systemic circulation
horizontal distance not to scale

Pulmonary circulation
horizontal distance not to scale

2. Explain the purpose of the valves in the heart: _____

_____

3. The heart is full of blood. Suggest two reasons why, despite this, it needs its own blood supply:

(a) _____

(b) _____

4. Predict the effect on the heart if blood flow through a coronary artery is restricted or blocked: _____

_____

_____

5. Identify the vessels corresponding to the letters A-D on the graph above:

A: _____   B: _____   C: _____   D: _____

6. (a) Explain why the pulmonary circuit must operate at a lower pressure than the systemic system: _____

_____

_____

_____

(b) Relate this to differences in the thickness of the wall of the left and right ventricles of the heart: _____

_____

_____

7. Explain what you are recording when you take a pulse: _____

_____

©2023 **BIOZONE** International
ISBN: 978-1-99-101408-5
Photocopying Prohibited

107 The Cardiac Cycle

Key Idea: The cardiac cycle refers to the sequence of events of a heartbeat and involves three main stages.

The heart pumps with alternate contractions (systole) and relaxations (diastole). Pressure changes within the heart's chambers generated by the cycle of contraction and relaxation are responsible for **blood** movement and cause the heart valves to open and close, preventing the back-flow of blood. The noise of the blood when the valves open and close produces the heartbeat sound (lubb-dupp). The heart beat occurs in response to electrical impulses, which can be recorded as a trace called an electrocardiogram or ECG. The ECG pattern is the result of the different impulses produced at each phase of the **cardiac cycle**, and each part is identified with a letter code. An ECG provides a useful method of monitoring changes in heart rate and activity and detection of heart disorders. The electrical trace is accompanied by volume and pressure changes (below).

The cardiac cycle

The pulse results from the rhythmic expansion of the arteries as the blood spurts from the left ventricle. Pulse rate therefore corresponds to heart rate.

Stage 1: Atrial contraction and ventricular filling
The ventricles relax and blood flows into them from the atria. Note that 70% of the blood from the atria flows passively into the ventricles. It is during the last third of ventricular filling that the atria contract.

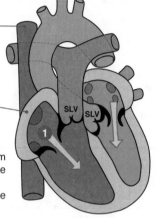

Heart during ventricular filling

Stage 2: Ventricular contraction
The atria relax, the ventricles contract, and blood is pumped from the ventricles into the aorta and the pulmonary artery. The start of ventricular contraction coincides with the first heart sound.

Stage 3: (not shown) There is a short period of atrial and ventricular relaxation. Semilunar valves (SLV) close to prevent backflow into the ventricles (see diagram, left). The cycle begins again. For a heart beating at 75 beats per minute, one cardiac cycle lasts about 0.8 seconds.

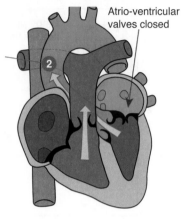

Atrio-ventricular valves closed

Heart during ventricular contraction

Cardiac cycle events in the left ventricle

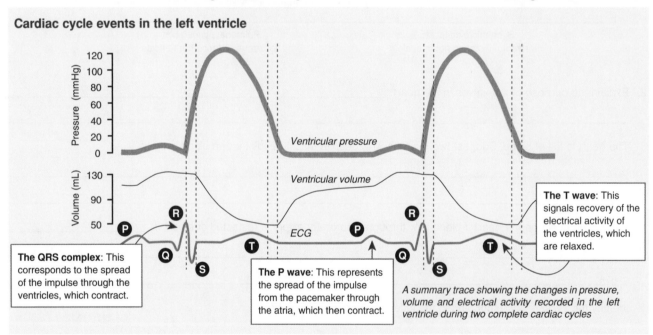

The QRS complex: This corresponds to the spread of the impulse through the ventricles, which contract.

The P wave: This represents the spread of the impulse from the pacemaker through the atria, which then contract.

The T wave: This signals recovery of the electrical activity of the ventricles, which are relaxed.

A summary trace showing the changes in pressure, volume and electrical activity recorded in the left ventricle during two complete cardiac cycles

1. Identify each of the following phases of an ECG by its international code:

   (a) Excitation of the ventricles and ventricular systole: _____

   (b) Electrical recovery of the ventricles and ventricular diastole: _____

   (c) Excitation of the atria and atrial systole: _____

2. Suggest the physiological reason for the period of electrical recovery experienced each cycle: _____

   _____

3. Identify the points on the trace above corresponding to each of the following, indicating which phase code(s) it is near:

   (a) Ejection of blood from the ventricle _____   (c) Filling of the ventricle _____

   (b) Closing of the atrioventricular valve _____   (d) Opening of the atrioventricular valve _____

©2023 **BIOZONE** International
ISBN: 978-1-99-101408-5
Photocopying Prohibited

108 Dissecting a Mammalian Heart

Key Idea: The dissection of a sheep's heart is a common practical activity and allows hands-on exploration of the physical appearance and structure of a mammalian heart.
A diagram of a heart is an idealized representation of an organ that may look quite different in reality. You must learn to transfer what you know from a diagram to the interpretation of the real organ. If you are lucky, you will have access to a fresh specimen, with most of the large vessels intact. The aim of this activity is to provide photographs of some aspects of a heart dissection to help you in identifying specific structures during your own dissection. It may also serve, in part, as a dissection replacement for those who, for personal reasons, do not wish to perform the dissection themselves.

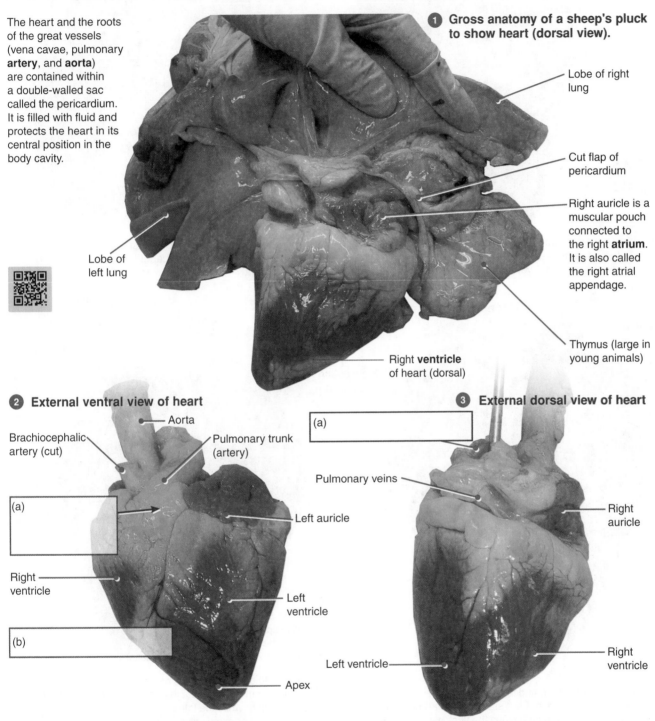

The heart and the roots of the great vessels (vena cavae, pulmonary **artery**, and **aorta**) are contained within a double-walled sac called the pericardium. It is filled with fluid and protects the heart in its central position in the body cavity.

① Gross anatomy of a sheep's pluck to show heart (dorsal view).

Lobe of right lung

Cut flap of pericardium

Right auricle is a muscular pouch connected to the right **atrium**. It is also called the right atrial appendage.

Thymus (large in young animals)

Lobe of left lung

Right **ventricle** of heart (dorsal)

② External ventral view of heart

Brachiocephalic artery (cut)

Aorta

Pulmonary trunk (artery)

Left auricle

(a)

Right ventricle

(b)

Left ventricle

Apex

③ External dorsal view of heart

(a)

Pulmonary veins

Right auricle

Left ventricle

Right ventricle

Note the main surface features of an isolated heart. The narrow pointed end forms the apex of the heart, while the wider end, where the blood vessels enter is the base. The ventral surface of the heart (above) is identified by a groove, the interventricular sulcus, which marks the division between the left and right ventricles. Fat and vessels sit within this groove.

1. Label the areas indicated in the external, ventral view of the heart above (a) and (b).

On the dorsal surface of the heart (above), locate the large thin-walled vena cavae and pulmonary **veins**. You may be able to distinguish between the anterior and posterior vessels. On the right side of the dorsal surface (as you look at the heart) at the base of the heart is the right atrium; the right ventricle is below it.

2. On the photograph above, label the vessel indicated by the probe (a).

4 Dorsal view of heart

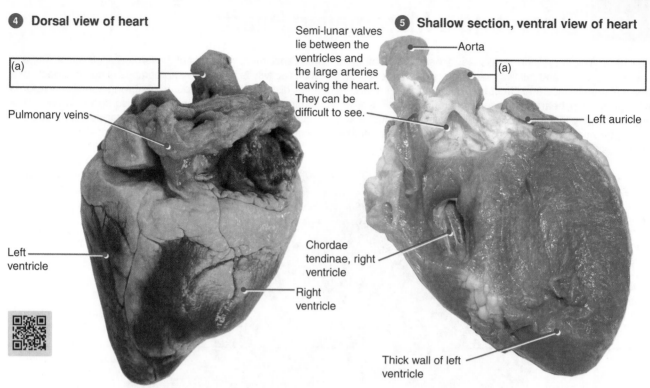

(a)

Pulmonary veins

Left ventricle

5 Shallow section, ventral view of heart

Semi-lunar valves lie between the ventricles and the large arteries leaving the heart. They can be difficult to see.

Aorta

(a)

Left auricle

Chordae tendinae, right ventricle

Right ventricle

Thick wall of left ventricle

3. On the dorsal view above, label the vessel indicated (a). Palpate the heart and feel the difference in the thickness of the left and right ventricle walls.

4. The photograph above shows a shallow section to expose the right ventricle. Label the vessel in the box indicated (a).

6 Frontal sections of heart to show chambers

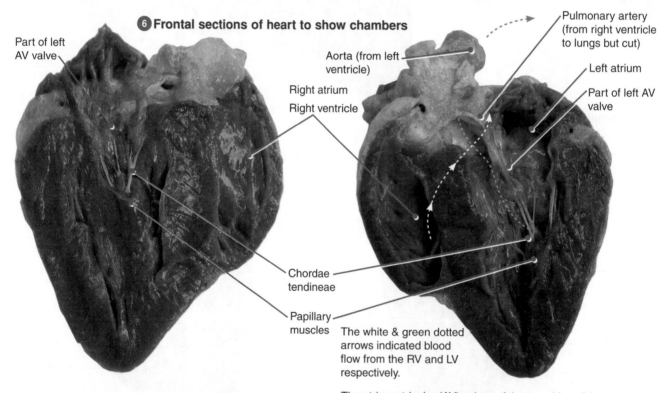

Part of left AV valve

Aorta (from left ventricle)

Right atrium

Right ventricle

Pulmonary artery (from right ventricle to lungs but cut)

Left atrium

Part of left AV valve

Chordae tendineae

Papillary muscles

The white & green dotted arrows indicated blood flow from the RV and LV respectively.

If the heart is sectioned and the two halves opened, the valves of the heart can be seen. Each side of the heart has a one-way valve between the atrium and the ventricle known as the atrioventricular valve. They close during ventricular contraction to prevent back-flow of the blood into the lower pressure atria.

The atrioventricular (AV) valves of the two sides of the heart are similar in structure except that the right AV valve has three cusps (tricuspid) while the left atrioventricular valve has two cusps (bicuspid or mitral valve). Connective tissue (chordae tendineae) runs from the cusps to papillary muscles on the ventricular wall.

5. Judging by their position and structure, what do you suppose is the function of the chordae tendineae?

_____

_____

6. What feature shown here most clearly distinguishes the left and right ventricles?

_____

_____

©2023 **BIOZONE** International
ISBN: 978-1-99-101408-5
Photocopying Prohibited

109 The Intrinsic Regulation of Heartbeat

Key Idea: The heartbeat is regulated by a conduction system consisting of specialized muscle cells called the pacemaker (sinoatrial node) and a tract of conducting Purkyne fibers. Given the right physiological conditions, an isolated heart will continue to beat. This shows that the origin of the heartbeat is myogenic (it can generate its own electrical impulse) and contraction is an intrinsic property of the cardiac muscle itself.

The pacemaker initiates the **cardiac cycle** by spontaneously generating action potentials. It sets a basic rhythm for the heart, although this rate is influenced by inputs from outside the heart itself in response to changing demands (see opposite). The diagram below illustrates the basic features of the heart's intrinsic control system.

Generation of the heartbeat

The basic rhythmic heartbeat is myogenic. The nodal cells (SAN and AVN - see diagram, right) spontaneously generate rhythmic action potentials without neural stimulation. The normal resting rate of self-excitation of the SAN is about 50 beats/min. The amount of **blood** ejected from the left **ventricle** per minute is called the cardiac output. It is determined by the stroke volume (the volume of blood ejected with each contraction) and the heart rate (number of heart beats per minute). Cardiac muscle responds to stretching by contracting more strongly. The greater the blood volume entering the ventricle, the greater the force of contraction. This relationship is known as Starling's Law of the heart and it is important in regulating stroke volume in response to demand.

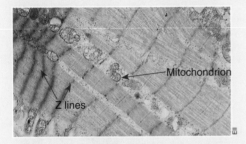

TEM of cardiac muscle showing striations in a fiber (muscle cell). Each fiber has one or two nuclei and many large mitochondria. Note the Z lines that delineate the contractile units (or sarcomeres) of the rod-like units (myofibrils) of the fiber. The fibers are joined by specialized electrical junctions called intercalated disks, which allow impulses to spread rapidly through the heart muscle.

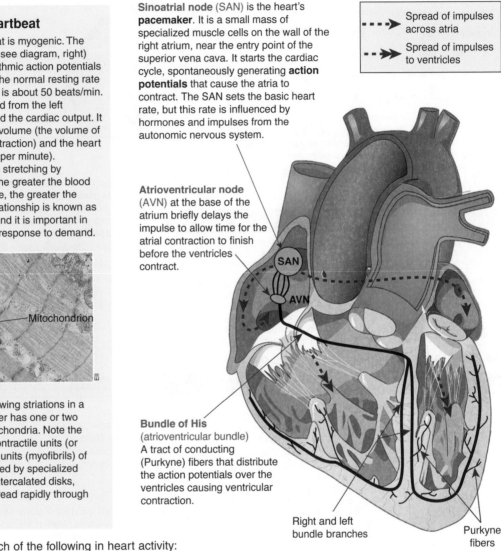

Sinoatrial node (SAN) is the heart's **pacemaker**. It is a small mass of specialized muscle cells on the wall of the right atrium, near the entry point of the superior vena cava. It starts the cardiac cycle, spontaneously generating **action potentials** that cause the atria to contract. The SAN sets the basic heart rate, but this rate is influenced by hormones and impulses from the autonomic nervous system.

Atrioventricular node (AVN) at the base of the atrium briefly delays the impulse to allow time for the atrial contraction to finish before the ventricles contract.

Bundle of His (atrioventricular bundle) A tract of conducting (Purkyne) fibers that distribute the action potentials over the ventricles causing ventricular contraction.

- - - - ▷ Spread of impulses across atria

- - - - ▶ Spread of impulses to ventricles

Right and left bundle branches

Purkyne fibers

1. Describe the role of each of the following in heart activity:

   (a) The sinoatrial node: _____

   (b) The atrioventricular node: _____

   (c) The bundle of His: _____

   (d) Intercalated discs: _____

2. What is the significance of delaying the impulse at the AVN? _____
   _____
   _____

3. (a) What is the physiological response of cardiac muscle to stretching? _____
   _____

   (b) What is the physiological advantage of this response? _____
   _____

110 Extrinsic Control of Heart Rate

Key Idea: The pacemaker sets the basic rhythm of the heart. This rate is influenced by the cardiovascular control center, primarily in response to sensory information from pressure receptors in the walls of the **blood** vessels entering and leaving the heart. Control of heart rate is complex and has some similarities to control of breathing rate. This is not surprising, given the importance of both systems in supplying oxygen to the tissues. However, the main trigger for changing the basic heart rate is change in blood pressure, whereas the main trigger for changing the basic rhythm of breathing is change in blood CO_2.

Cardiovascular control ....

Increase in rate   **+**

Decrease in rate   **−**

Higher brain centers influence the cardiovascular center, e.g. excitement or anticipation of an event.

Baroreceptors in **aorta**, carotid **arteries**, and vena cava give feedback to cardiovascular center on blood pressure. Blood pressure is directly related to the pumping action of the heart.

Cardiovascular center responds directly to norepinephrine (noradrenaline) and to low pH (high CO_2). It sends output to the sinoatrial node (SAN) to increase heart rate. Changing the rate and force of heart contraction is the main mechanism for controlling cardiac output in order to meet changing demands.

+ or **−**

Sympathetic output to heart via cardiac nerve increases heart rate. Sympathetic output predominates during exercise or stress. **+**

Parasympathetic output to heart via vagus nerve decreases heart rate. Parasympathetic (vagal) output predominates during rest. **−**

Influences on heart rate

Increase	Decrease
Increased physical activity	Decreased physical activity
Decrease in blood pressure	Increase in blood pressure
Secretion of epinephrine or norepinephrine	Re-uptake and metabolism of epinephrine or norepinephrine
Increase in H^+ or CO_2 concentrations in blood	Decrease in H^+ or CO_2 concentrations in blood

Reflex responses to changes in blood pressure

Reflex	Receptor	Stimulus	Response
Bainbridge reflex	Pressure receptors in vena cava and atrium	Stretch caused by increased venous return	Increase heart rate
Carotid reflex	Pressure receptors in the carotid arteries	Stretch caused by increased arterial flow	Decrease heart rate
Aortic reflex	Pressure receptors in the aorta	Stretch caused by increased arterial flow	Decrease heart rate

Extrinsic input to SAN

Opposing actions keep blood pressure within narrow limits

The intrinsic rhythm of the heart is influenced by the cardiovascular center, which receives input from sensory neurons and hormones.

1. Explain how each of the following extrinsic factors influences the basic intrinsic rhythm of the heart:

    (a) Increased venous return: _____

    (b) Release of epinephrine in anticipation of an event: _____

    (c) Increase in blood CO_2: _____

2. How do these extrinsic factors bring about their effects? _____
   _____

3. (a) Identify the nerve that brings about increased heart rate: _____

    (b) Identify the nerve that brings about decreased heart rate: _____

4. Account for the different responses to stretch in the vena cava and the aorta: _____
   _____
   _____

©2023 **BIOZONE** International
ISBN: 978-1-99-101408-5
Photocopying Prohibited

111 Stress and Heart Rate

Key Idea: The body releases hormones in response to stressors, called the "fight or flight" response and it puts the body on high alert and ready to respond quickly.

An important part of the fight or flight response is acceleration in heart rate. The heart's intrinsic rate of beating is influenced by higher brain function and by the cardiovascular control center in the medulla in response to sensory information.

Thus, when the body needs more oxygen, heart rate (as well as lung ventilation rate) will increase. Changes in the rate and force of heart contraction alter the cardiac output, i.e. the amount of **blood** pumped by the heart. When the body needs to prepare for physical exertion, cardiac output increases to meet the greater demand for gas exchange. Both nervous and endocrine controls are involved in regulating these changes.

Stress hormones and heart rate

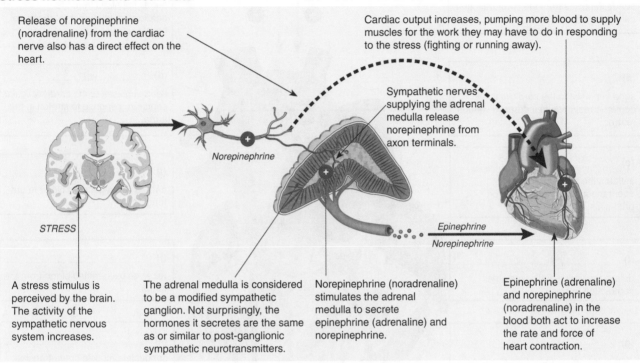

Release of norepinephrine (noradrenaline) from the cardiac nerve also has a direct effect on the heart.

Cardiac output increases, pumping more blood to supply muscles for the work they may have to do in responding to the stress (fighting or running away).

Sympathetic nerves supplying the adrenal medulla release norepinephrine from axon terminals.

Norepinephrine

STRESS

Epinephrine
Norepinephrine

A stress stimulus is perceived by the brain. The activity of the sympathetic nervous system increases.

The adrenal medulla is considered to be a modified sympathetic ganglion. Not surprisingly, the hormones it secretes are the same as or similar to post-ganglionic sympathetic neurotransmitters.

Norepinephrine (noradrenaline) stimulates the adrenal medulla to secrete epinephrine (adrenaline) and norepinephrine.

Epinephrine (adrenaline) and norepinephrine (noradrenaline) in the blood both act to increase the rate and force of heart contraction.

1. (a) Describe the effect of sympathetic nervous system stimulation of the heart: _____

   _____

   (b) Identify the hormones involved in this response: _____

2. Explain the adaptive value of an elevated heart rate during the "fight or flight" response: _____

   _____

   _____

3. Explain the role of norepinephrine as both a neurotransmitter and a hormone in the regulation of heart rate: _____

   _____

   _____

   _____

   _____

4. (a) What happens to the body's "high alert' system when the stress is removed? _____

   _____

   (b) Predict the consequences of continued stress without any resolution: _____

   _____

   _____

   _____

112 Review of the Human Heart

Key Idea: The heart has specific structures to carry out the role of moving blood around the body.

The heart enables the **circulatory system** to transport materials because diffusion is too inefficient and slow to supply all the cells of the body adequately. The circulatory system in humans transports nutrients, respiratory gases,

wastes, and hormones, aids in regulating body temperature and maintaining fluid balance, and has a role in internal defense. This activity summarizes key features of the structure and function of the human heart. The necessary information can be found in earlier activities in this chapter.

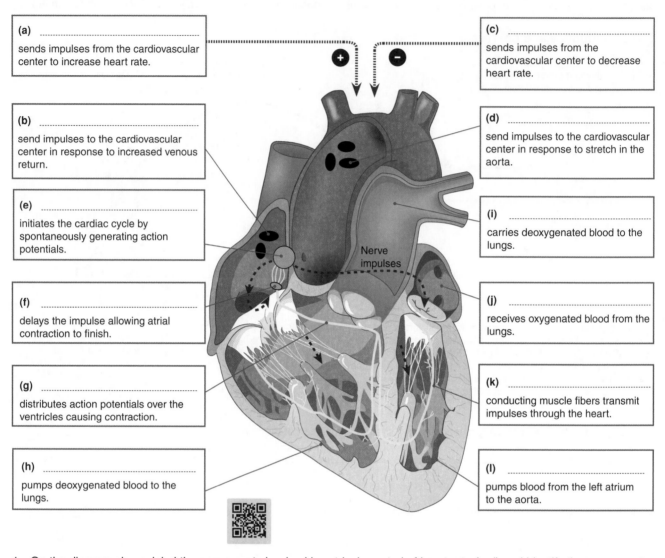

(a) ....
sends impulses from the cardiovascular center to increase heart rate.

(b) ....
send impulses to the cardiovascular center in response to increased venous return.

(e) ....
initiates the cardiac cycle by spontaneously generating action potentials.

(f) ....
delays the impulse allowing atrial contraction to finish.

(g) ....
distributes action potentials over the ventricles causing contraction.

(h) ....
pumps deoxygenated blood to the lungs.

(c) ....
sends impulses from the cardiovascular center to decrease heart rate.

(d) ....
send impulses to the cardiovascular center in response to stretch in the aorta.

(i) ....
carries deoxygenated blood to the lungs.

(j) ....
receives oxygenated blood from the lungs.

(k) ....
conducting muscle fibers transmit impulses through the heart.

(l) ....
pumps blood from the left atrium to the aorta.

Nerve impulses

1. On the diagram above, label the components involved in extrinsic control of heart rate (a-d) and identify the components of heart structure and intrinsic control (e-l).

2. An ECG is the result of different impulses produced at each phase of the cardiac cycle (the sequence of events in a heartbeat). For each electrical event indicated in the ECG below, describe the corresponding event in the cardiac cycle:

   (a) The spread of the impulse from the pacemaker (sinoatrial node) through the atria: _____

   (b) The spread of the impulse through the ventricles: _____

   (c) Recovery of the electrical activity of the ventricles: _____

3. (a) On the trace (right), between which letters is the ventricular pressure highest?

   _____

   (b) What is happening to the ventricular volume at this time in this region?

   _____

   _____

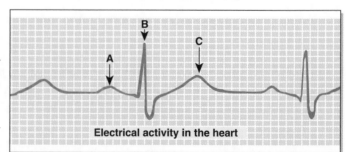

Electrical activity in the heart

©2023 **BIOZONE** International
ISBN: 978-1-99-101408-5

113 Investigating Cardiovascular Physiology

Key Idea: Cardiovascular fitness can be evaluated by measuring responses to changes in body position.
When lying down, heart rate decreases and blood vessels dilate. As you stand up there is a sudden decrease in blood pressure as gravity pulls **blood** towards your feet. The cardiovascular system must compensate for this by increasing heart rate and constricting the blood vessels. Its ability to do this can be measured using the Schneider index, a test of circulatory efficiency, which gives a score out of 18 (table 4, next page). In pairs, perform the following activity in the classroom to measure your own cardiovascular fitness.

The Schneider index uses both heart rate and blood pressure to determine circulatory efficiency. Blood pressure can be assessed using a sphygmomanometer. Heart rate in beats per minute (bpm) can be obtained from measuring the pulse for 30 seconds and doubling the number of pulses recorded. The pulse can be easily felt on the wrist just under the thumb or on the carotid artery on the neck just beneath the jaw.

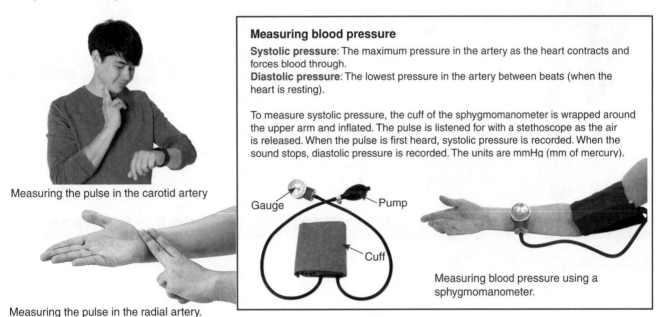

Measuring the pulse in the carotid artery

Measuring the pulse in the radial artery.

Measuring blood pressure

Systolic pressure: The maximum pressure in the artery as the heart contracts and forces blood through.
Diastolic pressure: The lowest pressure in the artery between beats (when the heart is resting).

To measure systolic pressure, the cuff of the sphygmomanometer is wrapped around the upper arm and inflated. The pulse is listened for with a stethoscope as the air is released. When the pulse is first heard, systolic pressure is recorded. When the sound stops, diastolic pressure is recorded. The units are mmHg (mm of mercury).

Gauge | Pump | Cuff

Measuring blood pressure using a sphygmomanometer.

Finding your score

Step 1

Have your lab partner lie down for five minutes before measuring and recording their heart rate and blood pressure on a separate sheet. For a heart rate (bpm) between 50-70 score 3 points, 71-80: 2 points, 81-90: 1 point, 91-100: 0 points, and 101-110+: -1 point. Record their score in table 5 (on the next page).

Step 2

Have your partner stand up and immediately measure their heart rate. Take this as their normal heart rate. For a heart rate between 61-80 bpm score 3 points, 81-90: 2 points, 91-110: 1 point, 111-130, 0 points, 131-140: -1 point.
After two minutes standing up, measure your partner's blood pressure and record it on a separate sheet. Use table 1 to score points for your partner based on how much systolic blood pressure changed upon standing, and table 2 to score points based on how much heart rate increased upon standing. Record the scores in table 5.

Table 1: Change in systolic pressure from reclining to standing	
Change in pressure	Points
Increase 8+ mmHg	3
Increase 2-7 mmHg	2
0 (+/- 1 mmHg)	1
Fall 2-5 mmHg	0
Fall 6+ mmHg	-1

Table 2: Difference in heart rate between standing and reclining					
Reclining rate (bpm)	Difference in pulse (bpm)				
	0-10	11-18	19-26	27-34	25-43
50-60	3	3	2	1	0
61-70	3	2	1	0	-1
71-80	3	2	0	-1	-2
81-90	2	1	-1	-2	-3
91-100	1	0	-2	-3	-3
101-110	0	-1	-3	-3	-3

Step 3

Use the height of a standard school chair for the following activity.

Have your partner step up onto the chair in the following pattern: right foot onto the chair followed by the left, then left foot back down to the floor followed by the right. Repeat this five times allowing no more than three seconds for each repetition. Immediately after the exercise, record your partner's heart rate for 15 seconds and multiply by four. Record the heart rate on a separate sheet. Record the heart rates at 30, 60, 90, and 120 seconds after the exercise, then for every 30 seconds until the pulse returns to normal.

Use table 3 to score your partner, based on the difference between heart rate immediately after the exercise and normal heart rate. For a heart rate that took between 0-30 seconds to return to normal score 3 points, 31-60 seconds: 2 points; 61-90 seconds: 1 point; 91-120 seconds: 0 points; and greater than 120 seconds: -1 point.

Score

1. Add all the points together and record them at the bottom of table 5 in your partner's workbook. Match this score to the scores in table 4 and rate your partner's cardiovascular fitness.

Table 3: Difference in normal and post-exercise heart rate

Standing rate (bpm)	Difference in pulse (bpm)				
	0-10	11-20	21-30	31-40	>40
61-70	3	3	2	1	0
71-80	3	2	1	0	-1
81-90	3	2	1	-1	-2
91-100	2	1	0	-2	-3
101-110	1	0	-1	-3	-3
111-120	1	-1	-2	-3	-3
121-130	0	-2	-3	-3	-3
131-140	0	-3	-3	-3	-3

Table 4: Scores cardiovascular fitness

Total score	Rating
17-18	Excellent
14-16	Good
8-13	Fair
0-7	Poor
Negative value	!!!!!

Table 5: Your scores

	Points
Reclining heart rate	
Change in systolic pressure	
Standing heart rate	
Difference in heart rate between standing and reclining	
Difference in normal and post-exercise heart rate	
Time for pulse to return to normal	
Score:	

2. The graph (right) compares the change in cardiac output (a measure of total blood flow in L) during rest and during exercise. The color of the bars indicates the proportion of blood flow in skeletal muscle relative to other body parts.

■ Blood flow to muscle

▢ Blood flow to other body parts

(a) What percentage of the blood goes to the muscles at rest?

_____

_____

(b) What percentage of the blood goes to the muscles during exercise?

_____

_____

Cardiac output (L)

Total 5.5 L: muscle 0.9 L

Resting

Total 22.5 L: muscle 17 L

Heavy exercise

3. (a) What happens to the total blood flow during heavy exercise compared to at rest? _____

_____

_____

(b) Why does this occur? _____

_____

(c) What would be happening to breathing rate during this time? _____

©2023 **BIOZONE** International
ISBN: 978-1-99-101408-5
Photocopying Prohibited

114 The Effects of Aerobic Training

Key Idea: The body has an immediate response to exercise, but over time responds to the stress of repeated exercise (or training) by adapting and improving both its capacity for exercise and the efficiency with which it performs.

Regular, intense exercise causes predictable physiological changes in muscular, cardiovascular, and respiratory performance. The heart adapts so that it can pump more **blood** per stroke. This increase in cardiac output is brought about not only by an increase in heart rate, but also by a training-induced increase in the stroke volume. The **circulatory system** also adapts to repeated exercise, with changes in blood flow facilitating an increased flow of blood to the muscles and skin and an increased rate of gas exchange. The pulmonary system adjusts accordingly, with greater efficiencies in ventilation rate and breathing rhythm.

The physiological effects of aerobic training

The pulmonary system

- Improvement in lung ventilation rate. The rate and depth of breathing increases during exercise but for any given level of exercise, the ventilation response is reduced with training.
- Improvement in ventilation rhythm, so that breathing is in tune with the exercise rhythm. This promotes efficiency.

Overall result
Improved exchange of gases.

The muscular system

- Improvement in aerobic generation of ATP.
- Larger mitochondria.
- More mitochondria.
- Increase in muscle myoglobin.
- Greater Krebs cycle enzyme activity.
- Improved ability to use fats as fuels.
- Increased capillary density.

Overall result
Improved function of the oxidative system and better endurance.

The cardiovascular system

- Exercise lowers blood plasma volume by as much as 20% and the cellular portion of the blood becomes concentrated. With training, blood volume at rest increases to compensate.
- Heart rate increases during exercise but aerobic training leads to a lower steady state heart rate overall for any given level of work.
- Increase in stroke volume (the amount of blood pumped with each beat). This is related to an increased heart capacity, an increase in the heart's force of contraction, and an increase in venous return.
- Increased cardiac output as a result of the increase in stroke volume.
- During exercise, systolic blood pressure increases as a result of increased cardiac output. In response to training, the resting systolic blood pressure is lowered.
- Blood flow changes during exercise so that more blood is diverted to working muscles and less is delivered to the gut.

Overall result
Meets the increased demands of exercise most efficiently.

1. (a) State what you understand by the term training: _____

    _____

    (b) In general terms, explain how training forces a change in physiology: _____

    _____

2. With respect to increasing functional efficiency, describe the role of each of the following effects of aerobic training:

    (a) Increase in stroke volume and cardiac output: _____

    _____

    _____

    (b) Increased ventilation efficiency: _____

    _____

Endurance refers to the ability to carry out sustained activity. Muscular strength and short term muscular endurance allows sprinters to run fast for a short time or body builders and weight lifters to lift an immense weight and hold it. Cardiovascular and respiratory endurance refer to the body as a whole; it is the ability to endure a high level of activity over a prolonged period. This type of endurance is seen in marathon runners, long distance swimmers, and cyclists.

Sprint-focused sports demand quite different training to that required for endurance sports, and the physiologies and builds of the athletes are quite different. Therefore, a body builder ready for a competition would be ill-equipped to complete a 90 km cycle race!

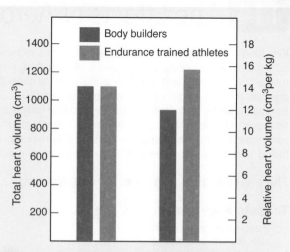

LocalFitness Pty Ltd

2008's Mr Olympia winner, Dexter Jackson: high muscular development and endurance.

Difference in heart size of highly trained body builders and endurance athletes. Total heart volume is compared to heart volume as related to body weight. Average weights as follows:
Body builders = 90.1 kg. Endurance athletes = 68.7 kg.

Distance runners have very good cardiovascular, respiratory, and muscular endurance; they sustain high intensity exercise for a long time. Typical sports needing overall endurance are distance running, cycling, and swimming. Triathletes combine all three.

3. Explain why heart size increases with endurance activity: _____
_____
_____

4. In the graph above right, explain why the relative heart volume of endurance athletes is greater than that of body builders, even though their total heart volumes are the same:
_____
_____

5. Heart stroke volume increases with endurance training. Explain how this increases the efficiency of the heart as a pump:
_____
_____
_____

6. The resting pulse is much lower in trained athletes compared with non-active people. Explain the health benefits of a lower resting pulse:
_____
_____
_____
_____

©2023 **BIOZONE** International
ISBN: 978-1-99-101408-5
Photocopying Prohibited

115 Cardiovascular Disease

Key Idea: Cardiovascular disease (CVD) describes all diseases affecting the heart and blood vessels.

It includes coronary heart disease, atherosclerosis (hardening of the arteries), hypertension (high blood pressure), peripheral vascular disease, stroke (reduced **blood** supply to the brain), and congenital heart disorders. CVD causes 20% of all deaths worldwide and is the principal cause of deaths in developed countries. Most CVD develops as a result of lifestyle factors, but a small proportion of the population (< 1%), are born with a CVD. This is called a congenital disorder. There are many types of congenital heart defects. Some obstruct blood flow in the heart or vessels near it, whereas others cause blood to flow through the heart in an abnormal pattern.

Atherosclerosis

Atherosclerosis (hardening of the arteries) is caused by deposits of fats and cholesterol in the inner walls of the arteries (see p205). Blood flow becomes restricted and increases the risk of blood clots (thrombosis). Complications arising as a result of atherosclerosis include heart attack (infarction), gangrene, and stroke. A stroke is the rapid loss of brain function due to a disturbance in the blood supply to the brain, and may result in death if the damage is severe. Speech, or vision and movement on one side of the body is often affected.

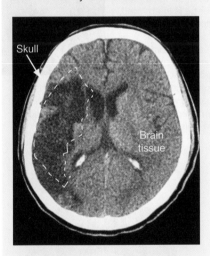

The CT scan (above) shows a brain affected by a severe cerebral infarction or ischemic stroke. The loss of blood supply results in tissue death (outlined area). Blood clots resulting from atherosclerosis are a common cause of ischemic stroke.

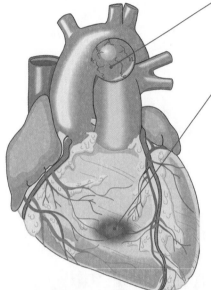

Aortic aneurysm

A ballooning and weakening of the wall of the **aorta**. Aneurysms usually result from generalized heart disease and high blood pressure.

Myocardial infarction

Otherwise known as a heart attack; this occurs when an area of the heart is deprived of blood supply, resulting in tissue damage or death. It is the major cause of death in developed countries. Symptoms of infarction include a sudden onset of chest pain, breathlessness, nausea, and cold, clammy skin. Damage to the heart may be so severe that it leads to heart failure, and even death (myocardial infarction is fatal within 20 days in 40-50% of all cases).

Valve defects

Unusual heart sounds (murmurs) can result when a valve (often the mitral valve) does not close properly, allowing blood back into the atria. Valve defects may be congenital (present at birth), but they can also occur as a result of rheumatic fever.

Septal defects

These hole-in-the-heart congenital defects occur where the dividing wall (septum) between the left and right sides of the heart is not closed. These defects may occur between the **atria** or the **ventricles**, and are sometimes combined with valve problems.

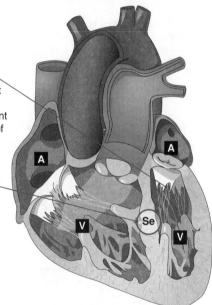

A Atrium
V Ventricle
Se Septum

1. Define the term cardiovascular disease (CVD): _____

_____

2. Suggest why CVD is the principal cause of death in developed countries? _____

_____

_____

_____

_____

3. Explain the difference between a congenital cardiovascular defect and a defect that develops later in life: _____

_____

_____

_____

116 Smoking and the Cardiovascular System

Key Idea: The nicotine and carbon monoxide in tobacco smoke have immediate and long term effects on the cardiovascular system.

These effects are associated with increased **blood** pressure and elevated heart rate. Together with the carcinogens in tar, nicotine and carbon monoxide are among the most harmful components of tobacco smoke. Nicotine is an addictive poison acting quickly to constrict arteries, increase blood pressure and heart rate, mobilize fat stores, and increase metabolic rate. Carbon monoxide is also toxic, displacing oxygen from hemoglobin and reducing the oxygen content of the blood. The effects of nicotine and carbon monoxide increase the workload of the heart and increase the risk of heart disease, peripheral vascular disease, and stroke.

Short term effects of smoking

After inhaling, nicotine enters the bloodstream rapidly and reaches the brain within 8 seconds where it increases the release of many chemical messengers, including acetylcholine and dopamine, and stimulates the brain's reward centers.

Nicotine raises blood pressure (10-30 points). Chronic high blood pressure is the single most important risk factor for stroke (cell death in the brain as a result of impaired blood flow).

Surface blood vessel constriction drops skin temperature by up to 5°C.

Very sharp rise in carbon monoxide levels in the lungs, contributing to breathlessness.

Nicotine causes a rapid increase in heart rate by up to 20 beats per minute.

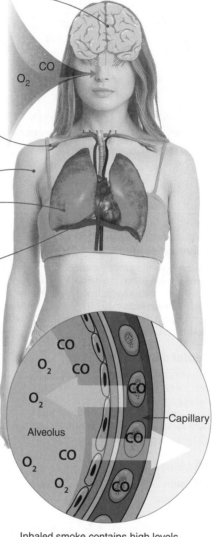

Long term effects of smoking

The nicotine and carbon monoxide in tobacco smoke increase the viscosity of the blood, which increases the risk of fatty plaques forming in the coronary and carotid **arteries**. These plaques increase the risk of heart attack and stroke. Heart attacks usually result when blood flow to the heart muscle is interrupted, often following rupture of a plaque. The muscle becomes starved of oxygen and dies. Chronic high blood pressure and elevated heart rate, coupled with high levels of CO make the heart work harder to deliver the oxygen needed by the cells and tissues of the body.

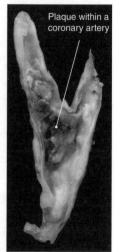

Plaque within a coronary artery

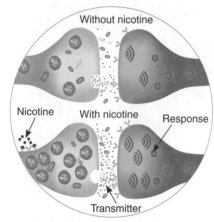

Nicotine affects communication between nerve cells and between nerve cells and muscles. It interacts with cell receptors, stimulating greater release of transmitter substance and increased response in target cells. It causes an immediate and longer term increase in blood pressure and heart rate and causes the body to mobilize fat stores.

Inhaled smoke contains high levels of carbon monoxide, which crosses the gas exchange membrane along with oxygen to enter the blood with the **capillaries** of the lung. Here, the carbon monoxide (CO) is preferentially picked up by the hemoglobin in the RBCs, which normally transport oxygen.

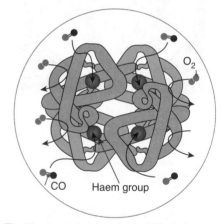

The blood protein hemoglobin (Hb) binds and carries oxygen within the red blood cells to supply the cells and tissues of the body. However, CO has a much higher affinity for Hb than oxygen, so when CO is inhaled, it displaces oxygen from Hb. As a result, less oxygen is supplied to the tissues. High levels of CO are fatal.

1. Describe the short and long term effects of nicotine and carbon monoxide on the cardiovascular system: _____

_____

_____

_____

_____

_____

©2023 **BIOZONE** International
ISBN: 978-1-99-101408-5

Atherosclerosis is a disease of the arteries caused by atheromas (fatty deposits) on the inner arterial walls. An atheroma is made up of cells (mostly macrophages) or cell debris, with associated fatty acids, cholesterol, calcium, and varying amounts of fibrous connective tissue. The accumulation of fat and plaques causes the lining of the arteries to degenerate. Atheromas weaken the arterial walls and eventually restrict blood flow through the arteries, increasing the risk of aneurysm (swelling of the artery wall) and thrombosis (blood clots). Complications arising as a result of atherosclerosis include heart attacks, strokes, and gangrene. A typical progression for the formation of an atheroma is illustrated below.

Initial lesion	**Fatty streak**	**Intermediate lesion**	**Atheroma**	**Fibroatheroma**	**Complicated plaque**
Atherosclerosis is triggered by damage to an artery wall caused by blood borne chemicals or persistent hypertension.	Low density lipoproteins (LDLs) accumulate beneath the endothelial cells. Macrophages follow and absorb them, forming foam cells.	Foam cells accumulate forming greasy yellow lesions called atherosclerotic plaques.	A core of extracellular lipids under a cap of fibrous tissue forms.	Lipid core and fibrous layers. Accumulated smooth muscle cells die. Fibres deteriorate and are replaced with scar tissue.	Calcification of plaque. Arterial wall may ulcerate. Hypertension may worsen. Plaque may break away and blood cells may then collect at the damaged site, forming a clot.

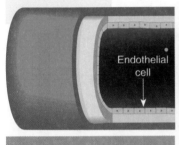
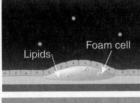
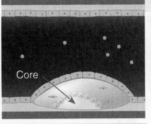

Earliest onset	From first decade	From third decade	From fourth decade
Growth mechanism	Growth mainly by lipid accumulation	Smooth muscle/ collagen increase	Thrombosis, hematoma
Clinical correlation	Clinically silent	Clinically silent or overt	

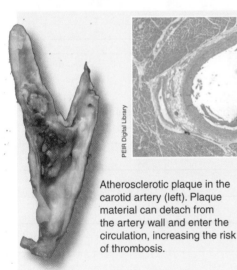

Atherosclerotic plaque in the carotid artery (left). Plaque material can detach from the artery wall and enter the circulation, increasing the risk of thrombosis.

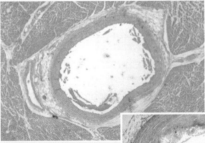

PEIR Digital Library

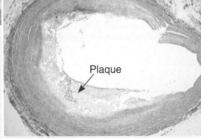

Plaque

Normal unobstructed coronary artery (left), and a coronary artery with moderately severe atheroma (below). Note the formation of the plaque on the inside surface of the artery.

Recent studies indicate that most heart attacks are caused by the body's inflammatory response to a plaque. The inflammatory process causes young, soft, cholesterol-rich plaques to rupture and break into pieces. If these block blood vessels, they can cause lethal heart attacks, even in previously healthy people.

Aorta opened lengthwise (above), with extensive atherosclerotic lesions (arrowed).

2. Explain why most people are unlikely to realize they are developing atherosclerosis until serious complications arise:

_____

_____

_____

3. Explain how an atherosclerotic plaque changes over time: _____

_____

_____

4. Describe some of the consequences of developing atherosclerosis: _____

_____

117 CVD Risk Factors

Key Idea: Several risk factors increase the likelihood of a person developing cardiovascular disease (CVD).

A risk factor is a variable that increases the risk of a certain disease developing. Some risk factors are controllable in that they can be modified by lifestyle changes. Controllable risk factors include diet, cigarette smoking, obesity, high blood cholesterol, high blood pressure, diabetes, and physical inactivity. Uncontrollable risk factors, such as advancing age, gender, and heredity, cannot be modified but overall risk can minimized by reducing the number of controllable risk factors. The more risk factors a person has, the greater the likelihood they will develop CVD (below). Increased levels of education and awareness about CVD and its risk factors have helped to reduce levels of the disease.

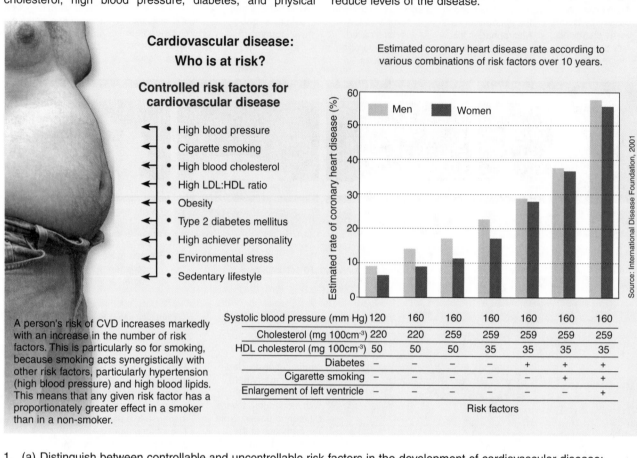

Cardiovascular disease: Who is at risk?

Controlled risk factors for cardiovascular disease

- High blood pressure
- Cigarette smoking
- High blood cholesterol
- High LDL:HDL ratio
- Obesity
- Type 2 diabetes mellitus
- High achiever personality
- Environmental stress
- Sedentary lifestyle

Estimated coronary heart disease rate according to various combinations of risk factors over 10 years.

Source: International Disease Foundation, 2001

A person's risk of CVD increases markedly with an increase in the number of risk factors. This is particularly so for smoking, because smoking acts synergistically with other risk factors, particularly hypertension (high blood pressure) and high blood lipids. This means that any given risk factor has a proportionately greater effect in a smoker than in a non-smoker.

Risk factors							
Systolic blood pressure (mm Hg)	120	160	160	160	160	160	160
Cholesterol (mg 100cm⁻³)	220	220	259	259	259	259	259
HDL cholesterol (mg 100cm⁻³)	50	50	50	35	35	35	35
Diabetes	–	–	–	–	+	+	+
Cigarette smoking	–	–	–	–	–	+	+
Enlargement of left ventricle	–	–	–	–	–	–	+

1. (a) Distinguish between controllable and uncontrollable risk factors in the development of cardiovascular disease:

_____

_____

_____

_____

(b) Suggest why some controllable risk factors often occur together: _____

_____

_____

_____

(c) Evaluate the evidence supporting the observation that patients with several risk factors are at a higher risk of CVD:

_____

_____

_____

_____

_____

_____

©2023 **BIOZONE** International
ISBN: 978-1-99-101408-5
Photocopying Prohibited

118 Correcting Heart Problems

Key Idea: Medical technology now provides the means to correct many heart problems, even if only temporarily.

Some symptoms of CVD, arising as a result of blockages to the coronary **arteries**, are now commonly treated using techniques such as coronary bypass surgery and angioplasty. Other cardiac disorders, such as disorders of heartbeat, are frequently treated using cardiac pacemakers. Valve defects, which are often congenital, can be successfully corrected with surgical valve replacement. The latest technology involves non-surgical replacement of aortic valves. The procedure, known as percutaneous (through the skin) heart valve replacement, will greatly reduce the trauma associated with correcting these particular heart disorders.

Coronary bypass surgery

This is a now commonly used surgery to bypass blocked coronary arteries with blood vessels from elsewhere in the body (e.g. leg **vein** or mammary artery). Sometimes, double or triple bypasses are performed.

Angioplasty

Angioplasty (below) is an alternative procedure used for some patients with coronary artery disease. A balloon tipped catheter is placed via the **aorta** into the coronary artery. The balloon is inflated to reduce the blockage of the artery and later removed. Heparin (an anticlotting agent) is given to prevent the formation of blood clots. The death rate from complications is about 1%.

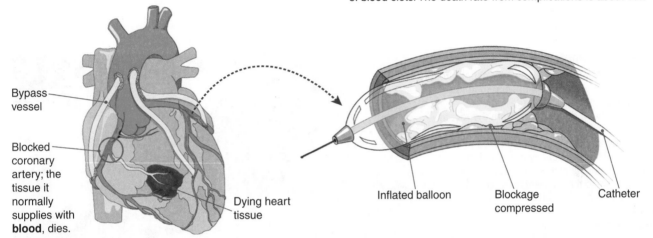

Bypass vessel

Blocked coronary artery; the tissue it normally supplies with **blood**, dies.

Dying heart tissue

Inflated balloon

Blockage compressed

Catheter

Cardiac pacemakers

▶ A cardiac pacemaker is sometimes required to maintain an effective heart rate in cases where the heart beats irregularly or too slowly.

▶ Pacemakers provide regular electrical stimulation of the heart muscle so that it contracts and relaxes with a normal rhythm. They stand by until the heart rate falls below a pre-set rate.

▶ Temporary pacemakers are often used after cardiac surgery or heart attacks, while permanent pacemakers are required for patients with ongoing problems.

▶ Pacemakers allow a normal (even strenuous) lifestyle.

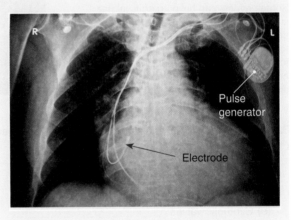

R   L

Pulse generator

Electrode

1. Compare the advantages and disadvantages of angioplasty and coronary bypass as different methods of correcting blocked arteries in the heart:

_____

_____

_____

2. Explain why patients who have undergone coronary bypass surgery or angioplasty require careful supervision of their diet and lifestyle following the operation, even though their problem has been alleviated:

_____

_____

_____

©2023 **BIOZONE** International
ISBN: 978-1-99-101408-5
Photocopying Prohibited

Heart valve replacement

Heart valves can be replaced with either biological (tissue) valves or synthetic valves. Tissue valves are sourced from animal, e.g. pig, or human donors. They last only 7-10 years, but there are relatively few blood clotting and tissue rejection problems associated with them. For these reasons, they are often used in older patients. Synthetic ball or disk valves (see below) are constructed from non-biological materials. They last a long time but tend to create blood clots, raising the risk of stroke. They are used on younger patients, who must take long-term anti-clotting drugs.

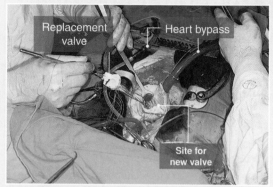

Above: Valve replacement operation in progress. The valve can be seen threaded up and ready for placement. Two large tubes bypass the heart so that circulation to the lungs and rest of the body is maintained.

Disk valve

Ball valve

Tissue valve

Heart transplants

Some heart damage is so severe, either through disease, injury, or congenital (inherited) disorder, that the heart needs to be replaced. Heart transplants use donor hearts from the recently deceased (within 4 hours normally), that have been carefully matched in blood type to the recipient. The chest cavity is opened (right), and the patient is placed on a heart bypass machine while the old heart is removed, and the donor heart is attached. Patients will need to permanently take immunosuppressants to avoid organ rejection, but a successful transplant will allow the patient to live a normal life for a decade or more.

Some patients can have an artificial heart surgically inserted, called a ventricular assist device (VAD), that can temporarily replace heart function while waiting for a transplant. Further technology is likely to produce a totally artificial heart, that can be permanently transplanted, and removes rejection issues.

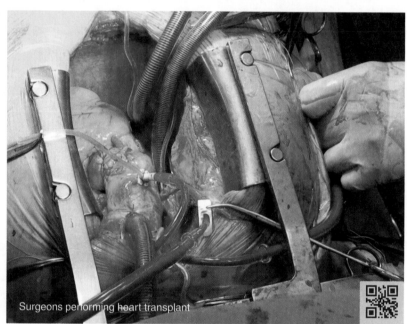

Surgeons performing heart transplant

3. Describe the problems associated with the use of each of the following type of replacement heart valve:

   (a) Tissue valves: _____

   _____

   (b) Synthetic valves: _____

   _____

4. Suggest why tissue valves are usually a preferred option for use in elderly patients: _____

   _____

   _____

5. What are some likely advantages and disadvantages of heart transplants, compared to other forms of heart correction treatment?

   _____

   _____

   _____

   _____

©2023 **BIOZONE** International
ISBN: **978-1-99-101408-5**
Photocopying Prohibited

119 Chapter Summary

1. Explain why blood cells are constantly being produced, when some other cells (e.g. neurons) are not: _____

_____

_____

2. Compare and contrast the structure of veins and arteries, linked to their functions within the cardiovascular system:

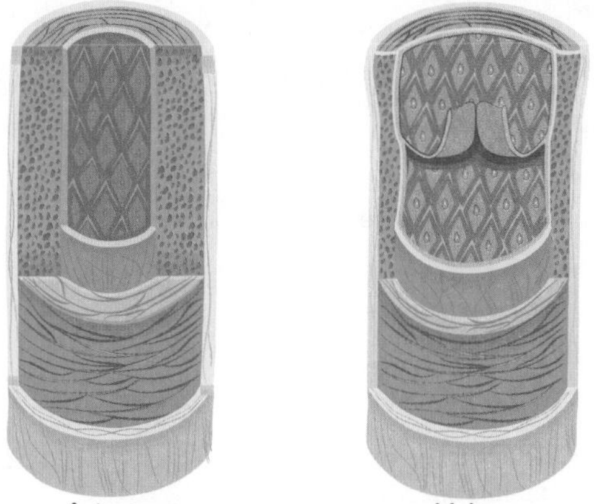

_____

_____

_____

_____

_____

_____

_____

_____

Artery   Vein

3. Summarize the key functions of blood, linked to the blood specific blood component(s) involved: _____

_____

_____

_____

_____

_____

4. Identify and name the numbered features in the heart diagram, (right):

(a) 1: _____

(b) 2: _____

(c) 3: _____

(d) 4: _____

(e) 5: _____

(f) 6: _____

(g) 7: _____

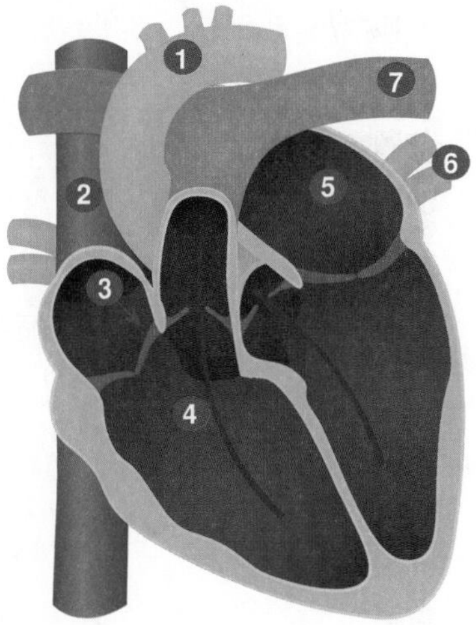

5. What stage of the cardiac cycle is the heart (right) showing, and what evidence can you provide for your answer?

_____

_____

_____

6. Distinguish between the mechanisms for the intrinsic and extrinsic control of the heart rate: _____

_____

_____

_____

_____

CHAPTER 8

The Lymphatic System and Immunity

KEY IDEAS

- The body can distinguish self from non-self.
- The body can defend itself against pathogens.
- Non-specific defenses target any foreign material.
- The immune response targets specific antigens and has a memory for antigens previously encountered.
- The properties of immune cells can be used to target specific antigens.

KEY TERMS

- Antibody
- Antigen
- Antigen presenting cell (APC)
- Autoimmune disease
- Hypersensitivity
- Inflammation
- Lymphocyte
- Major histocompatibility complex (MHC)
- Phagocytosis
- T cell
- Vaccine

RESOURCE HUB

Scan the QR code to access:

- weblinks
- videos
- 3D models
- interactives

LEARNING OBJECTIVES

		Activity number
☐ 1	Know that an antigen is any substance that promotes an immune response. Understand that the body is able to distinguish between harmless and potentially harmful material. Describe what is meant by an autoimmune disease and give examples of these, including symptoms and treatments.	120-122
☐ 2	Describe how blood is grouped according to the presence of different antigens on the red blood cells. Explain how blood clotting acts as a defense mechanism in the body.	123-124
☐ 3	Understand the difference between the innate and adaptive immune responses and describe the body's three lines of defense. Describe the different functions of macrophages, neutrophils, and dendritic cells in phagocytosis and explain, using a diagram, the stages in phagocytosis and pathogen destruction. Give examples of other cells and processes involved in the innate immune response.	125-127
☐ 4	Explain the stages in the inflammatory response and why it is beneficial. Understand the roles of antigen presenting cells (APCs) and the major histocompatibility complex receptors in the immune response. Describe the difference between class I and class II MHC receptors. Describe the stages of fever in the body.	128-130
☐ 5	Describe the components of the lymphatic system and its role in immunity. Know the difference between the humoral and cell mediated responses in the adaptive immune system. Explain the main differences between B cells and T cells.	131-132
☐ 6	Give an overview of the clonal selection theory. Describe ways in which antibodies help destroy antigens.	133-134
☐ 7	Understand what is meant by acquired immunity. Analyze data on the effect of the chickenpox vaccine over a specific time period. Describe different types of vaccine and what is meant by herd immunity. Describe how the disease HIV affects the immune system over both short and long terms.	135-137
☐ 8	Describe how monoclonal antibodies are made and give examples of their applications. Explain, using examples, how hypersensitivity occurs.	138-141
☐ 9	Give examples of different organ and tissue transplants that can be carried out. Explain why transplanted organs and tissues can be rejected by the body. Understand how stem cell technology can be used to produce organs suitable for transplant. Understand how gene therapy can be used to replace defective genes.	142-144

Background: Virus (abstract)

120 Antigens

Key Idea: Antigens are substances capable of producing an immune response. Some antigens are pathogens, i.e. infectious agents that cause disease.

An **antigen** is any substance that causes an immune response in an organism. Most antigens are foreign material and originate from outside the organism, e.g. a microbe, or other disease causing pathogen. They, or their toxins, generate an immune response in the host, which destroys them. However, an antigen can also originate inside the body, causing autoimmune disorders, such as multiple sclerosis.

Non-self antigens

Any foreign material provoking an immune response is termed a non-self antigen. Disease-causing organisms (pathogens) such as bacteria, viruses, and fungi are non-self antigens. The body recognizes them as foreign and will attack and destroy them before they cause harm.

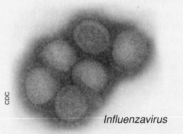

CDC

Influenzavirus

Pathogens have ways of avoiding detection. Mutations result in new surface antigens, delaying the immune response and allowing the pathogen to reproduce in its host undetected for a time, e.g. the flu virus, above. Some pathogens, e.g. the malaria-causing *Plasmodium*, switches off its surface antigens in order to enter cells undetected.

Self antigens

The body is usually tolerant of its own antigens. However, sometimes the self-tolerance system fails and the body attacks its own cells and tissues as though they were foreign. This can result in an autoimmune disorder in which tissue is destroyed, grows abnormally, or changes in function.

Autoimmune disorders, such as multiple sclerosis and rheumatoid arthritis, may be triggered by infection. The similarity of the pathogen and self antigens is thought to be behind this failure of self recognition.

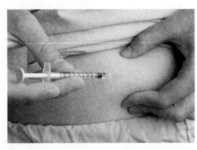

Type 1 diabetes is the result of autoimmune destruction of the insulin-producing pancreatic cells. Patients must inject insulin to maintain normal blood glucose levels.

Allergens

Antigens that cause allergic reactions are called allergens. An allergic reaction is a very specific type of immune response in which the **immune system** overreacts to a normally harmless substance. An allergic response can produce minor symptoms (itching, sneezing, rashes, swelling) or life-threatening anaphylaxis (respiratory and cardiovascular distress).

Common allergens include dust, chemicals, mold, pet hair, food proteins, or pollen grains.

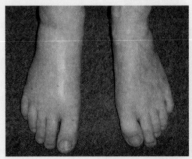

Kent Pryor

The swelling on the foot in the left of the photograph is a result of an allergic reaction to a bee sting.

1. What is an antigen? _____

_____

2. Define the following terms:

(a) Non-self antigen: _____

_____

(b) Self antigen: _____

_____

(c) Allergen: _____

_____

3. Why is it important that the body detects foreign antigens? _____

_____

_____

_____

_____

121 The Protective Microbiome and Recognizing Self

Key Idea: It is important that the body can distinguish its own tissues from foreign material so that it does not attack itself. In order for the body to present an effective defense against pathogens, it must be able to recognize its own tissues (self) and ignore the body's normal microflora, e.g. the bacteria of the skin and gastrointestinal tract. The body must also be able to deal with abnormal cells which may become cancerous. Failure of self/non-self recognition can lead to **autoimmune** **disorders**, in which the immune system mistakenly attacks its own tissues. The body's ability to recognize its own molecules has implications for procedures such as tissue grafts, organ transplants, and blood transfusions. Incompatible tissues (identified as foreign) are attacked by the body's immune system (rejected). Even pregnancy involves suppression of specific features of the self recognition system, allowing the mother to tolerate a nine month gestation with the fetus.

Role of the microbiome

After birth, normal and characteristic microbial populations begin to establish themselves on and in the body. A typical human body contains 1×10^{13} body cells, yet harbors 1×10^{14} bacterial cells. These microorganisms establish more or less permanent residence but, under normal conditions, do not cause disease. In fact, this normal microflora can benefit the host by preventing the overgrowth of harmful pathogens. They are not found throughout the entire body, but are located in certain regions.

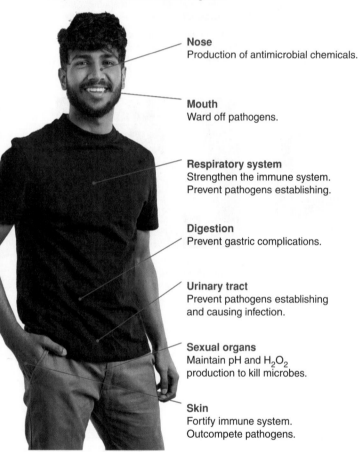

Nose
Production of antimicrobial chemicals.

Mouth
Ward off pathogens.

Respiratory system
Strengthen the immune system.
Prevent pathogens establishing.

Digestion
Prevent gastric complications.

Urinary tract
Prevent pathogens establishing and causing infection.

Sexual organs
Maintain pH and H_2O_2 production to kill microbes.

Skin
Fortify immune system.
Outcompete pathogens.

Distinguishing self from non-self

▶ Every type of cell has unique protein markers (antigens) on its surface. The type of antigen varies greatly between cells and between species. The immune system uses these markers to identify its own cells (self) from foreign cells (non-self). If the immune system recognizes the antigen markers, it will not attack the cell. If the antigen markers are unknown, the cell is attacked and destroyed.

▶ The system responsible for this property is the **major histocompatibility complex** (**MHC**). The MHC is a cluster of tightly linked genes on chromosome 6. One set comes from the mother (maternal) and one set from the father (paternal). These genes code for MHC antigens that are attached to the surface of body cells. The main role of MHC antigens is to bind to antigenic fragments and display them on the cell surface so that they can be recognized by the cells of the immune system.

▶ Class I MHC antigens are found on the surfaces of almost all human cells. Class II MHC antigens occur only on macrophages and **B cells** of the immune system, like the stylized neutrophil below.

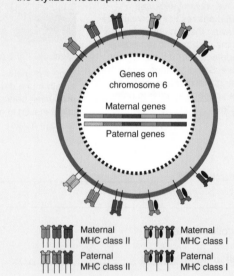

Genes on chromosome 6

Maternal genes

Paternal genes

Maternal MHC class II	Maternal MHC class I
Paternal MHC class II	Paternal MHC class I

---

1. Why is it healthy to have a natural population of microbes on and inside the body? _____

_____

_____

2. (a) Explain the nature and purpose of the major histocompatibility complex (MHC): _____

_____

_____

_____

(b) Explain the importance of the self-recognition system: _____

_____

©2023 **BIOZONE** International
ISBN: 978-1-99-101408-5
Photocopying Prohibited

122 Autoimmune Diseases

Key Idea: Autoimmune diseases are caused when the body's **immune system** begins to attack the body's own tissues.

The **immune system** normally distinguishes self from non-self (foreign **antigens**). However, when the normal self recognition system fails, the immune system may attack its own cells or tissues. This is called an **autoimmune disease**. Numerous diseases, including myasthenia gravis, multiple sclerosis, rheumatoid arthritis, celiac disease, and type 1 diabetes are the result of immune system malfunctions. The exact mechanisms behind autoimmune diseases are not fully understood but pathogens or drugs may play a role in triggering an autoimmune response in someone who already has a genetic predisposition. The reactions are similar to those that occur in allergies, except that in autoimmune disorders, the **hypersensitivity** response is to the body itself, rather than to an outside substance.

Multiple sclerosis

Multiple sclerosis (MS) is a progressive inflammatory disease of the central nervous system in which scattered patches of myelin (white matter) in the brain and spinal cord are destroyed. Myelin is the fatty connective tissue sheath surrounding conducting axons. When it is destroyed, the axons cannot transmit impulses effectively and this leads to the symptoms of MS: numbness, tingling, muscle weakness, and paralysis. MS can interfere with mobility (below).

MS usually starts early in adult life and the disease is characterized by a patchy pattern of disabilities, often with dramatic, unpredictable improvements. There is a genetic component to it, as relatives of affected people are far more likely to develop the disease.

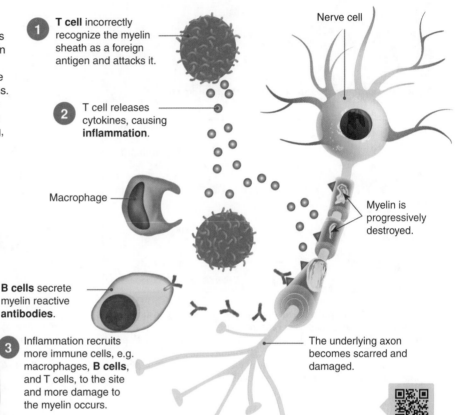

1. **T cell** incorrectly recognize the myelin sheath as a foreign antigen and attacks it.

2. T cell releases cytokines, causing **inflammation**.

Nerve cell

Macrophage

Myelin is progressively destroyed.

B cells secrete myelin reactive **antibodies**.

3. Inflammation recruits more immune cells, e.g. macrophages, **B cells**, and T cells, to the site and more damage to the myelin occurs.

The underlying axon becomes scarred and damaged.

1. What is an autoimmune disease? _____

_____

_____

2. Explain why autoimmune diseases can be regarded as an intolerance to self? _____

_____

_____

_____

3. Explain the basis of multiple sclerosis: _____

_____

_____

_____

_____

Myasthenia gravis

Myasthenia gravis (MG) is caused by a breakdown in the communication between nerves and muscles. Nerves release chemicals (neurotransmitters) that bind to specific receptor sites on muscles, stimulating them to contract. In MG, a person's own antibodies bind to the receptor sites on the muscles and block them, and some of the fibers in the muscle do not receive the stimulus strength required to contract. This results in muscle weakness and fatigue. Drooping eyelids (ptosis) is a common first symptom in MG sufferers (below), but it also affects muscles in the face, throat, neck, and limbs. MG has no cure, but can be treated by surgery, neurotransmitter inhibitors, and immunosuppressant drugs to reduce the autoimmune response.

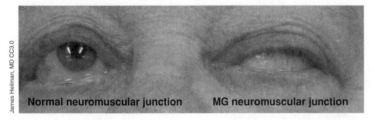

Normal neuromuscular junction   MG neuromuscular junction

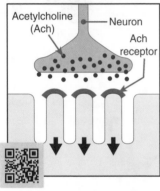 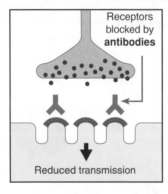

In MG, antibodies bind to the receptors on the post synaptic junction, preventing the neurotransmitter (acetylcholine) from binding. The excitatory effects of acetylcholine are reduced, and muscle contraction is impaired. Treatment often uses drugs that prevent acetylcholine from being broken down so that it remains at the neuromuscular junction longer than usual. This allows more receptor sites to be activated.

Celiac disease

 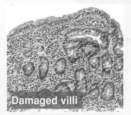

Celiac disease is a condition where the immune system attacks the small intestine when a person consumes gluten containing foods, e.g. wheat, rye, and barley products. This causes inflammation of the small intestine and the villi (finger like protrusions) are damaged and flattened (above right). The ability to absorb nutrients is greatly reduced because of the reduced surface area. Symptoms vary greatly, and a person can go undiagnosed for years. Undiagnosed celiac disease can result in a range of health issues including malnutrition, gastrointestinal issues, dermatitis, infertility, osteoporosis, and some cancers. There is no cure for celiac disease; people with the disease must eliminate all gluten containing foods from their diet for life.

Rheumatoid arthritis

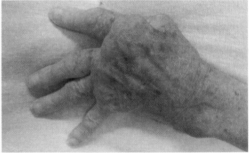

Rheumatoid arthritis is a type of joint inflammation, usually in the hands and feet, which results in destruction of cartilage and painful, swollen joints. The disease often begins in adulthood, but can also occur in children or the elderly. Rheumatoid arthritis affects more women than men and is treated with anti-inflammatory and immunosuppressant drugs, and physiotherapy.

4. Explain the basis of myasthenia gravis: _____

_____

_____

_____

5. How does preventing acetylcholine breakdown help to reduce the symptoms of myasthenia gravis? _____

_____

_____

_____

_____

6. (a) Why do the villi of the small intestine become damaged in a person with celiac disease? _____

_____

_____

(b) Suggest why malnutrition can occur in people with undiagnosed celiac disease? _____

_____

123 Blood Group Antigens

Key Idea: Blood is classified into groups according to the different marker molecules (antigens) on the surface of red blood cells.

The type of **antigens** present on the surface of a red blood cell (RBC) determines an individual's blood type. ABO blood group antigens (below) and Rh antigens are the most important in the blood typing system because they are strongly immunogenic, i.e. cause a strong immune response. Blood must be checked for compatibility before a patient can receive donated blood. Transfusion of incompatible blood may cause a fatal transfusion reaction in which RBCs from the donated blood clump together (agglutinate), block capillaries, and rupture (hemolysis). To prevent this occurring, blood is carefully matched before transfusion. Although human RBCs have more than 500 known antigens, fewer than 30 are regularly tested for and they are not common enough to be used for cross-matching. Blood typing can also be used to predict the possibilities of paternity.

	Blood type A	**Blood type B**	**Blood type AB**	**Blood type O**
Antigens present on the red blood cells	Antigen A	Antigen B	Antigens A and B	Neither antigen A nor B
Antibodies present in the plasma	Contains anti-B antibodies; but no antibodies that would attack its own antigen A	Contains anti-A antibodies; but no antibodies that would attack its own antigen B	Contains neither anti-A nor anti-B antibodies	Contains both anti-A and anti-B antibodies

1. Complete the table below to show the antibodies and antigens in each blood group, and donor/recipient blood types. The first row has been completed for you:

Blood Type	Freq. in US		Antigen	Antibody	Can donate blood to:	Can receive blood from:
	Rh+	**Rh−**				
A	34%	6%	A	anti-B	A, AB	A, O
B	9%	2%	a)			
AB	3%	1%	b)			
O	38%	7%	c)			

2. Why do you think blood from an incompatible donor causes a transfusion reaction in the recipient? _____

_____

_____

_____

3. Why is blood type O⁻ sometimes called the universal donor? _____

_____

_____

_____

4. Why is blood type AB⁺ sometimes called the universal recipient? _____

_____

_____

©2023 **BIOZONE** International
ISBN: 978-1-99-101408-5
Photocopying Prohibited

124 Blood Clotting and Defense

Key Idea: Blood clotting helps maintain blood volume and has a defensive role in reducing pathogen entry into the body. Apart from its transport role, blood has a role in the body's defense against infection and hemostasis (the prevention of bleeding and maintenance of blood volume). The tearing of a blood vessel initiates clotting. Clotting is normally a rapid process that seals off the tear, preventing blood loss and the invasion of bacteria into the site. Clot formation is triggered by the release of clotting factors from the damaged cells at the site of the tear or puncture. A hardened clot forms a scab, which acts to prevent further blood loss and acts as a mechanical barrier to the entry of pathogens.

Blood clotting

1 Injury to the lining of a blood vessels exposes collagen fibers to the blood. Platelets stick to the collagen fibers.

3 As the platelets clump together, more chemicals are released, accelerating the clot formation (positive feedback). The platelet plug forms immediate protection against blood loss.

When tissue is wounded, the blood quickly coagulates to prevent further blood loss and maintain the integrity of the circulatory system. For external wounds, clotting also prevents the entry of pathogens. Blood clotting involves a cascade of reactions involving at least twelve clotting factors in the blood. The end result is the formation of an insoluble network of fibers, which traps red blood cells and seals the wound.

Endothelial cell
Red blood cell
Exposed collagen fibers

Blood vessel

2 Platelet releases chemicals that make the surrounding platelets sticky.

Platelet plug

4 A fibrin clot reinforces the seal. The clot traps blood cells and the positive feedback loop ends. The clot eventually dries to form a scab.

Clotting factors from:

Platelets → ← Plasma clotting factors

Damaged cells → ← Calcium

Clotting factors catalyze the conversion of prothrombin (plasma protein) to thrombin (an active enzyme). Clotting factors include thromboplastin and factor VIII (antihemophilia factor).

Prothrombin ⟹ Thrombin

Fibrinogen ⟹ Fibrin

Hydrolysis

Fibrin clot traps red blood cells

1. Explain two roles of the blood clotting system in internal defense and hemostasis:

   (a) _____

   (b) _____

2. Explain the role of each of the following in the sequence of events leading to a blood clot:

   (a) Injury: _____

   _____

   (b) Release of chemicals from platelets: _____

   _____

   (c) Clumping of platelets at the wound site: _____

   _____

   (d) Formation of a fibrin clot: _____

   _____

3. (a) Explain the role of clotting factors in the blood in formation of the clot: _____

   _____

   (b) Explain why these clotting factors are not normally present in the plasma: _____

   _____

©2023 **BIOZONE** International
ISBN: **978-1-99-101408-5**
Photocopying Prohibited

125 The Body's Defenses: An Overview

Key Idea: The human body has a tiered system of defenses that, together, provide resistance against disease.

The human body has a range of physical, chemical, and biological defenses that provide resistance against pathogens. The first line of defense consists of external barriers to prevent pathogens entering the body. If this fails, a second line of defense targets any foreign bodies that enter. Lastly, the specific immune response provides a targeted third line of defense against the pathogen. The defense responses fall into two broad categories: the innate and the adaptive immune responses. The innate (or non-specific) response makes up the first and second lines of defense. It protects against a broad range of non-specific pathogens. This response is present in all animals. It involves blood proteins (e.g. complement), **inflammation**, and phagocytic white blood cells. The adaptive (or specific) immune response is the third line of defense. It is specific to identified pathogens and is present only in vertebrates. It involves defense by specific **T cells** (cellular immunity) as well as **antibodies**, which neutralize foreign **antigens** (humoral immunity).

Most microorganisms find it difficult to get inside the body. If they succeed, they face a range of other defenses that protect the body.

The natural populations of harmless microbes living on the skin and mucous membranes inhibit the growth of most pathogenic microbes.

Microorganisms are trapped in sticky mucus and expelled by cilia (tiny hairs that move in a wavelike fashion).

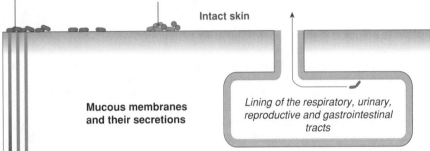

Intact skin

Mucous membranes and their secretions

Lining of the respiratory, urinary, reproductive and gastrointestinal tracts

1st line of defense

The skin provides a physical barrier to the entry of pathogens. Healthy skin is rarely penetrated by microorganisms. Its low pH is unfavorable to the growth of many bacteria and its chemical secretions, e.g. sebum, and antimicrobial peptides, inhibit growth of bacteria and fungi. Tears, mucus, and saliva also help to wash bacteria away.

2nd line of defense

A range of defense mechanisms operate inside the body to inhibit or destroy pathogens. These responses react to the presence of any pathogen, regardless of which species it is. White blood cells are involved in most of these responses. The 2nd line of defense includes the complement system, whereby blood plasma proteins work together to bind pathogens and induce inflammation to help fight infection.

  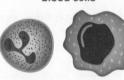

Antimicrobial substances

Inflammation and fever
40°C ↑ 37°C

Phagocytic white blood cells

Eosinophils
Produce toxic proteins against certain parasites, some phagocytosis

Basophils
Release heparin (an anticoagulant) and histamine which promotes inflammation

Neutrophils, macrophages
These cells engulf and digest cellular debris, cancer cells, and foreign material (e.g. bacteria).

3rd line of defense

Once the pathogen has been identified by the **immune system**, **lymphocytes** (specialized white blood cells) launch a range of specific responses to the pathogen, including the production of defensive proteins called antibodies. Each type of antibody is produced by a **B cell** clone and is specific against a particular antigen.

Antibody

Lymphocytes

B-cells: Recognize specific antigens and divide to form antibody-producing clones.

T-cells: Recognize specific antigens and activate specific defensive cells.

Tears contain antimicrobial substances as well as washing contaminants from the eyes.

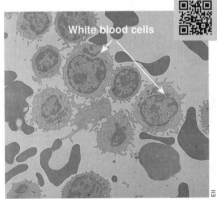

White blood cells

A range of white blood cells (the larger cells in the photograph) form the second line of defense.

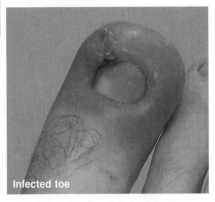

Infected toe

Inflammation is a localized response to infection characterized by swelling, pain, and redness.

The importance of the first line of defense

The skin is the largest organ of the body. It forms an important physical barrier against the entry of pathogens into the body. A natural population of harmless microbes live on the skin, but most other microbes find the skin inhospitable. The continual shedding of old skin cells (arrow, right) physically removes bacteria from the surface of the skin. Sebaceous glands in the skin (top right) produce sebum, which has antimicrobial properties, and the slightly acidic secretions of sweat inhibit microbial growth.

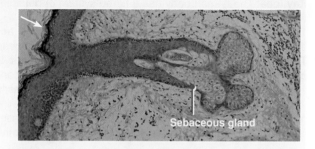
Sebaceous gland

Cilia line the epithelium of the respiratory tract (right) and regions of the urinary and reproductive tracts. Their wave-like movement sweeps foreign material out and keeps the passage free of microorganisms, preventing them from colonizing the body.

Antimicrobial chemicals are present in many bodily secretions. Tears, saliva, nasal secretions, and human breast milk all contain lysozymes and phospholipases. Lysozymes kill bacterial cells by catalyzing the hydrolysis of cell wall linkages, whereas phospholipases hydrolyze the phospholipids in bacterial cell membranes, causing bacterial death. Low pH gastric secretions also inhibit microbial growth, and reduce the number of pathogens establishing colonies in the gastrointestinal tract.

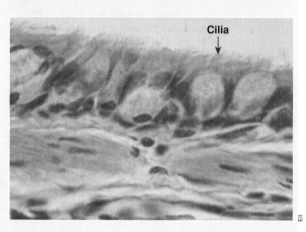
Cilia

1. What are the differences between the innate and adaptive immune responses? _____

_____

_____

_____

_____

_____

2. How does the skin act as a barrier to prevent pathogens entering the body? _____

_____

_____

_____

3. Describe the role of cilia and phospholipases in non-specific defense: _____

_____

_____

_____

4. Explain the value of a three tiered system of defense against microbial invasion: _____

_____

_____

_____

_____

_____

©2023 **BIOZONE** International
ISBN: 978-1-99-101408-5
Photocopying Prohibited

126 The Innate Immune Response

Key Idea: The innate immune response provides a rapid response to contain and destroy pathogens. Inflammation is an important part of this response.

The innate **immune system** provides protection against a pathogen, even if it has never encountered it before. The innate response is very fast and provides general protection (it is not **antigen** specific), but does not provide long lasting immunity. Many different cells and processes are involved. The primary outcome is to destroy and remove the cause of infection. This is achieved through containing the infection through **inflammation** and then recruiting immune cells to destroy the pathogen. During this process, a series of biochemical reactions (the complement system) is activated to destroy the pathogen and recruit immune cells to the site.

Phagocytic cells of the innate immune system

A phagocyte is any type of mobile white blood cell capable of **phagocytosis**. Phagocytes protect the body by engulfing and destroying antigenic material, including harmful foreign particles, microbes, and dead or dying cells tagged for destruction. Phagocytes move around the material to engulf it, then break it down into harmless fragments by enclosing it in a phagosome and digesting it. Macrophages, neutrophils, and dendritic cells are all phagocytes.

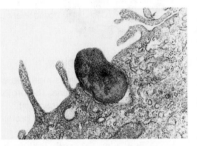
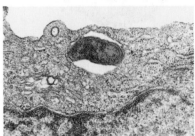

Photos: CDC

Photos above: A cell engulfs and ingests a bacterium by phagocytosis.

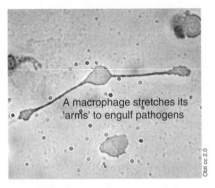

A macrophage stretches its 'arms' to engulf pathogens

Obli cc 2.0

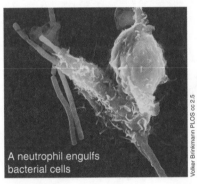

A neutrophil engulfs bacterial cells

Volker Brinkmann PLOS cc 2.5

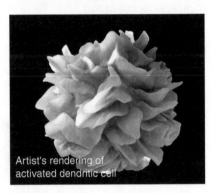

Artist's rendering of activated dendritic cell

Macrophage

Macrophages are very large and are highly efficient phagocytes. They are found throughout the body and move using an amoeboid movement (above) to hunt down and destroy pathogens. Macrophages also have a role in recruiting other immune cells to an infection site and eliminating diseased and damaged cells.

Neutrophil

Neutrophils are the most abundant type of phagocyte and are usually the first cells to arrive at an infection site. They contain toxic substances that kill or inhibit the growth of extracellular pathogens, such as bacteria and fungi. Neutrophils release cytokines, which amplify the immune response and recruit other cells to the infection site.

Dendritic cell

Dendritic cells are present in tissues that are in contact with the external environment, e.g. skin, and linings of the nose, lungs, and digestive tract. They act as messengers between the innate and adaptive immune systems by ingesting antigenic material and presenting it to the **T cells** of the immune system.

1. What feature do all phagocytic cells have in common? _____

_____

_____

2. Outline the role of the following phagocytes in the innate immune response:

(a) Macrophages: _____

_____

(b) Neutrophils: _____

_____

_____

(c) Dendritic cells: _____

_____

_____

Other cells and processes of the innate immune response

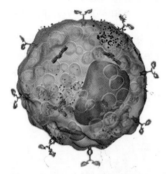

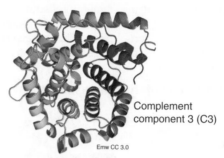

Complement component 3 (C3)

Emw CC 3.0

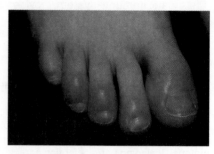

Mast cells

Mast cells contain a lot of histamine, a chemical involved in both inflammation and allergic responses. When a mast cell is activated, it releases histamine, which causes the surrounding blood vessels to dilate and become leaky. The increased permeability allows phagocytes to reach the site of infection easily.

Complement proteins

The complement system is made up of a number of different proteins. The proteins circulate as inactive precursors until they are activated. Complement proteins have three main roles: phagocytosis, attracting macrophages and neutrophils to the infection site, and rupturing the membranes of foreign cells.

The process of inflammation

The inflammatory process is a protective response to pathogen invasion. It has several functions: (1) to destroy the cause of the infection and remove it and its products from the body; (2) if this fails, to limit the effects on the body by confining the infection to a small area; (3) replacing or repairing tissue damaged by the infection.

Interferons

Interferons are signaling proteins released by immune cells when viruses are detected. Interferons disrupt viral replication, reducing infection of the host's cells. Interferons also activate immune cells, e.g. natural killer T cells and macrophages, and cause them to increase in number. Interferons also increase the rate of antigen presentation by increasing the expression of **major histocompatibility complex (MHC)** antigens.

Nevit Dilmen CC 3.0

Interferons (model, above left) belong to a large class of proteins called cytokines. They activate natural killer T cells (illustration, above right).

Natural killer cells

Natural killer T cells (NK cells) are a white blood cell important in the destruction of cancer cells and cells infected with viruses. Cytokines (including interferon) activate NK cells. Once activated, the NK cells release a protein called perforin, which forms holes in the cell membrane of the target cell. A series of events causes the cell to die and any viral particles inside to be destroyed.

3. What are the three main roles the proteins of the complement system play in immunity?

(a) _____

_____

(b) _____

_____

(c) _____

_____

4. (a) Briefly explain what interferons are and what stimulates their production: _____

_____

_____

(b) Explain the connection between interferons and natural killer cells: _____

_____

_____

_____

©2023 **BIOZONE** International
ISBN: 978-1-99-101408-5
Photocopying Prohibited

127 Phagocytes and Phagocytosis

Key Idea: Phagocytes are mobile white blood cells that ingest and destroy extracellular foreign material and dead or dying cells.

Phagocytosis is the process by which a cell engulfs another cell or particle. Cells that do this are called phagocytes. All types of phagocytes, such as neutrophils, dendritic cells, and macrophages, are white blood cells. These specialized cells have receptors on their surfaces that can detect antigenic material, such as microbes. They then ingest the microbes and digest them, rendering them harmless. As well as destroying microbes, phagocytes also release substances called cytokines, which help to coordinate the overall response to an infection. Macrophages and dendritic cells also play an important role in processing and presenting **antigens** from ingested microbes to other cells of the **immune system**.

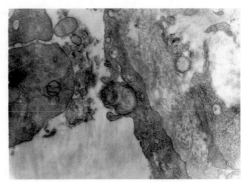

Stages in phagocytosis and destruction of a pathogen

1 Detection and interaction
Microbe coated in chemical markers is detected by the phagocyte, which attaches to it. Chemical markers coating the foreign material, e.g. a bacterial cell, mark it as a target for **phagocytosis**.

2 Engulfment
The markers trigger engulfment of the microbe by the phagocyte. The microbe is taken in by endocytosis.

3 Phagosome forms
A phagosome forms, enclosing the microbe in a membrane.

4 Fusion with lysosome
Phagosome fuses with a lysosome containing digestive enzymes. The fusion forms a phagolysosome.

5 Digestion
The microbe is broken down into its chemical constituents.

6 Discharge
Indigestible material is discharged from the phagocyte.

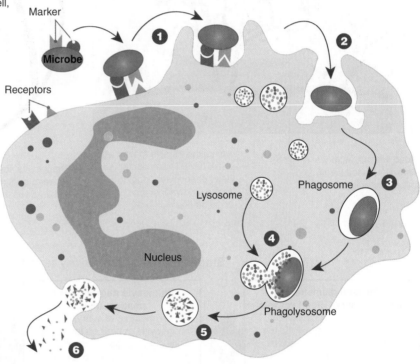

1. Explain the role of chemical markers and phagocyte receptors in enhancing phagocytosis: _____

_____

_____

2. What is the purpose of phagocytosis, and how is it involved in internal defense? _____

_____

_____

_____

_____

_____

3. Why do you think the foreign material has to be enclosed in a phagosome? _____

_____

©2023 **BIOZONE** International
ISBN: 978-1-99-101408-5
Photocopying Prohibited

128 Inflammation

Key Idea: Inflammation is a defensive response to damage. The inflammation process involves pain, redness, heat, and swelling.

Damage to the body's tissues can be caused by physical agents, e.g. sharp objects, heat, radiant energy, or electricity; microbial infection; or chemical agents, e.g. gases, acids and bases. The damage triggers a defensive response called **inflammation**. The inflammatory response is beneficial and the process of inflammation can be divided into three distinct stages. These are described below.

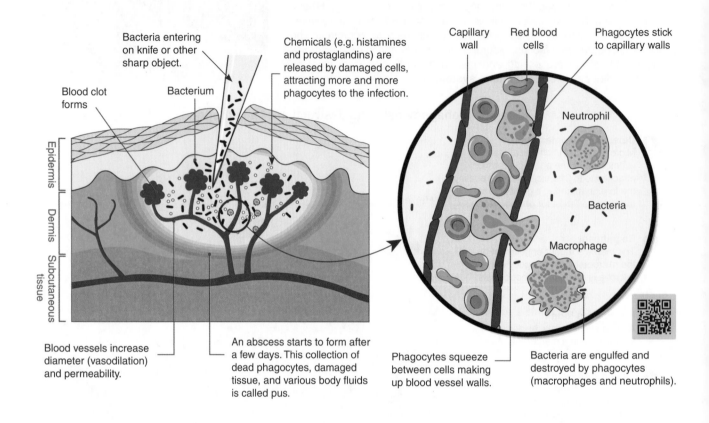

Bacteria entering on knife or other sharp object.

Bacterium

Blood clot forms

Chemicals (e.g. histamines and prostaglandins) are released by damaged cells, attracting more and more phagocytes to the infection.

Epidermis

Dermis

Subcutaneous tissue

Blood vessels increase diameter (vasodilation) and permeability.

An abscess starts to form after a few days. This collection of dead phagocytes, damaged tissue, and various body fluids is called pus.

Capillary wall

Red blood cells

Phagocytes stick to capillary walls

Neutrophil

Bacteria

Macrophage

Phagocytes squeeze between cells making up blood vessel walls.

Bacteria are engulfed and destroyed by phagocytes (macrophages and neutrophils).

Stages in the inflammatory response

Increased diameter and permeability of blood vessels	**Phagocyte migration and phagocytosis**	**Tissue repair**
Blood vessels increase their diameter and permeability in the area of damage. This increases blood flow to the area and allows defensive substances to leak into tissue spaces.	Within one hour of injury, phagocytes appear on the scene. They squeeze between cells of blood vessel walls to reach the damaged area, where they destroy invading microbes.	Functioning cells or supporting connective cells create new tissue to replace dead or damaged cells. Some tissue regenerates easily (skin) while others do not at all (cardiac muscle).

1. Outline the three stages of inflammation and identify the beneficial role of each stage:

    (a) _____

    _____

    (b) _____

    _____

    (c) _____

    _____

2. State the role of histamines and prostaglandins in inflammation: _____

    _____

    _____

©2023 **BIOZONE** International
ISBN: 978-1-99-101408-5
Photocopying Prohibited

129 Processing Antigens

Key Idea: Antigen processing prepares and displays antigens for presentation to the T cells of the immune system.

Antigen presenting cells (APCs) process and present **antigens** for recognition by **T cells**. During antigen processing, the APC digests the foreign antigen into smaller peptide fragments. These fragments are then displayed on the surface of the APC by **MHC** receptors. The immune response evoked by the T cells depends on which MHC receptor (MHCI or MHCII) is activated. Antigen presentation is necessary for T cells to recognize infection or abnormal growth and activate other cells of the **immune system**. Dendritic cells, macrophages, and **B cells** are APCs.

The role of MHC receptors

There are two types of MHC receptors, class I and class II (right). Both have similar functions in that they display antigens on cell surfaces so that they can be recognized and processed by the T cells of the immune system. T cells can only recognize antigens if they are displayed by the MHC receptors. MHC receptors presenting no foreign antigens are ignored by T cells and are recognized as 'self'. Only MHC receptors with foreign antigens bound to them will attract T cells and evoke an immune response.

The two classes of MHC receptors display different types of antigens. Class I MHC receptors display antigens from intracellular pathogens, e.g. viruses. Class II MHC receptors display antigens from pathogens that have been phagocytosed, e.g. bacteria.

Antigen binding site

Class I MHC
Antigens from within the cell, e.g. viral proteins.

Class II MHC
Antigens from outside the cell, e.g. proteins from phagocytosed microbes.

An overview of antigen processing

The diagram on the right represents antigen processing of an extracellular peptide antigen via a class II MHC receptor.

1 An APC encounters an antigen.

2 The antigen is engulfed via phagocytosis and digested into short peptide fragments.

3 Class II MHC receptors bind the fragments and form a MHC-antigen complex.

4 The MHC-antigen complex is displayed on the surface of the APC.

5 A receptor on the T helper cell recognizes the peptide as foreign. It binds, and a series of events stimulate the adaptive immune response.

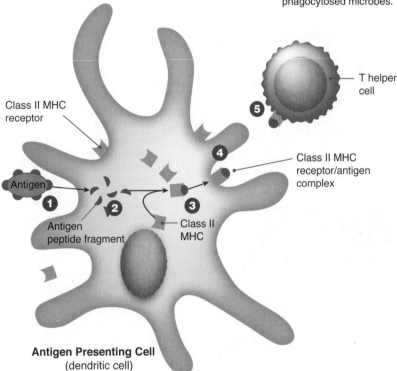

Antigen Presenting Cell
(dendritic cell)

1. What is the purpose of antigen processing? _____

2. Why do MHC receptors with no bound antigenic peptide not cause an immune response? _____

3. Describe the differences between class I and class II MHC receptors: _____

©2023 **BIOZONE** International
ISBN: 978-1-99-101408-5
Photocopying Prohibited

130 Fever

Key Idea: Fever is defined as an increase in body temperature above the normal range (36.2 - 37.2°C).

To a point, fever is beneficial, because it assists a number of the defense processes. The release of the protein interleukin-1 helps to reset the thermostat of the body to a higher level and increases production of **T cells**. High body temperature also intensifies the effect of interferon (an antiviral protein) and may inhibit the growth of some bacteria and viruses. Because high temperatures speed up the body's metabolic reactions, it may promote more rapid tissue repair. Fever also increases heart rate so that white blood cells are delivered to sites of infection more rapidly.

❶ Pathogen or toxin
The most frequent cause of fever is infection from bacteria (and their toxins) and viruses. A macrophage ingesting one of these will start the fever-causing process.

Toxins may be waste products or cell components.

Virus / Bacterium

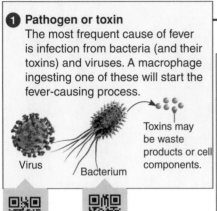

❷ Macrophages respond
Macrophage ingests bacterium, destroying it and releasing endotoxins. The endotoxins induce the macrophage to produce a small protein called interleukin-1.

Macrophage releases interleukin-1 into the bloodstream.

Macrophage digests bacterium in vacuole.

❸ Thermostat is reset
Interleukin-1 circulates to the brain and induces the hypothalamus to produce more prostaglandins, which resets the 'thermostat' to a higher temperature, producing fever.

The hypothalamus controls the body's temperature setting.

Fever

38.5 °C

❻ Crisis phase
Body temperature is maintained at the higher setting until the interleukin-1 has been eliminated. As the infection subsides, the thermostat is reset to 37°C. Heat losing mechanisms, such as sweating and vasodilation cause the person to feel warm. This crisis phase of the fever indicates that body temperature is falling.

❺ Chill phase
Although body temperature is elevated above normal, the skin remains cold, and shivering increases. This condition, called a chill, is a definite sign that body temperature is rising. When the body reaches the setting of the thermostat, the chill disappears.

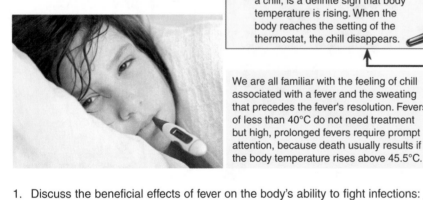

We are all familiar with the feeling of chill associated with a fever and the sweating that precedes the fever's resolution. Fevers of less than 40°C do not need treatment but high, prolonged fevers require prompt attention, because death usually results if the body temperature rises above 45.5°C.

❹ Fever onset
The body responds to a higher temperature set point by constricting blood vessels, increasing metabolic rate, and shivering. These responses raise body temperature beyond the normal range of 36.2 – 37.2°C.

1. Discuss the beneficial effects of fever on the body's ability to fight infections: _____

_____
_____
_____
_____

2. Summarize the key steps of how the body's thermostat is set at a higher level by infection: _____

_____
_____
_____
_____

©2023 **BIOZONE** International
ISBN: 978-1-99-101408-5
Photocopying Prohibited

131 The Lymphatic System and Immunity

Key Idea: The lymphatic system transports lymph, a fluid rich in white blood cells, throughout the body to attack antigens.
The **lymphatic system** is a network of tissues and organs that collects the tissue fluid leaked from the blood vessels and transports it to the heart. The lymphatic system has an important role in immunity because the fluid (lymph) transported by the lymphatic system is rich in infection-fighting white blood cells called **lymphocytes**. The thymus and red bone marrow are the primary organs of the lymphatic system, but it also has many secondary components.

Components of the lymphatic system

Tonsils
A collection of secondary lymphoid tissues in the throat. They provide defense against ingested or inhaled pathogens and produce activated **B** and **T cells**.

Thymus
A primary lymphoid organ located above the heart. It is large in infants and shrinks after puberty to a fraction of its original size. Important for maturation of T cells.

Spleen
The largest mass of lymphatic tissue in the body. It stores and releases blood in case of demand, e.g. in severe bleeding, produces mature B cells and **antibodies**, and removes antibody-coated antigenic material.

Lymph nodes
Ovoid masses of lymph tissue where lymphocytes are concentrated. Each node receives lymph through several incoming and outgoing vessels.

Red bone marrow
A primary lymphoid tissue where all the different kinds of blood cells, including white blood cells, are produced by cellular differentiation from stem cells. B cells also mature here.

Lymphatic vessels
When the fluid leaking from capillaries is picked up by lymph capillaries, it is called lymph. The lymph, carrying leukocytes, flows in lymphatic vessels through the secondary lymphoid tissues.

The lymphatic system and immunity

Lymphocytes (T and B cells) are types of white blood cells. They are important in fighting infection, e.g. destroying the microbes causing viral or bacterial infections.

Lymphocytes in circulation are constantly moving between sites where antigens may be encountered. The antigens are presented to T cells in the secondary lymphoid tissues. Recognition of the antigen leads to activation and rapid increase in the number of both T and B cells. After several days, antigen-activated lymphocytes begin leaving the lymphoid tissue.

Bone marrow: immature lymphocytes

Thymus

Bone marrow

Lymph nodes and other secondary lymphoid tissue

Circulation of activated lymphocytes

▪ Site of lymphocyte origin

▪ Sites of maturation of B and T cells

▪ Sites of antigen presentation and activation of B and T cells

---

1. What is the general role of the lymphatic system in immunity? _____

_____

_____

_____

2. (a) What is the role of lymph nodes in the immune response? _____

_____

_____

_____

   (b) Why do you think lymph nodes become swollen when someone has an infection? _____

_____

_____

132 The Adaptive Immune Response

Key Idea: Antigens, such as the cell walls of microbial cells, activate the immune system's B and T cells against specific pathogens when processed by antigen-presenting cells.

There are two main components of the adaptive immune system: the humoral and the cell-mediated responses. They work separately and together to protect against disease. The humoral immune response is associated with the serum (the non-cellular part of the blood) and involves the action of **antibodies** secreted by **B cells** (B lymphocytes). Antibodies

are found in extracellular fluids, including lymph, plasma, and mucus secretions, and protect against viruses, and bacteria and their toxins. The cell-mediated immune response is associated with the production of specialized **lymphocytes** called **T cells**. **Antigens** are recognized by T cells only after antigen processing. The antigen is first engulfed by an **antigen-presenting cell**, which processes the antigen and presents it on its surface. T helper cells can then recognize the antigen and activate other cells of the **immune system**.

Lymphocyles and their functions

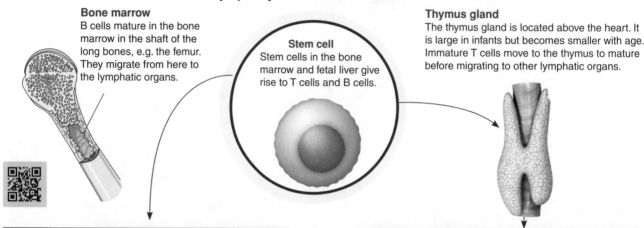

Bone marrow
B cells mature in the bone marrow in the shaft of the long bones, e.g. the femur. They migrate from here to the lymphatic organs.

Stem cell
Stem cells in the bone marrow and fetal liver give rise to T cells and B cells.

Thymus gland
The thymus gland is located above the heart. It is large in infants but becomes smaller with age. Immature T cells move to the thymus to mature before migrating to other lymphatic organs.

B CELLS	T CELLS

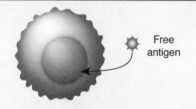

Free antigen

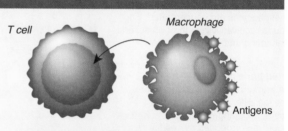

T cell   *Macrophage*

Antigens

B cells recognize and bind antigens. Each B cell recognizes one specific antigen. Helper T cells recognize specific antigens on B cell surfaces and induce their maturation and proliferation. A mature B cell may carry as many as 100,000 antigenic receptors embedded in its surface membrane. B cells defend against bacteria and viruses outside the cell and toxins produced by bacteria (free antigens).

T cells respond only to **antigen** fragments that have been processed and presented by specialized **antigen**-presenting cells (dendritic cells and macrophages). They defend against:
- Intracellular bacteria and viruses
- Protozoa, fungi, flatworms, and roundworms
- Cancerous cells and transplanted foreign tissue

Differentiate into two kinds of cells

Antibody

Differentiate into various kinds of cells

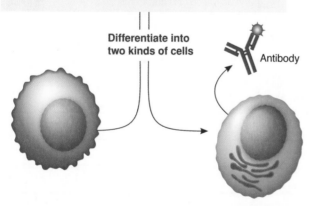

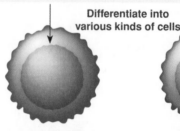

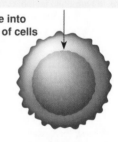

T helper cell activates T killer cells and other helper T cells. They are needed for B cell activation.

T killer cell destroys target cells on contact. Recognizes tumor or virus-infected cells by their surface markers. They are also called cytotoxic T cells.

Memory cells
Some B cells differentiate into long-lived memory cells (see Clonal Selection). When these cells encounter the same antigen again, even years or decades later, they rapidly differentiate into antibody-producing plasma cells.

Plasma cells
When stimulated by an antigen (see Clonal Selection), some B cells differentiate into plasma cells, which secrete antibodies into the bloodstream. The antibodies then inactivate the circulating antigens.

There are also other types of T cells:
T memory cells have encountered specific antigens before and can respond quickly and strongly when the same antigen is encountered again.

T regulator cells control the immune response by turning it off when no more antigen is present. They are important in the development of self tolerance.

©2023 **BIOZONE** International
ISBN: 978-1-99-101408-5
Photocopying Prohibited

Dendritic cells stimulate the activation and proliferation of lymphocytes

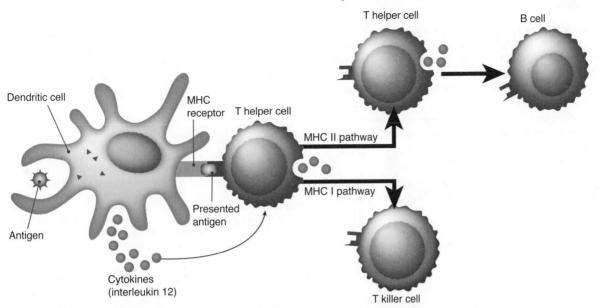

▸ Dendritic cells (DC) are antigen-presenting cells. Immature DC originate in bone marrow and migrate through the body to lymph nodes. When a DC encounters an antigen, it presents it to a T helper cell, stimulating it to secrete chemicals called cytokines. Cytokines stimulate the activation and proliferation (rapid increase in number) of T cells, activating the immune system against that specific antigen. T helper cells go on to stimulate the production of antibody-producing B cells.

▸ Dendritic cells with MHC I receptors stimulate the production of T killer cells.

▸ Dendritic cells with MHC II receptors stimulate the production of T helper cells.

1. Where do B cells and T cells originate (before maturing)? _____

2. (a) Where do B cells mature? _____

   (b) Where do T cells mature? _____

3. Describe the nature and general action of the two major divisions in the immune system:

   (a) Humoral immune system: _____

   _____

   _____

   (b) Cell-mediated immune system: _____

   _____

   _____

4. Explain how an antigen causes the activation and proliferation of T cells and B cells, including the role of dendritic cells:

   _____

   _____

   _____

   _____

5. In what way do dendritic cells act as messengers between the innate and the adaptive immune systems?

   _____

   _____

6. Describe the function of each of the following cells in the immune system response:

   (a) T helper cells: _____

   (b) T killer cells: _____

133 Clonal Selection

Key Idea: Clonal selection theory explains how lymphocytes can respond to a large and unpredictable range of antigens. The clonal selection theory explains how the **immune system** can respond to the large and unpredictable range of potential **antigens** in the environment. The diagram below describes clonal selection after antigen exposure for **B cells**. In the same way, a **T cell** stimulated by a specific antigen will multiply and develop into different types of T cells. Clonal selection and differentiation of **lymphocytes** provide the basis for immunological memory.

Five (a-e) of the many B cells generated during development. Each one can recognize only one specific antigen.

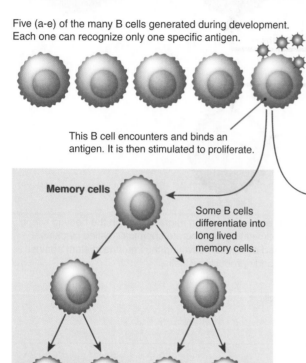

This B cell encounters and binds an antigen. It is then stimulated to proliferate.

Clonal selection theory

Millions of B cells form during development. Antigen recognition is randomly generated, so collectively they can recognize many antigens, including those that have never been encountered. Each B cell has receptors on its surface for specific antigens and produces antibodies that correspond to these receptors. When a B cell encounters its antigen, it responds by proliferating and producing many clones that produce the same kind of antibody. This is called clonal selection because the antigen selects the B cells that will proliferate.

Memory cells

Some B cells differentiate into long lived memory cells.

Some B cells differentiate into plasma cells.

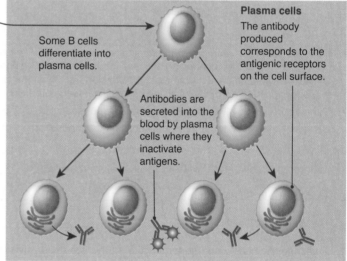

Plasma cells

The antibody produced corresponds to the antigenic receptors on the cell surface.

Antibodies are secreted into the blood by plasma cells where they inactivate antigens.

Some B cells differentiate into long lived memory cells. These are retained in the lymph nodes to provide future immunity (immunological memory). If the antigen returns a second time, memory B cells react more quickly and vigorously than the first time the antigen appeared.

Plasma cells secrete **antibodies** specific to the antigen that stimulated their development. Each plasma cell lives for only a few days, but can produce about 2000 antibody molecules per second. During development, any B cells that react to the body's own antigens are destroyed in a process that leads to self tolerance (acceptance of the body's own tissues).

1. Describe how clonal selection results in the proliferation of one particular B cell clone: _____

_____

_____

_____

2. (a) What is the function of the plasma cells in the immune system response? _____

_____

(b) What is the significance of B cells producing antibodies that correspond to (match) their antigenic receptors?

_____

_____

3. (a) Explain the basis of immunological memory: _____

_____

(b) Why are B memory cells able to respond so rapidly to an encounter with an antigen, long after an initial infection?

_____

_____

©2023 **BIOZONE** International
ISBN: 978-1-99-101408-5
Photocopying Prohibited

134 Antibodies

Key Idea: Antibodies are large, Y-shaped proteins, made by B cells, which destroy specific antigens.

Antibodies and **antigens** play key roles in the response of the **immune system**. Recall that antigens are foreign molecules that promote a specific immune response. Antigens include pathogenic microbes and their toxins, as well as substances such as pollen grains, blood cell surface molecules, and the

surface proteins on transplanted tissues. Antibodies (also called immunoglobulins) are proteins made in response to antigens. They are secreted from plasma **B cells** into the plasma where they can recognize, bind to, and help destroy **antigens**. There are five classes of antibodies, each playing a different role in the immune response. Each type of antibody is specific to only one particular antigen.

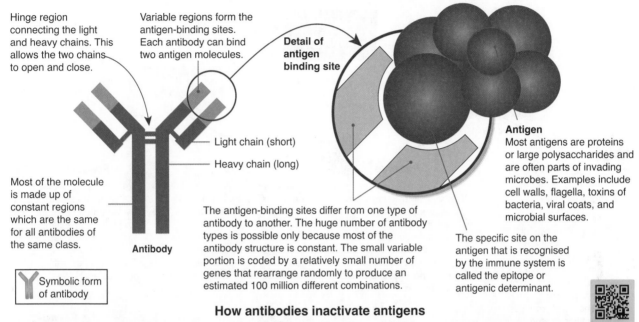

Hinge region connecting the light and heavy chains. This allows the two chains to open and close.

Variable regions form the antigen-binding sites. Each antibody can bind two antigen molecules.

Detail of antigen binding site

Light chain (short)

Heavy chain (long)

Most of the molecule is made up of constant regions which are the same for all antibodies of the same class.

Antibody

The antigen-binding sites differ from one type of antibody to another. The huge number of antibody types is possible only because most of the antibody structure is constant. The small variable portion is coded by a relatively small number of genes that rearrange randomly to produce an estimated 100 million different combinations.

Antigen
Most antigens are proteins or large polysaccharides and are often parts of invading microbes. Examples include cell walls, flagella, toxins of bacteria, viral coats, and microbial surfaces.

The specific site on the antigen that is recognised by the immune system is called the epitope or antigenic determinant.

Symbolic form of antibody

How antibodies inactivate antigens

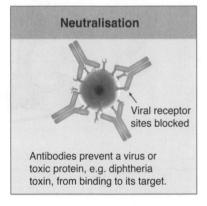

Neutralisation

Viral receptor sites blocked

Antibodies prevent a virus or toxic protein, e.g. diphtheria toxin, from binding to its target.

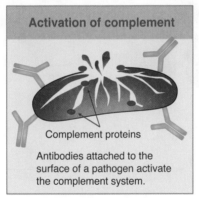

Activation of complement

Complement proteins

Antibodies attached to the surface of a pathogen activate the complement system.

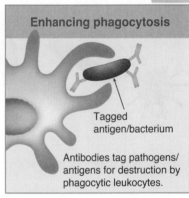

Enhancing phagocytosis

Tagged antigen/bacterium

Antibodies tag pathogens/ antigens for destruction by phagocytic leukocytes.

1. Describe the structure of an antibody, identifying the specific features of its structure that contribute to its function:

_____

_____

_____

2. Explain how the following actions by antibodies enhance the immune system's ability to stop infections:

(a) Acting as agglutinins: _____

_____

(b) Acting as antitoxins: _____

_____

(c) Tagging foreign cells with chemical markers: _____

_____

135 Acquired Immunity

Key Idea: Acquired immunity is a resistance to specific pathogens acquired over the life-time of an organism.
We are born with natural or innate resistance which provides non-specific immunity to certain illnesses. In contrast, acquired immunity is protection developed over time to specific **antigens**. Active immunity develops after the

immune system responds to being exposed to microbes or foreign substances. Passive immunity is acquired from gaining pre-formed **antibodies** without exposure to the antigen. Immunity can be naturally acquired, through natural exposure to microbes, or artificially acquired as a result of medical treatment (below).

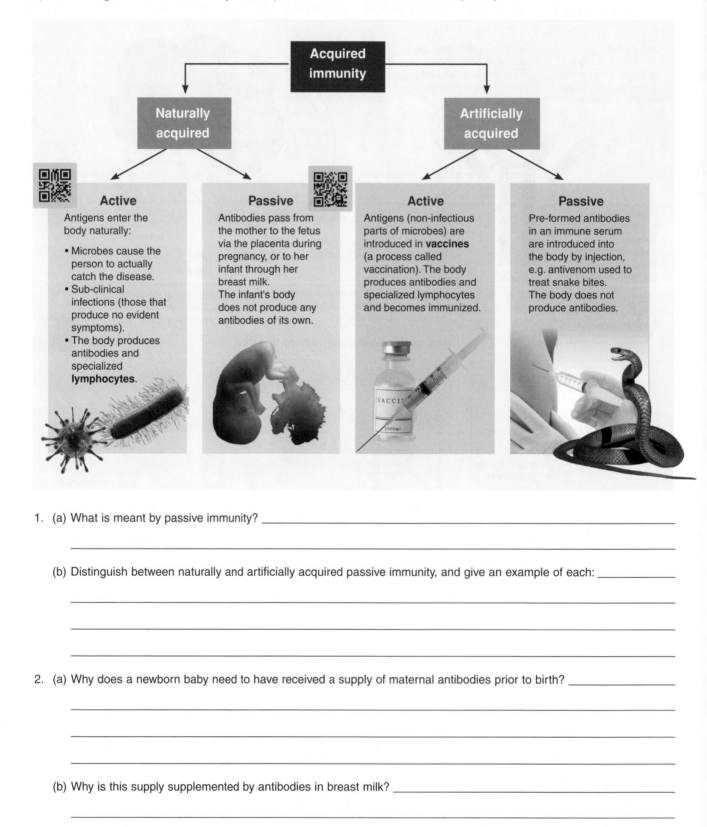

Acquired immunity

Naturally acquired

Active

Antigens enter the body naturally:

- Microbes cause the person to actually catch the disease.
- Sub-clinical infections (those that produce no evident symptoms).
- The body produces antibodies and specialized **lymphocytes**.

Passive

Antibodies pass from the mother to the fetus via the placenta during pregnancy, or to her infant through her breast milk.
The infant's body does not produce any antibodies of its own.

Artificially acquired

Active

Antigens (non-infectious parts of microbes) are introduced in **vaccines** (a process called vaccination). The body produces antibodies and specialized lymphocytes and becomes immunized.

VACCI
2000ml

Passive

Pre-formed antibodies in an immune serum are introduced into the body by injection, e.g. antivenom used to treat snake bites.
The body does not produce antibodies.

1. (a) What is meant by passive immunity? _____
   _____

   (b) Distinguish between naturally and artificially acquired passive immunity, and give an example of each: _____
   _____
   _____
   _____

2. (a) Why does a newborn baby need to have received a supply of maternal antibodies prior to birth? _____
   _____
   _____
   _____

   (b) Why is this supply supplemented by antibodies in breast milk? _____
   _____

3. (a) What is active immunity? _____
   _____

©2023 **BIOZONE** International
ISBN: 978-1-99-101408-5
Photocopying Prohibited

Primary and secondary response to antigens

When the **B cells** encounter antigens and produce antibodies, the body develops active immunity against that antigen.

The initial response to antigenic stimulation, caused by the sudden increase in B cell clones, is called the primary response. Antibody levels, as a result of the primary response, peak a few weeks after the response begins and then decline. However, because the immune system develops an immunological memory of that antigen, it responds much more quickly and strongly when presented with the same antigen subsequently (the secondary response).

This forms the basis of immunization programmes, where one or more booster shots are provided following the initial vaccination.

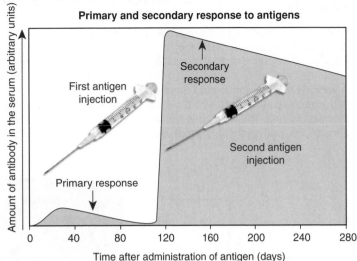

Primary and secondary response to antigens

(b) Distinguish between naturally and artificially acquired active immunity, and give an example of each: _____

_____

_____

_____

4. (a) Describe two differences between the primary and secondary responses to presentation of an antigen: _____

_____

_____

_____

(b) Why is the secondary response so different from the primary response? _____

_____

_____

_____

5. Chickenpox is a highly contagious disease caused by the varicella-zoster virus. It is a very serious disease and can be fatal. Study the graph on the right and answer the following questions:

(a) What year did the chickenpox vaccine program begin in the USA?

_____

(b) How many chickenpox deaths occurred in 1994 and 1995?

_____

_____

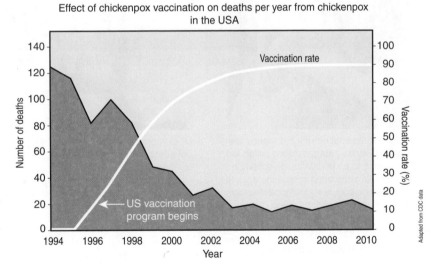

Effect of chickenpox vaccination on deaths per year from chickenpox in the USA

(c) Describe the effect of introducing the chickenpox vaccine into the US immunization schedule: _____

_____

_____

(d) Predict what would happen to the number of deaths per year if the chickenpox vaccination rates decreased:

_____

136 Vaccines and Vaccination

Key Idea: A vaccine is a suspension of antigens that is deliberately introduced into the body to protect against disease. If enough of the population is vaccinated, herd immunity provides protection to unvaccinated individuals.

A **vaccine** is a preparation of a harmless foreign **antigen** that is deliberately introduced into the body to protect against a specific disease. The antigen in the vaccine is usually some part of the pathogen. It triggers the **immune system** to produce **antibodies** against the antigen but it does not cause the disease. The immune system remembers its response and will produce the same antibodies if it encounters the antigen again. If enough of the population is vaccinated, herd immunity (indirect protection) provides unvaccinated individuals in the population with a measure of protection against the disease. There are two basic types of vaccine: subunit vaccines and whole-agent vaccines (below).

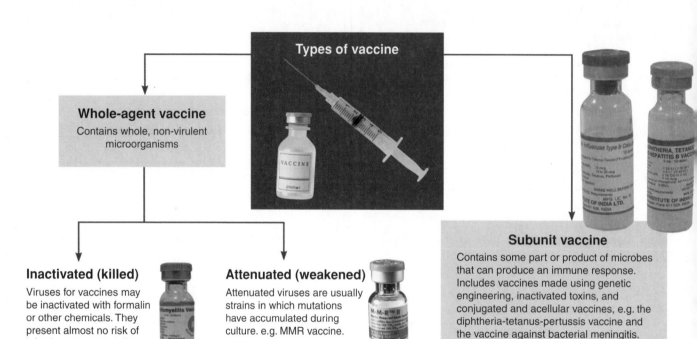

Types of vaccine

Whole-agent vaccine
Contains whole, non-virulent microorganisms

Inactivated (killed)
Viruses for vaccines may be inactivated with formalin or other chemicals. They present almost no risk of infection, e.g. most influenza vaccines, Salk polio vaccine.

Attenuated (weakened)
Attenuated viruses are usually strains in which mutations have accumulated during culture. e.g. MMR vaccine.

Subunit vaccine
Contains some part or product of microbes that can produce an immune response. Includes vaccines made using genetic engineering, inactivated toxins, and conjugated and acellular vaccines, e.g. the diphtheria-tetanus-pertussis vaccine and the vaccine against bacterial meningitis.

Why are vaccinations given?

Vaccines against common diseases are given at various stages during childhood, according to an immunization schedule. Vaccination has been behind the decline of some once-common childhood diseases, such as mumps and measles.

Most vaccinations are given in childhood, but adults may be vaccinated against a disease, e.g. TB, tetanus, if they are in a high risk group, e.g. the elderly or farmers, or to provide protection against seasonal diseases such as influenza.

Tourists may need specific **vaccines** if the country they are visiting has a high incidence of a certain disease. For example, travellers from Australia to South America should be immunized against yellow fever, because yellow fever does not occur in Australia.

1. (a) What is a vaccine? _____

_____

(b) Provide some examples of when vaccinations are needed: _____

_____

_____

_____

Vaccination can provide herd immunity

▶ Herd immunity occurs when the vaccination of a significant portion of a population provides some protection for individuals who have not developed immunity, e.g. have not been vaccinated and are not immunized. In order to be effective for any particular disease, a high percentage of the population needs to be vaccinated against that disease. High vaccination rates make it difficult for the disease to spread because there are very few susceptible people in the population.

▶ Herd immunity is important for people who cannot be vaccinated, e.g. the very young, people with immune system disorders, or people who are very sick, such as cancer patients.

High herd immunity: Most of the population is immunized. The spread of the disease is limited. Only a few people are susceptible and become infected.

Low herd immunity: Only a small proportion of the population is immunized. The disease spreads more readily through the population, infecting many more people.

Immunized and healthy

Not immunized and healthy

Not immunized, sick and contagious

The level of vaccination coverage to obtain herd immunity differs for each disease. Highly contagious diseases, e.g. measles, need a much higher vaccine uptake (95%) than a less contagious disease such as polio (80-85%).

2. Attenuated viruses provide long term immunity to their recipients and generally do not require booster shots. Why do you think attenuated viruses provide such effective long-term immunity when inactivated viruses do not?

_____

_____

_____

_____

3. (a) What is herd immunity? _____

_____

_____

(b) Why are health authorities concerned when the vaccination rates for an infectious disease fall? _____

_____

_____

4. Some members of the population, e.g. people with specific illnesses or undergoing certain treatments, are unable to be vaccinated. Give an example and explain why herd immunity is very important to them:

_____

_____

_____

137 HIV and the Immune System

Key Idea: The human immunodeficiency virus (HIV) infects lymphocyte cells, eventually causing AIDS, a fatal disease, which acts by impairing immune system function.

HIV (human immunodeficiency virus) is a retrovirus (a type of viral pathogen). It causes immune deficiency by destroying T helper cells, which are central to cellular immunity. Over time, a disease called AIDS (acquired immunodeficiency syndrome) develops and the **immune system** progressively loses its ability to fight infection. HIV is transmitted in blood, vaginal secretions, semen, breast milk, and across the placenta. There are a number of drugs available that are effective at slowing the progress of the disease or can help reduce the risk of infection.

HIV infects T helper cells

HIV infects T helper cells. It uses the cells to replicate itself in great numbers, then the newly formed viral particles exit the cell to infect more T helper cells. Many T helper cells are destroyed by the viral replication. Because of their role in cellular immunity, T helper cell destruction recruits more **T cells**, accelerating the infection of new cells.

Once the T helper cell population becomes depleted, the immune system's ability to fight infection is severely compromised.

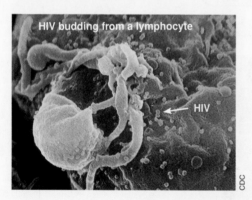

HIV budding from a lymphocyte

HIV

CDC

The graph below shows the relationship between the level of HIV infection and the number of T helper cells. AIDS is only the end stage of an HIV infection. Shortly after the initial infection, HIV **antibodies** appear in the blood. There are three clinical categories during progression of the disease.

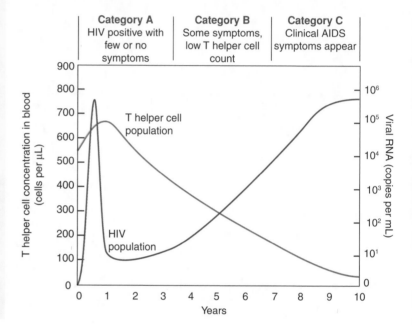

Category A HIV positive with few or no symptoms

Category B Some symptoms, low T helper cell count

Category C Clinical AIDS symptoms appear

T helper cell concentration in blood (cells per µL)

Viral RNA (copies per mL)

T helper cell population

HIV population

Years

HIV uses the cellular machinery of T helper cells to replicate

The genetic material of HIV is a single strand of RNA.

HIV hijacks the T helper cells' machinery to replicate itself. Reverse transcriptase produces double stranded DNA (dsDNA) from the viral RNA. The host cell transcribes the viral genes to produce new viruses.

The new HIV particles bud from the T helper cell. Between 1000 and 3000 new HIV particles can be released from a single infected cell.

The HIV particles mature and infect more T helper cells. As more T helper cells become infected, the body's immune response weakens.

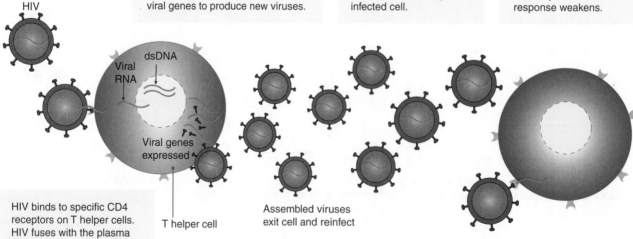

HIV

Viral RNA

dsDNA

Viral genes expressed

T helper cell

HIV binds to specific CD4 receptors on T helper cells. HIV fuses with the plasma membrane of the T helper cell. Its RNA enters the cell.

Assembled viruses exit cell and reinfect

©2023 **BIOZONE** International
ISBN: 978-1-99-101408-5
Photocopying Prohibited

AIDS: The end stage of an HIV infection

HIV/AIDS is a spectrum of disorders (right) arising as a consequence of impaired immune function, which prevents the body detecting and destroying pathogens or damaged cells.

People with healthy immune systems can fight off the challenges of pathogens and are able to detect and destroy damaged (pre-cancerous) cells. However, people with HIV are susceptible to all pathogens because their resistance to disease is so low. What's more, loss of the **T cell** population compromises the ability of HIV-infected people to detect and destroy pre-cancerous cells. Rare cancers are a common symptom of HIV/AIDS.

Medications

Antibiotics can be used to treat some of the infections contracted due to the reduced **immune system**, e.g. tuberculosis, but they cannot be used to treat the HIV infection itself because antibiotics are ineffective against viruses.

Although there is currently no cure for HIV/AIDS, some antiretoviral drugs can slow the progress of the disease by interfering with the replication of HIV and slowing the advance of the disease.

Pre-exposure prophylaxis (PrEP) medications (right) can be prescribed to people who do not have HIV, but are at risk of contracting it. Correct use of PrEP, along with other precautions, can reduce the risk of contracting HIV by up to 99%.

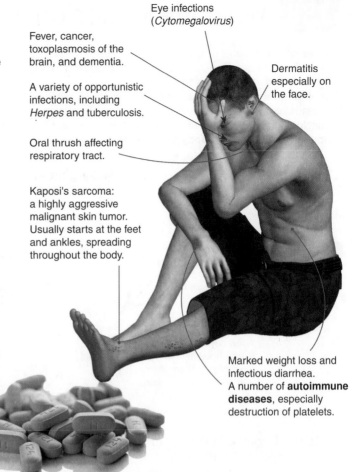

Eye infections (*Cytomegalovirus*)

Fever, cancer, toxoplasmosis of the brain, and dementia.

A variety of opportunistic infections, including *Herpes* and tuberculosis.

Oral thrush affecting respiratory tract.

Kaposi's sarcoma: a highly aggressive malignant skin tumor. Usually starts at the feet and ankles, spreading throughout the body.

Dermatitis especially on the face.

Marked weight loss and infectious diarrhea. A number of **autoimmune diseases**, especially destruction of platelets.

1. (a) What type of cells does HIV infect? _____

   (b) How does HIV recognize this type of cell? _____

   _____

   (c) What is the role of reverse transcriptase in HIV replication? _____

   _____

   _____

2. Study the graph on the previous page showing how HIV affects the number of T helper cells. Describe how the viral population changes with the progression of the disease:

   _____

   _____

   _____

   _____

3. (a) What effect does HIV have the cells of the immune system? _____

   _____

   _____

   (b) Describe the effect of this change on the long-term health of a person with HIV: _____

   _____

   _____

   _____

138 What Are Monoclonal Antibodies?

Key Idea: Monoclonal antibodies are artificially produced antibodies that neutralize specific antigens. They have many diagnostic and therapeutic applications.

A **monoclonal antibody** is an artificially produced antibody that binds to and neutralizes one specific type of **antigen**. A monoclonal antibody binds an antigen in the same way that a normally produced **antibody** does. Monoclonal antibodies are useful because they are identical, i.e. clones. They can be produced in large quantities and they are highly specific for a particular antigen. Most monoclonal antibodies are produced in mice, and in some people the foreign mouse proteins can cause an unwanted immune response. Monoclonal antibodies have wide applications in diagnosing and treating disease, in detecting pregnancy, and in food safety tests.

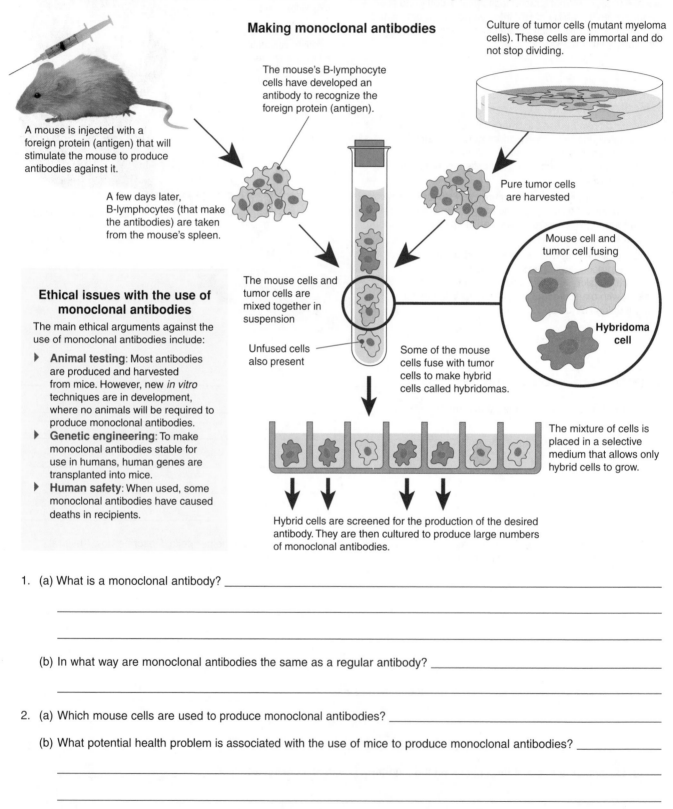

Making monoclonal antibodies

A mouse is injected with a foreign protein (antigen) that will stimulate the mouse to produce antibodies against it.

The mouse's B-lymphocyte cells have developed an antibody to recognize the foreign protein (antigen).

A few days later, B-lymphocytes (that make the antibodies) are taken from the mouse's spleen.

Culture of tumor cells (mutant myeloma cells). These cells are immortal and do not stop dividing.

Pure tumor cells are harvested

Mouse cell and tumor cell fusing

Hybridoma cell

The mouse cells and tumor cells are mixed together in suspension

Unfused cells also present

Some of the mouse cells fuse with tumor cells to make hybrid cells called hybridomas.

The mixture of cells is placed in a selective medium that allows only hybrid cells to grow.

Hybrid cells are screened for the production of the desired antibody. They are then cultured to produce large numbers of monoclonal antibodies.

Ethical issues with the use of monoclonal antibodies

The main ethical arguments against the use of monoclonal antibodies include:

▸ **Animal testing**: Most antibodies are produced and harvested from mice. However, new *in vitro* techniques are in development, where no animals will be required to produce monoclonal antibodies.

▸ **Genetic engineering**: To make monoclonal antibodies stable for use in humans, human genes are transplanted into mice.

▸ **Human safety**: When used, some monoclonal antibodies have caused deaths in recipients.

1. (a) What is a monoclonal antibody? _____

_____

_____

(b) In what way are monoclonal antibodies the same as a regular antibody? _____

_____

2. (a) Which mouse cells are used to produce monoclonal antibodies? _____

(b) What potential health problem is associated with the use of mice to produce monoclonal antibodies? _____

_____

_____

3. Which characteristic of tumor cells allows an ongoing culture of antibody-producing lymphocytes to be made? _____

_____

©2023 **BIOZONE** International
ISBN: 978-1-99-101408-5
Photocopying Prohibited

Using monoclonal antibodies to detect HIV

A monoclonal antibody test can be used to detect the presence of HIV (right) in blood serum. An outline of one testing method, using an enzyme-linked color change reaction, is given below.

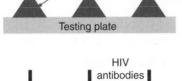

The HIV antigen is attached to a testing plate.

HIV antigen

Testing plate

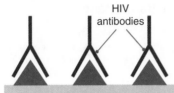

Blood serum from the patient being tested is passed over the plate. Any HIV antibodies naturally present in the blood will bind to the antigen. The plate is washed to remove unbound components.

HIV antibodies

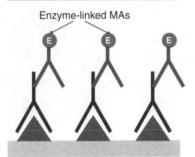

Enzyme-linked MAs

A monoclonal antibody (MA) is passed over the plate. Its antigen is the HIV antibody and it will bind to it if it is present. The MA has an enzyme (E) attached.

The amount of the monoclonal antibody that is bound is proportional to the amount of bound HIV antibody.

Chromogen dye (the enzyme's substrate)

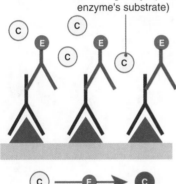

A chromogen dye (C) is passed over the plate. A chromogen is able to become colored and act as a dye after a reaction, e.g. oxidation.

The enzyme catalyzes a change in the color of the chromogen dye substrate. The more intense the color on the plate, the more HIV antibody present in the patient's serum.

HIV negative   **HIV positive**

Other applications of monoclonal antibodies

Diagnostic uses

- Detecting the presence of pathogens such as *Chlamydia* and streptococcal bacteria, distinguishing between *Herpesvirus* I and II, and diagnosing AIDS.
- Measuring protein, toxin, or drug levels in serum.
- Blood and tissue typing.
- Detection of antibiotic residues in milk.
- Pregnancy testing.

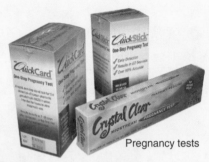

Pregnancy tests

Therapeutic uses

- Neutralizing endotoxins produced by bacteria in blood infections.
- Used to prevent organ rejection, e.g. in kidney transplants, by interfering with the **T cells** involved with the rejection of transplanted tissue.
- Used in the treatment of some auto-immune disorders such as rheumatoid arthritis and allergic asthma. The monoclonal antibodies bind to and inactivate factors involved in the cascade leading to the inflammatory response.
- Immunodetection and immunotherapy of cancer. Herceptin is a monoclonal antibody for the targeted treatment of breast cancer. Herceptin recognizes receptor proteins on the outside of cancer cells and binds to them. The **immune system** can then identify the antibodies as foreign and destroy the cell.
- Inhibition of platelet clumping, which is used to prevent reclogging of coronary arteries in patients who have undergone angioplasty. The monoclonal antibodies bind to the receptors on the platelet surface that are normally linked by fibrinogen during the clotting process.

4. (a) The test described above does not directly measure the HIV virus. What does it measure? _____

    _____

    _____

    (b) Explain how the presence of the substance you named in (a) indicates the presence of HIV: _____

    _____

    (c) What is the antigen for the monoclonal antibodies? _____

    (d) Why are the monoclonal antibodies linked to an enzyme? _____

    _____

    _____

139 Herceptin: A Modern Monoclonal

Key Idea: Herceptin is the patented name of a monoclonal antibody for the targeted treatment of breast cancer.

Herceptin (chemical name Trastuzumab) recognizes and is specific to the receptor proteins on the outside of cancer cells that are produced by the proto-oncogene HER2. The HER2 (Human Epidermal growth factor Receptor 2) gene codes for cell surface proteins that signal to the cell when it should divide. Cancerous cells contain 20-30% more of the HER2 gene than normal cells and this causes over-expression of HER2, and large amounts of HER2 protein.

The over-expression causes the cell to divide more often than normal, producing a tumor. Cancerous cells are designated HER2+ indicating receptor protein over-expression. The **immune system** fails to destroy these cells because they are not recognized as being abnormal. Herceptin's role is to recognize and bind to the HER2 protein on the surface of the cancerous cell. The immune system can then identify the **antibodies** as foreign and destroy the cell. The antibody also has the effect of blocking the cell's signaling pathway and thus stops the cell from dividing.

Herceptin targeted destruction of cancer cells

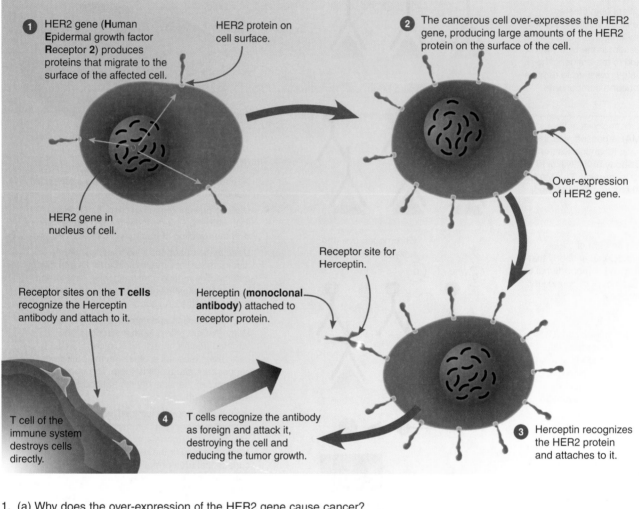

1 HER2 gene (**H**uman **E**pidermal growth factor **R**eceptor **2**) produces proteins that migrate to the surface of the affected cell.

HER2 protein on cell surface.

HER2 gene in nucleus of cell.

2 The cancerous cell over-expresses the HER2 gene, producing large amounts of the HER2 protein on the surface of the cell.

Over-expression of HER2 gene.

Receptor site for Herceptin.

Receptor sites on the **T cells** recognize the Herceptin antibody and attach to it.

Herceptin (**monoclonal antibody**) attached to receptor protein.

T cell of the immune system destroys cells directly.

4 T cells recognize the antibody as foreign and attack it, destroying the cell and reducing the tumor growth.

3 Herceptin recognizes the HER2 protein and attaches to it.

1. (a) Why does the over-expression of the HER2 gene cause cancer? _____

_____

(b) Why does the immune system require Herceptin to help target cancerous cells? _____

_____

_____

2. Describe the two ways in which Herceptin works to fight cancer:

(a) _____

(b) _____

3. Why is the use of Herceptin and other monoclonal antibody drugs called targeted drug therapy?

_____

_____

©2023 **BIOZONE** International
ISBN: 978-1-99-101408-5
Photocopying Prohibited

140 Monoclonals Against Autoimmune Disease

Key Idea: Monoclonal antibodies can help reduce the effects of autoimmune diseases by blocking specific cell receptors. Many **autoimmune diseases** result partly from the excessive production of, or hyper-sensitivity to, inflammation-promoting molecules. Such inflammatory autoimmune diseases include rheumatoid arthritis and multiple sclerosis. One of the most import molecules in these diseases is the protein interleukin 6. This is a cytokine (signal molecule) that promotes the inflammatory response. **Monoclonal antibodies** block the cell receptors for interleukin 6, reducing its effect.

IL-6 and inflammatory autoimmune disorders

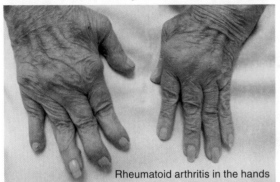

Rheumatoid arthritis in the hands

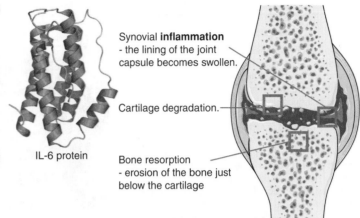

IL-6 protein

Synovial **inflammation** - the lining of the joint capsule becomes swollen.

Cartilage degradation.

Bone resorption - erosion of the bone just below the cartilage

▶ Interleukin 6 (IL-6) promotes **inflammation**. It is produced by immune cells and is involved in cell signaling, including stimulating **T** and **B cells**.

▶ In particular, IL-6 increases the number of pro-inflammatory T cells relative to regulatory T cells. This can result in inflammatory autoimmune diseases such as rheumatoid arthritis.

▶ Effects of IL-6 on joint inflammation are shown right.

Rheumatoid arthritis is an **autoimmune disease** that primarily affects the joints. Thickening of the synovial membrane invades and damages adjacent cartilage and bone.

It results in swollen and painful joints, but can include numerous other issues including low red blood cell count, and **inflammation** of the lungs and heart.

▶ In affected patients, IL-6 binds to the IL-6 receptor in the cell membrane. This triggers processes in the cell, resulting in the autoimmune effects of IL-6. Receptors can also be found in soluble form outside the cell. These bind with IL-6 and then dock with the cell membrane.

▶ Tocilizumab is a monoclonal antibody that binds to the IL-6 receptor and blocks IL-6 from binding. This then reduces the effect of IL-6 on the immune response.

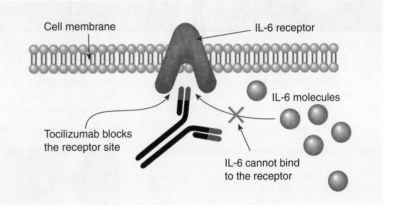

Cell membrane

IL-6 receptor

IL-6 molecules

Tocilizumab blocks the receptor site

IL-6 cannot bind to the receptor

1. What is the role of IL-6? _____

_____

_____

2. How does it cause autoimmune diseases such as rheumatoid arthritis? _____

_____

_____

3. How does Tocilizumab reduce the symptoms of autoimmune diseases like rheumatoid arthritis? _____

_____

_____

_____

4. Why is using a monoclonal antibody useful to target specific receptors? _____

_____

141 Allergies and Hypersensitivity

Key Idea: Sometimes the immune system may overreact, or react to the wrong substances instead of responding appropriately.

Overreaction of the immune systems is called **hypersensitivity** and the immunological response leads to tissue damage rather than immunity. Hypersensitivity reactions occur after a person has been sensitized to an **antigen**. In some cases, this causes only localized discomfort, as in the case of hayfever. More generalized reactions, such as anaphylaxis from insect venom or drug injections, or localized reactions that affect essential body systems, such as asthma, can cause death through asphyxiation and/or circulatory shock.

Hypersensitivity

A person becomes sensitized when they form **antibodies** to harmless substances in the environment, such as pollen or spores (steps 1-2 right). These substances, or allergens, act as antigens to induce antibody production and an allergic response. Once a person is sensitized, the antibodies respond to further encounters with the allergen by causing the release of histamine from mast cells (steps 4-5). Histamine mediates the symptoms of hypersensitivity reactions such as hay fever and asthma. These symptoms include wheezing and airway constriction, **inflammation**, itching and watering of the eyes and nose, and/or sneezing.

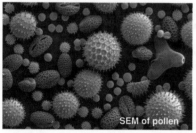 
SEM of pollen | Ragweed

Hay fever is an allergic reaction to airborne substances, such as dust, molds, pollens, and animal fur. Allergy to wind-borne pollen is the most common, and certain plants, e.g. ragweed and privet, are highly allergenic. There appears to be a genetic susceptibility to hay fever, as it is common in people with a family history of eczema, hives, and/or asthma. The best treatment for hay fever is to avoid the allergen, although anti-histamines, decongestants, and steroid nasal sprays will assist in alleviating symptoms.

Asthma is a common disease affecting more than 15 million people in the US. It usually occurs as a result of an allergic reaction to allergens such as the feces of house dust mites, pollen, and animal dander. As with all hypersensitivity reactions, it involves the production of histamines from mast cells. The site of the reaction is the respiratory bronchioles where the histamine causes constriction of the airways, accumulation of fluid and mucus, and inability to breathe. During an attack, sufferers show labored breathing with overexpansion of the chest cavity (right).

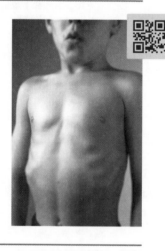

Asthma attacks are often triggered by environmental factors, such as cold air, exercise, air pollutants, and viral infections. Recent evidence has also indicated the involvement of a bacterium, *Chlamydia pneumoniae*, in about half of all cases of asthma in susceptible adults.

The basis of hypersensitivity

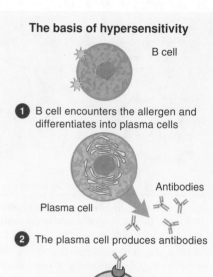

B cell

1 B cell encounters the allergen and differentiates into plasma cells

Plasma cell

Antibodies

2 The plasma cell produces antibodies

Mast cell

3 Antibodies bind to specific receptors on the surface of the mast cells

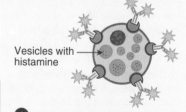

Vesicles with histamine

4 The mast cell binds the allergen when it encounters it again.

5 The mast cell releases histamine and other chemicals, which together cause the symptoms of an allergic reaction.

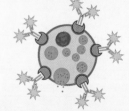

---

1. Explain the role of histamine in hypersensitivity responses: _____

_____

2. Explain what is meant by becoming sensitized to an allergen: _____

_____

3. Explain the effect of bronchodilators and explain why they are used to treat asthma: _____

_____

©2023 **BIOZONE** International
ISBN: 978-1-99-101408-5
Photocopying Prohibited

142 Organ and Tissue Transplants

Key Idea: Transplant surgery replaces a damaged organ or tissue with a healthy, living one from a donor. Transplants can be carried out on many parts of the human body.

Transplants replace damaged organs. The donor is usually someone who is brain dead (their breathing and heartbeat are maintained artificially) or has just died, but transplant material, e.g. bone marrow, blood, kidney, can also be taken from a living donor. Two major problems associated with organ transplants are the lack of donors and tissue rejection. Recall that the genetically determined **MHC** antigens on the surface of all cells are responsible for the **immune system's**

recognition of the body's own tissues. Cells from donor tissue will have different MHC antigens to those of the recipient, and the donor tissue will be recognized as foreign and attacked (rejected). The success of transplants is continually increasing. The reasons for this increase include better tissue-typing and more effective immunosuppressant drugs, both of which decrease the MHC response. Surgical techniques and methods for organ preservation and transport also continue to improve. Tissue engineering and stem cell technology has also been used to create bioartificial organs (organs created from donor cells grown on an artificial scaffold).

Organ transplants

Currently, there are five organs that are routinely transplanted (below). In addition to organs, whole hand transplants and partial or whole face transplants are now possible.

Face: Facial reconstructions began initially with reconnection of a patient's own facial components damaged in accidents. More recently, medical techniques have developed so that partial reconstructions (usually of nose and mouth) are possible, using facial material from a dead donor. In 2008, a French medical team completed the world's first full face transplant. These types of transplants require careful connection of blood vessels, skin, muscles, and bone, tendons, and other connective tissues. Performing face transplants also involves addressing a number of ethical concerns.

Lungs: Replacement of organs damaged by cystic fibrosis or emphysema. Typically, lungs are transplanted together, but single lung transplants and heart-lung transplants are also possible.

Heart: These transplants are carried out after a patient suffers heart failure due to heart attack, viral infections of the heart, or congenital, irreparable defects.

Liver: Substitute for a liver destroyed by cirrhosis, congenital defects, or hepatitis.

Hands: In 1999, the first successful hand transplant was performed on Matthew Scott, in the USA. A year and a half after the operation, he could sense temperature, pressure and pain, and could write, turn the pages of a newspaper, tie shoelaces and throw a baseball. Many successful hand transplants have been undertaken since.

Pancreas: Restores insulin production in Type I diabetics (caused by autoimmune destruction of the insulin-producing cells of the pancreas).

Kidneys: Used in cases of renal failure, diabetes, high blood pressure, inherited illnesses, and infection. The failing kidneys are usually left *in situ* and the transplant (Kt) is placed in a location different from the original kidney.

Tissue transplants

A large number of tissues are currently used in transplant procedures. An estimated 200 patients can potentially benefit from the organs and tissues donated from a single body.

Cornea: Transplants can restore impaired vision.

Dental powder: This tissue is prepared to help rebuild defects in the mandible (which supports the teeth).

Jaw: The mandible is used in facial reconstruction.

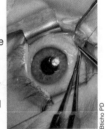
Bticho PD

Ear bones: The three bones of the inner ear can be transplanted to improve some forms of deafness.

Pericardium: The pericardium surrounding the heart is made of tough tissue that can be used to cover the brain after surgery. Transplants of the brain coverings themselves are no longer performed because of the risk of transmitting prion infections.

Blood and blood vessels: Blood transfusions are transplants of blood tissue. Blood vessels, mostly veins, can be transplanted to reroute blood around blockages, such as this atherosclerotic plaque (right) in the body.

Plaque

Ed Uthman CC 2.0

Hip joints: Joints can be reconstructed by transplanting the head of the femur.

Bone marrow: Marrow is extracted from living donors and used to help people with a wide variety of illnesses, such as leukemia.

Bones: Long bones of the arms and legs can be used in limb reconstruction; ribs can be used for spinal fusions and facial repair.

Cartilage and ligaments: Orthopedic surgeons use these materials to rebuild ankle, knee, hip, elbow, and shoulder joints.

Skin: Skin can be used as a temporary covering for burn injuries until the patient's own skin grows back.

Second degree burn

Westchaser PD

Commonly performed transplants

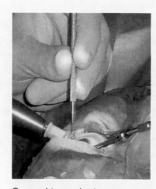

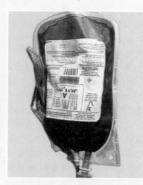

Corneal transplants can be used to restore sight in patients with damaged vision. The cornea naturally has a poor blood supply, so rejection is less of a problem than with some other tissues

For many amputees, being fitted with an artificial limb is the first step towards mobility. In the future, such prostheses may be replaced with limb transplants, in much the same way as current hand transplants.

Transplants of whole blood, blood plasma, platelets, and other blood components are crucial to many medical procedures. The donor blood is carefully typed to ensure compatibility with the recipient.

Many patients with kidney failure rely on regular dialysis in order to function. This is expensive and inconvenient, and carries health risks. Such patients are usually waiting for a kidney transplant.

1. What are the five most commonly transplanted organs? _____

   _____

2. (a) Explain the basis for organ and tissue rejection: _____

   _____

   (b) Explain the role of tissue typing and immunosuppressant drugs in reducing or preventing this response:

   _____

   _____

   _____

3. Debate some reasons for and against organ transplants. Consider costs, benefits, source of tissue, and criteria for choosing recipients. Summarize a justification for or against organ transplants below:

   _____

   _____

   _____

   _____

   _____

   _____

   _____

   _____

   _____

   _____

   _____

   _____

   _____

   _____

   _____

143 Stem Cell Technology

Key Idea: Stems cells can potentially be used to produce organs for transplant.

Stem cells are undifferentiated cells, able to give rise to a number of other specialized cell types. Their two important properties, self renewal and potency, make them valuable as a source of cell lines for research and therapy. Two types of stem cell are important in medicine and research: embryonic stems cells, which are found in the early embryo, and adult stem cells, which occur in some tissues of adults and children. There is still much to learn in stem cell research about the environments that cells require in order to differentiate into specific cell types. However, potential applications include tissue engineering and cell therapy to replace diseased or damaged cells with new ones grown in culture.

Embryonic stem cells

Embryonic stem cells (ESCs) are pluripotent stem cells from the inner cell mass of blastocysts (below). Blastocysts are embryos of about 50-150 cells that are about five days old. Most ESCs come from IVF embryos, which have been donated for research. When grown *in vitro*, ESCs retain their pluripotency for many cell divisions, provided they are not stimulated to differentiate.

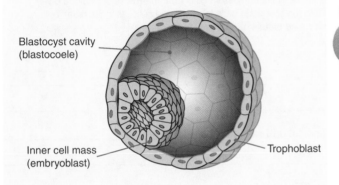

- Blastocyst cavity (blastocoele)
- Inner cell mass (embryoblast)
- Trophoblast

Stem cell properties

Self renewal: The ability to divide many times while maintaining an unspecialized state.

Potency: The ability to differentiate into specialized cells.

The potency of stem cells

Totipotent: Stem cells that can differentiate into all the cells in an organism. In humans, only the zygote and its first few divisions are totipotent.

Pluripotent: Stem cells that can become any cells of the body, except extra-embryonic cells, such as the placenta. Embryonic stem cells are pluripotent.

Multipotent: Stem cells that give rise a limited number of cell types, usually related to their tissue of origin (e.g. hematopoietic stem cells give rise to all blood cell types).

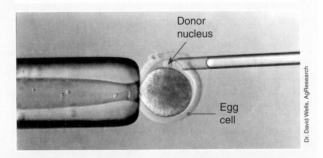

- Donor nucleus
- Egg cell

Dr. David Wells, AgResearch

Histocompatibility refers to the compatibility of cells and tissues between different individuals. If donor material is poorly matched to the recipient, the recipient's **immune system** rejects the donor cells. Stem cell cloning, also called therapeutic cloning, provides a way around this problem. Stem cell cloning produces cells that have been derived from the recipient, and are therefore histocompatible. Transplantation success rates are much improved and immunosuppressant drugs are no longer required.

Embryonic stem cell cloning

When ESCs are provided with appropriate growth conditions, they will differentiate into specialized cell types. Scientists can control this process by manipulating the *in vitro* culture conditions to produce cells of a particular type for a particular purpose, e.g. heart cells to replaced damaged heart tissue.

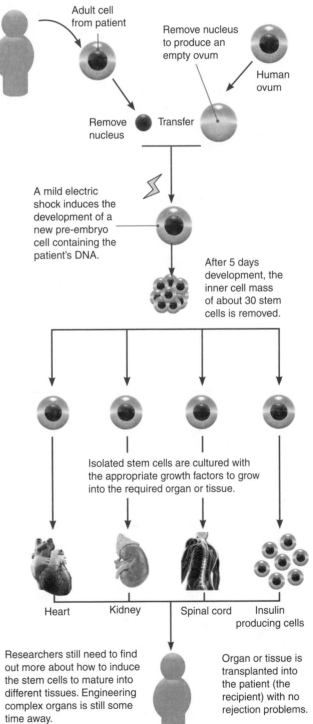

- Adult cell from patient
- Remove nucleus to produce an empty ovum
- Human ovum
- Remove nucleus — Transfer

A mild electric shock induces the development of a new pre-embryo cell containing the patient's DNA.

After 5 days development, the inner cell mass of about 30 stem cells is removed.

Isolated stem cells are cultured with the appropriate growth factors to grow into the required organ or tissue.

- Heart
- Kidney
- Spinal cord
- Insulin producing cells

Researchers still need to find out more about how to induce the stem cells to mature into different tissues. Engineering complex organs is still some time away.

Organ or tissue is transplanted into the patient (the recipient) with no rejection problems.

Adult stem cells

- Adult stem cells (ASC) are undifferentiated cells found in several types of tissues in adults and children, e.g. brain, bone marrow, skin, and liver; and in umbilical cord blood. ASCs are also called somatic stem cells.

- ASCs are multipotent, meaning they can only differentiate into a limited number of cell types, usually related to the tissue of origin.

- The function of ASCs in the body is to replace dying cells and repair damaged tissue.

- There are fewer ethical issues associated with using ASCs because they are derived from adult tissues, whereas ESCs are harvested from human embryos.

- ASCs are already used to treat a number of diseases, including leukemia and other blood disorders.

- In many countries, parents of newborns have blood from the umbilical cord stored in a cord blood bank, which can be used for self transplants to treat a range of diseases.

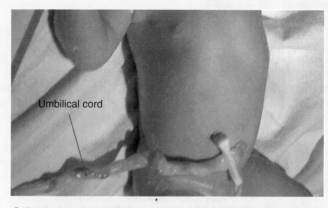

Umbilical cord

Cells obtained from umbilical cord blood (above) or bone marrow could be used to treat patients with a variety of diseases, including leukemia, lymphomas, anemia, and a range of congenital diseases. Multipotent stem cells from marrow or cord blood give rise to the precursor cells for red blood cells, all white blood cell types, and platelets.

1. (a) Identify the two defining properties of stem cells: _____

   _____

   (b) Why do these properties make stem cells valuable for medical and research purposes? _____

   _____

2. Describe the main differences between embryonic stem cells (ESC) and adult stem cells (ASC): _____

   _____

   _____

   _____

   _____

3. Why are ASC therapies less controversial than therapies using ESC? _____

   _____

   _____

   _____

   _____

4. Discuss the techniques or the applications of therapeutic stem cell cloning (including ethical issues where relevant):

   _____

   _____

   _____

   _____

   _____

   _____

   _____

   _____

   _____

   _____

144 Gene Therapy for Immune Dysfunction

Key Idea: Gene therapy involves correcting genetic disorders by replacing a defective or missing gene with a normally functioning version.

Gene therapies vary in their technical detail, but all are based around the same technique. Normal (non-faulty) DNA containing the correct copy of the gene is inserted into a vector, which transfers the DNA into the patient's cells in a process called transfection. Viruses and liposomes are commonly used vectors. The vector is introduced into a sample of the patient's cells and these are cultured to amplify the gene. The cultured cells are then transferred back to the patient, and the corrected gene begins to be expressed. The treatment of somatic cells or stem cells may be therapeutic, but the changes are not inherited. Modification of gametes (germ-line therapy) would enable genetic changes to be inherited. Gene therapy has had limited success because transfection of targeted cells is usually inefficient and the side effects can be severe or even fatal.

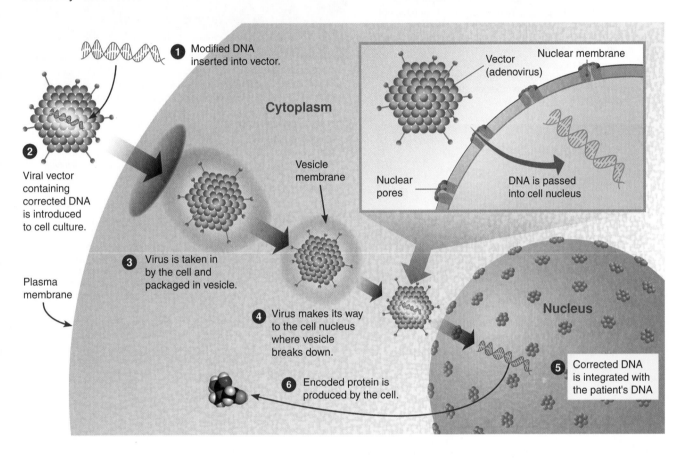

1. (a) Describe the general principle of gene therapy: _____

_____

_____

_____

(b) Describe the medical areas where gene therapy might be used: _____

_____

_____

2. Explain the significance of transfecting germ-line cells rather than somatic (body) cells: _____

_____

_____

_____

_____

3. What do you think is the purpose of amplifying the gene prior to transferring the cultured cells back to the patient?

_____

Treating SCID using gene therapy

What is SCID?

▶ SCID (severe combined immunodeficiency) describes a group of inherited disorders affecting production of **B-** and **T cells**. Children born with SCID have no specific **immune system** and are susceptible to life-threatening infections. Without early diagnosis and treatment, they usually die before their second birthday.

▶ X-linked SCID is the most common and most severe form of the disease. It is caused by a single mutation to a gene on the X chromosome. The gene encodes a protein that forms part of a receptor complex on white blood cells. Without the protein, **lymphocytes** do not develop normally, and the body is susceptible to infections. SCID is more common in males because they lack a second X chromosome to compensate for the defective one.

▶ The second most common form of SCID (ADA-SCID) results from an enzyme deficiency. Both forms have been treated with transplants of modified stem cells.

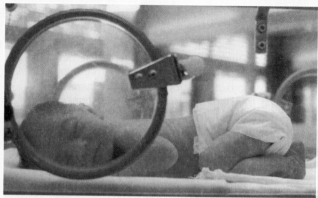

Jacoplane CC 3.0

Detecting SCID is difficult in the first months because the mother's **antibodies** still circulate in the infant's blood. If SCID is suspected, patients are kept in sterile conditions to avoid infection.

Conventional treatment

▶ SCID is most commonly treated using a bone marrow transplant from a compatible donor. The stem cells in the donor bone marrow develop into new, functional, white blood cells. However, it is not effective for all types of SCID, and tissue rejection or infection may develop.

Gene therapy

▶ Patients treated for SCID using gene therapy have now been medically followed for many years. Gene therapy treatments began in 1990. Of 20 patients treated, 18 showed long term success in regeneration of the immune system. However six patients developed leukemia, which was fatal in one patient. Treatments were stopped while a second generation gene therapy was developed.

▶ Data from 2014 shows that 8 out of 9 patients of the 2nd generation trials showed long term survival and successful recovery of the immune system. Analysis of the DNA shows a much less likely chance of developing cancer and, so far, none of the patients have.

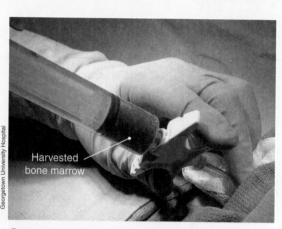

Georgetown University Hospital

Harvested bone marrow

Bone marrow, which contains stem cells, is extracted from the patient. The corrected gene is inserted into the stem cells, and the stem cells are returned to the patient.

4. What is SCID? _____

_____

5. (a) How are bone marrow transplants used to treat SCID? _____

_____

_____

(b) What are some of the disadvantages of bone marrow transplants? _____

_____

_____

(c) What are some of the advantages of treating SCID with gene therapy? _____

_____

_____

6. Discuss the potential risks associated with gene therapy: _____

_____

_____

_____

_____

145 Chapter Summary

1. Contrast the innate and the adaptive immune responses, with reference to the basic action and the cells involved:

_____

_____

_____

_____

_____

_____

_____

2. The diagram below shows a model of part of the adaptive immune system reaction when an antigen is encountered.

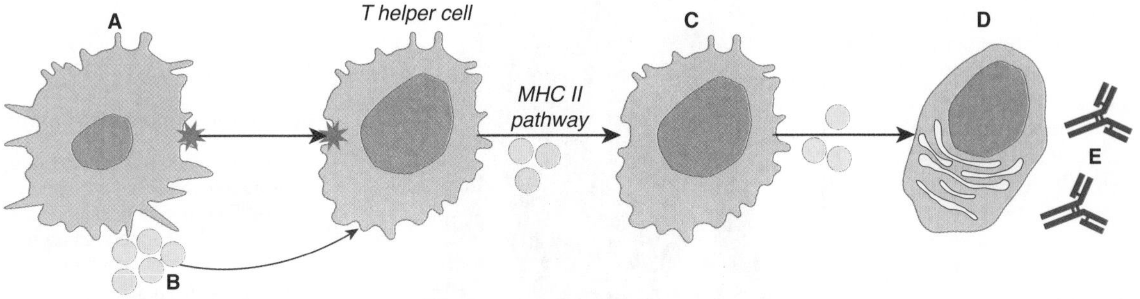

(a) What type of cell is A and what is its role? _____

_____

_____

(b) Identify the structures labeled B and state their role in this part of the process: _____

_____

_____

(c) What type of cell is C? _____

(d) What type of cell is D? _____

(e) Identify the structures labeled E and state their role: _____

_____

3. Explain how monoclonal antibodies are able to be used against specific diseases: _____

_____

_____

_____

4. Identify each of the following components of, or processes in, the adaptive immune system, by the description provided:

(d) These T cells destroy target cells on contact: _____

(e) These cells are responsible for immunological memory: _____

(f) This class of proteins is made by B cells and destroy specific antigens: _____

(g) These chemicals activate T cells and cause them to multiply rapidly: _____

(h) This immune system organ synthesizes antibodies and removes antibody-coated material: _____

(i) T cells mature in this organ: _____

Cardiovascular system

- Blood transports respiratory gases.
- The carbonate-bicarbonate system in blood contributes to blood buffering.
- Blood proteins (e.g. immunoglobulins) also contribute to blood buffering.

Skeletal system

- Bones enclose and protect the lungs and bronchi from damage.
- Expansion and elastic recoil of ribcage produce volume changes necessary for inhalation and exhalation (breathing).

Digestive system

- Digestive system provides nutrients required by the respiratory system.

Reproductive system

- Pregnancy has significant effects on breathing, largely through sex hormones. The enlarged uterus at full term pushes abdominal organs up and outwards and compromises the functioning of the diaphragm.

Urinary system

- Kidneys dispose of waste products of respiratory metabolism (other than CO_2 which is breathed out).

Integumentary system

- Skin forms a surface barrier, protecting the organs of the respiratory system.

Nervous system

- Control centers in the medulla and the pons regulate the rate and depth of breathing.
- Sensory feedback to the respiratory control centers is provided by stretch receptors in the bronchioles and chemoreceptors in the aorta and carotid arteries.

Lymphatic system and immunity

- Immune system provides general protection against pathogens; specifically the tonsils protect against pharyngeal and upper respiratory tract infections.
- Lymphatic system helps to maintain blood volume required for efficient transport of respiratory gases.

Endocrine system

- Epinephrine (from the adrenal medulla above the kidneys) acts as a bronchodilator.
- Testosterone promotes enlargement of the larynx at puberty in males.
- Cortisol has a role in lung maturation. A number of other hormones directly or indirectly influence breathing rates.

Muscular system

- Diaphragm and intercostal muscles produce the volume changes necessary for breathing.
- Regular aerobic exercise improves efficiency of the respiratory system.

General functions and effects on all systems

The respiratory system provides an interface for gas exchange with the external environment. It is ultimately responsible for providing all the cells of the body with oxygen and disposing of waste carbon dioxide produced as a result of cellular Respiration. These respiratory gases are transported in the blood.

Symptoms of disease
- Chest pain
- Excessive mucus production
- Coughing, sneezing
- Difficulty breathing, cyanosis

Infectious respiratory diseases
- Viral pneumonia
- Covid-19
- Influenza

Non-infectious respiratory diseases
- Asthma
- Fibrosis (scarring)
- Smoking-related diseases
- Inherited diseases (e.g. CF)
- Sleep apnea

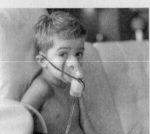
- Asthma
- Lung cancer
- Chronic bronchitis
- Emphysema
- Asbestosis
- Covid-19 induced ARDS

Diagnosis of disorders
- Chest X-ray and CT scans
- Pulmonary function tests
- Sputum cultures and biopsy
- DNA tests and screening

Preventing diseases of the respiratory system
- Education
- Exercise
- Behavior modification

Treating diseases of the respiratory system
- Drug therapies (e.g. antibiotics)
- Vaccination
- Surgery
- Radiotherapy
- Behavior modification

- Stem cell therapy
- Gene therapy
- X-rays
- Vaccination

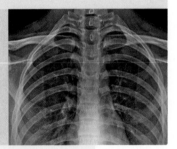

Taking a Breath
The Respiratory System

The respiratory system can be affected by disease and undergoes changes associated with training and aging.

Medical technologies can be used to diagnose and treat respiratory disorders. Exercise and lifestyle management can prevent some respiratory diseases.

- Lung cancer
- Chronic bronchitis
- Emphysema

Aging and the respiratory system
- Decline in respiratory capacity
- Decline in aerobic capacity (VO_2 max)
- Increased incidence of chronic respiratory disease

- VO_2max
- Ventilation efficiency
- Ventilation rhythm

Effects of exercise on the respiratory system
- Increased rate and depth of breathing
- Increased aerobic capacity (VO_2 max)
- Increased respiratory efficiency
- Improved oxygen loading/unloading
- Better diaphragmatic performance

The Respiratory System

KEY IDEAS

- Respiratory gases are exchanged with the environment across gas exchange membranes in the alveoli of the lungs.
- The specific features of the gas exchange system maximize exchange rates.
- Hemoglobin transports oxygen in the blood and delivers it to the tissues.
- The respiratory center responds to changes in oxygen demand by changing the breathing rate.
- Lung function can be measured using spirometry.

KEY TERMS

- Alveoli
- Asthma
- Bronchi
- Bronchioles
- Bronchitis
- COPD
- Diaphragm
- Hemoglobin
- Respiratory center
- Spirometry
- Trachea
- Vital capacity

LEARNING OBJECTIVES

Activity number

☐ 1   Know that the lungs are the primary organs in the body for gas exchange. Describe the location and functions of the gas exchange surfaces and related structures in the lung and explain how their features contribute to efficient gas exchange.   146-147

☐ 2   Understand the role of hemogobin in transport and delivery of oxygen to the tissues. Describe how carbon dioxide is transported by the body.   148

☐ 3   Explain the mechanism of breathing, with reference to muscle action. Understand how the respiratory center in the brain controls breathing and explain the roles of the phrenic and vagus nerves. Describe sleep apnea as a breathing disorder during sleep.   149-150

☐ 4   Understand how a spirometer can be used to measure lung function and know how to interpret a spirogram. Define the term, vital capacity and describe some factors that can affect it.   152-154

☐ 5   Explain the effect of respiratory diseases on lung function, generally.   155

☐ 6   Describe the effects of COVID-19 on the respiratory system. Know the risk factors that contribute to COPD and describe the effects of this disease on the body. Describe the risk factors for lung diseases, in general and explain the differences between asbestosis and mesothelioma as two serious lung diseases.   156-158

☐ 7   Describe how smoking affects the lungs and know that this activity leads to increased risk of many cancers and other harmful diseases. Understand the impacts of vaping on the body.   159-160

☐ 8   Understand the effects of exercise on the cardiac and respiratory system. Describe how the body makes physiological adjustments, in response to being at high altitude.   161

☐ 9   Describe some of the effects of aging on the respiratory system.   38

RESOURCE HUB

Scan the QR code to access:

- weblinks
- videos
- 3D models
- interactives

146 The Respiratory System

Key Idea: The tissues and organs of the human gas exchange system work together to enable the exchange of gases between the body's cells and the environment.

The gas exchange system consists of the passages of the mouth and nose, the **trachea**, and the tubes and air sacs of the lungs. Cooperation with the muscles of the **diaphragm** and ribcage contribute to its function. Each region is specialized to perform a particular role in the organ system's overall function, which is to exchange respiratory gases (O_2 and CO_2) between the body's cells and the environment.

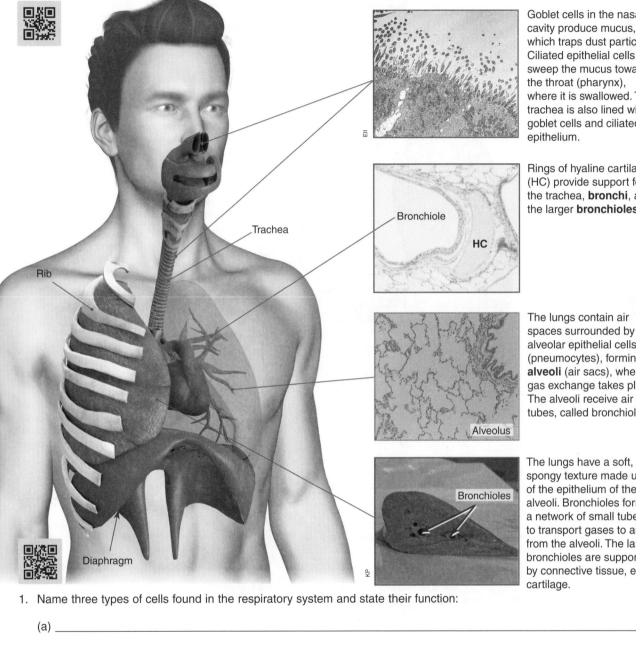

Goblet cells in the nasal cavity produce mucus, which traps dust particles. Ciliated epithelial cells sweep the mucus towards the throat (pharynx), where it is swallowed. The trachea is also lined with goblet cells and ciliated epithelium.

Rings of hyaline cartilage (HC) provide support for the trachea, **bronchi**, and the larger **bronchioles**.

Bronchiole

HC

The lungs contain air spaces surrounded by alveolar epithelial cells (pneumocytes), forming **alveoli** (air sacs), where gas exchange takes place. The alveoli receive air from tubes, called bronchioles.

Alveolus

The lungs have a soft, spongy texture made up of the epithelium of the alveoli. Bronchioles form a network of small tubes to transport gases to and from the alveoli. The larger bronchioles are supported by connective tissue, e.g. cartilage.

Bronchioles

Trachea

Rib

Diaphragm

1. Name three types of cells found in the respiratory system and state their function:

(a) _____

_____

(b) _____

_____

(c) _____

_____

2. What is the primary organ of gas exchange? _____

3. Which cells form the alveoli? _____

4. What is the purpose of the hyaline cartilage in the gas exchange system? _____

_____

147 The Lungs

Key Idea: Lungs are internal, sac-like organs connected to the outside by a system of airways. The smallest airways end in thin-walled alveoli, where gas exchange occurs.

The respiratory system includes all the structures needed for exchanging respiratory gases with the environment. In mammals, the gas exchange organs are paired lungs connected to the outside air by way of a system of tubular passageways: the **trachea**, **bronchi**, and **bronchioles**.

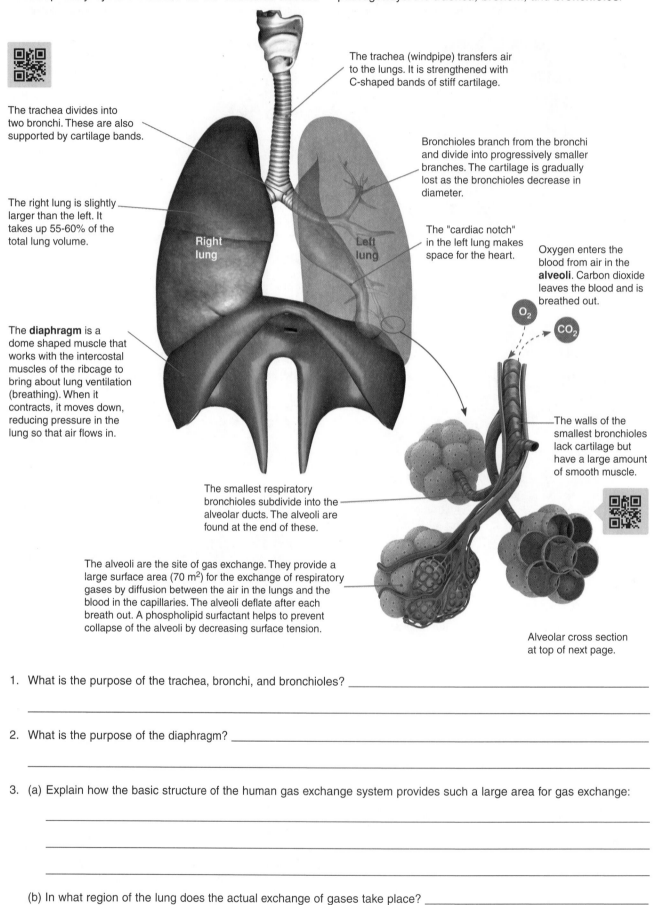

The trachea (windpipe) transfers air to the lungs. It is strengthened with C-shaped bands of stiff cartilage.

The trachea divides into two bronchi. These are also supported by cartilage bands.

Bronchioles branch from the bronchi and divide into progressively smaller branches. The cartilage is gradually lost as the bronchioles decrease in diameter.

The right lung is slightly larger than the left. It takes up 55-60% of the total lung volume.

Right lung

Left lung

The "cardiac notch" in the left lung makes space for the heart.

Oxygen enters the blood from air in the **alveoli**. Carbon dioxide leaves the blood and is breathed out.

O_2

CO_2

The **diaphragm** is a dome shaped muscle that works with the intercostal muscles of the ribcage to bring about lung ventilation (breathing). When it contracts, it moves down, reducing pressure in the lung so that air flows in.

The walls of the smallest bronchioles lack cartilage but have a large amount of smooth muscle.

The smallest respiratory bronchioles subdivide into the alveolar ducts. The alveoli are found at the end of these.

The alveoli are the site of gas exchange. They provide a large surface area (70 m^2) for the exchange of respiratory gases by diffusion between the air in the lungs and the blood in the capillaries. The alveoli deflate after each breath out. A phospholipid surfactant helps to prevent collapse of the alveoli by decreasing surface tension.

Alveolar cross section at top of next page.

1. What is the purpose of the trachea, bronchi, and bronchioles? _____

_____

2. What is the purpose of the diaphragm? _____

_____

3. (a) Explain how the basic structure of the human gas exchange system provides such a large area for gas exchange:

_____

_____

_____

(b) In what region of the lung does the actual exchange of gases take place? _____

©2023 **BIOZONE** International
ISBN: 978-1-99-101408-5
Photocopying Prohibited

Cross section through an alveolus

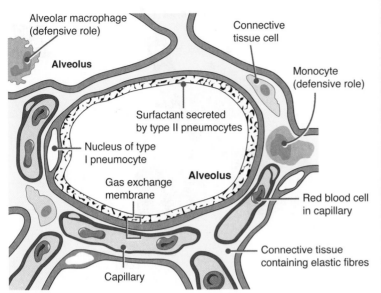

Alveolar macrophage
(defensive role)

Alveolus

Surfactant secreted
by type II pneumocytes

Nucleus of type
I pneumocyte

Gas exchange
membrane

Alveolus

Capillary

Connective
tissue cell

Monocyte
(defensive role)

Red blood cell
in capillary

Connective tissue
containing elastic fibres

Above: The physical arrangement of the alveoli to the capillaries
through which the blood moves. The alveolus is lined with
pneumocytes (alveolar epithelial cells). Phagocytes (monocytes
and macrophages) are present to protect the lung tissue. Elastic
connective tissue gives the alveoli their ability to expand and recoil.

The gas exchange membrane

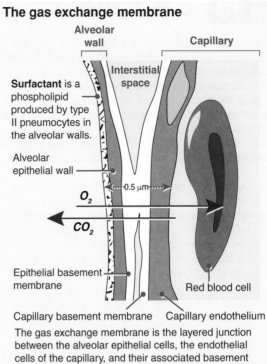

Alveolar
wall

Capillary

Surfactant is a
phospholipid
produced by type
II pneumocytes in
the alveolar walls.

Interstitial
space

Alveolar
epithelial wall

O_2

CO_2

0.5 µm

Epithelial basement
membrane

Red blood cell

Capillary basement membrane   Capillary endothelium

The gas exchange membrane is the layered junction
between the alveolar epithelial cells, the endothelial
cells of the capillary, and their associated basement
membranes (thin connective tissue layers under the
epithelia). Gases move freely across this membrane.

4. Describe the structure and purpose of the alveolar-capillary (gas exchange) membrane: _____

_____

_____

_____

5. The diagram below shows the different types of cells and their positions and occurrence in the lungs. Use it to answer
    the following questions:

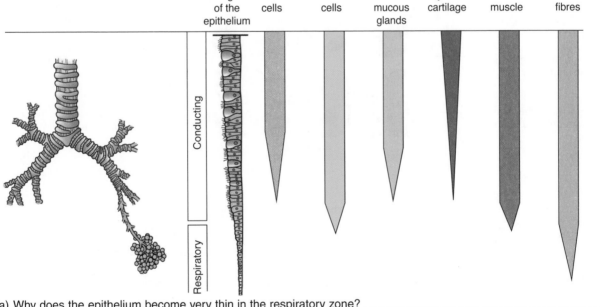

Height
of the
epithelium

Goblet
cells

Ciliated
cells

Serous and
mucous
glands

Hyaline
cartilage

Smooth
muscle

Elastic
fibres

Conducting

Respiratory

Holly Fischer cc3.0

(a) Why does the epithelium become very thin in the respiratory zone? _____

_____

_____

(b) Why would elastic fibers be present in the respiratory zone, whereas hyaline cartilage is not? _____

_____

_____

148 Gas Transport

Key Idea: Hemoglobin is a respiratory pigment in red blood cells that binds oxygen and increases the efficiency of its transport and delivery to tissues throughout the body. The transport of respiratory gases around the body is the role of the blood. Most of the carbon dioxide in the blood is carried as bicarbonate in the plasma. Oxygen does not dissolve in blood easily, so it is transported throughout the body, chemically bound to the respiratory protein **hemoglobin** (Hb) inside the red blood cells.

In the muscles, oxygen from hemoglobin is transferred to and retained by myoglobin, a molecule that is chemically similar to hemoglobin except that it consists of only one heme-globin unit. Myoglobin has a greater affinity for oxygen than hemoglobin and acts as an oxygen store within muscles, releasing the oxygen during periods of prolonged or extreme muscular activity.

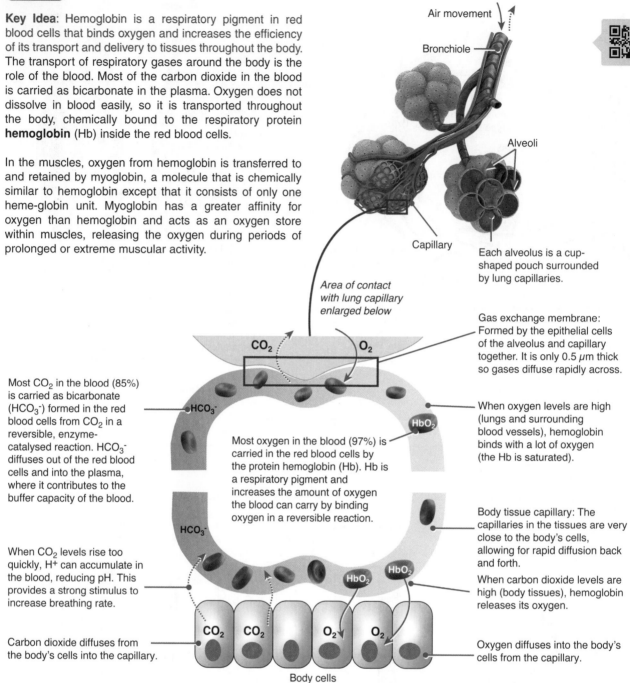

Air movement

Bronchiole

Alveoli

Capillary

Each alveolus is a cup-shaped pouch surrounded by lung capillaries.

Area of contact with lung capillary enlarged below

Gas exchange membrane: Formed by the epithelial cells of the alveolus and capillary together. It is only 0.5 μm thick so gases diffuse rapidly across.

CO_2 O_2

Most CO_2 in the blood (85%) is carried as bicarbonate (HCO_3^-) formed in the red blood cells from CO_2 in a reversible, enzyme-catalysed reaction. HCO_3^- diffuses out of the red blood cells and into the plasma, where it contributes to the buffer capacity of the blood.

HCO_3^-

HbO_2

When oxygen levels are high (lungs and surrounding blood vessels), hemoglobin binds with a lot of oxygen (the Hb is saturated).

Most oxygen in the blood (97%) is carried in the red blood cells by the protein hemoglobin (Hb). Hb is a respiratory pigment and increases the amount of oxygen the blood can carry by binding oxygen in a reversible reaction.

HCO_3^-

Body tissue capillary: The capillaries in the tissues are very close to the body's cells, allowing for rapid diffusion back and forth.

When CO₂ levels rise too quickly, H⁺ can accumulate in the blood, reducing pH. This provides a strong stimulus to increase breathing rate.

HbO_2 HbO_2

When carbon dioxide levels are high (body tissues), hemoglobin releases its oxygen.

Carbon dioxide diffuses from the body's cells into the capillary.

CO_2 CO_2 O_2 O_2

Oxygen diffuses into the body's cells from the capillary.

Body cells

Transport of carbon dioxide in the blood

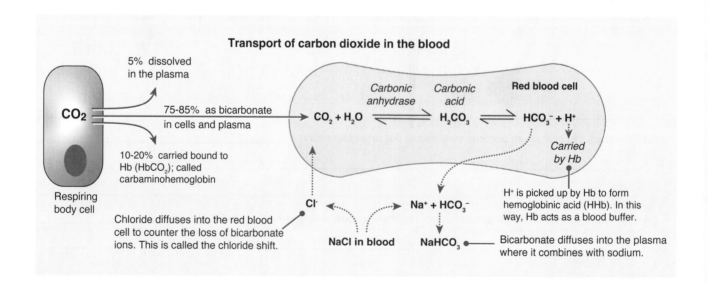

CO_2

Respiring body cell

5% dissolved in the plasma

75-85% as bicarbonate in cells and plasma

10-20% carried bound to Hb (HbCO₂); called carbaminohemoglobin

Chloride diffuses into the red blood cell to counter the loss of bicarbonate ions. This is called the chloride shift.

Cl⁻

NaCl in blood

Carbonic anhydrase   *Carbonic acid*   **Red blood cell**

$CO_2 + H_2O \rightleftharpoons H_2CO_3 \rightleftharpoons HCO_3^- + H^+$

Carried by Hb

Na⁺ + HCO₃⁻

NaHCO₃

H⁺ is picked up by Hb to form hemoglobinic acid (HHb). In this way, Hb acts as a blood buffer.

Bicarbonate diffuses into the plasma where it combines with sodium.

©2023 **BIOZONE** International
ISBN: 978-1-99-101408-5
Photocopying Prohibited

Oxygen does not easily dissolve in blood, but is carried in chemical combination with hemoglobin (Hb) in red blood cells. The most important factor determining how much oxygen is carried by Hb is the level of oxygen in the blood. The greater the oxygen tension, the more oxygen will combine with Hb. This relationship can be illustrated with an oxygen-hemoglobin dissociation curve, as shown below (Fig. 1). In the lung capillaries, (high O_2), a lot of oxygen is picked up and bound by Hb. In the tissues, (low O_2), oxygen is released. In skeletal muscle, myoglobin picks up oxygen from hemoglobin and therefore serves as an oxygen store when oxygen tensions begin to fall. The release of oxygen is enhanced by the Bohr effect (Fig. 2).

Respiratory pigments and the transport of oxygen

Fig. 1: Dissociation curves for hemoglobin and myoglobin at normal body temperature for fetal and adult human blood.

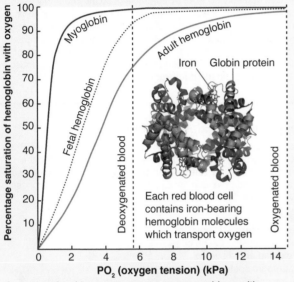

Fig.2: Oxygen-hemoglobin dissociation curves for human blood at normal body temperature at different blood pH.

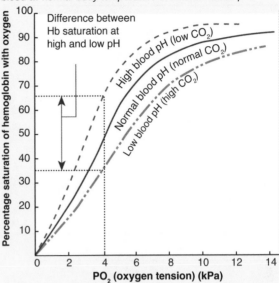

As oxygen level increases, more oxygen combines with hemoglobin (Hb). Hb saturation remains high, even at low oxygen tensions. Fetal Hb has a high affinity for oxygen and carries 20-30% more than maternal Hb. Myoglobin in skeletal muscle has a very high affinity for oxygen and will take up oxygen from hemoglobin in the blood.

As pH increases (lower CO_2), more oxygen combines with Hb. As the blood pH decreases (higher CO_2), Hb binds less oxygen and releases more to the tissues (the Bohr effect). The difference between Hb saturation at high and low pH represents the amount of oxygen released to the tissues.

1. (a) Identify two regions in the body where oxygen levels are very high: _____

    (b) Identify two regions where carbon dioxide levels are very high: _____

    _____

2. Explain the significance of the reversible binding reaction of hemoglobin (Hb) to oxygen: _____

    _____

    _____

3. (a) Hemoglobin saturation is affected by the oxygen level in the blood. Describe the nature of this relationship:

    _____

    _____

    (b) Comment on the significance of this relationship to oxygen delivery to the tissues: _____

    _____

4. (a) Describe how fetal Hb is different from adult Hb: _____

    (b) Explain the significance of this difference to oxygen delivery to the fetus: _____

    _____

5. At low blood pH, less oxygen is bound by hemoglobin and more is released to the tissues. Name this effect and comment on its significance to oxygen delivery to respiring tissue:

    _____

    _____

149 Breathing

Key Idea: Breathing provides a continual supply of air to the lungs to maintain the concentration gradients for gas exchange. Different muscles are used in inspiration and expiration to force air in and out of the lungs.

Breathing (ventilation) provides a continual supply of oxygen-rich air to the lungs and expels air high in carbon dioxide. Together with the cardiovascular system, which transports respiratory gases between the alveolar and the cells of the body, breathing maintains concentration gradients for gas exchange. Breathing is achieved by the action of muscles.

1. Explain the purpose of breathing: _____

_____

_____

2. In general terms, how is breathing achieved?

_____

_____

_____

_____

3. (a) Describe the sequence of events involved in quiet breathing:

_____

_____

_____

_____

_____

(b) What is the essential difference between this and the situation during forced breathing?

_____

_____

_____

4. During inspiration, which muscles are:

(a) Contracting: _____

_____

(b) Relaxed: _____

_____

5. During forced expiration, which muscles are:

(a) Contracting: _____

_____

(b) Relaxed: _____

_____

6. Explain the role of antagonistic muscles in breathing:

_____

_____

_____

Breathing and muscle action

Muscles can only do work by contracting, so they can only perform movement in one direction. To achieve motion in two directions, muscles work as antagonistic pairs. Antagonistic pairs of muscles have opposing actions and create movement when one contracts and the other relaxes. Breathing in humans involves two sets of antagonistic muscles. The external and internal intercostal muscles of the ribcage, and the **diaphragm** and abdominal muscles.

Inspiration (inhalation or breathing in)

During quiet breathing, inspiration is achieved by increasing the thoracic volume (therefore decreasing the pressure inside the lungs). Air then flows into the lungs in response to the decreased pressure inside the lung. Inspiration is always an active process involving muscle contraction.

1 External intercostal muscles contract causing the rib cage to expand and move up. Diaphragm contracts and moves down.

Air in

2 Thoracic volume increases, lungs expand, and the pressure inside the lungs decreases.

3 Air flows into the lungs in response to the pressure gradient.

Diaphragm down

Expiration (exhalation or breathing out)

In quiet breathing, expiration is a passive process, achieved when the external intercostals and diaphragm relax and thoracic volume decreases. Air flows passively out of the lungs to equalize with the air pressure. In active breathing, muscle contraction is involved in bringing about both inspiration and expiration.

1 In quiet breathing, external intercostals and diaphragm relax. The elasticity of the lung tissue causes recoil. In forced breathing, the internal intercostals and abdominal muscles contract to compress the thoracic cavity and increase the force of the expiration.

Air out

2 Thoracic volume decreases and the pressure inside the lungs increases.

3 Air flows passively out of the lungs in response to the pressure gradient.

Diaphragm up

©2023 **BIOZONE** International
ISBN: 978-1-99-101408-5
Photocopying Prohibited

150 Control of Breathing

Key Idea: The basic rhythm of breathing is controlled by the respiratory center, a cluster of neurons located in the medulla oblongata, situated in the brain stem.
This rhythm is adjusted in response to the physical and chemical changes that occur when we carry out different activities. Although the control of breathing is involuntary, we can exert some degree of conscious control over it. The diagram below illustrates these controls.

The respiratory center and the control of breathing

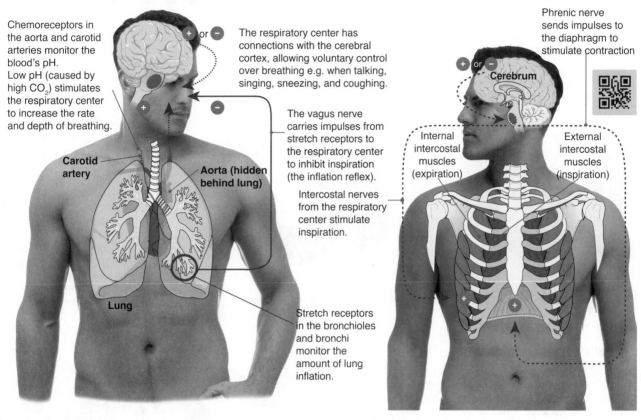

Chemoreceptors in the aorta and carotid arteries monitor the blood's pH.
Low pH (caused by high CO_2) stimulates the respiratory center to increase the rate and depth of breathing.

The respiratory center has connections with the cerebral cortex, allowing voluntary control over breathing e.g. when talking, singing, sneezing, and coughing.

The vagus nerve carries impulses from stretch receptors to the respiratory center to inhibit inspiration (the inflation reflex).

Intercostal nerves from the respiratory center stimulate inspiration.

Stretch receptors in the bronchioles and bronchi monitor the amount of lung inflation.

Carotid artery

Aorta (hidden behind lung)

Lung

Phrenic nerve sends impulses to the diaphragm to stimulate contraction

Cerebrum

Internal intercostal muscles (expiration)

External intercostal muscles (inspiration)

Sensory input

Stretch receptors in the **bronchioles** monitor lung inflation and send impulses to inhibit the **respiratory center**. Input from sensory receptors and the higher brain centers influence the basic rhythm.

Motor output

The respiratory center sends rhythmic impulses to the intercostal muscles and the **diaphragm** to bring about breathing.

1. Explain how the basic rhythm of breathing is controlled: _____

_____

2. Describe the role of each of the following in the regulation of breathing:

(a) Phrenic nerve: _____

(b) Intercostal nerves: _____

(c) Vagus nerve: _____

_____

(d) Inflation reflex: _____

3. (a) Describe the effect of low blood pH on the rate and depth of breathing: _____

_____

(b) Explain how this effect is mediated: _____

_____

(c) Suggest why blood pH is a good mechanism by which to regulate breathing rate: _____

_____

151 Sleep Apnea

Key Idea: Sleep apnea is a condition where air, and therefore oxygen, are prevented from entering the lungs during sleep. There are two main conditions responsible: obstructive sleep apnea and the less common, central sleep apnea.

Obstructive sleep apnea occurs when the air passage through the **trachea** is blocked by relaxed throat muscles, which causes the back of the tongue and soft palate to fall back and block the airway. Central sleep apnea occurs due to lack of nervous signaling between the brain stem and muscles, preventing the muscles responsible for the breathing mechanism from contracting. Both conditions create a low oxygen environment, and the higher levels of CO_2 usually wake the sleeper, forcing them to take a gasping breath and recommence normal breathing.

Obstructive sleep apnea

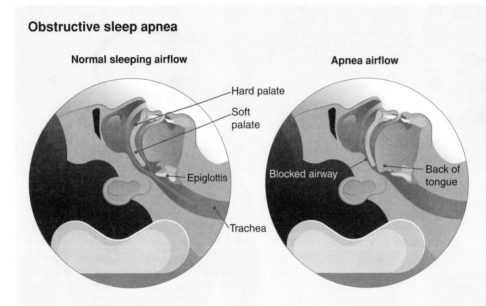

Normal sleeping airflow

- Hard palate
- Soft palate
- Epiglottis
- Trachea

Apnea airflow

- Blocked airway
- Back of tongue

Complete or partial blockage of the upper airway, due to relaxed throat muscles during sleep is called obstructive sleep apnea, causing hypoxia (too little oxygen). This causes the breathing to stop, the heart rate to drop, which then stimulates a sudden spike of heart rate and blood pressure increase. Chest muscles and the **diaphragm** need to work harder to increase pressure to open the airway, and each episode usually ends with the person waking to take a gasp of breath to restore oxygen levels in the lungs. Ongoing apnea can lead to stroke, arrhythmias, diabetes, obesity, and heart attacks.

Central sleep apnea

Central sleep apnea also causes hypoxia, but is the result of insufficient or absent nervous signals from the breathing center of the brain stem to the muscles responsible for breathing. The person can be observed to stop and start breathing, often causing wakening with shortness of breath. Other events, such as heart failure and stroke, can lead to this type of apnea developing, as well as sleeping at high altitude.

Both obstructive and central sleep apnea can be remediated with a device called a continuous positive airway pressure machine (CPAP), which is worn at night (see right). This machine forces air gently into the mouth at a set pressure, which prevents the collapse of the airway, as well as stimulating the breathing mechanism. More serious apnea can be corrected with recently developed surgery to implant a device that stimulates the phrenic (diaphragm) nerve.

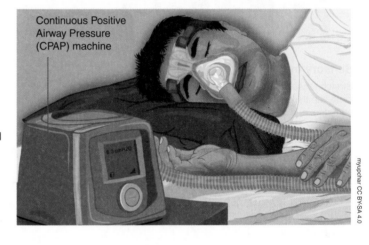

Continuous Positive Airway Pressure (CPAP) machine

myupchar CC BY-SA 4.0

1. Discuss the similarities between the two types of sleep apnea: _____

_____

_____

2. Discuss the differences between the two types of sleep apnea: _____

_____

_____

3. Describe the link between sleep apnea in the respiratory system and possible consequences in other body systems:

_____

_____

_____

©2023 **BIOZONE** International
ISBN: 978-1-99-101408-5
Photocopying Prohibited

152 Measuring Lung Function

Key Idea: A lung function test, called spirometry, measures changes in lung volume and can be used diagnostically.
The volume of gases exchanged during breathing varies according to the physiological demands placed on the body, e.g. by exercise, and an individual's lung function. **Spirometry** measures changes in lung volume by measuring how much air a person can breathe in and out and how fast the air can be expelled. Spirometry can measure changes in ventilation rates during exercise and can be used to assess impairments in lung function, as might occur as a result of disease. In humans, the total adult lung capacity varies between 4 and 6 L and is greater in males.

Determining changes in lung volume using spirometry

The apparatus used to measure the amount of air exchanged during breathing and the rate of breathing is a spirometer (also called a respirometer). A simple spirometer consists of a weighted drum, containing oxygen or air, inverted over a chamber of water. A tube connects the air-filled chamber with the subject's mouth, and soda lime in the system absorbs the carbon dioxide breathed out. Breathing results in a trace called a spirogram, from which lung volumes can be measured directly.

During inspiration

Air is removed from the chamber, the drum sinks, and an upward deflection is recorded on the paper on the rotating drum.

During expiration

Air is added to the chamber, the drum rises, and a downward deflection is recorded.

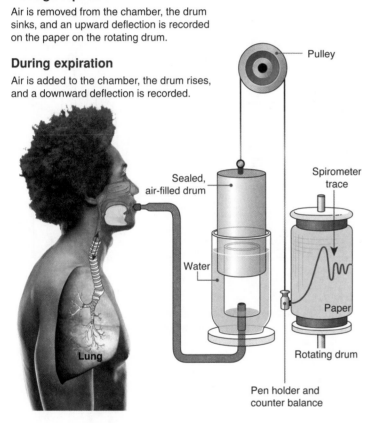

Pulley

Sealed, air-filled drum

Spirometer trace

Water

Paper

Rotating drum

Lung

Pen holder and counter balance

Lung volumes and capacities

The air in the lungs can be divided into volumes. Lung capacities are combinations of volumes.

Description of volume	Vol (L)
Tidal volume (TV) Volume of air breathed in and out in a single breath.	0.5
Inspiratory reserve volume (IRV) Volume breathed in by a maximum inspiration at the end of a normal inspiration.	3.3
Expiratory reserve volume (ERV) Volume breathed out by a maximum effort at the end of a normal expiration.	1.0
Residual volume (RV) Volume of air remaining in the lungs at the end of a maximum expiration.	1.2

Description of capacity

Inspiratory capacity (IC) = TV + IRV Volume breathed in by a maximum inspiration at the end of a normal expiration.	3.8
Vital capacity (VC) = IRV + TV + ERV Volume that can be exhaled after a maximum inspiration.	4.8
Total lung capacity (TLC) = VC + RV The total volume of the lungs. Only a fraction of TLC is used in normal breathing.	6.0

Primary indicators of lung function

Forced expiratory volume in 1 second (FEV_1)
The volume of air that is maximally exhaled in the first second of exhalation.

Forced vital capacity (FVC)
The total volume of air that can be forcibly exhaled after a maximum inspiration.

---

1. Describe how each of the following might be expected to influence values for lung volumes and capacities obtained using spirometry:

   (a) Height: _____

   (b) Gender: _____

   (c) Age: _____

2. A percentage decline in FEV_1 and FVC (to <80% of normal) are indicators of impaired lung function, e.g. in asthma:

   (a) Explain why a forced volume is a more useful indicator of lung function than tidal volume: _____

   _____

   (b) Asthma is treated with drugs to relax the airways. Suggest how spirometry could be used during asthma treatment:

   _____

©2023 **BIOZONE** International
ISBN: 978-1-99-101408-5
Photocopying Prohibited

Respiratory gas	Approximate percentages of O_2 and CO_2		
	Inhaled air	Air in lungs	Exhaled air
O_2	21.0	13.8	16.4
CO_2	0.04	5.5	3.6

Above: The percentages of respiratory gases in air (by volume) during normal breathing. The percentage volume of oxygen in the alveolar air (in the lung) is lower than that in the exhaled air because of the influence of the dead air volume (the air in the spaces of the nose, throat, larynx, **trachea**, and **bronchi**). This air (about 30% of the air inhaled) is unavailable for gas exchange.

Left: During exercise, the breathing rate, tidal volume, and PV increase up to a maximum (as indicated below).

Spirogram for a male during quiet and forced breathing, and during exercise

Lung volume (L)

Inspiratory reserve volume (IRV) = 3.3 L

A
B
C
D E F G
Resting Exercise

PV = breathing rate X tidal volume
L/min = breaths/min X L

Time

3. Using the definitions given on the previous page, identify the volumes and capacities indicated by the letters A-F on the spirogram above. For each, indicate the volume (vol) in liters (L). The inspiratory reserve volume has been identified:

(a) : _____ Vol: _____   (d) : _____ Vol: _____

(b) : _____ Vol: _____   (e) : _____ Vol: _____

(c) : _____ Vol: _____   (f) : _____ Vol: _____

4. Explain what is happening in the sequence indicated by the letter G: _____

5. Calculate PV when breathing rate is 15 breaths per minute and tidal volume is 0.4 L: _____

6. (a) Describe what would happen to PV during strenuous exercise: _____

   (b) Explain how this is achieved: _____

7. The table above gives approximate percentages for respiratory gases during breathing. Study the data and then:

   (a) Calculate the difference in CO_2 between inhaled and exhaled air: _____

   _____

   (b) Explain where this 'extra' CO_2 comes from: _____

   (c) Explain why the dead air volume raises the oxygen content of exhaled air above that in the lungs: _____

   _____

   _____

©2023 **BIOZONE** International
ISBN: 978-1-99-101408-5
Photocopying Prohibited

153 Investigating Vital Capacity

Key Idea: Vital capacity is the greatest volume of air expelled from the lungs after taking the deepest possible breath.
Vital capacity is easily measured using a spirometer or a bell jar system, as described below. In healthy adults, vital capacity ranges between 4-6 L, but is influenced by several factors including gender, age, height, ethnicity, and fitness.

Measuring vital capacity

Vital capacity can be measured using a 6 L calibrated, glass bell jar, supported in a sink of water (right). The jar is calibrated by inverting it, pouring in known volumes of water, and marking the level on the bell jar with a marker pen.

To measure vital capacity, a person breathes in as far as possible (maximal inhalation), and then exhales as far as possible (maximal exhalation) into a mouth piece connected to tubing. The drop in volume within the bell jar is measured; this gives the vital capacity in L.

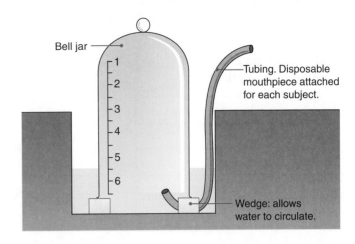

Bell jar

Tubing. Disposable mouthpiece attached for each subject.

Wedge: allows water to circulate.

Investigating vital capacity

A class of high school biology students investigated the vital capacity of the whole class using the bell jar method described above.

The students recorded their heights as well as their vital capacity. The results are presented on the table (right).

1. Calculate the mean vital capacity for:

   (a) Females: _____

   (b) Males: _____

   (c) Explain whether these results are what you would expect:

   _____

   _____

   _____

   _____

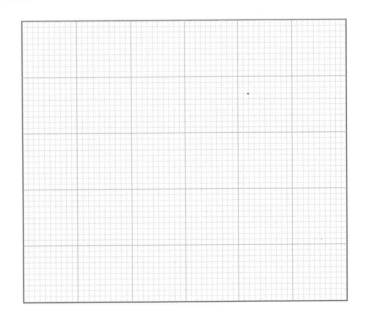

Females		Males	
Height cm	Vital capacity L	Height cm	Vital capacity L
156	2.75	181	4.00
145	2.50	163	2.50
155	3.25	167	4.00
170	4.00	174	4.00
162	2.75	177	4.00
164	2.75	177	3.75
163	3.40	176	3.75
158	2.75	177	3.25
167	4.00	178	4.00
165	3.00	178	3.75

2. (a) Plot height versus vital capacity as a scatter graph on the grid provided (right). Use different symbols or colors for each set of data (female and male).

   (b) Draw a line of best fit through each set of points. For a line of best fit, the points should fall equally either side of the line.

   (c) Describe the relationship between height and vital capacity:

   _____

   _____

   _____

   _____

   _____

   _____

154 Review of Lung Function

Key Idea: The respiratory system includes the lungs and the system of tubes through which the air reaches them.
Breathing (ventilation) provides a continual supply of fresh air to the lungs and helps to maintain a large diffusion gradient for respiratory gases across the gas exchange surface.

The basic rhythm of breathing is controlled by the **respiratory center** in the medulla of the hindbrain. The following activity summarizes the key features of respiratory system structure and function. The information can be found in earlier exercises in this chapter.

Components of the respiratory system

(a)

(b)

(c)

(d)

(e)

(f)

(g)

The control of breathing

(h) .... controls the rate and depth of breathing. Connections with the cerebral cortex allow voluntary control over breathing.

(i) .... carries impulses from stretch receptors to the respiratory center to inhibit inspiration (the inflation reflex).

(j) .... from the respiratory center, stimulate inspiration.

(k) .... in the aorta and carotid arteries, monitor blood pH. Low pH stimulates an increase in the rate and depth of breathing.

(l) .... in the bronchioles and bronchi, monitor the amount of lung inflation.

(m) .... sends impulses to the diaphragm to stimulate contraction.

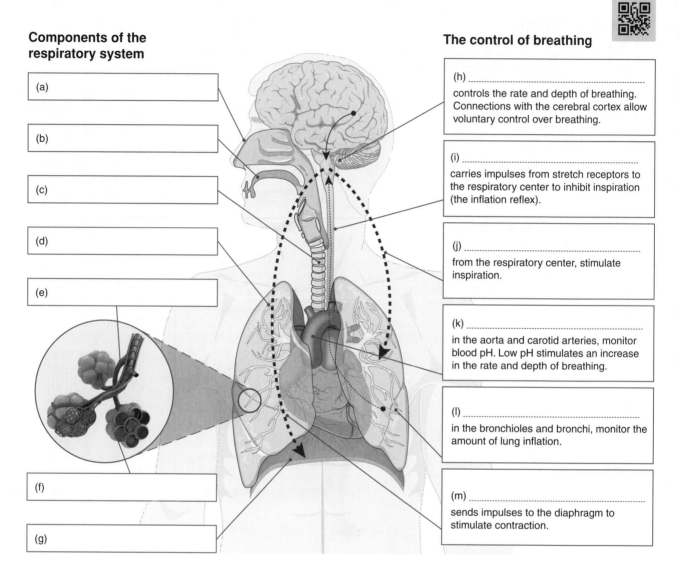

1. On the diagram above, label the components of the respiratory system (a-g) and the components that control the rate of breathing (h-m).

2. Identify the volumes and capacities indicated by the letters A - E on the diagram of a spirogram (right).

   (a): _____

   (b): _____

   (c): _____

   (d): _____

   (e): _____

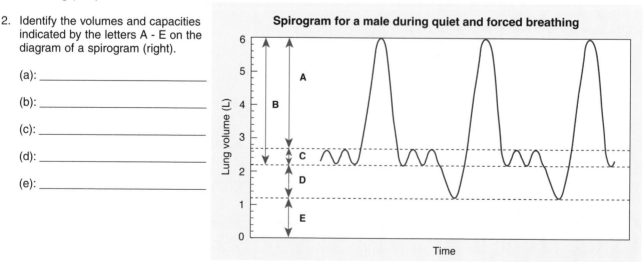

Spirogram for a male during quiet and forced breathing

155 Respiratory Diseases

Key Idea: Respiratory diseases are diseases of the gas exchange system, including diseases of the lung, bronchial tubes, trachea, and upper respiratory tract.

Respiratory diseases range from mild, self-limiting diseases such as the common cold, to life-threatening infections such as tuberculosis. One in six people in the US is affected by some form of chronic lung disease, the most common being **asthma** and chronic obstructive pulmonary disease (including emphysema and chronic **bronchitis**). Non-infectious respiratory diseases are categorized according to whether they prevent air reaching the **alveoli** (obstructive) or whether they affect the gas exchange tissue itself (restrictive).

Such diseases have different causes and different symptoms (below) but all are characterized by difficulty in breathing and the end result is similar in that gas exchange rates are too low to meet metabolic requirements. Non-infectious respiratory diseases are strongly correlated with certain behaviors and are made worse by exposure to air pollutants. Obstructive diseases, such as emphysema, are associated with an inflammatory response of the lung to noxious particles or gases, most commonly tobacco smoke. In contrast, scarring (fibrosis) of the lung tissue underlies restrictive lung diseases such as asbestosis and silicosis. Such diseases are often called occupational lung diseases.

Chronic bronchitis
Excess mucus blocks airway, leading to inflammation and infection

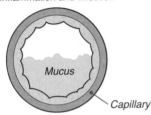

Asthma
Thickening of bronchiole wall and muscle hypertrophy. Bronchioles narrow.

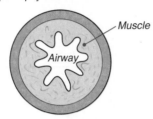

Emphysema
Destruction of capillaries and structures supporting the small airways and lung tissue

Cross sections through a bronchiole with various types of obstructive lung disease

Obstructive lung disease – passage blockage –

In obstructive lung diseases, a blockage prevents the air getting to the gas exchange surface.

The flow of air may be obstructed because of constriction of the airways (as in **asthma**), excess mucus secretion (as in chronic **bronchitis**), or because of reduced lung elasticity, which causes alveoli and small airways to collapse (as in emphysema). Shortness of breath is a symptom in all cases and chronic bronchitis is also associated with a persistent cough.

Chronic bronchitis and emphysema often occur together and are commonly associated with cigarette smoking, but can also occur with chronic exposure to air pollution.

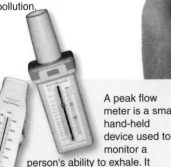

A peak flow meter is a small, hand-held device used to monitor a person's ability to exhale. It measures the airflow through the **bronchi** and therefore the degree of obstruction in the airways.

Scarring (fibrosis) makes the lung tissue stiffer and prevents adequate gas exchange

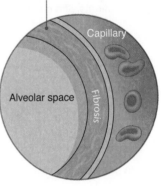

Capillary

Alveolar space

Fibrosis

Restrictive lung disease – scarring –

Restrictive lung diseases are characterized by scarring or fibrosis within the gas exchange tissue of the lung (above). As a result of the scarring, the lung tissue becomes stiffer and more difficult to expand, leading to shortness of breath.

Restrictive lung diseases are usually the result of exposure to inhaled substances (especially dusts) in the environment, including inorganic dusts such as silica, asbestos, or coal dust, and organic dusts, such as those from bird droppings or moldy hay. Like most respiratory diseases, the symptoms are exacerbated by poor air quality (such as occurs in smoggy cities).

Lungs

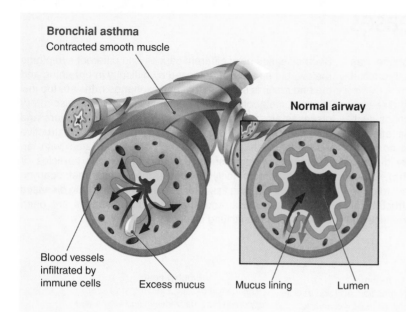

Bronchial asthma
Contracted smooth muscle

Normal airway

Blood vessels infiltrated by immune cells

Excess mucus

Mucus lining

Lumen

Asthma and the respiratory system

Asthma is a common disease affecting millions of people worldwide (20 million in the US alone). Asthma is the result of a hypersensitive reaction to allergens such as house dust or pollen, but attacks can be triggered by environmental factors such as cold air, exercise, or air pollutants.

Mast cells, a specific type of immune cell, release histamine and other compounds that induce the smooth muscle around the bronchi to contract. The lumen diameter reduces to limit airflow. During an attack, sufferers show labored breathing with overexpansion of the chest cavity. Asthma is treated with drugs that help to expand the airways (bronchodilators). These are usually delivered via a nebulizer or inhaler. Chronic asthma can cause swelling and excess mucus, which may not respond to treatment as readily.

1. Distinguish between obstructive and restrictive lung diseases, and provide some examples: _____

_____

_____

_____

_____

2. Physicians may use spirometry to diagnosis certain types of respiratory disease. (See activity 152 to recall terminology) Explain the following typical results:

(a) In patients with chronic obstructive pulmonary disease, the FEV_1 / FVC ratio declines (to <70% of normal): _____

_____

_____

(b) Patients with asthma also have a FEV_1 / FVC ratio of <70%, but this improves following use of bronchodilators:

_____

_____

(c) In patients with restrictive lung disease, both FEV_1 and FVC are low but the FEV_1 / FVC ratio is normal to high:

_____

_____

3. Describe the mechanisms by which restrictive lung diseases reduce lung function and describe an example: _____

_____

_____

_____

4. Suggest why many restrictive lung diseases are also classified as occupational lung diseases: _____

_____

_____

5. Describe the role of histamine in the occurrence of an asthma attack: _____

_____

_____

156 Covid-19 and Lung Damage

Key Idea: In serious cases, SARS-CoV-2, the coronavirus that causes Covid-19, causes the development of pneumonia and Acute Respiratory Distress Syndrome (ARDS) in the respiratory system.

Viral pneumonia, a common consequence of severe Covid-19, impacts breathing due to lungs filling with fluid, and associated lung inflammation. Surviving patients usually face many weeks of lingering symptoms, such as coughing and shortness of breath. ARDS is not a single respiratory disease, but a set of related syndromes. Developing Covid-19 induced ARDS is commonly fatal, and life-threatening damage to both the **alveoli** and surrounding capillaries normally requires

the patient to be placed on mechanical ventilation while the lungs heal. The SARS-CoV-2 protein binds to ACE receptors on the epithelial calls of the alveoli, setting off a 'cytokinetic storm', an exaggerated immune response, and creates 'leaky' capillaries surrounding the alveoli. Cytokines, released by immune cells in the blood, cause an inflammatory response. Alveoli swell and fluid from the capillaries leak in to fill the alveoli sacs, preventing oxygen from entering the capillaries. Covid-19 induced ARDS resulted in a mortality rate of 39% of those hospitalized at the peak of the pandemic, impacting older patients, and those with other underlying health conditions, to a greater extent.

Covid-19 induced ARDS and the effect on the respiratory system

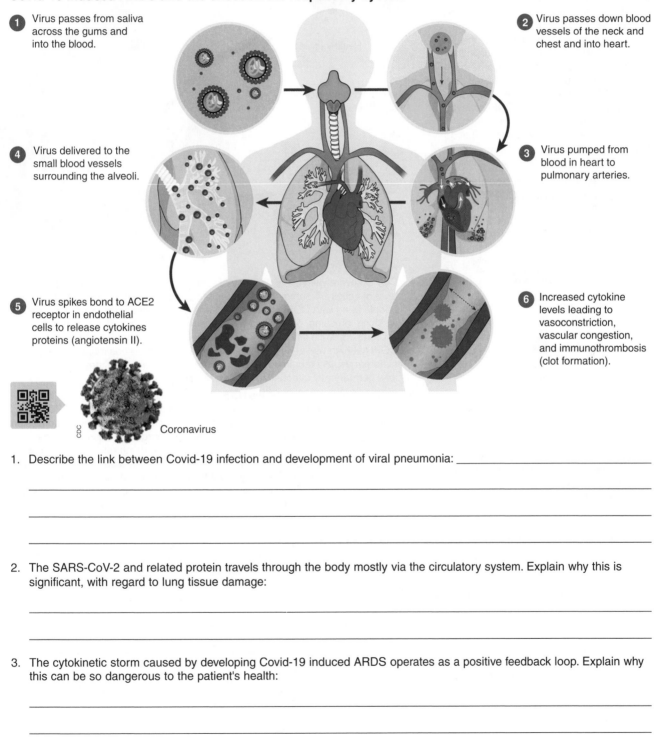

1 Virus passes from saliva across the gums and into the blood.

2 Virus passes down blood vessels of the neck and chest and into heart.

4 Virus delivered to the small blood vessels surrounding the alveoli.

3 Virus pumped from blood in heart to pulmonary arteries.

5 Virus spikes bond to ACE2 receptor in endothelial cells to release cytokines proteins (angiotensin II).

6 Increased cytokine levels leading to vasoconstriction, vascular congestion, and immunothrombosis (clot formation).

Coronavirus

1. Describe the link between Covid-19 infection and development of viral pneumonia: _____

_____

_____

_____

2. The SARS-CoV-2 and related protein travels through the body mostly via the circulatory system. Explain why this is significant, with regard to lung tissue damage:

_____

_____

3. The cytokinetic storm caused by developing Covid-19 induced ARDS operates as a positive feedback loop. Explain why this can be so dangerous to the patient's health:

_____

_____

_____

157 Living with COPD

Key Idea: COPD (chronic obstructive pulmonary disease) is a type of chronic lung disease that causes persistent respiratory symptoms, including difficulty in breathing. Major contributors to **COPD** are emphysema (the formation of air-filled spaces in the lungs) and chronic **bronchitis** (excess mucus in the lungs). The most common cause of COPD is tobacco smoking. Other risk factors include pollution, exposure to irritant substances, and genetics. As this disease is progressive, the prevalence in many populations still continues to increase, even though tobacco use has decreased over time.

The impact of COPD in the US

Chronic obstructive pulmonary disease (COPD) is a serious lung disease which makes it difficult for people to breathe because their airways are partially blocked or because the **alveoli** of the lungs lose their elasticity or become damaged. COPD includes chronic bronchitis and emphysema, and affects about 12 million people in the US. Most of those affected are over the age of 40 and smoking is the cause in the vast majority of cases. This relationship is clear; people who have never smoked rarely develop COPD. The symptoms of COPD and **asthma** are similar, but COPD causes permanent damage to the airways, and so symptoms are chronic (persistent) and treatment is limited.

Healthy bronchus

Healthy alveoli

Inflammation and excess mucus (bronchitis)

Breakdown of alveoli walls (emphysema)

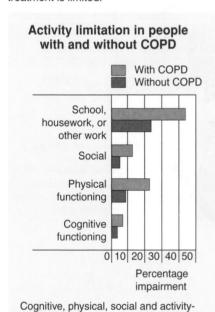

Activity limitation in people with and without COPD

- With COPD
- Without COPD

School, housework, or other work

Social

Physical functioning

Cognitive functioning

0 | 10 | 20 | 30 | 40 | 50

Percentage impairment

Cognitive, physical, social and activity-related limitations are more common among people with chronic obstructive pulmonary disease.

▶ COPD severely limits the capacity of sufferers to carry out even a normal daily level of activity. A survey by the American Lung Association of hundreds of people living with COPD found that nearly half became short of breath while washing, dressing, or doing light housework (left). Over 25% reported difficulty in breathing while sitting or lying still. Lack of oxygen also places those with COPD at high risk of heart failure. As the disease becomes more severe, sufferers usually require long-term oxygen therapy, in which they are more or less permanently attached to an oxygen supply.

▶ COPD is estimated to cost the US $32 billion dollars each year, $14 billion of which are indirect costs, such as lost working days. A 'flare-up' of COPD, during which the symptoms worsen, is one of the most common reasons for admission to hospital and the disease places a substantial burden on health services. COPD is the only major disease with an increasing death rate in the US, rising 16%, and is the third leading cause of death. At least 120,000 people die each year from the end stages of COPD but the actual number may be higher, as COPD is often present in patients who die from heart failure and stroke. Many of these people have several years of ill health before they die.

1. COPD is a chronic inflammatory disease associated with smoking:

(a) What does chronic mean? _____

(b) What symptoms are associated with COPD? _____

_____

_____

(c) How are these related to the changes in the lung tissue itself? _____

_____

_____

_____

©2023 **BIOZONE** International
ISBN: 978-1-99-101408-5
Photocopying Prohibited

158 Risk Factors for Lung Disease

Key Idea: Risk factors associated with lung disease include age, sex, occupational hazards, and behavioral factors.

Lung disease includes a wide range of aliments, including lung cancer, obstructive diseases such as emphysema, and restrictive diseases, such as asbestosis. In the US, about 15 million people live with **COPD**, and 120,000 die from it every year. Risk factors include behavioral, genetic, occupational, age, and socio-economic.

Behavioral
Smoking is the number one behavioral risk factor for lung disease, with lung cancer rates being 15 times higher in smokers than in non-smokers. Second-hand smoke also contributes to lung disease. Indoor living increases the risk of lung disease, due to increased levels of radon gas released from the soil which becomes trapped indoors, especially in basement areas.

Genetic and socio-economic factors
Occurrence of lung disease increases in those with a family history of lung disease. Some socioeconomic factors, e.g. living in poorly heated and ventilated housing, also increase the risk of lung disease. Crowded urban areas can be more at risk of smog and air pollution.

Occupational
Occupations that involve the use of, or proximity to, hazardous substances increase the risk of lung diseases. Many of these substances cause change to the DNA (mutation) and include paints, machine exhaust, and airborne particles such as industrial dusts, e.g. concrete, asbestos, and coal dust, which are inhaled.

Age and sex
The risk of developing lung disease increases with age. Frequent occurrences of lung disease when young increases the risk of chronic lung disease later in life. Males tend to have slightly higher risk of developing lung disease than females.

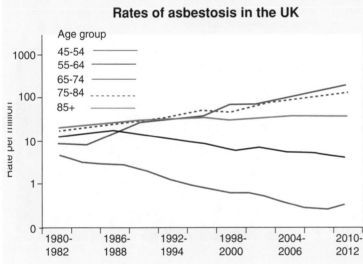

Rates of asbestosis in the UK

Age group
- 45-54
- 55-64
- 65-74
- 75-84
- 85+

rate per million

1980-1982 · 1986-1988 · 1992-1994 · 1998-2000 · 2004-2006 · 2010-2012

Asbestosis is a restrictive lung disease caused by breathing in asbestos fibers. The asbestos fibers make their way into the **alveoli**, where they cause damage and scarring. Symptoms may not appear for 20 years or more. Asbestos has not been widely used as building or insulating material for many decades. In the photo (right), workers removing old asbestos sheets must wear full protective equipment.

1. In the UK, cases of asbestosis between age groups were not significantly different in the 1970s and early 1980s. Since then, there has been a steady fall in young to middle age people with asbestosis, but a rising incidence rate in older age groups. Explain why this has occurred:

_____

_____

_____

2. Asbestos has different toxicity depending on the type. Some types of asbestos are very friable and, when dry, form a powder that can become airborne. Degradation can make some asbestos types become friable. Discuss friability as a risk factor:

Asbestos fibers

_____

_____

_____

_____

©2023 **BIOZONE** International
ISBN: 978-1-99-101408-5
Photocopying Prohibited

Mesothelioma vs asbestosis

▶ Asbestos is a naturally occurring substance and was used as building insulation and ceiling coatings in older buildings. Asbestos is a carcinogen and exposure to it, especially during removal, can lead to cancer as well as severe lung disease.

▶ A second disease linked to asbestos exposure, asbestosis, has higher survivability rates but requires long term treatment to mediate the effects.

▶ Mesothelioma is a rare, mostly fatal, type of cancer that is almost exclusively acquired from asbestos exposure. However, more common types of lung cancer can also develop.

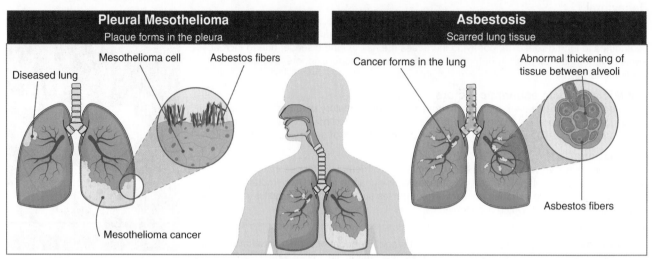

Pleural Mesothelioma	Asbestosis
Plaque forms in the pleura	Scarred lung tissue

Asbestos exposure is the main cause of pleural mesothelioma, but not the only cause. Asbestos fibers travel to the pleura (lining) of the lungs. Mesothelioma is an aggressive and deadly cancer with no cure. Symptoms include unexplained weight loss, unusual lumps under the skin, fluid accumulating in chest, and difficulty swallowing.

The only cause of asbestosis is environmental exposure to asbestos. Asbestos fibers travel and are lodged into the lung alveoli. The effects of this chronic disease can be reduced, and patients can live a long period. Specific symptoms include shortness of breath and coughing, pain and, in advanced cases, wider and rounder fingertips and toes (clubbing).

Environmental air pollution and lung disease

Pollutants from vehicles, households, and industry in the form of small, airborne particles can travel in the air and be inhaled by humans. Air pollution is often seen as smog, especially in built up, urban areas, and in atmospheric conditions that prevent low-level smog moving away (see right).

Ultra-fine particles can enter the lungs and cause a range of respiratory disorders. The World Heath Organization (WHO) estimates that air pollution is responsible for around 16% of all lung cancer deaths, 26% of respiratory infection deaths, and 25% of COPD deaths.

Some regions and cities send out warnings to citizens to remain inside, or wear respiratory masks, when air pollution levels are high.

Smog in urban city

3. What are the common causes of both pleural mesothelioma and asbestosis? _____

_____

_____

4. What are common disease symptoms of both pleural mesothelioma and asbestosis? _____

_____

_____

5. Air pollution is a significant factor in the development of respiratory diseases, and subsequent death:

(a) What is the link between air pollution and lung function? _____

_____

(b) Why is air pollution caused lung disease more likely to impact lower socio-economic populations? _____

_____

_____

©2023 **BIOZONE** International
ISBN: 978-1-99-101408-5
Photocopying Prohibited

159 Smoking and the Lungs

Key Idea: Tobacco smoking is a major health hazard associated with nicotine addiction, cancer, and chronic diseases of the cardiovascular and gas exchange systems. Despite its practice in Western countries for more than 400 years, and much longer elsewhere, tobacco smoking has only been accepted as a major health hazard relatively recently. Cigarettes became popular at the end of World War I because they were cheap, convenient, and easy to smoke. The mild smoke is readily inhaled, allowing nicotine (an addictive poison) to be quickly absorbed into the bloodstream. Cigarette smoke also contains poisonous gases, such as carbon monoxide, and the tar contains many carcinogens. Smoking is associated with a large number of diseases, including cancers, **COPD**, and heart disease.

The effects of tobacco smoking on the gas exchange system

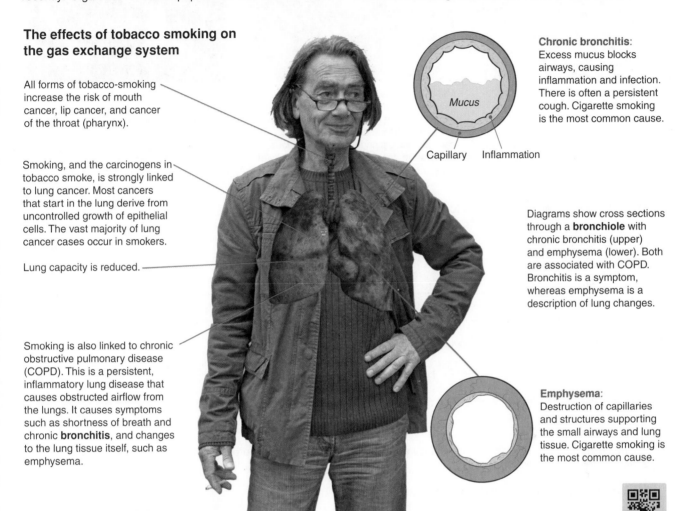

All forms of tobacco-smoking increase the risk of mouth cancer, lip cancer, and cancer of the throat (pharynx).

Smoking, and the carcinogens in tobacco smoke, is strongly linked to lung cancer. Most cancers that start in the lung derive from uncontrolled growth of epithelial cells. The vast majority of lung cancer cases occur in smokers.

Lung capacity is reduced.

Smoking is also linked to chronic obstructive pulmonary disease (COPD). This is a persistent, inflammatory lung disease that causes obstructed airflow from the lungs. It causes symptoms such as shortness of breath and chronic **bronchitis**, and changes to the lung tissue itself, such as emphysema.

Mucus

Capillary   Inflammation

Chronic bronchitis: Excess mucus blocks airways, causing inflammation and infection. There is often a persistent cough. Cigarette smoking is the most common cause.

Diagrams show cross sections through a **bronchiole** with chronic bronchitis (upper) and emphysema (lower). Both are associated with COPD. Bronchitis is a symptom, whereas emphysema is a description of lung changes.

Emphysema: Destruction of capillaries and structures supporting the small airways and lung tissue. Cigarette smoking is the most common cause.

How smoking damages the lungs

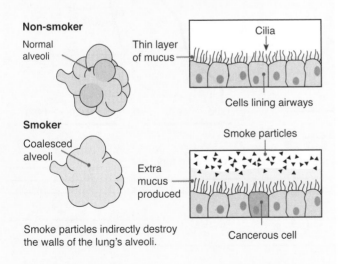

Non-smoker

Normal alveoli

Thin layer of mucus

Cilia

Cells lining airways

Smoker

Coalesced alveoli

Extra mucus produced

Smoke particles

Cancerous cell

Smoke particles indirectly destroy the walls of the lung's alveoli.

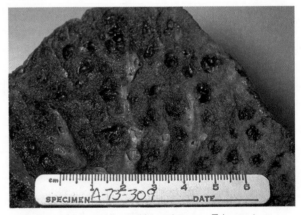

Lung tissue from a patient with emphysema. Tobacco tar deposits can be seen. Tar is a toxic, resinous residue of tobacco smoke and contains at least 17 known carcinogens (cancer-causing agents), including benzene, acrylamide, and acrylonitrile. Tar damages the teeth and gums, desensitizes taste buds, and accumulates in the lung tissue (above). The carcinogenic components of tar cause DNA mutations in the delicate epithelial cells of the lung, leading to lung cancer.

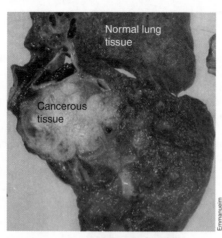

Emphysema, which is characterized by narrowing of the small airways and breakdown of lung tissue, is typical of COPD. The breakdown of the lung tissue causes the formation of large air pockets (above) and airflow and gas exchange rates are poor.

Most lung cancers begin in the epithelial cells of the lung. DNA damage from exposure to the carcinogens in tar leads to cell proliferation and tumor formation. Lung cancer is the second most common form of cancer in the UK and the vast majority of cases are associated with cigarette smoking.

Chronic bronchitis is associated with COPD, although there are other causes. It is accompanied by a persistent, productive cough, where sufferers attempt to cough up the mucus that accumulates in the airways. It leads to inflammation. The poor airflow is not improved with bronchodilator therapy.

1. Discuss the physical changes to the lung that result from long-term smoking: _____

_____

_____

_____

_____

2. Describe how the inhalation of particulates, such as tar, in tobacco smoke can lead to lung cancer: _____

_____

_____

_____

3. A long term study showed the correlation between smoking and lung cancer, providing supporting evidence for the adverse effects of smoking (right):

(a) Explain why a long term study was important:

_____

_____

_____

_____

(b) The study made a link between cigarette consumption and mortality from lung cancer. What else did it show?

_____

_____

_____

4. Discuss the link between tobacco smoking and emphysema, including the loss of lung function: _____

_____

_____

_____

_____

©2023 **BIOZONE** International
ISBN: 978-1-99-101408-5
Photocopying Prohibited

160 Vaping and the Lungs

Key Idea: The inhalation of a vapor containing nicotine and other products is called vaping. This activity may have negative health effects.

Nicotine 'vaping', through an electronic device, is a relatively new phenomenon. Research links its uptake to a decrease in tobacco smoking. Although vaping is often promoted as a safe alternative to tobacco smoking, developing evidence shows many possible negative health impacts, including cardiovascular and lung disease. Long-term health impacts are still unknown.

Vaping and lung damage

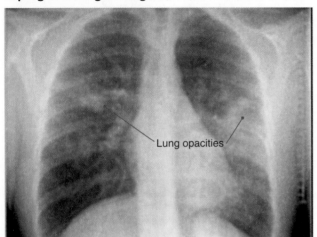

Chest radiograph showing lung damage in patient due to vaping, typical of EVALI.

Vaping has been linked to lung damage in patients. This damage was defined by the CDC (Centres for Disease Control and prevention) in 2019 as e-cigarette or vaping product use-associated lung injury (EVALI). Symptoms include coughing, chest pain, and shortness of breath. Studies concluded that additives to the vaping liquid, such as Vitamin E acetate, were likely to be major contributors to lung damage. Over 2800 people in the US, and over 68 deaths, by early 2020 were attributed to Vitamin E acetate. Although this additive was mainly linked to THC-containing vape liquids, other additives in nicotine-based vape liquids are thought to contribute to EVALI. Health specialists are concerned about the lack of research on health impacts of vaping, the possible poisons and carcinogens that may cause future lung damage and disease, as well as the increase in marketing to young people.

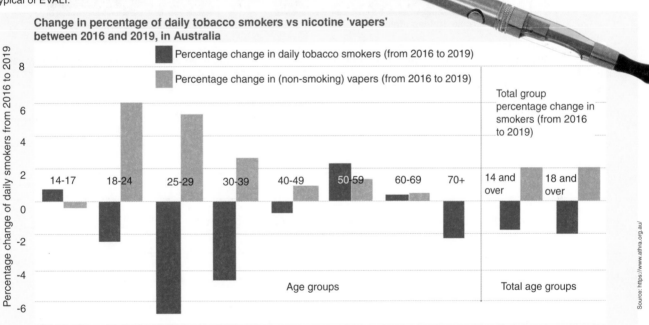

Change in percentage of daily tobacco smokers vs nicotine 'vapers' between 2016 and 2019, in Australia

- Percentage change in daily tobacco smokers (from 2016 to 2019)
- Percentage change in (non-smoking) vapers (from 2016 to 2019)

Total group percentage change in smokers (from 2016 to 2019)

Age groups: 14-17, 18-24, 25-29, 30-39, 40-49, 50-59, 60-69, 70+

Total age groups: 14 and over, 18 and over

Source: https://www.athra.org.au/

1. From the graph above, describe the patterns you see in the data for tobacco smoking vs 'vaping': _____

_____

_____

2. Research studies done in 2022 by CDC shows around 9% of middle school and high school students in the US have vaped in the past 30 days, 3 times higher than the rate of adults. Why is promoting vaping as a healthy alternative to tobacco smoking in the 18-24 youth age scientifically and statistically incorrect?

_____

_____

3. Summarize the impacts to lung health caused by vaping: _____

_____

_____

©2023 **BIOZONE** International
ISBN: 978-1-99-101408-5
Photocopying Prohibited

161 Responding to Exercise

Key Idea: Maintaining homeostasis during exercise is principally the job of the circulatory and respiratory systems, although the skin, kidneys, and liver are also important.

Physical exercise places greater demands on the abilities of the body to maintain a steady state. Extra heat generated during exercise must be dissipated, oxygen demands increase, and more waste products are produced. The body has an immediate response to exercise but also, over time,

responds to the stress of repeated exercise (training) by adapting and improving its capacity and the efficiency with which it performs. This concept is illustrated below. Training causes tissue damage and depletes energy stores but the body responds by repairing the damage, replenishing energy stores, and adjusting its responses in order to minimize the impact of exercise in the future.

Exercise effects on the cardiac and respiratory system

Cardiac output (total blood flow)

Muscle / Other body parts

5.5 L total: muscle 0.8-1.0 L
Resting man

20-25 L total: muscle 15-20 L
Heavy exercise: average man

30-35 L total: muscle 26-31 L
Heavy exercise: trained athlete

Oxygen consumption

0.25 L total: muscle 0.05 L
Resting man

3-3.5 L total: muscle 2.8-3.3 L
Heavy exercise: average man

5-6 L total: muscle 4.8-5.8 L
Heavy exercise: trained athlete

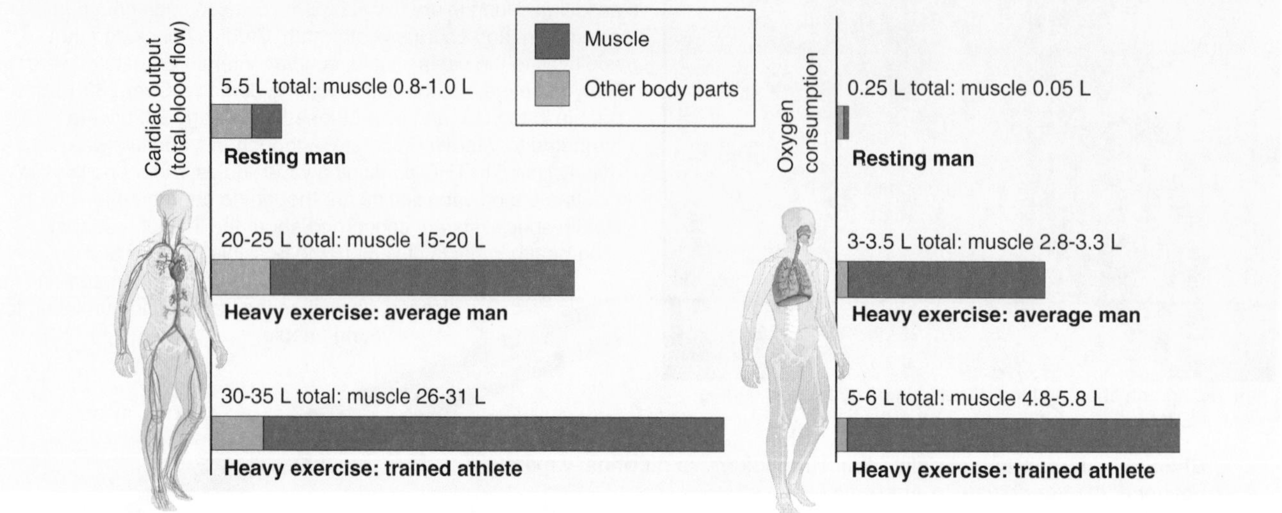

1. The graph above shows the change in cardiac output (a measure of total blood flow) and oxygen consumption between resting and exercise in an athlete and an average man. The different shading on the bars indicates the proportion of oxygen or blood flow in skeletal muscle, compared to other body parts.

   (a) Describe what happens to the output of the heart (total blood flow) during heavy exercise: _____

   _____

   (b) Explain why this is the case: _____

   _____

   (c) List the organ(s) and tissues responsible for adjusting blood flow during exercise: _____

   _____

2. (a) Describe what happens to oxygen consumption during heavy exercise: _____

   _____

   (b) Explain why this is the case: _____

   _____

   (c) Explain the change in the proportion of oxygen consumed by the muscles during exercise: _____

   _____

   _____

3. Explain the difference in oxygen consumption and blood flow between a trained athlete and an average man:

   _____

   _____

   _____

   _____

   _____

162 The Effects of High Altitude

Key Idea: Air pressure decreases with altitude so the pressure (therefore amount) of oxygen in the air also decreases. Many of the physiological effects of high altitude arise from the low oxygen pressure, not the actual low air pressure.

Sudden exposure to an altitude of 2000 m causes breathlessness and above 7000 m most people would become unconscious. Humans can make both short and long term physiological adjustments to altitude. These changes are referred to as acclimation, and are different from the evolutionary adaptations of high altitude populations, which are inherited.

Physiological adjustments to altitude

When exposed to high altitude, the body makes several short and long term physiological adjustments to compensate. Two immediate responses are to increase both the rate of breathing (hyperventilation) and heart rate.

Normally, the rate of breathing is regulated by a sensitivity to blood pH (CO_2 level). However, low oxygen pressures (pO_2) in the blood induce a hypoxic response, stimulating oxygen-sensitive receptors in the aorta and inducing hyperventilation. Breathing rates increase over several days and may remain elevated for up to a year.

Heart rate at altitude increases up to 50% above the rate at sea level, although the stroke volume (the amount of blood pumped per contraction) remains the same. Fluid loss also becomes an issue, as water evaporates more easily at low pressure. Water losses from breathing thus become much higher and the body must compensate by taking in more fluids. Longer term changes in physiology include acid-base readjustment and an increase in red blood cells (RBCs).

The kidneys also produce the hormone erythropoietin (EPO). This stimulates an increase in the production of RBCs within about 15 hours of exposure to altitude. The blood of a high altitude miner in the Andes contains about 38% more RBCs than that of a low altitude person. This is about the limit of benefit, as any more RBCs would cause blood viscosity to be too high.

Ascending to altitude (4500 m+) too rapidly results in mountain sickness. The symptoms include breathlessness and nausea. Continuing to ascend with mountain sickness can result in fatal accumulation of fluid on the lungs and brain.

Time scales of physiological changes at altitude

Effect	Minutes	Days	Weeks
Increased heart rate	→		
Increased breathing	→		
Concentration of blood		→	
Increased red blood cell production			↔
Increased capillary density			↔

The human body can make adjustments to life at altitude. Some of these changes, e.g. increased breathing and heart rates, take place almost immediately. Other adjustments, such as increasing the number of red blood cells and associated **hemoglobin** level, may take weeks (see above and below). These responses are all aimed at improving the rate of supply of oxygen to the body's tissues. When the more permanent adjustments to physiology are made (increased blood cells and capillary networks), heart and breathing rates can return to normal.

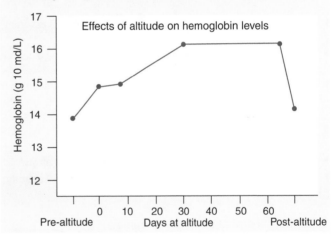

Effects of altitude on hemoglobin levels

Hemoglobin (g 10 md/L) vs Days at altitude: Pre-altitude, Days at altitude (0, 10, 20, 30, 40, 50, 60), Post-altitude

1. (a) Describe the initial effects of high altitude on the body in people who are not acclimated: _____

_____

_____

   (b) Name the general term given to describe these effects: _____

2. (a) Name one short term and long term physiological adjustment that humans make to high altitude: _____

_____

   (b) Explain how these adjustments help to increase the amount of oxygen the body receives: _____

_____

_____

_____

_____

©2023 **BIOZONE** International
ISBN: 978-1-99-101408-5
Photocopying Prohibited

163 Aging and the Respiratory System

Key Idea: Aging impacts the respiratory system, often as a decline in respiratory capacity and VO$_2$ max, and an increase in incidence of chronic respiratory disease.

The amount of respiratory function loss in an aging person depends on a combination of genetic factors, fitness, health complications, and lifestyle choices. Muscle fibers deteriorate as people age, including those around the **diaphragm**, so breathing becomes weaker. Ribcage bones become more brittle, making breathing less effective. **Alveoli** sacs lose their shape and become less efficient at transferring oxygen across them and into the blood stream. A weakening immune system can mean respiratory diseases become more complicated, causing tissue damage that may become permanent. Clearing mucus from the airway and lungs can become more difficult, as nervous responses to trigger coughing are slower.

Astronaut taking VO$_2$ max test on the ISS

NASA, Public domain, via Wikimedia Commons

Respiratory system function loss and aging

▶ Reduction in VO$_2$ max measurement, and therefore utilization of the oxygen in the air, and exercise capacity.

▶ Decrease in maximum oxygen intake due to weakening diaphragm muscles and rib cage bones.

▶ Higher incidence of respiratory disease complications, such as from pneumonia, influenza, and Covid-19, due to decreasing function of immune system.

▶ Loss of function of alveoli gas exchange due to loss of shape and increase of 'dead space' in sac.

▶ Impairment of coughing reflex to remove phlegm from airway.

▶ Reduction of FEV - forced expiratory volume and **vital capacity**.

VO$_2$ max and respiratory function

Recall from activity 48 that the VO$_2$ max test determines the amount of oxygen that a person can utilize from inhalation of air. It is measured in milliliters of oxygen used by a person during one minute of exercise per kilogram of body weight. The quantity of oxygen remaining in the expired air is measured when a person is performing an exercise at maximum effort, usually by stationary cycling or running. This test is often used as the 'gold standard' to measure athletic endurance fitness. The VO$_2$ max averages decrease from their peak at around 20 years old, to more than 30% once a person reaches 65. Males also tend to average 20% higher than equivalently aged women. VO$_2$ max can be improved with aerobic training, but is also partly determined by genetic factors.

1. (a) Describe what VO$_2$ max measures: _____

_____

(b) How is aging likely to effect VO$_2$ max in a person? _____

_____

2. (a) Why is aging likely to reduce a person's speed and duration of endurance exercise? _____

_____

_____

_____

(b) How is aging linked to greater chance of complications and mortality when contacting a respiratory disease?

_____

_____

_____

©2023 **BIOZONE** International
ISBN: 978-1-99-101408-5
Photocopying Prohibited

164 Chapter Summary

1. Summarize the path of oxygen from the air to entering the heart, using correct terminology:

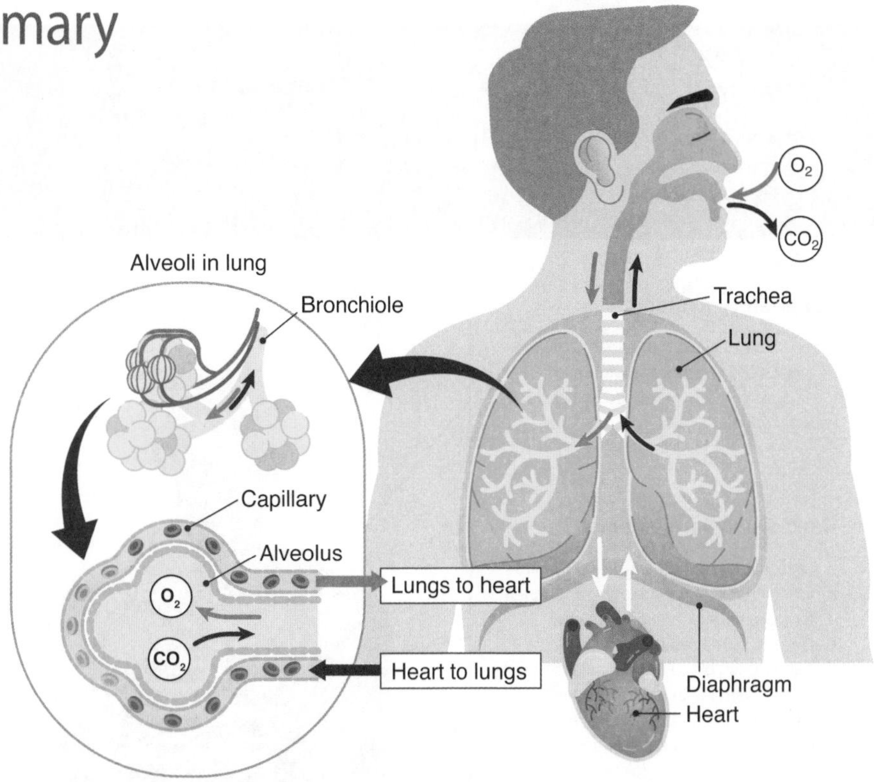

_____

_____

_____

_____

_____

_____

_____

_____

_____

_____

_____

Alveoli in lung

Bronchiole

Capillary

Alveolus

O_2

CO_2

Lungs to heart

Heart to lungs

O_2

CO_2

Trachea

Lung

Diaphragm

Heart

2. Discuss how breathing is controlled and how central sleep apnea can effect that control: _____

_____

_____

3. Explain the potential effects of a Covid-19 infection on the respiratory system: _____

_____

_____

4. Describe the impacts of tobacco smoking on the respiratory system: _____

_____

_____

_____

_____

_____

5. Discuss the potential issues of promoting nicotine vaping to replace tobacco smoking: _____

_____

_____

_____

6. Compare and contrast between short-term and long-term physiological changes when living at high altitude: _____

_____

_____

_____

7. Describe several changes that occur in the respiratory system due to old age: _____

_____

_____

The Digestive System

Respiratory system

- Respiratory system provides O_2 to the organs of the digestive system and disposes of CO_2 produced by cellular respiration.

Cardiovascular system

- Digestive system absorbs iron required for synthesis of hemoglobin, and water for maintenance of blood volume.
- Hepatic portal system transports nutrient-rich blood from substantial parts of the gastrointestinal tract to the liver. Ultimately the cardiovascular system distributes nutrients throughout the body.
- The liver produces angiotensinogen, a precursor of the protein angiotensin, which is involved in the system regulating blood pressure and fluid volume.
- Blood distributes hormones of the digestive tract.

Urinary system

- Kidneys excrete toxins and the breakdown products of hormones which have been metabolized by the liver.
- Final activation of vitamin D, which is involved in calcium and phosphorus metabolism, occurs in the kidneys.

Skeletal system

- Digestive system absorbs calcium needed for bone maintenance, growth, and repair.
- Skeletal system protects some of the digestive organs from major damage.
- Bone acts as a storage site for some nutrients, e.g. calcium.

Integumentary system

- Digestive system provides fats for insulation in dermal and subcutaneous tissues.
- Skin provides external covering to protect the digestive organs.
- The skin synthesizes a precursor to vitamin D, which is required for absorption of calcium from the gut.

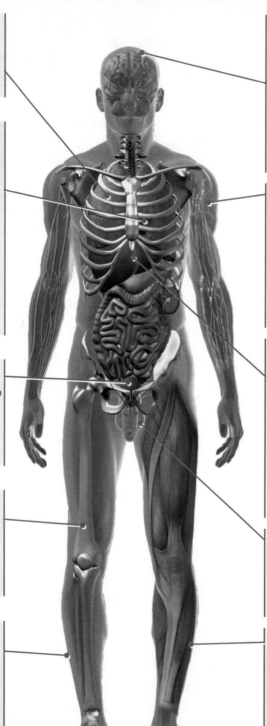

Nervous system

- The feeding center of the hypothalamus stimulates hunger. The satiety center suppresses the feeding center's activity after eating.
- Autonomic NS activity regulates much of gut function. Generally, parasympathetic stimulation increases and sympathetic stimulation decreases gut activity.
- There are reflex and voluntary controls over defecation.

Lymphatic system and immunity

- The lymphatic vessels of the small intestine (the lacteals) drain fat-laden lymph from the gut to the liver.
- Acidic gastric secretions destroy pathogens (non-specific defense).
- Lymphoid tissues in the gut mesenteries and intestinal wall house macrophages and leukocytes that protect against infection.

Endocrine system

- The liver removes hormones from circulation and prevents their continued activity.
- Pancreas contains endocrine cells that produce hormones for regulating blood sugar.
- Local hormones, e.g. gastrin from the stomach, cholecystokinin and secretin from the intestinal mucosa, help to regulate digestive function, including secretion of digestive juices and gut motility.

Reproductive system

- The digestive system provides nutrients required both for normal growth and repair, and nutrition required to support pregnancy and lactation in females.

Muscular system

- Liver removes and metabolizes lactic acid produced by intense muscular activity.
- Calcium absorbed in the gut as part of the diet is required for muscle contraction.
- Activity of skeletal muscles increases the motility of the gastrointestinal tract, aiding passage of food through the gut.

General functions and effects on all systems

The digestive system is responsible for the physical and chemical digestion and absorption of ingested food. Ultimately, it provides the nutrients required by all body systems for energy metabolism, growth, repair, and maintenance of tissues. Some nutrients may be stored (e.g. in bone, liver, and adipose tissue).

Disease

Symptoms of disease
- Pain (moderate to severe)
- Bleeding/change in bowel function
- Gastric reflux, nausea, vomiting
- Nutritional deficiencies

Infectious diseases of the digestive system
- Cholera
- Viral hepatitis
- Bacterial food poisoning
- Viral gastroenteritis

Non infectious disorders of the digestive system
- Bowel cancer
- Appendicitis
- Inflammatory bowel diseases
- Food allergies or intolerance
- Cirrhosis of the liver

 Medicine and Technology

Diagnosis of disorders
- Endoscopy and colonoscopy
- Gastrointestinal biopsy
- MRI scans and barium enema
- Blood tests

Preventing diseases of the digestive system
- Dietary management
- Behavior modification

Treatment of diseases of the digestive system
- Drug therapies
- Surgery
- Radiotherapy

- Appendicitis
- Lactose intolerance
- Celiac disease
- Salmonellosis

- Endoscopy
- MRI scanning
- Diet for health

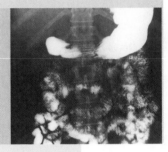

Eating to Live
The Digestive System

The digestive system provides for the energy and nutritional needs of all the body's systems.

While the digestive system is fairly robust against degenerative changes, gastrointestinal disorders are common. Gut function is improved by moderate exercise.

- Constipation
- Gastric emptying
- Bowel cancer

- GI blood flow
- Sports nutrition
- Carb loading
- Nutrition and recovery

Effects of aging on the digestive system
- Increased risk of bowel cancers
- Slower food passage, constipation
- Fibrosis of some organs (pancreas)
- Decline in gastric emptying rate
- Reduced gastric capacity

Effects of exercise on the digestive system
- Reduced blood flow to gut
- Decreased intestinal transit time
- Improved digestive function

 The Effects of Aging

 Exercise

The Digestive System

KEY IDEAS

- The digestive system takes in and processes food, making it available for assimilation.

- Food moves through the gut by peristalsis.

- Food is broken down by enzymes secreted by the organs of the digestive tract.

- Nutrients are absorbed across the gut wall into the blood. The liver is important in nutrient processing.

- Nervous and hormonal signals regulate digestion.

- Dietary and digestive disorders may be associated with inadequate nutrient intake and infection.

KEY TERMS

- Absorption
- Deficiency disease
- Digestive system
- Large intestine
- Malnutrition
- Peristalsis
- Small intestine
- Sphincter
- Stomach
- Villi

RESOURCE HUB

Scan the QR code to access:

- weblinks
- videos
- 3D models
- interactives

LEARNING OBJECTIVES

Activity number

☐ 1   Describe, giving examples, different models that can be used to help people choose a healthy diet.   **165**

☐ 2   Describe the overall process of digestion, including the role of the oral cavity and teeth, peristalsis, and the digestive sphincters. Understand the steps involved in the processing of food as ingestion, digestion, absorption, and egestion.   **166-168**

☐ 3   Describe the structure and function of the stomach and explain the role of gastric glands. Describe the role of the small intestine and explain how the structure of villi relate to their function.   **169**

☐ 4   Understand that digestion often involves the breakdown of large molecules into smaller molecules that can be absorbed by the body. Explain, in detail, the process of nutrient absorption by the villi. Describe the role of the large intestine.   **170-171**

☐ 5   Understand that digestion is controlled by both nervous and hormonal mechanisms. Describe the roles of named examples of hormones, and the vagus nerve.   **172**

☐ 6   Describe using annotated diagrams, the basic structure and histology of the liver. Understand the homeostatic function of the liver and describe, using examples, how it processes nutrients. Describe the urea/ornithine cycle in the conversion of ammonia to urea.   **173-176**

☐ 7   Analyze data that shows the effect of exercise on gut function. Understand the difference between soluble and insoluble fiber.   **177**

☐ 8   Understand that malnutrition takes many forms and that obesity is an example of malnutrition. Analyze and compare data on prevalence of clinical obesity in selected countries over time.   **178**

☐ 9   Describe examples of specific nutrient deficiency conditions.   **179**

☐ 10   Explain some effects of infection and inflammation on gut function, giving specific examples.   **38**

Background: Stomach lining (abstract)

165 A Balanced Diet

Key Idea: A balanced diet is required for optimum health. Different models can be used to represent the amounts of various food groups that should be eaten daily.

Nutrients are required for metabolism, tissue growth and repair, and as an energy source. Diet refers to the quantity and nature of food consumed and a balanced diet is one that provides all the nutrients and energy to maintain good health. Poor nutrition (**malnutrition**) may cause ill-health or **deficiency diseases.** While not all foods contain all nutrients, we can obtain the required balance of different nutrients by eating a wide variety of foods. The health benefits of unsaturated fats such as olive and canola oils, fish oils, and whole grains have been recognized, and people are being urged to reduce their consumption of highly processed foods and saturated (rather than total) fats. Those on diets that restrict certain food groups, e.g. vegans, must take care to balance their intake of foods to ensure an adequate supply of protein and other nutrients, e.g. iron and B vitamins. Different food pyramids have been used in the past to help guide food choices but a new plate model was introduced in 2011.

Nutrition models

▶ Over the years, a number of nutrition models have been developed to help people make good dietary choices. Various forms of food pyramids were developed to demonstrate that some food types should only be eaten in small amounts, and that some foods should compose the bulk of the diet (below left).

▶ Pyramid models were criticized as they encouraged people to eat a lot of carbohydrate and less fat, and a diet of low fat, high carbohydrate, highly processed 'junk foods' is not a healthy one. Not all fats are bad. Unsaturated fats, such as olive oil and fats found in oily fish, are healthier than the saturated fats found in red meat and dairy products.

▶ In 2011, the USDA introduced "My Plate" as a new dietary guideline model. This portioned plate graphic aims to give people a better image of how to balance food groups in daily meals, for a healthy diet.

Key
- MM: include at most meals
- AB: eat in abundance
- 2-3: number of servings per day
- S: eat these sparingly

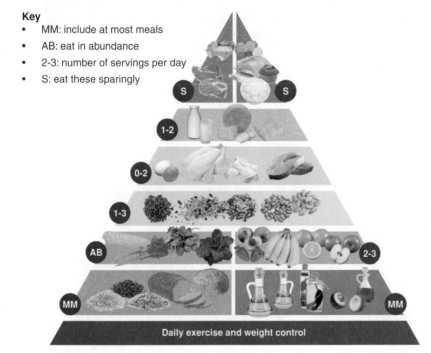

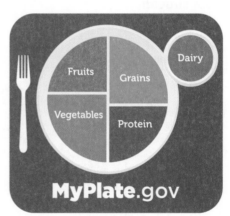

1. Identify two major roles of nutrients in the diet:

    (a) _____

    (b) _____

2. Compare the two nutrition models (above) and discuss how they differ in their recommendations for a healthy diet:

    _____

    _____

    _____

3. Explain why nutritional planning is especially important for vegans, who eat no animal products at all:

    _____

    _____

    _____

166 The Mouth and Pharynx

Key Idea: The mouth (oral cavity) is the first part of the gut and is where food is ingested.

The oral cavity comprises the cheeks, hard and soft palate, and tongue, and leads to the pharynx (the first part of the throat). The tongue moves food around and the teeth, and the salivary glands, which produce saliva, begin digestion. The oral cavity is divided into quadrants and the number of teeth in each quadrant is given by a dental formula. Children have 20 deciduous (milk) teeth and there are 32 adult (permanent) teeth, organized as shown below left. The basic structure of a tooth is described (below left).

The oral cavity and teeth

Adult (permanent) teeth per quadrant

Molar: 3

Premolar: 2

Canine: 1

Incisor: 2

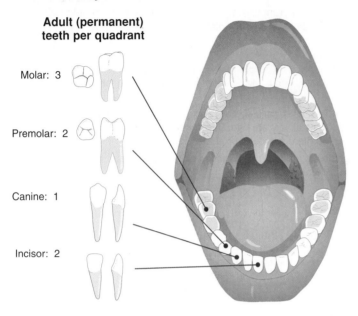

The 20 deciduous or milk teeth are lost at various stages during childhood. They are important placeholders for the permanent teeth.

The third molars usually erupt in the late teens or early twenties, hence their name as the wisdom teeth (right). They are frequently extracted because there is not enough room in the oral cavity for them.

Tooth structure

The crown is coated with enamel, the hardest substance in the body.

The root of the tooth extends down into the jaw, where the nerves and blood vessels join to form larger units.

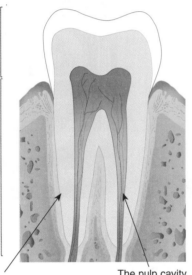

Dentin is a bone-like substance forming the bulk of the tooth. It gives the tooth its shape, but is not resistant to wear.

The pulp cavity contains the nerves and blood vessels supplying the tooth.

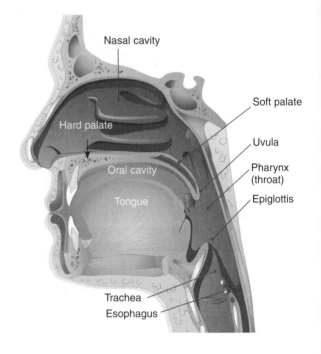

Nasal cavity

Hard palate

Soft palate

Uvula

Oral cavity

Pharynx (throat)

Tongue

Epiglottis

Trachea

Esophagus

1. Describe two major roles of the oral cavity and its associated structures in digestion: _____

   (a) _____

   (b) _____

2. Based on its position projecting up behind the tongue and guarding the tracheal entrance, infer the role of the epiglottis:

   _____

   _____

   _____

©2023 **BIOZONE** International
ISBN: 978-1-99-101408-5
Photocopying Prohibited

167 Moving Food Through the Gut

Key Idea: Solid food is chewed into a small mass called a bolus and swallowed. Further digestion produces chyme. Food is moved through the gut by waves of muscular contraction called peristalsis.

Ingested food is chewed and mixed with saliva to form a small mass called a bolus. Wave-like muscular contractions called **peristalsis** move the food, first as a bolus and then as semi-fluid chyme, through the digestive tract as described below.

Peristalsis

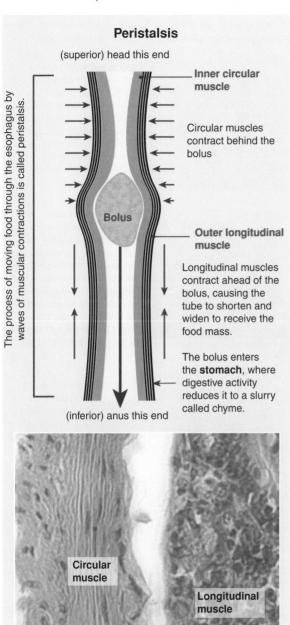

(superior) head this end

The process of moving food through the esophagus by waves of muscular contractions is called peristalsis.

Inner circular muscle

Circular muscles contract behind the bolus

Bolus

Outer longitudinal muscle

Longitudinal muscles contract ahead of the bolus, causing the tube to shorten and widen to receive the food mass.

The bolus enters the **stomach**, where digestive activity reduces it to a slurry called chyme.

(inferior) anus this end

Circular muscle

Longitudinal muscle

Ell

Cross section through the small intestine

A cross section through the **small intestine** shows the outer longitudinal and inner circular muscles involved in peristalsis.

Peristaltic movement in the colon

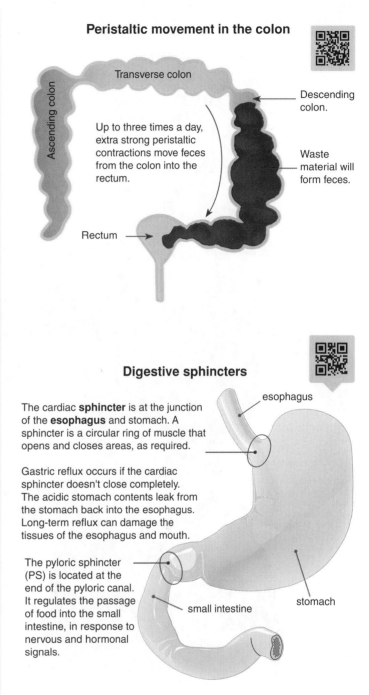

Transverse colon

Ascending colon

Up to three times a day, extra strong peristaltic contractions move feces from the colon into the rectum.

Descending colon.

Waste material will form feces.

Rectum

Digestive sphincters

esophagus

The cardiac **sphincter** is at the junction of the **esophagus** and stomach. A sphincter is a circular ring of muscle that opens and closes areas, as required.

Gastric reflux occurs if the cardiac sphincter doesn't close completely. The acidic stomach contents leak from the stomach back into the esophagus. Long-term reflux can damage the tissues of the esophagus and mouth.

The pyloric sphincter (PS) is located at the end of the pyloric canal. It regulates the passage of food into the small intestine, in response to nervous and hormonal signals.

small intestine

stomach

1. Describe how peristalsis moves food through the gut: _____

_____

_____

2. What are the two main functions of peristalsis? _____

_____

168 The Digestive System

Key Idea: The digestive tract is specialized for digestion of food, absorption of nutrients, and elimination of undigested material.

The **digestive system** (gut) is a tubular tract, divided into a complex series of organs and glands. These work in sequence to maximize the efficiency by which food is processed. Collectively, the organs of the digestive tract carry out the physical and chemical breakdown (digestion) of food, **absorption** of nutrients, and elimination of undigested material. The gut is a hollow, open-ended, muscular tube, and the food within it is essentially outside the body, having contact only with the cells lining the tract. Several accessory organs and glands lie external to the digestive tract. These secrete enzyme-rich fluids to the food to aid digestion.

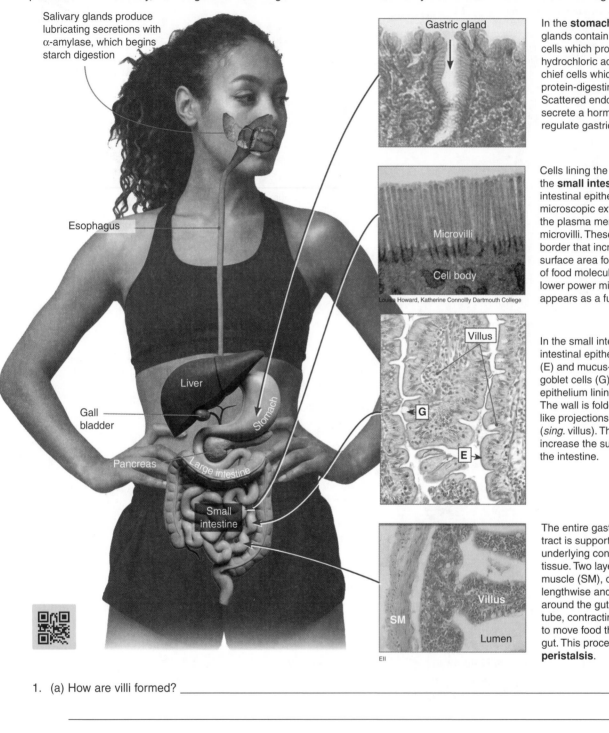

Salivary glands produce lubricating secretions with α-amylase, which begins starch digestion

Esophagus

Liver

Gall bladder

Pancreas

Large intestine

Stomach

Small intestine

Gastric gland

In the **stomach**, gastric glands contain parietal cells which produce hydrochloric acid, and chief cells which produce a protein-digesting enzyme. Scattered endocrine cells secrete a hormone to regulate gastric activity.

Microvilli

Cell body

Louisa Howard, Katherine Connollly Dartmouth College

Cells lining the walls on the **small intestine** (the intestinal epithelium) have microscopic extensions of the plasma membrane called microvilli. These form a brush border that increases the surface area for absorption of food molecules. Under lower power microscopy, it appears as a fuzzy edge.

Villus

G

E

In the small intestine, the intestinal epithelial cells (E) and mucus-producing goblet cells (G) make up the epithelium lining the gut wall. The wall is folded into finger-like projections called **villi** (*sing*. villus). These further increase the surface area of the intestine.

Villus

SM

Lumen

EII

The entire gastrointestinal tract is supported by underlying connective tissue. Two layers of smooth muscle (SM), one running lengthwise and one running around the gut, encircle the tube, contracting in waves to move food through the gut. This process is called **peristalsis**.

1. (a) How are villi formed? _____

_____

(b) What is the purpose of microvilli? _____

_____

2. What is the purpose of the smooth muscle surrounding the intestine? _____

_____

_____

©2023 **BIOZONE** International
ISBN: 978-1-99-101408-5
Photocopying Prohibited

169 The Stomach and Small Intestine

Key Idea: The stomach produces acid and a protein-digesting enzyme, which breaks food down into a slurry, called chyme. The **stomach** is a hollow, muscular organ between the esophagus and **small intestine**. In the stomach, food is mixed in an acidic environment to produce a semi-fluid mixture called chyme. The low pH of the stomach destroys microbes, denatures proteins, and activates a protein-digesting enzyme precursor. There is very little **absorption**, although small molecules (glucose, alcohol) are absorbed across the stomach wall into the surrounding blood vessels.

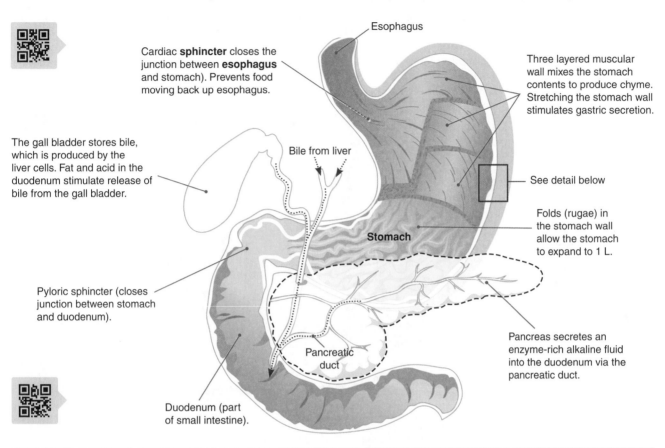

Cardiac **sphincter** closes the junction between **esophagus** and stomach). Prevents food moving back up esophagus.

Esophagus

Three layered muscular wall mixes the stomach contents to produce chyme. Stretching the stomach wall stimulates gastric secretion.

The gall bladder stores bile, which is produced by the liver cells. Fat and acid in the duodenum stimulate release of bile from the gall bladder.

Bile from liver

See detail below

Stomach

Folds (rugae) in the stomach wall allow the stomach to expand to 1 L.

Pyloric sphincter (closes junction between stomach and duodenum).

Pancreatic duct

Pancreas secretes an enzyme-rich alkaline fluid into the duodenum via the pancreatic duct.

Duodenum (part of small intestine).

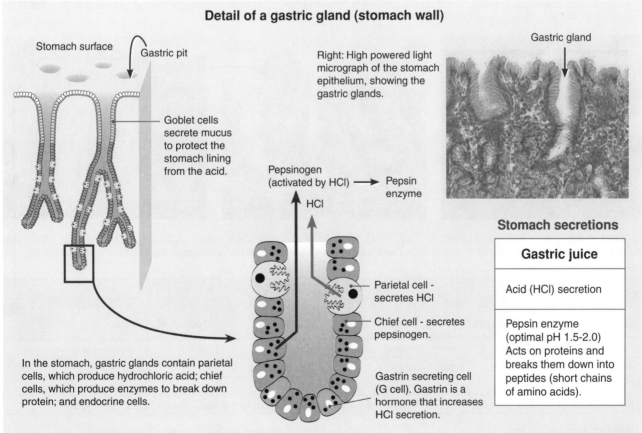

Detail of a gastric gland (stomach wall)

Stomach surface — Gastric pit

Right: High powered light micrograph of the stomach epithelium, showing the gastric glands.

Gastric gland

Goblet cells secrete mucus to protect the stomach lining from the acid.

Pepsinogen (activated by HCl) → Pepsin enzyme

HCl

Parietal cell - secretes HCl

Chief cell - secretes pepsinogen.

Gastrin secreting cell (G cell). Gastrin is a hormone that increases HCl secretion.

In the stomach, gastric glands contain parietal cells, which produce hydrochloric acid; chief cells, which produce enzymes to break down protein; and endocrine cells.

Stomach secretions

Gastric juice
Acid (HCl) secretion
Pepsin enzyme (optimal pH 1.5-2.0) Acts on proteins and breaks them down into peptides (short chains of amino acids).

The small intestine

▶ The small intestine receives the chyme directly from the stomach. The small intestine is divided into three regions which are distinguished by the cell types present: the duodenum, where most chemical digestion occurs, and then the jejunum, and finally the ileum. Most absorption occurs in the jejunum and ileum.

▶ The intestinal lining is folded into many intestinal villi which project into the gut lumen (the space enclosed by the gut). The **villi** increase the surface area for nutrient absorption. The epithelial cells that make up the lining of each villus have their own brush-border of many microvilli, which are primarily responsible for nutrient absorption. The membrane of the microvilli is packed with enzymes that break down food molecules for absorption.

▶ Enzymes bound to the microvilli of the epithelial cells, and in the pancreatic and intestinal juices, break down fats, peptides, and carbohydrates (see tables below). The small molecules produced by this digestion are then absorbed into the underlying blood and lymph vessels.

▶ Tubular exocrine glands and goblet cells secrete alkaline fluid and mucus into the lumen. This neutralizes the acidity of the chyme entering the small intestine from the stomach and protects the lining of the intestine from damage.

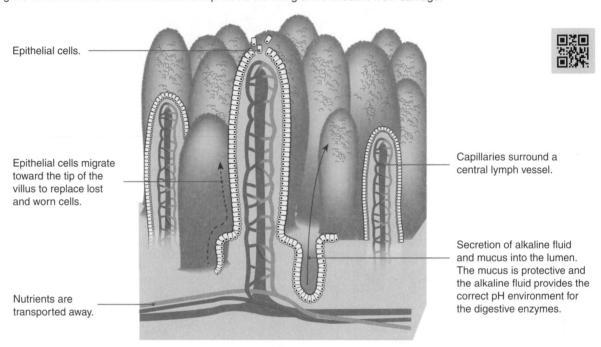

Epithelial cells.

Epithelial cells migrate toward the tip of the villus to replace lost and worn cells.

Nutrients are transported away.

Capillaries surround a central lymph vessel.

Secretion of alkaline fluid and mucus into the lumen. The mucus is protective and the alkaline fluid provides the correct pH environment for the digestive enzymes.

Photographs below: The intestinal villi are shown projecting into the gut lumen in a scanning electron micrograph (left image) and in a light microscope image (center). The microvilli forming the brush border of a single intestinal epithelial cell are shown in the transmission electron micrograph (right).

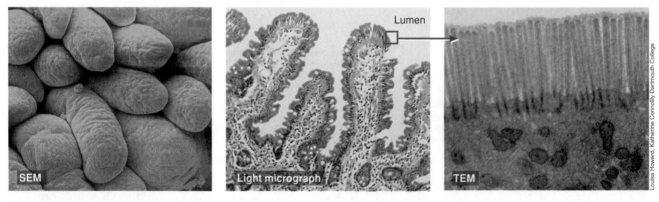

Lumen

SEM

Light micrograph

TEM

Louisa Howard, Katherine Connolly Dartmouth College

Enzymes in the small intestine break down food into small molecules that can be absorbed through the gut wall. Enzymes are present in the pancreatic juice added to the duodenum, in intestinal juice, and are bound to the surfaces of the intestinal epithelial cells.

Enzymes in pancreatic juice		
Enzyme	**Optimal pH**	**Action**
Pancreatic amylase	6.7-7.0	Starch → maltose
Trypsin*	7.8-8.7	Protein → peptides
Chymotrypsin*	7.8	Protein → peptides
Pancreatic lipase	8.0	Fats → fatty acids & glycerol

Enzymes in intestinal juice (IJ) and epithelium (E)		
Enzyme	**Optimal pH**	**Action**
Maltase (E)	6.0-6.5	Maltose → glucose
Peptidases (IJ, E)	~ 8.0	Polypeptides → amino acids
Sucrase (E)	~6.0	Protein → peptides
Enteropeptidase (IJ)	8.0	Activates trypsin**

* Secreted in an inactive form

**Once activated, trypsin activates chymotrypsin

©2023 **BIOZONE** International
ISBN: 978-1-99-101408-5
Photocopying Prohibited

1. Summarize the structure and role of each of the following regions of the human digestive tract:

   (a) Stomach: _____

   _____

   _____

   _____

   (b) Small intestine: _____

   _____

   _____

   _____

2. (a) What is the purpose of the hydrochloric acid produced by the parietal cells of the stomach? _____

   _____

   _____

   (b) Explain why protein-digesting enzymes, e.g. pepsin, are secreted in an inactive form and then activated after release:

   _____

   _____

3. Identify an endocrine cell in the stomach epithelium and state its purpose: _____

   _____

4. How does the stomach achieve the mixing of acid and enzymes with food? _____

   _____

5. (a) What is the purpose of the intestinal villi? _____

   _____

   _____

   (b) What is the purpose of the microvilli (brush border) on intestinal epithelial cells? _____

   _____

   _____

6. Identify two sites for secretion of enzymes active in the small intestine. Identify an enzyme produced there, and its role:

   (a) Site: _____ Enzyme: _____

   Enzyme's role: _____

   _____

   (b) Site: _____ Enzyme: _____

   Enzyme's role: _____

   _____

   (c) In general, do the enzymes act in acidic or alkaline conditions? _____

   _____

   (d) How is this pH environment generated? _____

   _____

   _____

170 Absorption and Transport

Key Idea: Food must be digested into components small enough to be absorbed by the body's cells and assimilated. Nutrient absorption involves both active and passive transport. Digestion breaks down food into small molecules that can pass through the intestinal lining into the underlying blood and lymph vessels. For example, starch is broken down first into maltose and short chain carbohydrates, such as dextrose, before being hydrolyzed to the simple sugar, glucose (below).

Breakdown products of other foods include amino acids, from proteins; and fatty acids, glycerol, and monoglycerides, from fats. The passage of these molecules from the gut into the blood or lymph is called **absorption**. Nutrients are then transported directly or indirectly to the liver for storage or processing. After they have been absorbed, nutrients can be assimilated, i.e incorporated into the body itself.

Digestion of starch

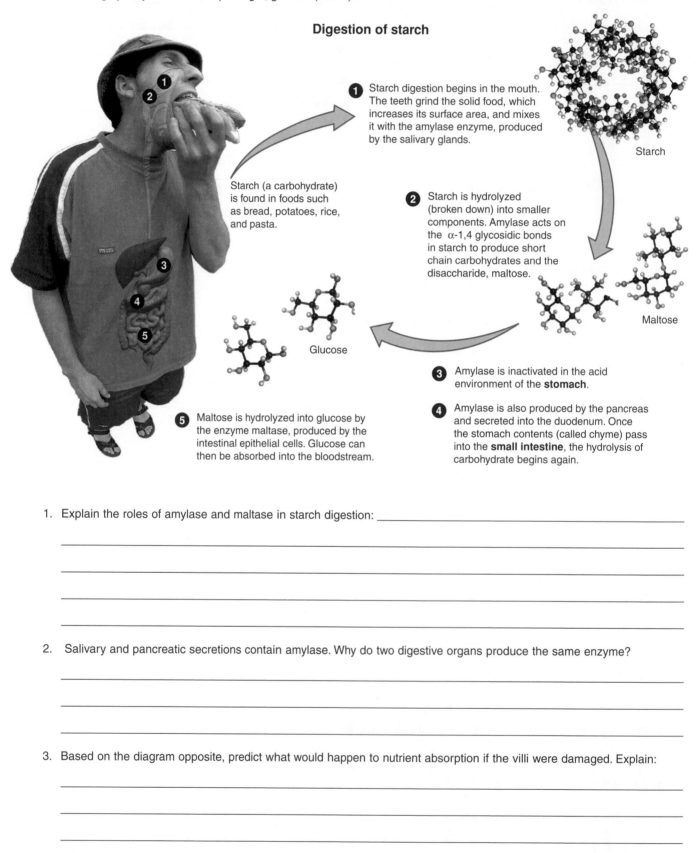

① Starch digestion begins in the mouth. The teeth grind the solid food, which increases its surface area, and mixes it with the amylase enzyme, produced by the salivary glands.

Starch (a carbohydrate) is found in foods such as bread, potatoes, rice, and pasta.

Starch

② Starch is hydrolyzed (broken down) into smaller components. Amylase acts on the α-1,4 glycosidic bonds in starch to produce short chain carbohydrates and the disaccharide, maltose.

Maltose

Glucose

③ Amylase is inactivated in the acid environment of the **stomach**.

④ Amylase is also produced by the pancreas and secreted into the duodenum. Once the stomach contents (called chyme) pass into the **small intestine**, the hydrolysis of carbohydrate begins again.

⑤ Maltose is hydrolyzed into glucose by the enzyme maltase, produced by the intestinal epithelial cells. Glucose can then be absorbed into the bloodstream.

1. Explain the roles of amylase and maltase in starch digestion: _____

_____

_____

_____

_____

2. Salivary and pancreatic secretions contain amylase. Why do two digestive organs produce the same enzyme?

_____

_____

_____

3. Based on the diagram opposite, predict what would happen to nutrient absorption if the villi were damaged. Explain:

_____

_____

_____

©2023 **BIOZONE** International
ISBN: 978-1-99-101408-5
Photocopying Prohibited

Nutrient absorption by intestinal villi

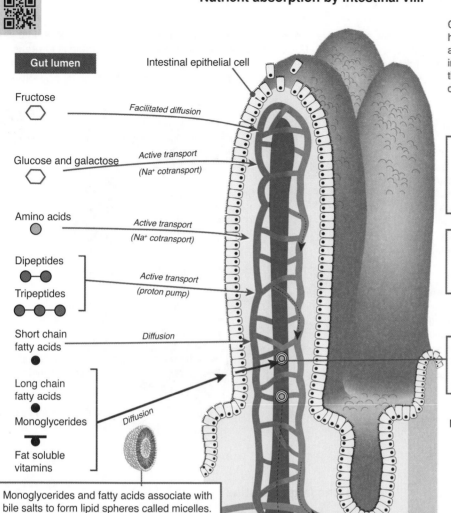

Gut lumen

Intestinal epithelial cell

Fructose — *Facilitated diffusion*

Glucose and galactose — *Active transport (Na⁺ cotransport)*

Amino acids — *Active transport (Na⁺ cotransport)*

Dipeptides / Tripeptides — *Active transport (proton pump)*

Short chain fatty acids — *Diffusion*

Long chain fatty acids / Monoglycerides / Fat soluble vitamins — *Diffusion*

Cross section through a villus, showing how the products of digestion are absorbed across the intestinal epithelium into the capillaries or into the lacteals of the lymphatic system. The nutrients are delivered to the liver.

Glucose and amino acids are actively transported by cotransport proteins along with sodium (sodium symport). This maintains a sodium gradient which helps with the absorption of water.

Active transport of di- and tripeptides is coupled to the downhill movement of H⁺ across the plasma membrane of the intestinal epithelial cells.

Once the monoglycerides and fatty acids are absorbed, triglycerides are re-formed and transported to the liver lacteals of the lymphatic system.

Monoglycerides and fatty acids associate with bile salts to form lipid spheres called micelles. Micelles hold the poorly soluble fatty acids and monoglycerides in suspension and transport them to the surface of the epithelial cells where they can be absorbed. The micelles themselves are not absorbed.

Lacteal Artery Vein

Monoglyceride

```
   H
   |
   C — O
   |       R
   C — OH  ‖
   |       O
   C — OH
   |
   H
```

Triglyceride

```
   H
   |
   C — O
   |       R
   C — O   ‖
   |       O
   C — O   R
   |       ‖
   H       O
           R
```

R = hydrocarbon chain

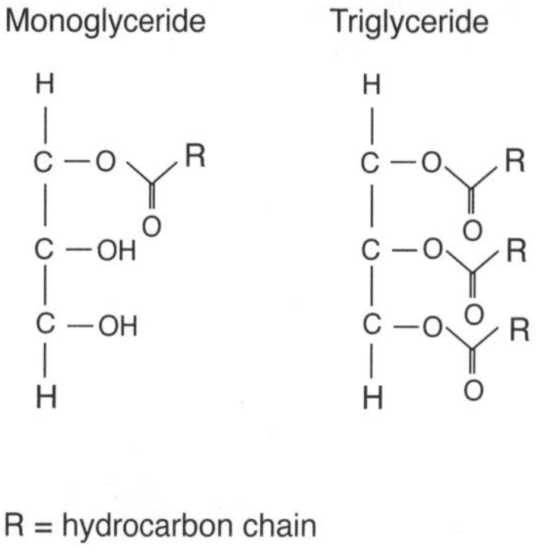

4. Describe how each of the following nutrients is absorbed by the intestinal villi:

(a) Glucose: _____

(b) Fructose: _____

(c) Amino acids: _____

(d) Di- and tripeptides: _____

5. Describe the two purposes of the sodium symport in the intestinal epithelium: _____

_____

_____

6. What is the role of micelles in the absorption of lipids? _____

_____

_____

7. How are concentration gradients maintained for the absorption of nutrients by diffusion? _____

_____

_____

171 The Large Intestine

Key Idea: The large intestine absorbs water and solidifies the indigestible material before passing it to the rectum. Undigested waste is egested as feces from the anus. After most of the nutrients have been absorbed in the **small intestine**, the remaining semi-fluid contents pass into the **large intestine**. The large intestine's main role is to reabsorb water and electrolytes and to consolidate the waste material into feces, which is eliminated from the anus by **egestion**.

▶ After most of the nutrients have been absorbed in the small intestine, the remaining semi-fluid contents pass into the large intestine (appendix, cecum, and colon). This mixture includes undigested or indigestible food, (such as cellulose), bacteria, dead cells, mucus, bile, ions, and water. In humans and other omnivores, the large intestine's main role is to reabsorb water and electrolytes and consolidate the undigested material for egestion (elimination) from the anus.

▶ The rectum stores the waste fecal material before it is discharged out the anus. Fullness in the rectum produces the urge to defecate. If too little water is absorbed, the feces will be watery, as in diarrhea. If too much water is absorbed, the feces will become compacted and difficult to pass.

▶ Defecation is controlled by the anal **sphincters**, whose usual state is to be contracted (closing the orifice). Defecation is under nervous control.

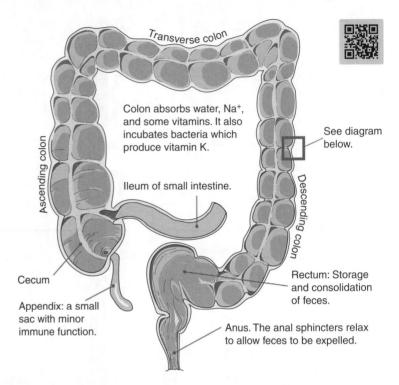

Transverse colon

Ascending colon

Colon absorbs water, Na⁺, and some vitamins. It also incubates bacteria which produce vitamin K.

Ileum of small intestine.

Descending colon

See diagram below.

Cecum

Appendix: a small sac with minor immune function.

Rectum: Storage and consolidation of feces.

Anus. The anal sphincters relax to allow feces to be expelled.

Lining of the large intestine

The lining of the large intestine has a simple epithelium containing tubular glands (crypts) with many mucus-secreting cells. The mucus lubricates the colon wall and helps to form and move the feces. In the photograph, some of the crypts are in cross section and some are in longitudinal section.

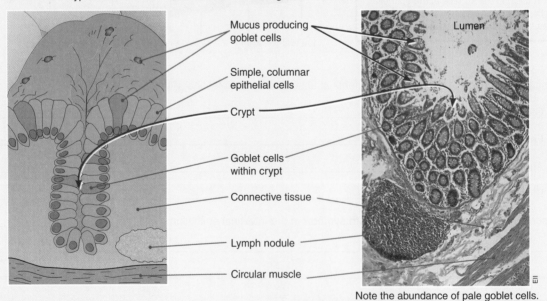

Mucus producing goblet cells

Simple, columnar epithelial cells

Crypt

Goblet cells within crypt

Connective tissue

Lymph nodule

Circular muscle

Lumen

Note the abundance of pale goblet cells.

1. What is the main purpose of the large intestine? _____

_____

2. What are the effects of absorbing too little and too much water in the large intestine? _____

_____

©2023 **BIOZONE** International
ISBN: 978-1-99-101408-5
Photocopying Prohibited

172 The Control of Digestion

Key Idea: Digestion is controlled by both nervous and hormonal mechanisms.

Most digestive juices are secreted only when there is food in the gut, and both nervous and hormonal mechanisms are involved in coordinating and regulating this activity. The **digestive system** is innervated (supplied with nerves) by branches of the autonomic nervous system. Hormonal regulation is achieved through the activity of several hormones, which are released into the bloodstream in response to nervous or chemical stimuli and influence activity of the gut and associated organs.

Feeding center:
The feeding center in the hypothalamus is constantly active. It monitors metabolites in the blood and stimulates hunger when these metabolites reach low levels. After a meal, the neighboring satiety center suppresses the activity of the feeding center for a period of time.

Pancreatic secretions and bile:
Cholecystokinin (CCK) stimulates secretion of enzyme-rich fluid from the pancreas and release of bile from the gall bladder. Secretin stimulates the pancreas to increase its secretion of alkaline fluid and the production of bile from the liver cells.

Intestinal secretion of hormones:
The entry of chyme (especially fat and gastric acid) into the small intestine stimulates the intestinal mucosa to secrete the hormones cholecystokinin (CCK) and secretin.

Salivation:
Entirely under nervous control. Some saliva is secreted continuously. Food in the mouth stimulates the salivary glands to increase their secretions.

Parasympathetic stimulation of the **stomach** and pancreas via the vagus nerve increases their secretion. **Sympathetic stimulation** has the opposite effect. These are simple reflexes in response to the sight, smell, or taste of food.

Gastric secretion:
Physical distension and the presence of food in the stomach causes release of the hormone gastrin from cells in the gastric mucosa. Gastrin in the blood increases gastric secretion and motility.

Vagus nerve

Gastrin

CCK and secretin

1. Describe the role of each of the following stimuli in the control of digestion, identifying both the response and its effect:

(a) Presence of food in the mouth: _____

_____

(b) Presence of fat and acid in the small intestine: _____

_____

_____

(c) Stretching of the stomach by the presence of food: _____

_____

_____

2. Outline the role of the vagus nerve in regulating digestive activity: _____

_____

_____

173 The Liver

Key Idea: The liver is a large organ located just below the diaphragm. It has many roles in digestion and metabolism. The liver is the body's largest solid organ, making up 3-5% of body weight. The liver performs a vast number of functions, including production of bile, storage and processing of nutrients, and detoxification of poisons and metabolic wastes.

The liver receives a dual blood supply from the hepatic portal vein and hepatic arteries, and up to 20% of the total blood volume flows through it at any one time. This high level of blood flow allows the liver to play a key role in regulating activities associated with the blood and circulatory system.

The liver (L on the diagram above) is located in the upper right-hand region of the abdominal cavity, it sits beneath the diaphragm, and on top of the stomach, right kidney, and intestines.

Dr I-Chen Tasi CC3.0

The liver has a fairly unique trait as far as human visceral organs go: it can regenerate (grow back) if it is damaged. There are limitations to its regenerative powers as excessive damage can damage the liver beyond repair, e.g. through prolonged high alcohol consumption or an untreated hepatitis infection. When this happens, a liver transplant is needed. A number of checks for tissue compatibility and size are needed before a liver, or part of a liver, can be transplanted. Volume rendering imaging (above in pink) is a non-invasive process used to see if the donor has enough liver volume for donation.

The gross structure of the liver

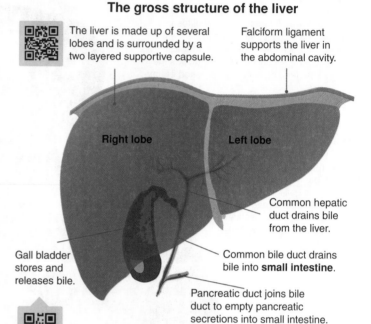

The liver is made up of several lobes and is surrounded by a two layered supportive capsule.

Falciform ligament supports the liver in the abdominal cavity.

Right lobe

Left lobe

Common hepatic duct drains bile from the liver.

Common bile duct drains bile into **small intestine**.

Gall bladder stores and releases bile.

Pancreatic duct joins bile duct to empty pancreatic secretions into small intestine.

The internal structure of the liver

Schematic of the arrangement of lobules and portal triad in the liver.

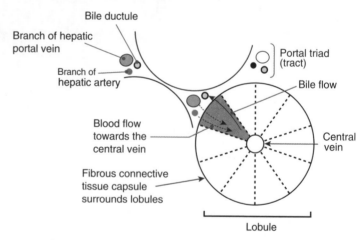

Bile ductule

Branch of hepatic portal vein

Branch of hepatic artery

Portal triad (tract)

Bile flow

Blood flow towards the central vein

Central vein

Fibrous connective tissue capsule surrounds lobules

Lobule

The liver is divided into functional units called lobules, with rows of liver cells arranged around a central vein. Branches of the hepatic artery, hepatic portal vein, and bile duct lie between the lobules, forming a portal triad (tract).

1. What unique property does the liver possess (for a visceral organ)? _____

2. Identify the components of a portal triad: _____
_____

3. What is the purpose of the gall bladder? _____
_____

©2023 **BIOZONE** International
ISBN: 978-1-99-101408-5
Photocopying Prohibited

174 The Liver's Homeostatic Role

Key Idea: The liver is the body's largest homeostatic organ and interacts with other systems to maintain homeostasis. The liver performs a vast number of functions that affect all other body systems. It has a unique, double blood supply and a large throughput (around 20% of the total blood volume at any one time). 25% of the blood flowing through the liver comes from the hepatic artery and 75% comes from the hepatic portal vein. The ability of the liver to receive, process, and dispatch so much blood is central to it homeostatic and digestive role in the body.

Homeostatic functions of the liver

The liver is one of the largest and most complex organs in the body, with a large number of homeostatic functions. The liver:

- Secretes bile, important in emulsifying fats in digestion.
- Metabolizes amino acids, fats, and carbohydrates (below).
- Synthesizes glucose from non-carbohydrate sources when glycogen stores are exhausted (gluconeogenesis).
- Stores iron, copper, and some vitamins (A, D, E, K, B_{12}).
- Converts unwanted amino acids to urea (urea cycle, right).
- Manufactures heparin and plasma proteins, e.g. albumin, essential in maintaining oncotic pressure (this is the opposing force to hydrostatic pressure in the movement of fluids across membranes, e.g. into and out of capillaries).
- Detoxifies poisons or turns them into less harmful forms.
- Some liver cells phagocytose worn-out blood cells.
- Synthesizes cholesterol from acetyl coenzyme A.

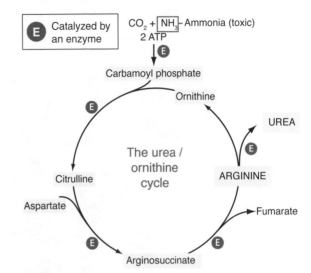

Nutrient processing in the liver

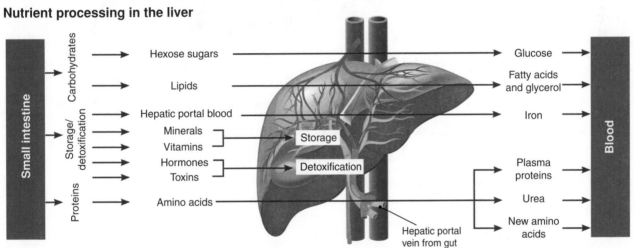

1. Explain how the liver's interactions with other body systems make it central to homeostatic regulation: _____

_____

_____

_____

_____

2. (a) Explain how the liver's rich blood supply enables it to regulate activities associated with the circulatory system:

_____

_____

(b) What is the significance of the liver receiving blood from the gut via a portal system? _____

_____

_____

3. Predict what would happen if the enzyme converting ammonia to carbamoyl phosphate was inhibited: _____

_____

175 The Histology of the Liver

Key Idea: The functional unit of the liver is the lobule.
The lobule is the functional unit of the liver and is made up of tightly packed rows (cords) of liver cells radiating from a central vein and surrounded by small blood vessels called sinusoids. Branches of the hepatic artery and the hepatic portal vein supply the lobules. This highly vascular structure is a reflection of the liver's important role as a dynamic blood

reservoir, able to both store and release blood as required. More than half of the 10-20% of the total blood volume normally in the liver resides in the sinusoids. Sinusoids are similar to capillaries but have a more porous endothelium. The increased permeability of the sinusoids allows small and medium-sized proteins, such as albumin, to readily enter and leave the bloodstream.

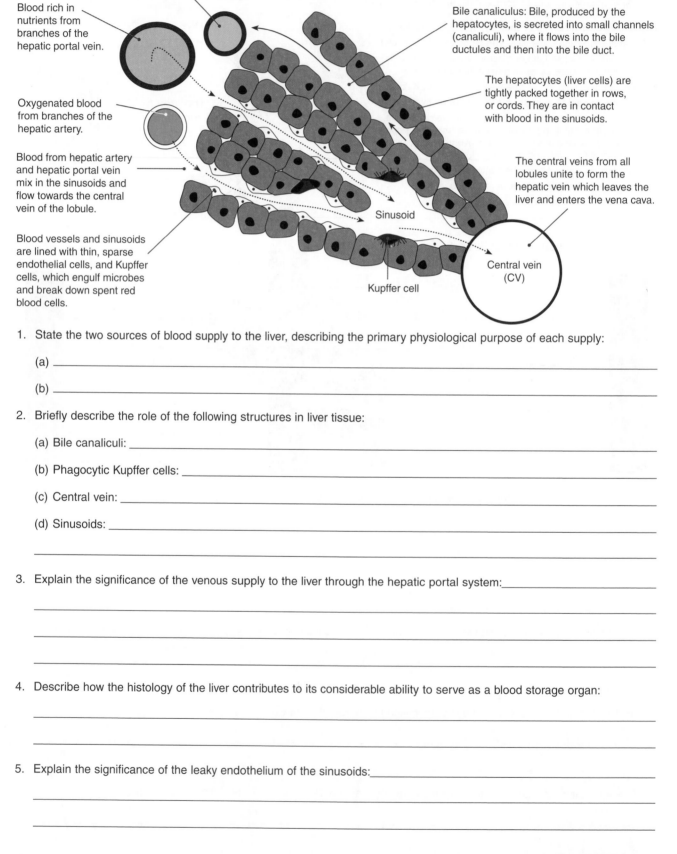

Bile ductule

Blood rich in nutrients from branches of the hepatic portal vein.

Bile canaliculus: Bile, produced by the hepatocytes, is secreted into small channels (canaliculi), where it flows into the bile ductules and then into the bile duct.

The hepatocytes (liver cells) are tightly packed together in rows, or cords. They are in contact with blood in the sinusoids.

Oxygenated blood from branches of the hepatic artery.

Blood from hepatic artery and hepatic portal vein mix in the sinusoids and flow towards the central vein of the lobule.

The central veins from all lobules unite to form the hepatic vein which leaves the liver and enters the vena cava.

Blood vessels and sinusoids are lined with thin, sparse endothelial cells, and Kupffer cells, which engulf microbes and break down spent red blood cells.

Sinusoid

Kupffer cell

Central vein (CV)

1. State the two sources of blood supply to the liver, describing the primary physiological purpose of each supply:

   (a) _____

   (b) _____

2. Briefly describe the role of the following structures in liver tissue:

   (a) Bile canaliculi: _____

   (b) Phagocytic Kupffer cells: _____

   (c) Central vein: _____

   (d) Sinusoids: _____

   _____

3. Explain the significance of the venous supply to the liver through the hepatic portal system: _____

   _____

   _____

   _____

4. Describe how the histology of the liver contributes to its considerable ability to serve as a blood storage organ:

   _____

   _____

5. Explain the significance of the leaky endothelium of the sinusoids: _____

   _____

   _____

©2023 **BIOZONE** International
ISBN: 978-1-99-101408-5
Photocopying Prohibited

176 Protein Metabolism in the Liver

Key Idea: The liver has a crucial role in the metabolism of proteins and in the storage and detoxification of hormones, and ingested or absorbed poisons (including alcohol).

The most critical aspects of protein metabolism occurring in the liver are deamination and transamination of amino acids, removal of ammonia from the body by synthesis of urea,

and synthesis of non-essential amino acids. Hepatocytes are responsible for synthesis of most of the plasma proteins, including albumins, globulins, and blood clotting proteins. Urea is formed from ammonia and carbon dioxide via the ornithine, also known as the urea cycle, which occurs primarily in the liver.

Storage and detoxification

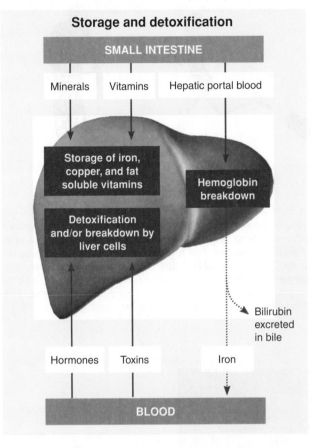

Protein metabolism

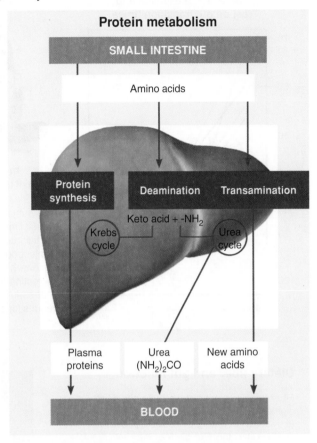

1. Explain three aspects of protein metabolism in the liver:

   (a) _____

   _____

   (b) _____

   _____

   (c) _____

2. Identify the waste products arising from deamination of amino acids and describe their fate:

   _____

   _____

   _____

3. An X-linked disorder of the ornithine cycle results in sufferers lacking the enzyme to convert ornithine to citrulline. Suggest what the symptoms and the prognosis might be:

   _____

   _____

   _____

Recall the urea/ornithine cycle from Activity 174. Ammonia (NH_3), the product of protein metabolism, is toxic in even small amounts and must be removed. It is converted to less toxic urea via the ornithine cycle (also known as the urea cycle) and is excreted from the body by the kidneys. The liver contains a system of carrier molecules and enzymes (E) which quickly convert the ammonia (and CO_2) into urea. One turn of the cycle consumes two molecules of ammonia (one comes from aspartate) and one molecule of CO_2, creates one molecule of urea and regenerates a molecule of ornithine.

©2023 **BIOZONE** International
ISBN: 978-1-99-101408-5
Photocopying Prohibited

177 Exercise, Fiber, and Gut Function

Key Idea: Exercise has both short and long term effects on the function of the digestive system.

Regular light to moderate exercise has several advantages, including strengthening the muscles which support the **digestive system**, and stimulating intestinal contractions.

However, people undertaking strenuous and prolonged exercise can suffer from digestive disorders such as vomiting, diarrhea, and reflux. Exercise and diet influence the time taken for food to move through the digestive tract.

The effect of exercise and rest on gut transition times

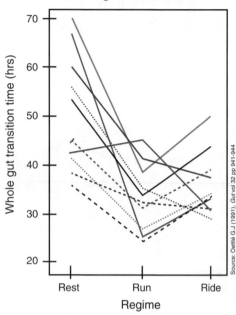

Source: Oettlé G.J (1991), Gut vol 32 pp 941-944

Rest
Gut transit time: 51.2 hrs

Run
Gut transit time: 34 hrs

Ride
Gut transit time: 36.6 hrs

Ten subjects were involved in a study to determine if exercise influenced gut transit time. The study was divided into three one week periods, and each subject participated in a different regime each week. Over the experimental period, each subject completed all three regimes. The regimes were: running on a treadmill for one hour each day, cycling on a stationary bicycle for one hour each day, or resting in a chair for one hour each day. Gut transit time was determined by measuring how long a radio-labelled pellet took to be egested as feces. The results for each of the ten subjects, are presented in the graph (left).

Dietary fiber and gut function

Fiber refers to plant material that cannot be digested. Fiber is classified as either soluble (it dissolves in water), or insoluble (it does not dissolve in water). Soluble fiber may help regulate lipid metabolism and blood sugar. Insoluble fiber passes through the digestive system largely intact. This regulates bowel activity and prevents constipation by:

- Increasing stool bulk
- Decreasing gut transit time
- Increasing the frequency of bowel movements
- Allowing the colon walls to grip the feces easily so they can be moved

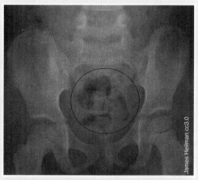

James Hellman cc3.0

Difficulty or infrequency in passing bowel motions is called constipation. A lack of dietary fiber is one cause. The X-ray above shows hard and compacted feces in the colon of a patient with constipation.

Most plant-based foods contain dietary fiber. Whole-wheat flour, wheat bran, nuts, beans, and vegetables, are good sources of insoluble fiber.

1. Study the graph above showing the effect of exercise on gut transit times.

   (a) What effect did each of the three regimes have on gut transit times? _____

   _____

   _____

   (b) Explain how exercise may have influenced gut transition times: _____

   _____

2. Why is dietary fiber important in maintaining healthy gut function? _____

   _____

   _____

178 Malnutrition and Obesity

Key Idea: Malnutrition is the term for nutritional disorders resulting from not having enough food or not enough of the right food. Obesity is an example of malnutrition.

In economically developed areas of the world, most (but not all) forms of **malnutrition** are the result of poorly balanced nutrient intakes rather than an actual lack of food. Amongst the most common of these is obesity, defined as BMI values in excess of 30 (see below). Although some genetic and hormonal causes are known, obesity is commonly the result

of excessive energy intake, usually associated with a highly processed diet, high in fat and sugar. In addition, incidental physical activity is declining: we drive more, use labor-saving machines, and exercise less. Obesity is a risk factor in a number of chronic diseases, including hypertension, cardiovascular disease, and type 2 diabetes. Obesity in developed countries is more common in poorly educated, lower socio-economic groups than amongst the wealthy, who often have more options in terms of food choices.

Obesity and malnutrition

▶ In adults, the level of obesity is determined by reference to the Body Mass Index (BMI). A score of 30+ on the BMI indicates mild obesity, while those with severe or morbid obesity have BMIs of 40+. Child obesity is based on BMI-for-age, and is assessed in relation to the weight of other children of a similar age and gender.

▶ Central or abdominal obesity refers to excessive fat around the abdomen and is now classified as an independent risk factor for some serious diseases. While the explanation for excessive body fat is simple (energy in exceeds energy out), a complex of biological and socio-economic factors are implicated in creating the problems of modern obesity.

Body mass index

A common method for assessing obesity is the **body mass index** (BMI).

$$BMI = \frac{\text{weight of body (in kg)}}{\text{height (in meters) squared}}$$

A BMI of: 17 to 20 = underweight
20 to 25 = normal weight
25 to 30 = overweight
over 30 = obesity

$$BMI = \frac{90 \text{ kg}}{(1.68 \text{ m})^2} = 32$$

Although BMI is simple to calculate, because of this simplicity it only provides information with limited use. The BMI fails to take into account lean muscle, which weighs more per volume that fat.

As a result, people such as muscular athletes who have little fat and are very fit, can often be classed as overweight when their BMI is calculated.

Measuring BMI is therefore only part of a tool kit for indicating a person's health. It may alert doctors or health officials to carry out further health tests rather than produce a definitive result.

Health effects of obesity

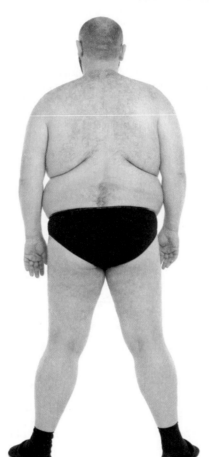

Obesity more than doubles the risk of hypertension and stroke.

Obesity is a major risk factor for cardiovascular disease because it is associated with an increased prevalence of cardiovascular risk factors, including type 2 diabetes, and high blood lipids.

The heaviness of the chest wall and a higher than normal oxygen requirement in obese people restricts normal physical activity and increases respiratory problems.

Obesity is associated with high bile cholesterol levels, gallstones, and gall bladder disease.

Obesity is associated with a higher risk of certain cancers including rectal, colon, and breast cancer. Cancer survival rates are also lower amongst obese patients.

Obese people are at higher risk of osteoarthritis in their weight bearing joints.

Obesity in pre-menopausal women is associated with irregular menstrual cycles and infertility.

1. (a) Explain why obesity is regarded as a form of malnutrition: _____

_____

(b) Describe the two basic energy factors that determine how a person's weight will change: _____

_____

2. Using the BMI, calculate the minimum and maximum weight at which a 1.85 m tall man would be considered:

(a) Overweight: _____

(b) Obese: _____

Prevalence of clinical obesity in the population

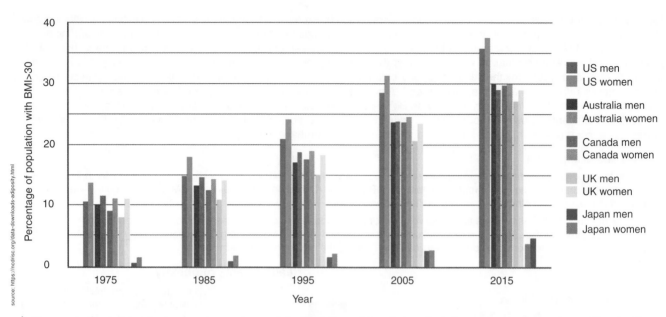

source: https://ncdrisc.org/data-downloads-adiposity.html

▶ The graph above shows the increase in prevalence of obesity at 5 year intervals for selected countries, for both males and females. It can be seen that obesity is increasing in all countries.

▶ Often, the highest rates of obesity occur amongst the most poorly educated, impoverished sectors of the population. Highly processed foods containing large quantities of carbohydrate and sugar may represent the lowest-cost option to consumers. These are often easier to ship and have a longer shelf life than fresh foods. Poverty and food insecurity are often associated with lower food expenditures, low fruit and vegetable consumption, and lower-quality diets.

▶ Increased urbanization around the world has also contributed to obesity levels. People are now less likely to walk to work or school, often work longer hours, and generally have less time for exercise than decades ago. Many jobs are desk and screen based, and children often spend more of their leisure time on screens than engaging in physical activities.

Examine the graph above:

3. (a) Which sex has higher obesity rates, generally? _____

    (b) In which country and in what year is this not the case? _____

    (c) In which three countries and in what years is the prevalence of obesity very similar for both men and women?

    _____

4. Suggest why obesity rates are increasing in all countries shown in the graph above: _____

    _____

    _____

    _____

5. Suggest why obesity in Japan is found at much lower rates than in the other countries shown above. You may have to carry out some research:

    _____

    _____

    _____

6. Discuss the factors that contribute to nutritional deficiencies among the obese: _____

    _____

    _____

    _____

7. Apart from diet, what other factor is contributing towards increasing levels of obesity around the world?

    _____

©2023 **BIOZONE** International
ISBN: 978-1-99-101408-5
Photocopying Prohibited

179 Deficiency Diseases

Key Idea: A deficiency disease can occur when there is an inadequate intake of a specific nutrient.

In developing countries, protein and energy deficiencies commonly cause disease, whereas, vitamin and mineral deficiencies are more common in western diets. Specific vitamin and mineral deficiencies are associated with specific disorders, e.g. scurvy (vitamin C), rickets (vitamin D), visual defects (vitamin A), osteoporosis (calcium), anemia (iron). In developed countries, **deficiency diseases** were once limited to people with very restricted diets, intestinal disorders, or drug and alcohol problems. However, some deficiencies, e.g. iron or vitamin D deficiencies, are relatively more common. This is mainly because diets often lack the nutrients in the quantities required to maintain good health and normal development. Children and pregnant women are particularly susceptible to nutritional deficiencies because of their specific metabolic requirements.

Vitamin A, found in animal livers, eggs, and dairy products, is required for the production of light-absorbing pigments in the eye and for the formation of cell structures. Symptoms of deficiency include loss of night vision, inflammation of the eye, corneal damage, and the presence of Bitots spots (foamy patches on the white of the eye, arrow on photo).

Iodine
Iodine is essential for the production of thyroid hormones, which control growth, metabolic rate, and development. Shortage of iodine in the diet may lead to goiter (enlargement of the thyroid). Iodine deficiency is also responsible for some cases of thyroid underactivity.

Goiter on neck

Vitamin C deficiency causes the disease, scurvy, once the scourge of sailors but now rare in developed countries. Inadequate vitamin C intake disturbs the body's normal production of collagen, an essential protein in the connective tissue that holds body structures together. This results in poor wound healing, rupture of small blood vessels (visible bleeding in the skin), swollen gums, and loose teeth.

Iron
Anaemia results from lower than normal levels of hemoglobin in red blood cells. Iron from the diet is required to produce hemoglobin. People most at risk include women during pregnancy and those with an inadequate dietary intake. Symptoms include fatigue, fainting, breathlessness, and heart palpitations.

Vitamin B$_{12}$ found primarily in meat, but also in eggs and dairy products, is required for nucleic acid and protein metabolism, and for the maturation of red blood cells. It is essential for proper growth and nervous system function. Deficiency results in pernicious anemia, poor appetite, weight loss, growth failure, fatigue, brain damage, nervousness, muscle tics, depression, spinal cord degeneration, and lack of balance.

Zinc
Zinc is found in red meat, poultry, fish, whole grain cereals, breads, legumes, and nuts. It is important for enzyme activity, production of insulin, making of sperm, and perception of taste. A deficiency in zinc causes growth retardation, a delay in puberty, muscular weakness, dry skin, and a delay in wound healing.

Vitamin D deficiency in children produces the disease, rickets. In adults a similar disease is called osteomalacia. Sufferers typically show skeletal deformities, e.g. bowed legs, because inadequate amounts of phosphorus and calcium are incorporated into the bones. Vitamin D is found in cod liver oil and is produced by the skin when exposed to sunlight. It is vital for the absorption of calcium from the diet.

Calcium
Calcium is required for enzyme function, formation of bones and teeth, blood clotting, and muscular contraction. Calcium deficiency causes poor bone growth and structure, increasing the tendency of bones to fracture and break. It also results in muscular spasms and poor blood clotting.

Fracture

Protein and energy deficiencies

Marasmus is the most common deficiency disease. It is a severe form of protein and energy **malnutrition** that usually occurs in famine conditions. Children suffering from marasmus are stunted and extremely emaciated. They have loose folds of skin on the limbs and buttocks, due to the loss of fat and muscle tissue. Sufferers have no resistance to disease and common infections are typically fatal.

Kwashiorkor is a severe type of protein-energy deficiency in young children (1-3 years old), occurring mainly in poor rural areas in the tropics. Kwashiorkor occurs when a child is weaned on to a diet that is low in calories, protein, and essential micronutrients. Children have poor growth, low resistance to infection, edema (accumulation of fluid in the tissues), and are inactive, apathetic, and weak.

Alcohol abuse and nutritional deficiency

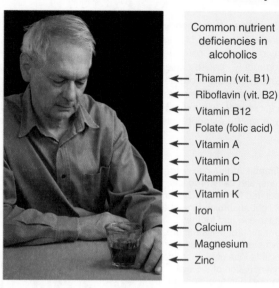

Common nutrient deficiencies in alcoholics

← Thiamin (vit. B1)
← Riboflavin (vit. B2)
← Vitamin B12
← Folate (folic acid)
← Vitamin A
← Vitamin C
← Vitamin D
← Vitamin K
← Iron
← Calcium
← Magnesium
← Zinc

People who regularly consume excessive alcohol are at increased risk of nutritional deficiencies. Even when food intake is adequate, alcohol interferes with the metabolism of food by affecting digestion, storage, utilization, and excretion of nutrients. Alcohol damages the cells lining the **small intestine** and impairs **absorption** of nutrients. For example, alcohol inhibits fat absorption, impairs the digestion of proteins, and interferes with glucose metabolism.

1. What is meant by the term, "deficiency disease"? _____
_____

2. Why are young children, pregnant women, and athletes the most susceptible to dietary deficiencies?
_____
_____
_____

3. (a) Explain why a lack of iron leads to the symptoms of anemia (fatigue and breathlessness):
_____
_____
_____

(b) Explain why iron deficiency is relatively more common in women of child-bearing age than in men:
_____
_____

4. Using the example of iodine, explain how artificial dietary supplementation can be achieved and discuss its benefits:
_____
_____
_____

5. Suggest why a zinc deficiency is associated with muscular weakness and a delay in puberty:
_____
_____
_____

©2023 **BIOZONE** International
ISBN: 978-1-99-101408-5
Photocopying Prohibited

180 Infection, Inflammation, and Gut Function

Key Idea: Gut function can be affected by diseases such as cholera and through inflammation, leading to Crohn's disease. Celiac disease is an autoimmune disorder which can be severe.

Cholera is an acute intestinal infection caused by the bacterium, *Vibrio cholerae*. Cholera is spread primarily by the consumption of contaminated drinking water or food.

Inflammatory Bowel Disease (IBD) is a collective term for any illness that causes inflammation in the digestive tract. The most common of these are Crohn's disease and ulcerative colitis. Celiac disease is an autoimmune disease which causes tissue damage to the **villi** of the **small intestine**, reducing the body's ability to absorb nutrients.

Cholera and diarrhea

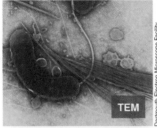
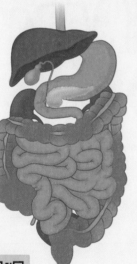

▶ The cholera bacterium, *Vibrio cholerae* (images, left), produces an enterotoxin which binds to membrane receptors on the small intestine, increasing permeability to chloride ions. Water follows the salt across the membrane by osmosis, resulting in copious, painless, watery diarrhea that can lead to severe dehydration, electrolyte imbalance, kidney failure, and death within hours if untreated.

▶ Each year there are 1.3 to 4.0 million cases of cholera, and 21,000 to 143,000 deaths. It is endemic in many countries.

▶ Cholera transmission is closely linked to inadequate access to clean water and sanitation facilities but the bacteria can also be found in coastal and brackish waters, and consumption of raw shellfish has been a source of infection.

▶ Fast treatment with oral rehydration salts is recommended. These contain water and salts in ratios designed to replenish fluids and electrolytes. Carbohydrates, such as glucose or sucrose, are added to enhance electrolyte **absorption** in the intestinal tract. Sugars may actually increase the rate of diarrhea at first, but they are essential for the co-transport of sodium into the intestinal cells

▶ Oral cholera vaccines are used in conjunction with other public health approaches, particularly during severe outbreaks.

Inflammatory bowel disease

Crohn's Disease
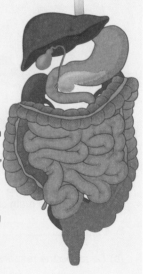

▶ Crohn's Disease is one of many conditions grouped under the heading of Irritable Bowel Disease, or IBS. Symptoms can vary but often include abdominal cramps, diarrhea (sometimes containing blood), nausea, and fatigue.

▶ Crohn's Disease is characterized by inflammation of parts of the digestive tract. Any part of the tract can be affected at any time, although it most commonly affects the end of the small intestine and the beginning of the **large intestine**.

▶ Recent studies in both the US and UK have demonstrated that the prevalence of Crohn's disease has been increasing.

Ulcerative Colitis
▶ Ulcerative colitis also comes under the generic heading of IBS and is characterized by continuous damage to one section of the digestive tract, usually the large intestine and rectal areas.

▶ Four main forms of the disease are recognized according to the location of inflammation: in ulcerative proctitis, inflammation is confined to the area closest to the anus; in proctosigmoiditis, the inflammation affects both the rectum and the sigmoid colon; in left sided colitis, inflammation is from the rectum and through both the ascending and descending portions of the colon; and pancolitis can affect the whole colon.

1. Which organism causes cholera? _____

2. Why is the severe diarrhea caused by cholera dangerous, if not treated quickly? _____

3. Describe the main differences between Crohn's disease and ulcerative colitis: _____

Celiac disease

▶ Celiac disease is an autoimmune condition characterized by injury to the mucosal tissue of the small intestine, leading to poor absorption of nutrients. Symptoms include diarrhea, fatigue, weight loss, bloating and discomfort, abdominal pain, and nausea/vomiting.

▶ The disease results from intolerance to a group of proteins, collectively known as gluten, found in wheat. Gluten itself contains two major protein fractions, the gliadins and the glutenins, which both contain disease-activating proteins. Barley and rye are closely related to wheat and contain similar proteins that also cause celiac disease. Oats are less closely related and are less commonly a cause.

▶ The amino acids glutamine and proline, found in high levels in gliadins and glutenins, can be relatively resistant to digestion by enzymes in the gut. The undigested gliadin fragments can pass through the gut wall, into the laminia propria, the layer of tissue below the intestinal epithelial cells.

▶ The undigested gliadins form complexes with antigens, which activate antigen presenting cells. The body reacts to these by releasing an immune response, which ultimately leads to intestinal tissue damage. The extent of intestinal damage can vary markedly in individuals and is measured on the Marsh Scale (1: mild, 4: advanced).

▶ A strong genetic component to celiac disease exists. Specific alleles of the genes HLA-DQ2 and HLA-DQ8 are present in almost all individuals diagnosed. Sufferers must completely exclude gluten from their diet to restore normal villi function.

Gliadin

BallenaBlanca CC 4.0

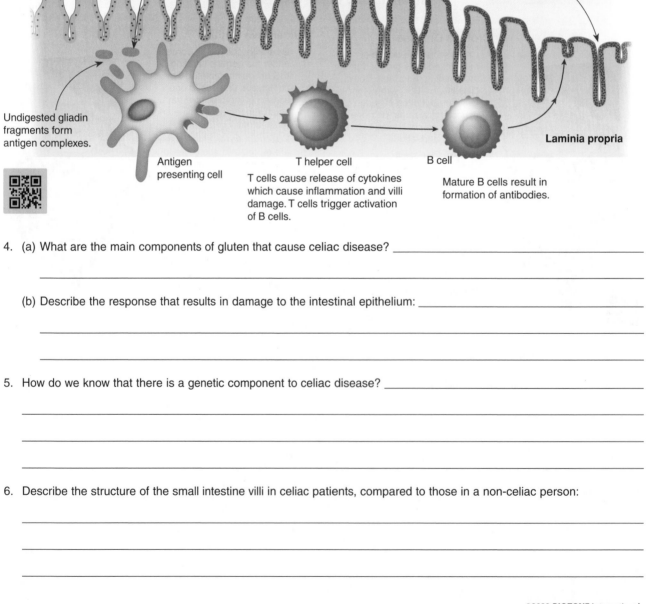

Undigested gluten fragments

Undigested gliadins pass through the epithelium.

Intestinal lumen

Damaged intestinal epithelium, resulting in blunting of villi and damage to crypts.

Undigested gliadin fragments form antigen complexes.

Antigen presenting cell

T helper cell

T cells cause release of cytokines which cause inflammation and villi damage. T cells trigger activation of B cells.

B cell

Mature B cells result in formation of antibodies.

Laminia propria

4. (a) What are the main components of gluten that cause celiac disease? _____

_____

(b) Describe the response that results in damage to the intestinal epithelium: _____

_____

_____

5. How do we know that there is a genetic component to celiac disease? _____

_____

_____

_____

6. Describe the structure of the small intestine villi in celiac patients, compared to those in a non-celiac person:

_____

_____

_____

181 Chapter Summary

1. Suggest why the small intestine is so long: _____

_____

2. Discuss the role of nerves and hormones in controlling digestion: _____

_____

_____

_____

_____

3. Label the parts of the liver shown in the diagram,(right):

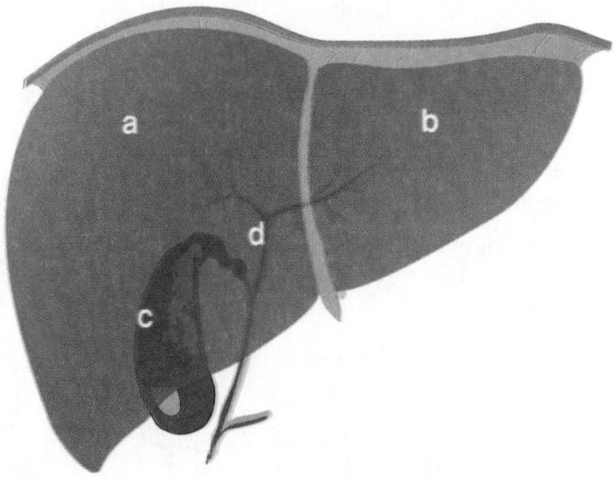

   (a) _____

   (b) _____

   (c) _____

   (d) _____

4. (a) Name one vascular function of the liver: _____

_____

   (b) Name two metabolic functions of the liver: _____

_____

_____

   (c) Name one digestive function of the liver: _____

   (d) Name one excretory function of the liver: _____

   (e) Name one storage function of the liver: _____

5. Explain why alcoholics are likely to be deficient in fat soluble vitamins (A, D, K) even when food intake is adequate:

_____

_____

_____

6. Suggest some changes that could be made to the meal on the right to make it healthier:

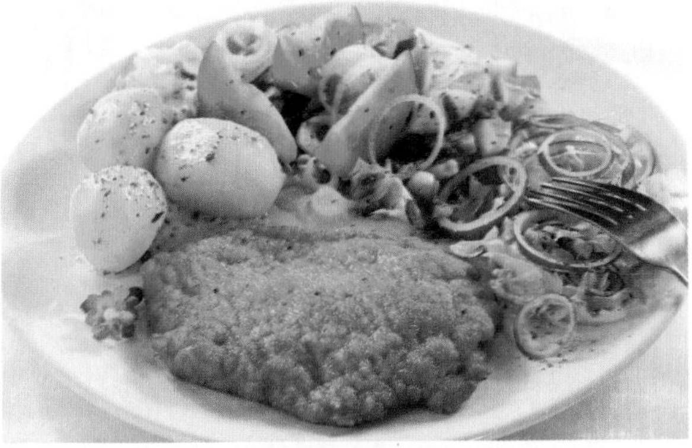

_____

_____

_____

_____

_____

7. Describe some lifestyle changes that people could make to reduce their risk of becoming obese, apart from making changes to their diet.

_____

_____

The Urinary System

Respiratory system

- Respiratory system provides O_2 to the urinary system and disposes of CO_2 produced by cellular respiration.
- An enzyme in the cells of the lung capillaries converts angiotensin I to angiotensin II (involved in regulation of glomerular filtration).

Cardiovascular system

- Regulation of salt and water balance in the kidney is important in regulation of blood pressure.
- Regulation of blood composition of Na^+, K^+, and Ca^{2+} helps maintain heart function.
- Arterial blood pressure is the driving force for glomerular filtration.
- Heart muscle cells secrete a peptide (ANP) in response to high blood pressure. ANP results in greater excretion of Na^+ and water from the kidney.
- Blood distributes the hormones that influence renal function, e.g. ADH and aldosterone.

Digestive system

- The final activation of vitamin D occurs in the kidneys. Bioactive vitamin D is required for calcium absorption in the gut.
- The liver synthesizes most of the body's urea, which is then excreted via the kidneys.
- The digestive system provides nutrients for maintenance and health of the urinary organs

Skeletal system

- Bones of the ribcage provide some protection for the kidneys.
- Erythropoietin from the kidneys promotes the formation of red blood cells in the bone marrow.

Integumentary system

- The skin provides an external protective barrier.
- Final activation of vitamin D (synthesized in the skin) occurs in the kidneys.
- Skin is a site of water loss.

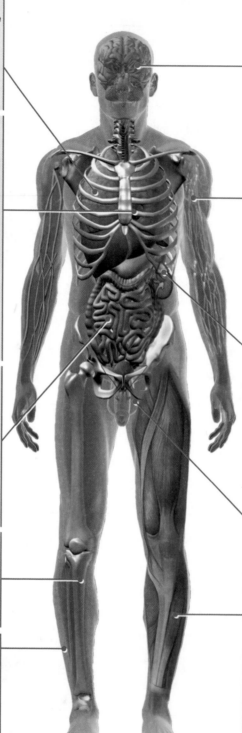

Nervous system

- Renal regulation of the Na^+, K^+, and Ca^{2+} content in the extracellular fluid is necessary for nerve function.
- Micturition (urination) is controlled by voluntary and reflex nervous activity.
- Sympathetic NS activity triggers the renin-angiotensin system for regulation of blood volume.

Lymphatic system and immunity

- The lymphatic vessels return leaked fluid to the general circulation and help to maintain the blood volume/pressure required for kidney function.
- The immune system protects the urinary organs from infection and cancer.

Endocrine system

- Kidneys produce erythropoietin, a hormone which promotes the formation of red blood cells in the bone marrow.
- Regulation of salt and water balance by the kidneys maintains the blood volume necessary for hormone transport.
- ADH, ANP, aldosterone and other hormones interact to regulate reabsorption of water and electrolytes in the kidney.

Reproductive system

- Urinogenital systems are closely aligned. Urethra has an excretory function in both sexes and a reproductive function in males, for the passage of semen.

Muscular system

- Renal regulation of the Na^+, K^+, and Ca^{2+} content in the extracellular fluid is necessary for muscle function.
- Muscles of the pelvic floor and external urethral sphincter are involved in voluntary control of micturition.
- Creatinine, which is a break-down product of creatine phosphate in muscle, is produced at a fairly constant rate by the body and must be excreted by the kidneys.

General functions and effects on all systems

The urinary system (kidneys and associated structures) is responsible for disposing of nitrogenous wastes toxins, and metabolic breakdown products. The kidneys maintain the fluid, electrolytes, and acid-base balance of the body fluids, which is essential for the proper functioning of all body systems.

 **Disease**

Symptoms of disease
- Pain (moderate to severe)
- Abnormal urine composition or volume
- Abnormal electrolyte balance
- Abnormal fluid balance

Diseases and disorders of the urinary system
- Kidney stones
- Hereditary disorders
- Nephrotic syndrome
- Congenital diseases
- Bladder and kidney cancer
- Chronic kidney disease (CKD)
- Incontinence

- Kidney stones
- CKD & renal failure
- Polycystic kidney disease

 Medicine and Technology

Diagnosis of disorders
- MRI scans
- Kidney biopsy
- Urine tests
- Blood tests

Prevention of urinary system disorders
- Control of hypertension
- Control of diabetes
- Control of weight
- Behavior to control risk of UTIs

Treatment of urinary system disorders
- Drug therapy, e.g. antibiotics
- Surgery, e.g. removal of kidney stones
- Transplant (e.g. of donor kidney)
- Renal dialysis

- MRI scans
- Urine analysis
- Kidney transplants
- Renal dialysis

Waste Removal
The Urinary System

The urinary system had a primary role in excretion of nitrogenous wastes, and in fluid and electrolyte balance.

Degenerative changes in kidney and bladder function can be severe and debilitating. Renal dialysis and transplants are options for sufferers of kidney disease.

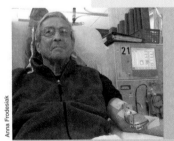

Anna Frodesiak

- Prostate enlargement
- Poor renal function
- Incontinence

- Effects of exercise on health
- Creatine metabolism
- Dehydration

Effects of aging on the urinary system
- Lower number of functional nephrons
- Reduction in glomerular filtration rate
- Reduced response to ADH
- Prostate enlargement (males)
- Loss of bladder/sphincter muscle tone

Effects of exercise on the urinary system
- Lowered blood pressure
- Reduced risk of chronic kidney disease
- Increased rates of creatinine excretion
- (Rarely) exercise-induced renal failure (dehydration or electrolyte imbalance)

 The Effects of Aging

 Exercise

CHAPTER 11

The Urinary System

KEY IDEAS

- The urinary system is the primary system for the excretion of nitrogenous and other wastes.
- The composition of the body's fluids is regulated through feedback mechanisms involving the blood, and respiratory and urinary systems.
- Urine production in the kidney is the result of ultrafiltration, secretion, and reabsorption.
- Urine analysis can assist in detecting disease.
- Renal failure can be addressed through dialysis or kidney transplant.

KEY TERMS

- Aldosterone
- Antidiuretic hormone (ADH)
- Cortex
- Electrolyte
- Excretion
- Kidney
- Medulla
- Nephron
- Renal dialysis
- Ultrafiltration
- Urine

RESOURCE HUB

Scan the QR code to access:

- weblinks
- videos
- 3D models
- interactives

LEARNING OBJECTIVES

Activity number

☐ 1 Understand that excretion is the elimination of waste products and that it is different from egestion. Describe, using examples, the roles of different organs in excretion. Explain the importance of water budget in humans.
183-184

☐ 2 Describe, using annotated diagrams, the blood vessels and ducts of the kidney. Describe the gross structure of the kidney.
185

☐ 3 Describe in detail the structure of a nephron and explain its role in ultrafiltration of the blood.
186

☐ 4 Understand the roles of antidiuretic hormone (ADH) and aldosterone in control of urine output.
187

☐ 5 Explain, using examples, the role of urine analysis as a diagnostic tool for a wide range of conditions.
188

☐ 6 Explain the importance of fluid and electrolyte balance to metabolic function. Understand the role of the renin-angiotensin system.
189

☐ 7 Understand the importance of maintaining a stable pH in the body. Explain the role of a buffer and describe some ways in which the body maintains pH homeostasis.
190

☐ 8 Describe some diseases of the kidney and distinguish between genetic and non-genetic disorders. Explain how technology can be used to treat kidney failure.
191-192

182 Waste Products in Humans

Key Idea: Metabolism produces a number of waste products that must be excreted from the body. Excretion is primarily the job of the kidneys, although other organs also play a role. **Excretion** refers to the elimination of the waste products of metabolism. It should not be confused with the elimination or egestion of undigested and unabsorbed food material from the gut as feces. A number of organs are involved in excretion, primarily the **kidneys**, which produce **urine**, forming part of the urinary system, but also the liver, lungs, and skin. The liver is very important in processing wastes, particularly in detoxifying poisons, breaking down hemoglobin, and forming urea from ammonia. The breakdown products of hemoglobin are excreted in bile and passed out with the feces, but they are not a result of digestion.

CO_2
Water

Lungs
Excretion of carbon dioxide (CO_2) with some loss of water.

Skin
Excretion of water, CO_2, hormones, salts and ions, and small amounts of urea as sweat.

Liver
Produces urea from ammonia in the urea cycle. Breakdown of hemoglobin in the liver produces the bile pigments e.g. bilirubin. These pass out with the feces, but are not the result of digestion.

Gut
Excretion of bile pigments in the feces. Also loss of water, salts, and carbon dioxide.

Bladder
Storage of urine before it is expelled from the body.

All cells
All the cells that make up the body carry out cellular respiration, breaking down glucose to release energy and produce the waste products carbon dioxide and water.

Converting and removing toxins

The kidneys excrete many toxins that are taken in from the environment. These are added to urine by glomeruli filtration, passive diffusion in the distal tubules, or active transport from the blood. Many toxic substances, such as alcohol, are rendered harmless by detoxification in the liver, but transported to the kidneys by blood vessels.

Kidney
Filtration of the blood to remove urea. Unwanted ions, particularly hydrogen (H^+) and potassium (K^+), and some hormones are also excreted by the kidneys. Some poisons and drugs, e.g. penicillin, are excreted by active secretion into the urine. Water is lost in excreting these substances and extra water may be voided if necessary.

Substance	Origin*	Organ(s) of excretion
Carbon dioxide		
Water		
Bile pigments		
Urea		
Ions (K^+, HCO_3^-, H^+)		
Hormones		
Poisons		
Drugs		

*Origin refers to location in the body from where each substance originates.

1. Explain the need for excretion: _____
_____

2. Complete the table above, summarizing the origin of excretory products and the main organ(s) of excretion for each:

3. What is the role of the liver in excretion, even though it is not primarily an excretory organ? _____
_____
_____

4. Based on the information on this page, predict the effects on the body if the kidneys did not function correctly: _____
_____
_____
_____
_____

183 Water Budget in Humans

Key Idea: We cannot live without water for more than about 100 hours, and adequate water is a requirement for physiological function and health.

Body water content varies between individuals and through life, from approximately 90% of total weight as a fetus to 74% as an infant, 60% as a child, and around 50-59% in adults, depending on gender and age. Gender differences (males usually have a higher water content than females) are the result of differing fat levels. Water intake and output are highly variable but closely matched to less than 0.1% over an extended period. Typical values for water gains and losses, as well as daily water transfers, are given below. Men need more water than women due to their higher (on average) fat-free mass and energy expenditure. Infants and young children need more water in proportion to their body weight, as they cannot concentrate their **urine** as efficiently as adults. They also have a greater surface area relative to weight, so water losses from the skin are greater.

Daily water transfers in an adult

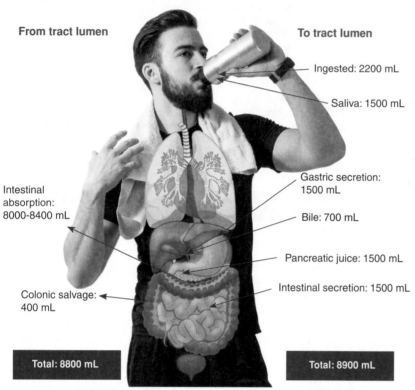

From tract lumen

To tract lumen

Ingested: 2200 mL

Saliva: 1500 mL

Gastric secretion: 1500 mL

Bile: 700 mL

Pancreatic juice: 1500 mL

Intestinal secretion: 1500 mL

Intestinal absorption: 8000-8400 mL

Colonic salvage: 400 mL

Total: 8800 mL

Total: 8900 mL

100 mL water (200 mL feces)

About 63% of our daily requirement for water is met through drinking fluids, 25% is obtained from food, and the remaining 12% comes from metabolism (the oxidation of glucose to ATP, CO_2, and water).

Typically, we lose 60% of body water through urination, 36% through the skin and lungs, and 4% in feces. Losses through the skin and from the lungs (breathing) average about 900 mL per day or more during heavy exercise. These are called insensible losses.

Water losses

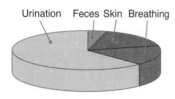

Urination Feces Skin Breathing

Skin and lungs: 900 mL per day
Urine: 1500 mL per day Feces: 100 mL per day

Water gains

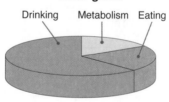

Drinking Metabolism Eating

Food and drink: 2200 mL per day
Metabolism: 300 mL per day

1. Explain how metabolism provides water for the body's activities: _____

_____

2. Describe four common causes of physiological dehydration:

    (a) _____   (c) _____

    (b) _____   (d) _____

3. Why is it important to maintain a water budget in humans? _____

_____

_____

©2023 **BIOZONE** International
ISBN: 978-1-99-101408-5
Photocopying Prohibited

184 The Urinary System

Key Idea: The urinary system is responsible for filtering and removing metabolic wastes from the blood, and hence body. The human urinary system consists of the **kidneys** and bladder, and their associated blood vessels and ducts. The kidneys have a plentiful blood supply from the renal artery.

The blood plasma is filtered by the kidneys to form **urine**, which is produced continuously, passing along the ureters to the bladder. Kidneys are very efficient, producing a urine that is concentrated to varying degrees, depending on fluid requirements at the time.

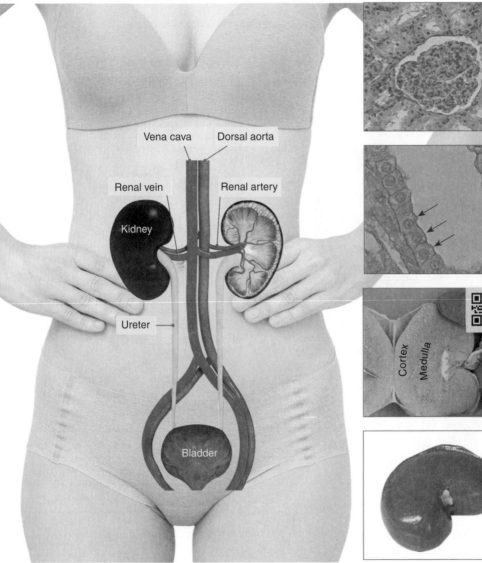

Blood is filtered in the kidneys by the glomerulus: a dense knot of capillaries. Blood pressure forces fluid through the capillary walls in a process called **ultrafiltration**. The filtrate is collected in the Bowman's capsule surrounding the glomerulus.

The filtrate moves from Bowman's capsule to the convoluted tubules. In the proximal tubule, the cuboidal epithelial cells (arrowed) have microvilli which increase the reabsorption of substances from the substrate. Most reabsorption occurs in the proximal tubule.

The glomerulus, capsule, and tubules form the **nephron** (the functional unit of the kidney). The thousands of nephrons are aligned and organized in an orderly way. The glomeruli and convoluted tubules are found in the outer **cortex**, while the "loop of Henle" is found in the inner **medulla** region.

The filtrate passes to the renal ducts and then to the ureter and finally to the bladder. The kidney itself is bean shaped and is around 10 cm long in humans.

1. What is the purpose of the microvilli in the epithelial cells of the convoluted tubules? _____

_____

2. (a) How is filtrate formed? _____

_____

_____

(b) How is the filtrate modified? _____

_____

3. The circulation rate of blood through the renal artery is about 1.2 L/min, about one quarter of the heart's total output. Why does so much blood need to pass through the kidneys every minute?

_____

_____

_____

The important roles of the kidneys in the urinary system

▶ The central organs of the urinary system in humans, and other mammals, are the kidneys. These are bean shaped organs that lie at the back of the abdominal cavity to either side of the spine (below right).

▶ The kidneys act as a selective filter of the blood, removing nitrogenous wastes (urea) and toxins and regulating blood composition and pH, while retaining useful substances, such as valuable ions and glucose. The kidneys receive blood under relatively high pressure via the arterioles from the renal artery. This relatively high pressure forces blood plasma out of the capillaries, forming a fluid called filtrate, which is then modified as it passes through the kidney to form the urine.

▶ Human kidneys (below left) are ~100-120 mm long and 25 mm thick. Each day they filter about 180 L of plasma. Most of this is reabsorbed, leaving a daily urine output of about 1 L.

▶ The kidneys help to maintain the body's internal chemical homeostasis, by adjusting the composition of the fluid excreted.

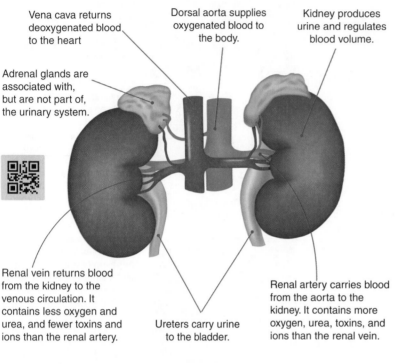

Vena cava returns deoxygenated blood to the heart

Dorsal aorta supplies oxygenated blood to the body.

Kidney produces urine and regulates blood volume.

Adrenal glands are associated with, but are not part of, the urinary system.

Renal vein returns blood from the kidney to the venous circulation. It contains less oxygen and urea, and fewer toxins and ions than the renal artery.

Ureters carry urine to the bladder.

Renal artery carries blood from the aorta to the kidney. It contains more oxygen, urea, toxins, and ions than the renal vein.

Kidneys *in-situ* (rat)

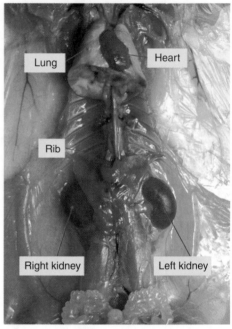

Lung

Heart

Rib

Right kidney

Left kidney

4. What are the important functions of the kidney? _____

_____

_____

5. Calculate the percentage of the plasma reabsorbed by the kidneys: _____

6. The kidneys are located near the lower part of the rib cage. What do you think is the significance of this location?

_____

_____

7. A person can live more or less normally with just one kidney. What does this tell you about the kidneys? _____

_____

_____

_____

8. The functional unit of the kidney is a filter element called a nephron. There are at least 1 million nephrons in each kidney. If a person filters 180 L of plasma a day, approximately what volume of plasma does each nephron filter?

_____

9. Describe the general passage of the blood through the kidney, and any changes to its composition: _____

_____

_____

_____

©2023 **BIOZONE** International
ISBN: 978-1-99-101408-5
Photocopying Prohibited

Internal structure of the human kidney

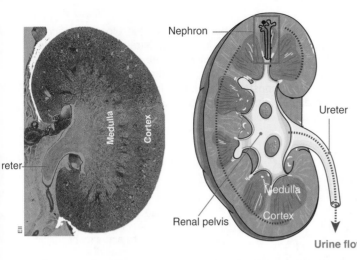

Nephron

Medulla

Cortex

reter

EII

Nephron

Ureter

Renal pelvis

Medulla

Cortex

Urine flow

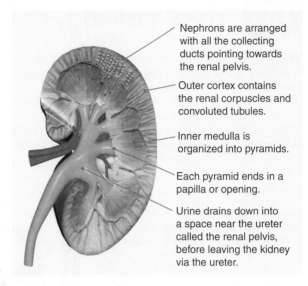

Nephrons are arranged with all the collecting ducts pointing towards the renal pelvis.

Outer cortex contains the renal corpuscles and convoluted tubules.

Inner medulla is organized into pyramids.

Each pyramid ends in a papilla or opening.

Urine drains down into a space near the ureter called the renal pelvis, before leaving the kidney via the ureter.

The outer cortex and inner medulla can be seen in a low power LM of the kidney. The ureter is seen extending into the fat and connective tissue surrounding and protecting the kidney.

The functional units of the kidney are selective filter elements called nephrons. Each kidney contains more than 1 million nephrons and they are precisely aligned so that urine is concentrated as it flows towards the ureter (model and diagram above). The alignment of the nephrons makes the kidney tissue appear striated (striped) and also makes it possible to fit in all the filtering units needed.

The bladder

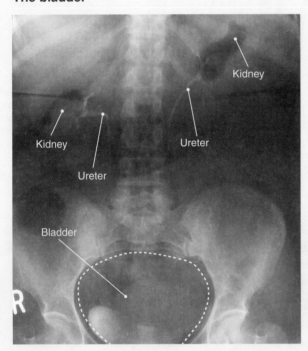

Kidney

Kidney

Ureter

Ureter

Bladder

R

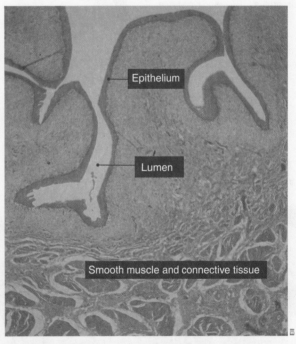

Epithelium

Lumen

Smooth muscle and connective tissue

EII

The bladder is a hollow stretchable organ, which stores the urine before it leaves the body via the urethra. In this X-ray, it is empty and resembles a deflated balloon. The dotted line shows where it would sit if full.

The bladder is lined with transitional epithelium. This type of epithelium is layered, or stratified, so it can be stretched without the outer cells breaking apart from each other. This image shows the bladder in a deflated state.

10. Describe the location and orientation of the nephrons in a kidney: _____

_____

_____

_____

11. Describe the structure and function of the bladder: _____

_____

185 The Physiology of the Kidney

Key Idea: The functional unit of the kidney is the nephron. It is a selective filter element, comprising a renal corpuscle and its associated tubules and ducts.

Ultrafiltration, i.e. forcing fluid and dissolved substances through a membrane by pressure, occurs in the first part of the **nephron**, across the membranes of the capillaries and the glomerular capsule. The formation of the glomerular filtrate depends on the pressure of the blood entering the nephron (below). If it increases, filtration rate increases; when it falls, glomerular filtration rate also falls. This process is precisely regulated so that glomerular filtration rate per day stays constant. The initial filtrate, now called **urine**, is modified through secretion and tubular reabsorption, according to body's needs at the time.

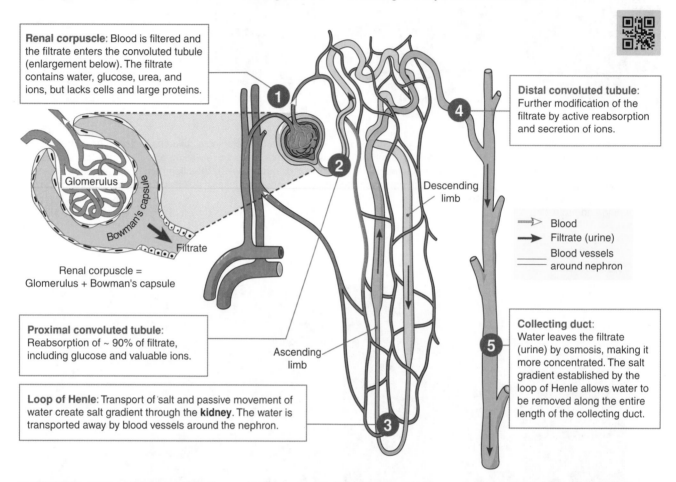

Renal corpuscle: Blood is filtered and the filtrate enters the convoluted tubule (enlargement below). The filtrate contains water, glucose, urea, and ions, but lacks cells and large proteins.

Glomerulus

Bowman's capsule

Filtrate

Renal corpuscle =
Glomerulus + Bowman's capsule

Proximal convoluted tubule: Reabsorption of ~ 90% of filtrate, including glucose and valuable ions.

Loop of Henle: Transport of salt and passive movement of water create salt gradient through the **kidney**. The water is transported away by blood vessels around the nephron.

Distal convoluted tubule: Further modification of the filtrate by active reabsorption and secretion of ions.

Descending limb

Ascending limb

⇒ Blood
→ Filtrate (urine)
— Blood vessels around nephron

Collecting duct: Water leaves the filtrate (urine) by osmosis, making it more concentrated. The salt gradient established by the loop of Henle allows water to be removed along the entire length of the collecting duct.

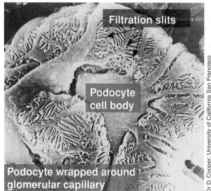

The epithelium of Bowman's capsule is made up of specialized cells called podocytes. The finger-like cellular processes of the podocytes wrap around the capillaries of the glomerulus, and the plasma filtrate passes through the filtration slits between them.

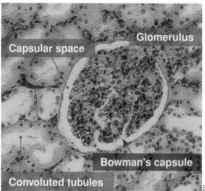

Bowman's capsule is a double walled cup, lying in the **cortex** of the kidney. It encloses a dense capillary network called the glomerulus. The capsule and its enclosed glomerulus form a renal corpuscle. In this section, the convoluted tubules can be seen surrounding the renal corpuscle.

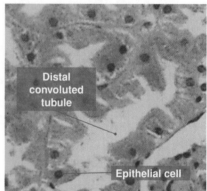

There are around 16 different types of epithelial cells in the kidney, lining the surface of tubules, each with different functions. The kidney tissue also contains endothelial cells that line blood vessels, interstitial cells (in the space between functional cells), and immune cells.

1. Explain how water is reabsorbed in the kidneys? _____

_____

_____

©2023 **BIOZONE** International
ISBN: 978-1-99-101408-5
Photocopying Prohibited

Summary of activities in the kidney nephron

Urine formation begins by ultrafiltration of the blood, as fluid is forced through the capillaries of the glomerulus, forming a filtrate similar to blood but lacking cells and proteins. The filtrate is then modified by secretion and reabsorption to add or remove substances, e.g. ions. The processes involved in urine formation are summarized below for each region of the nephron (glomerulus, proximal convoluted tubule, loop of Henle, and distal convoluted tubule), and the collecting duct. The loop of Henle acts as a countercurrent multiplier, establishing and increasing the salt gradient through the medullary region. This is possible because the descending loop is freely permeable to water but the ascending loop is not.

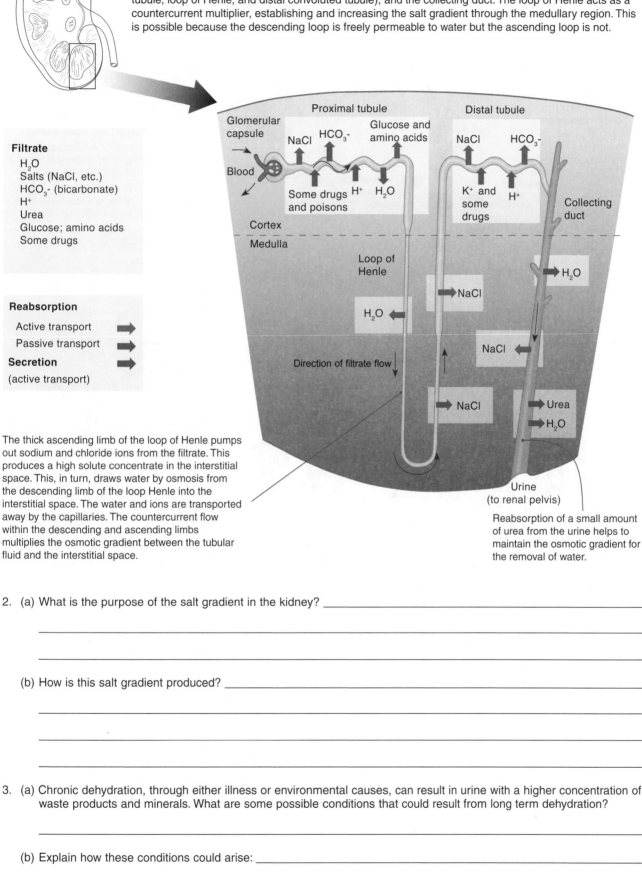

Filtrate

H_2O
Salts (NaCl, etc.)
HCO_3^- (bicarbonate)
H^+
Urea
Glucose; amino acids
Some drugs

Reabsorption

Active transport ➡
Passive transport ➡

Secretion

(active transport) ➡

The thick ascending limb of the loop of Henle pumps out sodium and chloride ions from the filtrate. This produces a high solute concentrate in the interstitial space. This, in turn, draws water by osmosis from the descending limb of the loop Henle into the interstitial space. The water and ions are transported away by the capillaries. The countercurrent flow within the descending and ascending limbs multiplies the osmotic gradient between the tubular fluid and the interstitial space.

Reabsorption of a small amount of urea from the urine helps to maintain the osmotic gradient for the removal of water.

2. (a) What is the purpose of the salt gradient in the kidney? _____

_____

_____

(b) How is this salt gradient produced? _____

_____

_____

_____

3. (a) Chronic dehydration, through either illness or environmental causes, can result in urine with a higher concentration of waste products and minerals. What are some possible conditions that could result from long term dehydration?

_____

(b) Explain how these conditions could arise: _____

_____

_____

186 Control of Urine Output

Key Idea: The body's balance of fluid and electrolytes is regulated by varying the composition and volume of urine. This is achieved through the action of the hormones antidiuretic hormone (ADH) and aldosterone.

The body regulates the composition and volume of the blood to compensate for variations in salt and water intake, and environmental conditions. This is achieved by varying the volume and composition of the **urine** and is under hormonal control. **Antidiuretic hormone (ADH)**, from the posterior pituitary, regulates water reabsorption from the kidney collecting duct. **Aldosterone**, from the adrenal cortex, regulates sodium absorption from the kidney tubules.

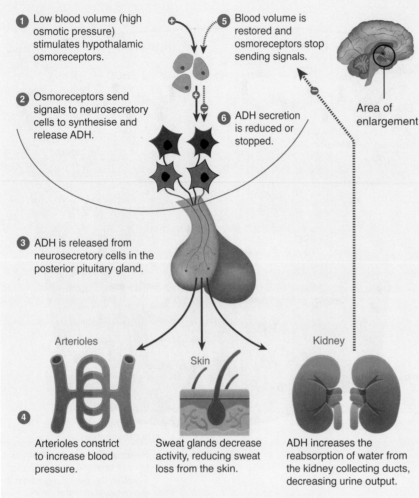

① Low blood volume (high osmotic pressure) stimulates hypothalamic osmoreceptors.

② Osmoreceptors send signals to neurosecretory cells to synthesise and release ADH.

③ ADH is released from neurosecretory cells in the posterior pituitary gland.

⑤ Blood volume is restored and osmoreceptors stop sending signals.

⑥ ADH secretion is reduced or stopped.

Area of enlargement

Arterioles

Skin

Kidney

④ Arterioles constrict to increase blood pressure.

Sweat glands decrease activity, reducing sweat loss from the skin.

ADH increases the reabsorption of water from the kidney collecting ducts, decreasing urine output.

Osmoreceptors in the hypothalamus of the brain respond to changes in blood volume. A fall in blood volume stimulates the synthesis and secretion of the hormone ADH (antidiuretic hormone), which is released from the posterior pituitary into the blood. ADH increases the permeability of the kidney collecting duct to water so that more water is reabsorbed and urine volume decreases. A second hormone, aldosterone, helps by increasing sodium reabsorption.

Factors causing ADH release
▶ Low blood volume
  = More negative water potential
  = High blood sodium levels
  = Low fluid intake
▶ Nicotine and morphine

Factors inhibiting ADH release
▶ High blood volume
  = Less negative water potential
  = Low blood sodium levels
▶ High fluid intake
▶ Alcohol consumption

Factors causing the release of aldosterone
Low blood volumes also stimulate secretion of aldosterone from the adrenal cortex. This is mediated through a complex pathway involving osmoreceptors near the kidney glomeruli and the hormone renin from the **kidney**.

1. State what happens to urine volume and blood volume when:

   (a) ADH secretion increases: _____

   (b) ADH secretion decreases: _____

2. Diabetes insipidus is caused by a lack of ADH. From what you know about ADH, describe the symptoms of this disease:

   _____

   _____

3. Explain why alcohol consumption (especially to excess) causes dehydration and thirst: _____

   _____

4. (a) State the effect of aldosterone on the kidney nephron: _____

   (b) What would be the net result of this effect? _____

5. Explain the role of negative feedback in the regulation of blood volume and urine output: _____

   _____

   _____

©2023 **BIOZONE** International
ISBN: **978-1-99-101408-5**
Photocopying Prohibited

187 Urine Analysis

Key Idea: Urine analysis is commonly used as diagnostic medical tool and to screen for the presence of illicit substances. **Urine** analysis (urinalysis) is used as a medical diagnostic tool for a wide range of metabolic disorders. In addition, urine analysis can be used to detect the presence of illicit (non-prescription) drugs and for diagnosing pregnancy.

Diagnostic urinalysis

A urinalysis (UA) is an array of tests performed on urine. It is a common method of medical diagnosis, as most tests are quick and easy to perform, non-invasive, and well understood diagnostically. A typical urinalysis usually includes a macroscopic analysis, a dipstick chemical analysis, in which the test results can be read as color changes, and a microscopic analysis, which involves centrifugation of the sample and examination for crystals, blood cells, or microbial contamination.

Macroscopic urinalysis

The first part of a urinalysis is direct, visual observation. Normal, fresh urine is pale to dark yellow or amber in color, and clear.

Turbidity or cloudiness may be caused by excessive cellular material or protein in the urine. A red or red-brown (abnormal) color could be from a food dye, eating fresh beets, a drug, or the presence of either hemoglobin or myoglobin. If the sample contained many red blood cells, it would be cloudy as well as red, as in this sample, indicating hematuria.

Dipstick urinalysis

Commonly, dipstick tests indicate:
Urine pH: normal range is 4.5-8.0.
Specific gravity: Normal is 1.002 - 1.035 Specific gravity measures urine density, or the ability of the **kidney** to concentrate or dilute the urine over that of plasma.
Protein: Normal total protein **excretion** does not exceed 10 mg per 100 ml in any single specimen. More than 150 mg per day is defined as proteinuria.
Glucose: Less than 0.1% of glucose filtered by the glomerulus normally appears in urine. Excess sugar in urine generally indicates diabetes mellitus.
Ketones: Ketones in the urine result from diabetic ketosis or some other form of calorie deprivation (starvation).
Nitrite: Nitrites indicate that bacteria may be present in significant numbers.
Leukocyte esterase: A positive leukocyte esterase test results from the presence of whole or lysed white blood cells.

Testing for anabolic steroids

Anabolic steroids are synthetic steroids related to the male sex hormone, testosterone (right). They work by increasing protein synthesis within cells, causing tissue, especially skeletal muscle, to build mass. They are used legitimately to stimulate bone growth and appetite, induce male puberty, and treat chronic wasting conditions. Misuse of anabolic steroids can have many adverse effects, including elevated blood pressure, cardiovascular disease, and altered cholesterol ratios.

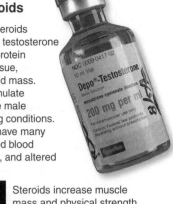

Steroids increase muscle mass and physical strength, and are used illegally by some athletes to gain an unfair advantage over their competitors.

Anabolic steroid use is banned by most major sporting bodies but some athletes continue to use them illegally. Athletes are routinely tested for the presence of performance enhancing drugs, including anabolic steroids.

Anabolic steroids break down into known metabolites which are excreted in the urine. The presence of specific metabolites indicates which substance has been used by the athlete.

Some steroid metabolites stay in the urine for weeks or months after being taken, while others are eliminated quite rapidly. Athletes using anabolic steroids can escape detection by stopping use of the drugs prior to competition. This allows the body time to break down and eliminate the components, and the drug use goes undetected.

1. Explain why urinalysis is a frequently used diagnostic technique for many common disorders: _____

_____

_____

2. Explain why the pH of normal urine (4.5-8.0) is much more variable than the pH of the blood (pH 7.35-7.45):

_____

3. Identify what each of the following might indicate in a urine sample:

   (a) Cloudy, red color: _____   (b) Positive leukocyte esterase test: _____

4. Explain why athletes exploiting illegal drugs might withhold them for a period before competition: _____

_____

188 Fluid and Electrolyte Balance

Key Idea: The body's fluid and electrolyte balance is critical to metabolic function.

Water makes up around 60% of the body and is found within two main fluid compartments. The intracellular fluid makes up 60-65% of the water in the body and is found within the body's cells. The extracellular fluid makes up the rest of the body's water and can be divided into intravascular fluid (mostly blood) and the extravascular fluid (interstitial fluid around the cells). Electrolytes in the body fluids are responsible for maintaining osmotic gradients and permitting ion exchanges. For example, in the blood plasma, electrolytes

help to maintain blood volume by keeping water moving into the capillaries. When **electrolyte** (mostly Na^+) levels fall, water moves out of the capillaries and into the tissues. This causes blood volume and pressure to fall and plasma to thicken. Two hormones are involved in regulating blood volume: **ADH**, which promotes water reabsorption in the **kidney** collecting ducts, and **aldosterone**, which promotes sodium reabsorption in the kidney tubules and is the most important mechanism for regulating its release is the renin-angiotensin system (RAS). The RAS is mediated by the juxtaglomerular (JG) apparatus in the renal tubules.

The renin-angiotensin system

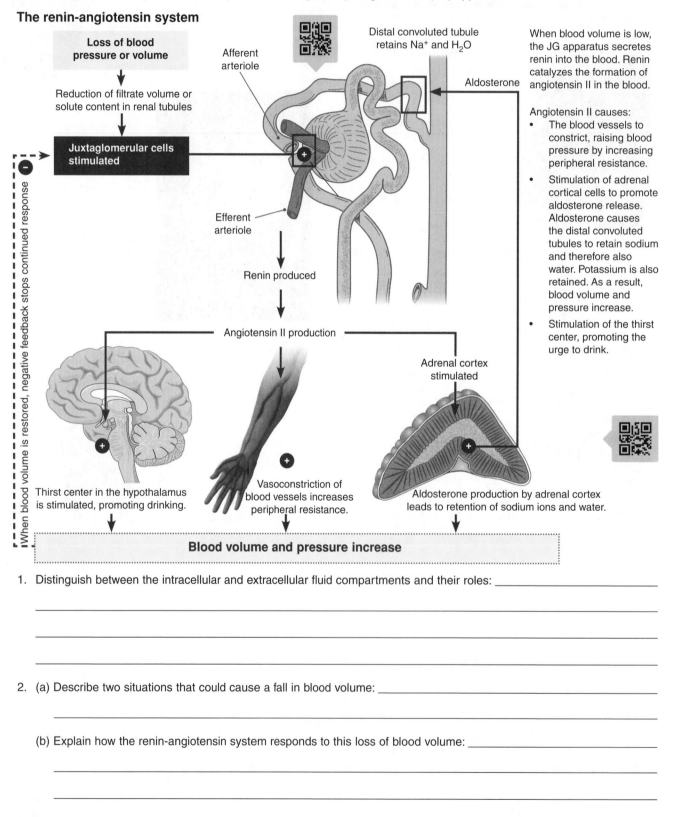

Loss of blood pressure or volume

Reduction of filtrate volume or solute content in renal tubules

Juxtaglomerular cells stimulated

When blood volume is restored, negative feedback stops continued response

Afferent arteriole

Efferent arteriole

Renin produced

Angiotensin II production

Thirst center in the hypothalamus is stimulated, promoting drinking.

Vasoconstriction of blood vessels increases peripheral resistance.

Distal convoluted tubule retains Na^+ and H_2O

Aldosterone

Adrenal cortex stimulated

Aldosterone production by adrenal cortex leads to retention of sodium ions and water.

When blood volume is low, the JG apparatus secretes renin into the blood. Renin catalyzes the formation of angiotensin II in the blood.

Angiotensin II causes:
- The blood vessels to constrict, raising blood pressure by increasing peripheral resistance.
- Stimulation of adrenal cortical cells to promote aldosterone release. Aldosterone causes the distal convoluted tubules to retain sodium and therefore also water. Potassium is also retained. As a result, blood volume and pressure increase.
- Stimulation of the thirst center, promoting the urge to drink.

Blood volume and pressure increase

1. Distinguish between the intracellular and extracellular fluid compartments and their roles: _____
_____
_____
_____

2. (a) Describe two situations that could cause a fall in blood volume: _____
_____

    (b) Explain how the renin-angiotensin system responds to this loss of blood volume: _____
_____
_____

©2023 **BIOZONE** International
ISBN: 978-1-99-101408-5
Photocopying Prohibited

189 Acid–Base Balance

Key Idea: The body's acid-base balance is maintained by interactions between three body systems.

Normal functioning of the body requires that the pH of the body's fluids are maintained between pH 7.35 and 7.45. The products of metabolic activity are generally acidic and could alter pH considerably without a buffer system to counteract pH changes. The carbonic acid-bicarbonate buffer works throughout the body to maintain the pH of blood plasma close to 7.40. The body maintains the buffer by eliminating either the acid (carbonic acid) or the base (bicarbonate ions). The blood buffers, the lungs, and the **kidneys** interact to maintain pH homeostasis. Changes in breathing rate bring about rapid changes in pH. The renal system acts more slowly, controlling pH by either excreting or retaining ions.

The blood buffer system

A buffer is able to resist changes to the pH of a fluid when either an acid or base is added to it. The bicarbonate ion (HCO_3^-) and its acid, carbonic acid (H_2CO_3), work in the following way:

$$H^+ + HCO_3^- \rightleftharpoons H_2CO_3$$

$$H_2CO_3 \rightleftharpoons H^+ + HCO_3^-$$

If a strong acid (such as HCl) is added to the system a weak acid is formed and thus the pH falls only slightly.

Strong base neutralized to weak base

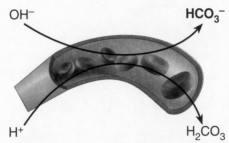

OH^- HCO_3^-

H^+ H_2CO_3

Strong acid neutralized to weak acid

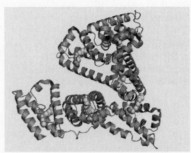

The blood also contains proteins, such as serum albumin (above) which contain basic and acidic groups that may accept or donate H^+ to help maintain blood pH.

The respiratory system

Carbon dioxide (CO_2) in the blood, an end-product of cellular respiration, forms carbonic acid (H_2CO_3) which dissociates to form H^+ and bicarbonate (HCO_3^-).

As CO_2 rises in the blood so too does the H^+ concentration. Chemoreceptors in the brain detect the rise in H^+ ions and increase the rate of breathing to expel the CO_2.

Low levels of CO_2 have the effect of depressing the respiratory system so that H^+ builds up and the pH is once again restored.

Signal to brain
$$CO_2 + H_2O \rightleftharpoons H_2CO_3$$

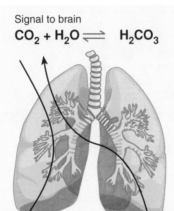

Increase in breathing rate
$$H_2CO_3 \rightleftharpoons H^+ + HCO_3^-$$

Anxiety can make some people hyperventilate. They breathe too deeply and quickly and breathe out more CO_2 than their body is producing, raising their blood pH. They can help reduce the effects by breathing into a paper bag.

1. Why must the blood must be kept at a pH between 7.35 and 7.45? _____

2. A drop in the blood pH to below 7.35 is called metabolic acidosis. If prolonged, it can be life threatening:

(a) From information above, explain how metabolic acidosis might arise: _____

(b) What would you expect the levels of bicarbonate ions to be in the blood of someone with metabolic acidosis?

The renal system

A net loss of HCO_3^- effectively results in the gain of H^+.

Bicarbonate is reabsorbed by the kidney tubules all the time so pH is regulated mainly through retaining or secreting H^+. When blood pH rises, H^+ is retained by the tubule cells. When blood pH falls, H^+ is actively secreted into the kidney tubules. The kidneys can also produce HCO_3^- which enters the body fluids.

Urine pH normally varies from 4.5 to 8.0, reflecting the ability of the renal tubules to lose or retain ions to maintain blood pH homeostasis.

Rise in pH
stimulates:

Retain H^+

Equates to
removal of HCO_3^-

Fall in pH
stimulates:

Removal H^+

Equates to
gain of HCO_3^-

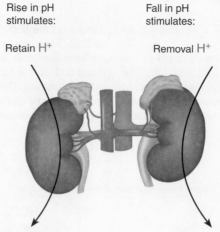

Urine is slightly acid, being pH 6, but can range from pH 4.5-8.0. Diet, and certain disease processes and medications can alter urine pH, showing that the kidneys are working to retain or excrete H^+ to regulate blood pH.

3   (a) How does the blood buffer system maintain blood pH? _____

_____

_____

_____

_____

(b) What happens when a base, e.g. ingestion of alkaline substance, is added to the system? _____

_____

_____

4.   (a) Describe the respiratory response to excess H^+ in the blood: _____

_____

(b) Where do these H^+ ions come from? _____

_____

5.   An abnormal increase in blood CO_2 is called respiratory acidosis.

(a) Explain the consequences to blood pH of increased CO_2: _____

(b) Explain how respiratory acidosis might arise: _____

_____

_____

6.   (a) What would happen to the blood pH of someone who was hyperventilating during an anxiety attack? _____

_____

(b) Why does breathing into a paper bag help someone who is hyperventilating? _____

_____

7.   Explain the role of the renal system in maintaining the pH of the blood: _____

_____

_____

_____

©2023 **BIOZONE** International
ISBN: 978-1-99-101408-5
Photocopying Prohibited

190 Kidney Disorders and Disease

Key Idea: Kidneys play a vital role in the urinary system and various diseases, either inherited, nutritional, or environmental, can impact their ability to function.

Disorders that prevent proper functioning of the **kidneys** can allow harmful build-up of waste, blood glucose, and toxins in the blood. Damage to the **nephrons**, by increased blood pressure, kidney stones, or cysts, can result in kidney failure, a fatal condition that is normally only controlled by **dialysis**. Sufferers may eventually require a kidney transplant. Aging increases the likelihood of developing a kidney disorder.

Genetically inherited kidney disorders

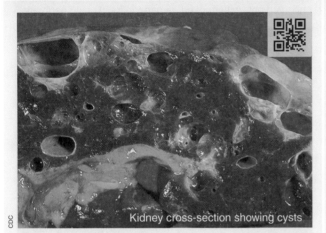

Kidney cross-section showing cysts

Polycystic kidney disease causes clusters of fluid filled sacs to build up in the nephrons, altering their shape. Initial symptoms from kidney damage are pain, kidney stones, blood in **urine**, and repeated kidney infections. Eventually, without treatment, this leads to kidney failure, requiring dialysis and, at end-stage, complete transplant if both kidneys are effected.

Two main forms of this disease exist: one is autosomal dominant, and the presence of only one mutated gene is required for the condition to be present; the other is autosomal recessive and, if both parents are carriers, their offspring have a 25% chance of inheriting the disease.

Non-genetic kidney disorders

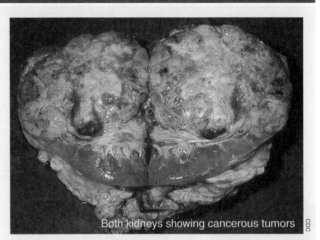

Both kidneys showing cancerous tumors

Kidney cancer, usually develops in the cells, most commonly as renal cell carcinoma. Early stage cancer has few symptoms, but can be diagnosed with CT scan, MRI, and follow-up biopsy. Complete removal, called a nephrectomy, is the usual treatment.

Kidney stones, often due to excessive salt in the diet, crystallize and create pressure damage, sometimes leading to kidney failure.

Chronic kidney disease is often caused by hypertension (high blood pressure) that damages nephrons. Type 1 and type 2 diabetes also cause progressive damage, due to uncontrolled blood glucose.

1. Explain how some lifestyle choices could reduce the risk of chronic kidney disease? _____

_____

_____

_____

2. (a) Describe the possible impact to urine production and constitution due to diseased kidneys: _____

_____

_____

(b) What are some common impacts to other body systems and organs due to diseased kidneys? _____

_____

_____

3. Diabetes causes damage to the blood vessels, causing them to thicken and work inefficiently. With reference to kidney structure and function, describe the outcome of such damage:

_____

_____

_____

Renal failure

Renal failure (also called kidney failure) arises when the kidneys fail to function adequately and filtrate formation decreases or stops. In cases of renal failure, normal blood volume levels and **electrolyte** balances are not maintained, and waste products build up in the body.

Common symptoms of renal failure include decreased urine output, swelling and edema of the extremities due to fluid retention, loss of appetite, chest pain and irregular heartbeat, shortness of breath, fatigue, nausea, and general body weakness.

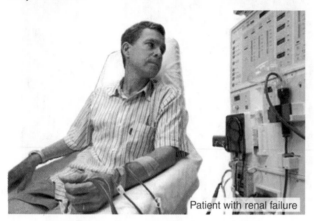
Patient with renal failure

If kidney deterioration is ignored, the kidneys will fail completely. The patient then requires dialysis (photo above and next activity) until a kidney transplant can be arranged.

Kidney failure is classified as acute (rapid onset) or chronic (developing over a period of months or years). There are many causes of kidney failure, including decreased blood supply, drug overdose, chemotherapy, infection, and poorly controlled diabetic or hypertensive conditions. Recovery from acute renal failure is possible with correct care, but chronic renal damage cannot be reversed.

In the US, as of 2022, 37 million Americans (15% of all adults) live with chronic kidney disease (CKD), and many are unaware they have the condition. Of those with CKD, around 660,000 have progressed to renal failure. Around 100,000 people are on a waiting list for a kidney transplant and there is an acute shortage of kidney donors.

Indicators of renal failure

Kidney (renal) failure is indicated by levels of serum creatinine, as well as by kidney size on ultrasound and the presence of anemia (chronic kidney disease generally leads to anemia and small kidney size). Creatinine is a break-down product of creatine phosphate in muscle, and is usually produced at a fairly constant rate by the body (depending on muscle mass). It is chiefly filtered out of the blood by the kidneys, although a small amount is actively secreted by the kidneys into the urine. A rise in blood creatinine levels is observed only with marked damage to functioning nephrons.

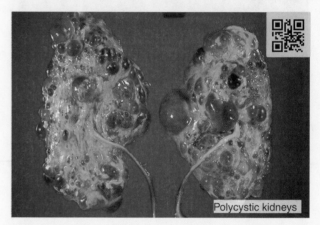
Polycystic kidneys

Acute renal failure (ARF) is characterized by decreased urine production (<400mL per day), and commonly arises because of low blood volume (blood loss), dehydration, or widespread infection. In contrast, chronic renal failure, which develops over months or years, is commonly the result of poorly controlled diabetes, poorly controlled high blood pressure, or polycystic kidney disease, a genetic disorder characterized by the growth of numerous cysts in the kidneys (above).

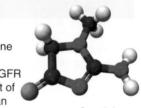
Creatinine

Creatinine levels in both blood and urine is used to calculate the creatinine clearance (CrCl), which reflects the glomerular filtration rate (GFR). The GFR is a clinically important measurement of renal function and more accurate than serum creatinine alone, since serum creatinine only rises when nephron function is very impaired.

4. Distinguish between acute and chronic renal failure and contrast their causes: _____

_____

_____

5. (a) Explain why a rise in blood (serum) levels of creatinine would indicate a failure of nephron function: _____

_____

(b) Explain why a creatinine clearance is a more accurate indicator of renal function than a serum creatinine test alone:

_____

_____

6. Summarize the symptoms that a medical physician may observe, which would indicate the kidneys are no longer functioning, leading to a diagnosis of acute renal failure:

_____

_____

_____

©2023 **BIOZONE** International
ISBN: 978-1-99-101408-5
Photocopying Prohibited

191 Technology to Treat Renal Failure

Key Idea: Diet and medication can be used to treat kidney failure but when the damage is extensive, kidney dialysis or a kidney transplant are required to keep the patient alive.

A kidney dialysis machine acts as an artificial kidney, removing waste, such as urea, from the blood. It is used when the **kidneys** fail, or when blood acidity, urea, or potassium levels increase much above normal. In kidney **dialysis**, blood flows through a system of tubes composed of partially permeable membranes. Dialysis fluid (dialysate) has a composition similar to blood, except that the concentration

of wastes is low. It flows in the opposite direction to the blood on the outside of the dialysis tubes. Consequently, waste products like urea diffuse from the blood into the dialysis fluid, which is constantly replaced. The dialysis fluid flows at a rate of several 100 cm³ per minute over a large surface area. For some people, dialysis is an ongoing procedure, but for others dialysis just allows the kidneys to rest and recover from injury or the effects of drugs or other metabolic disturbance. A kidney transplant allows a patient to come off dialysis and resume a reasonably normal life.

Hemodialysis for renal failure

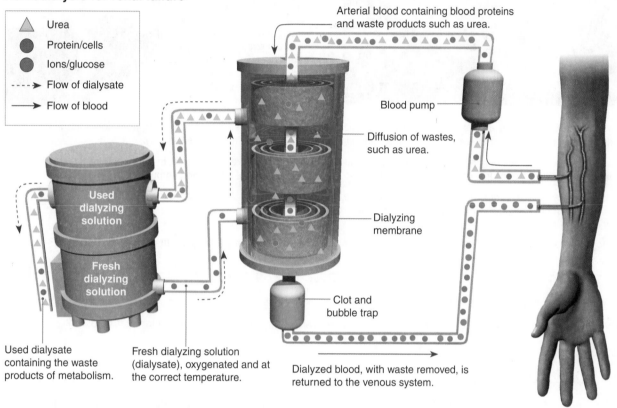

Legend:
△ Urea
● Protein/cells
● Ions/glucose
- - -▶ Flow of dialysate
——▶ Flow of blood

Arterial blood containing blood proteins and waste products such as urea.

Blood pump

Diffusion of wastes, such as urea.

Dialyzing membrane

Clot and bubble trap

Used dialyzing solution

Fresh dialyzing solution

Used dialysate containing the waste products of metabolism.

Fresh dialyzing solution (dialysate), oxygenated and at the correct temperature.

Dialyzed blood, with waste removed, is returned to the venous system.

1. In kidney dialysis, explain why the dialyzing solution is constantly replaced rather than being recirculated:

_____

_____

2. Explain why ions such as potassium and sodium, and small molecules, e.g. glucose, do not diffuse rapidly from the blood into the dialyzing solution along with the urea. Use the countercurrent flow diagram (right) to help you:

_____

_____

_____

3. Explain why the urea passes from the blood into the dialyzing solution: _____

_____

_____

4. Give a reason why the dialyzing solution flows in the opposite direction from the blood: _____

_____

_____

Countercurrent flow

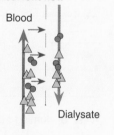

Blood

Dialysate

△ Urea
● Ions/glucose

Countercurrent flow occurs when two fluids move past each other, separated by a semi-permeable membrane. Substances move from high concentration to low concentration (gradient) by the process of diffusion.

Kidney transplant

▶ Transplantation of a healthy kidney from an organ donor is the preferred treatment for end-stage kidney failure. The organ is usually taken from a person who has just died, although kidneys can also be taken from living donors. The damaged kidneys are left in place and the new kidney is transplanted into the lower abdomen (below).

▶ As long as recipients comply with medical requirements, including correct diet and medication, over 85% of kidney transplants are successful and achieve full functionality.

A kidney transplant being performed.

Xenotransplantation

When cross-species transplants are used, the procedure is called xenotransplantation. In late 2021, a trial kidney transplant took place using a genetically modified pig kidney inserted into a human body. The kidney continued to function properly until the investigation was stopped 72 hours later. Pigs have a similar kidney structure and physiology to humans. The genetic modified kidney, called the UKidney, has genes removed to prevent excessive growth of the kidney, as well as genes added to prevent immuno rejection and blood clotting.

▶ Two major problems are associated with kidney transplants: lack of donors and tissue rejection. Cells from donor tissue have different antigens to those of the recipient, and the body's immune system will attack the new kidney.

▶ Tissue-typing and the use of immunosuppressant drugs help to decrease organ rejection rates. In future, the transplant of genetically modified organs from other species may help to solve the problems of supply and immune rejection.

▶ Life expectancy of kidney transplant patients is, on average, 10-15 years more than if they remained on dialysis alone. Some patients have more than one kidney transplant in their lifetime.

5. Kidney transplants can occur from live donors, unlike many other types of organ transplants. Why might this be?

_____

_____

6. What factors might be considered when selecting a patient with kidney failure to receive a kidney transplant? _____

_____

_____

7. Dialysis is usually an effective method to replace kidney function, yet there is still a large demand for kidney transplants. Why might a patient prefer a kidney transplant over dialysis, despite the invasive surgery, difficulty in securing a donor, and risk of organ rejection?

_____

_____

_____

_____

_____

_____

8. When evaluating new technology, scientists and medical practitioners need to consider many factors, including ethics.

(a) What might be some 'pros' of xenotransplantation? _____

_____

_____

(b) What might be some 'cons' of xenotransplantation? _____

_____

_____

©2023 **BIOZONE** International
ISBN: 978-1-99-101408-5
Photocopying Prohibited

192 Chapter Summary

1. Annotate the diagram below to indicate the direction of movement of water, ions, urea, and glucose in the nephron:

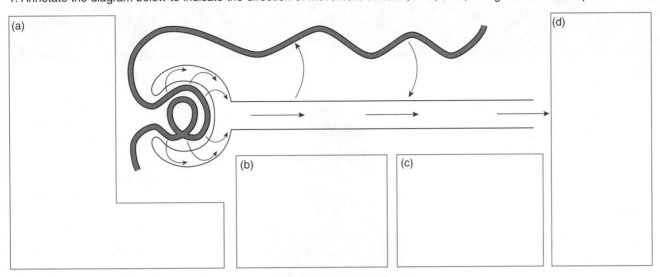

(a)

(b)

(c)

(d)

2. (a) Summarize the function of the kidneys in the urinary system: _____

_____

(b) What role do the kidneys have in maintaining body homeostasis? _____

_____

_____

3. Some recent sports events have received media coverage because athletes have collapsed after excessive water intake. This condition, called hyponatremia or water intoxication, causes nausea, confusion, diminished reflex activity, stupor, and eventually coma. From what you know of fluid and electrolyte balances in the body, explain these symptoms:

_____

_____

4. Label the following diagram of hemodialysis (dialysis of the blood) with the correct name and purpose of each part indicated:

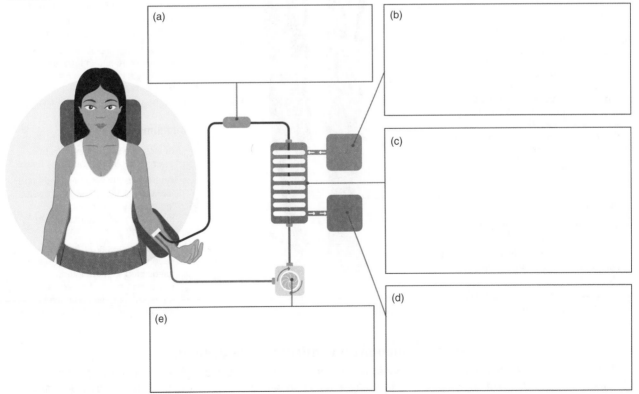

(a)

(b)

(c)

(d)

(e)

The Reproductive System

Respiratory system

- Respiratory system provides O_2 to the reproductive system and disposes of CO_2 produced by cellular respiration.
- Vital capacity and breathing rate increase in pregnancy. Enlarged uterus impairs descent of the diaphragm and can cause shortness of breath late in pregnancy.

Cardiovascular system

- Estrogens increase blood HDL cholesterol levels and promote cardiovascular health in premenopausal women.
- Pregnancy places extra demands on the cardiovascular system. Blood volume increases 40-50% during pregnancy.
- Local vasodilation is responsible for aspects of the sexual response
- Blood transports sex hormones to target tissues.

Endocrine system

- Reproductive hormones from the ovaries (in females) and testes (in males) are responsible for the development of secondary sexual characteristics. They are regulated via feedback mechanisms to the hypothalamic-pituitary axis.
- Gonadotropins, e.g. LH and FSH, help to regulate gonadal function.
- Placental hormones maintain pregnancy.

Skeletal system

- Sex hormones are responsible for secondary sexual characteristics associated with the skeleton: in males, androgens masculinize the skeleton (broad shoulders and expanded chest) and increase bone density; in females, estrogen causes pelvic widening and maintains bone mass.
- Bony pelvis protect organs.

Muscular system

- Androgens promote an increase in muscle mass in post-pubertal males.
- Pelvic floor muscles provide support for the reproductive organs and are involved in aspects of response.
- Abdominal, uterine, and pelvic floor muscles are active in childbirth

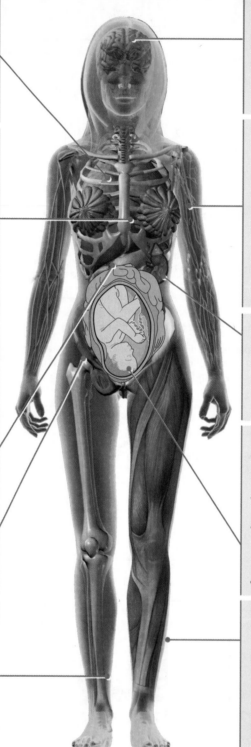

Nervous system

- Sex hormones masculinize or feminize brain, influence sex drive.
- The neurohormone, GnRH from the hypothalamus regulates the timing of puberty.
- Reflexes regulate aspects of the sexual response (e.g. orgasm).

Lymphatic system and immunity

- Immune cells protect against pathogens. Regulatory T cells important in the immune tolerance to the developing fetus.
- Lymphatic (and blood) vessels transport sex hormones.
- Maternal antibodies pass to the fetus *in-utero* and are present in breast milk, providing passive immunity.
- Increased abdominal pressure in pregnancy impairs lymphatic return leading to edema.

Digestive system

- Digestive organs are crowded in late pregnancy and constipation and heartburn are common.
- Increased hormone levels result in nausea and vomiting in early pregnancy.

Reproductive system

- Increased frequency and urgency of urination in pregnancy as a result of pressure on the bladder, pelvic floor.
- Enlargement of prostate (usually) in older men can impede urination.
- Kidneys dispose of nitrogenous waste and maintain fluid and electrolyte balance of mother and fetus in pregnancy.
- Urethra provides passage for semen.

Integumentary system

- In lactating women, milk from mammary glands nourishes infant.
- Androgens activate oil glands and lubricate skin and hair. Estrogen increases skin hydration and increases skin pigmentation in pregnancy.
- Sex hormones are responsible for secondary sexual characteristics associated with the integument, e.g. appearance of pubic hair and changes in fat distribution associated with male and female body shape

General functions and effects on all systems

The reproductive system in adults is responsible for reproduction, i.e. the production of gametes and offspring. Unlike other body systems, which are functioning almost continuously since birth, the reproductive system is quiescent until puberty, at which time it begins development towards maturity.

Symptoms of disease
- Pain (moderate to severe)
- Abnormal bleeding
- Infertility

Disorders and diseases of the male reproductive system
- Sexually transmitted infections
- Cancers, e.g. prostate cancer
- Congenital abnormalities
- Functional disorders, e.g. erectile dysfunction, premature ejaculation

Disorders and diseases of the female reproductive system
- Sexually transmitted infections
- Cancers (e.g. cervical cancer)
- Congenital abnormalities
- Functional disorders, e.g. infertility, ectopic pregnancy, endometriosis

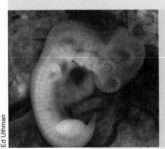
Ed Uhtman

- Osteomalacia
- Osteoarthritis
- Osteoporosis
- Sarcomas
- Muscular dystrophy

Diagnosis of disorders
- MRI scan and ultrasound
- Semen analysis
- Laparoscopy
- Blood and DNA (genetic) tests

Treating reproductive disorders
- Drug therapy, e.g. antibiotics
- Hormone therapy
- Surgery, e.g. hysterectomy

Treatment of infertility
- Assisted reproductive technologies
- Hormone therapy, e.g. clomiphene
- Laparoscopic surgery

Contraception
- Physical (barrier) methods
- Hormonal, e.g. oral contraceptive pill
- Surgical, e.g. vasectomy

- Ultrasound
- HRT
- Oral contraception
- Pregnancy testing
- IVF and GIFT

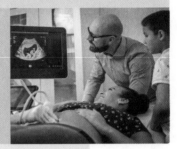

The Human Life Span
The Reproductive System

The reproductive system undergoes marked changes associated with aging and the end of fertility. Disease may affect it both directly and indirectly.

Medical technologies are used to detect, diagnose and treat reproductive disorders and control fertility.

- Menopause
- Decline in hormone level
- Declie in fertility

Aging and the reproductive system
- Decline in sperm production and erectile function
- Cessation of menses (women)
- Thinning and prolapse of organs

Excessive exercise may lead to:

- Exercise induced amenorrhea
- GNRH depression

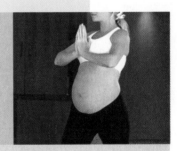

Effects of exercise on the reproductive system
- Improved muscle tone
- Reduced risk of reproductive cancers
- Heavy endurance exercise can lead to hormonal and menstrual irregularities
- Exercise beneficial during pregnancy

The Reproductive System

KEY IDEAS

- The reproductive system is responsible for production of gametes and offspring.

- Its activity is regulated by reproductive hormones from the pituitary and gonads.

- Birth follows a period of gestation in which the fetus is supported by the placenta.

- The human life span is characterized by distinct developmental stages.

- Humans can intervene in their own fertility.

KEY TERMS

- Apoptosis
- Contraception
- Estrogen
- IVF
- Lactation
- Menstrual cycle
- Oogenesis
- Ovulation
- Oxytocin
- Progesterone
- Spermatogenesis
- Testosterone

RESOURCE HUB

Scan the QR code to access:

- weblinks
- videos
- 3D models
- Interactives

LEARNING OBJECTIVES

		Activity number
☐	1 Know that gametes are the sex cells of organisms. Describe what is meant by the term gametogenesis in males and females. Describe, using an annotated diagram, the structures of the ovum and sperm.	193
☐	2 Identify the parts of the male reproductive system. Describe the process of spermatogenesis and name and describe the functions of the hormones involved. Identify the parts of the female reproductive system. Describe the process of ovulation and implantation.	194-196
☐	3 Describe the stages of the menstrual cycle.	197
☐	4 Describe the development of the follicle and oocyte in the ovary. Explain the roles of the hormones that control the menstrual cycle.	198-199
☐	5 Describe the structure and function of the placenta. Explain the stages of fertilization and the stages of the early development of the embryo.	200-201
☐	6 Describe the stages of apoptosis and its role in embryonic development. Describe, in general terms, how apoptosis is regulated.	202
☐	7 Explain the roles of the hormones secreted during pregnancy. Explain how pregnancy detection kits work through the use of antibodies that bind with the hormone HCG. Describe the stages of the birth process and control of lactation.	203-205
☐	8 Describe some methods of contraception and explain how they prevent pregnancy.	206
☐	9 Know that both the male and female reproductive systems can be affected by a number of diseases that can affect fertility or threaten life. Understand that infertility can be treated in females through use of hormonal drugs.	207-209
☐	10 Explain how *in vitro* fertilization can be used as a treatment for both male and female infertility and describe, using examples, some ethical issues associated with IVF.	209
☐	11 Describe the main changes that take place as a human develops from birth to maturity, including sexual development. Describe, giving examples, changes that take place as the human body ages.	210-212

Background: Sperm gametes (abstract)

193 Gametes

Key Idea: Gametes are the sex cells of organisms. Male and female gametes differ in their size, shape, and number.

Gametes (sex cells) are produced for the purposes of sexual reproduction. The gametes of males and females differ greatly in size, shape, and number. These differences reflect their different roles in fertilization and reproduction.

Male gametes (sperm) are highly motile and are produced in very large numbers throughout life. Female gametes (eggs or ova) are large, relatively few in number, and immobile. Eggs and sperm are produced by meiosis in a process called gametogenesis. Gametogenesis in males is called **spermatogenesis**. In females, it is called **oogenesis**.

Egg structure and function

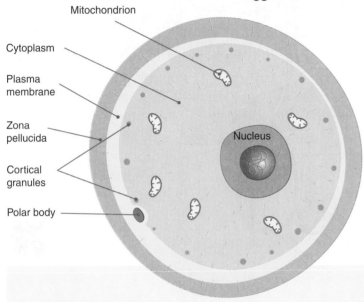

Labels: Mitochondrion, Cytoplasm, Plasma membrane, Zona pellucida, Cortical granules, Polar body, Nucleus

▶ The ovum is a simpler structure than the sperm cell. It has no propulsion mechanism and moves as a result of the wave-like motion of the ciliated cells lining the fallopian tubes of the female reproductive tract. The ovum is required to survive for a much longer time than a sperm, so it contains many more nutrients and metabolites and, as a result, it is much larger than a sperm cell (up to 100μm).

▶ The contents of the ovum are similar to that of a typical human cell, although it is externally surrounded by a jelly-like glycoprotein called the zona pellucida. A small polar body (the remnants of a sister cell) lies between the plasma membrane and zona pellucida. Cortical granules around the inner edge of the plasma membrane contain enzymes that are released once a sperm has penetrated the egg, forming a block to prevent further sperm entry (the cortical reaction).

Sperm structure and function

▶ Mature spermatozoa (sperm) are produced in the testes. Meiotic division of spermatocytes produces spermatids, which then differentiate into mature sperm.

▶ The sperm's structure reflects its purpose, which is to swim through the female reproductive tract to the ovum, penetrate the ovum's protective barrier, and donate its genetic material. A sperm cell comprises three regions: a headpiece, containing the nucleus and penetrative enzymes, an energy-producing mid-piece, and a tail for propulsion.

▶ Human sperm live for only about 48 hours, but they swim quickly and there are so many of them (millions per ejaculation) that usually some are able to reach the egg to fertilize it.

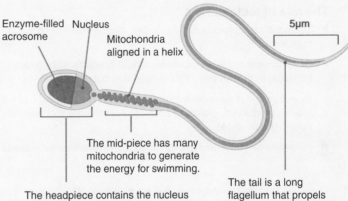

Labels: Enzyme-filled acrosome, Nucleus, Mitochondria aligned in a helix, 5μm

The mid-piece has many mitochondria to generate the energy for swimming.

The tail is a long flagellum that propels the sperm in its swim to the egg.

The headpiece contains the nucleus and the acrosome, which contains the enzymes that help penetrate the egg.

1. Why do sperm need to be motile? _____

_____

2. (a) How does an egg move along the Fallopian tube? _____

_____

(b) Why does a mature egg need to be so many times larger than a sperm? _____

_____

_____

3. Describe how each of the following three features of a sperm cell contribute to its role in reproduction:

(a) Tail: _____

(b) Mitochondria: _____

(c) Acrosome: _____

©2023 **BIOZONE** International
ISBN: 978-1-99-101408-5
Photocopying Prohibited

194 The Male Reproductive System

Key Idea: The male reproductive system produces sperm cells for reproduction, and testosterone which the drives the development of male characteristics.

The male reproductive system (below) is concerned with producing sperm and delivering them to the female urogenital tract. Mature sperm are ejaculated with fluids from the seminal vesicles and prostate as semen. When a sperm combines with an egg, it contributes half the genetic material of the offspring and, in humans and other mammals, determines its sex.

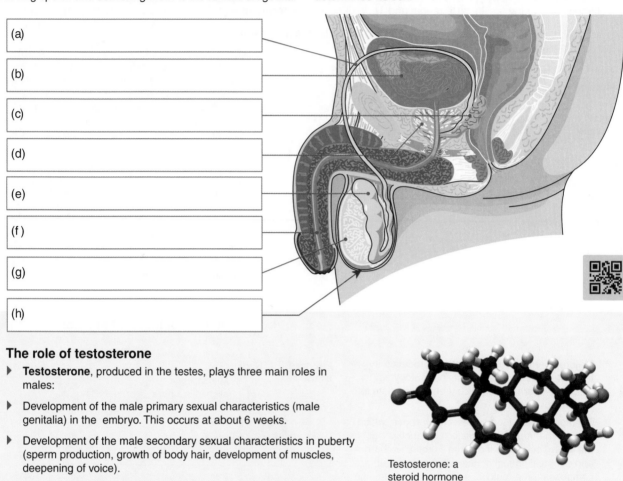

(a)

(b)

(c)

(d)

(e)

(f)

(g)

(h)

The role of testosterone

▶ **Testosterone**, produced in the testes, plays three main roles in males:

▶ Development of the male primary sexual characteristics (male genitalia) in the embryo. This occurs at about 6 weeks.

▶ Development of the male secondary sexual characteristics in puberty (sperm production, growth of body hair, development of muscles, deepening of voice).

▶ Maintains sex drive and sperm production in adults after puberty.

Testosterone: a steroid hormone

1. The male human reproductive system and associated structures are shown above. Using the following word list and the **BIOZONE Resource Hub** links below, identify the labeled parts in the spaces provided on the diagram.
   Word list: *bladder, scrotal sac, sperm duct (vas deferens), epididymis, seminal vesicle, testis, urethra, prostate gland*

2. Describe the three roles of testosterone in male development and the male reproductive system:

_____

_____

_____

_____

3. State the two main roles of the male reproductive system:

_____

_____

4. Distinguish between male primary and secondary characteristics: _____

_____

_____

_____

©2023 **BIOZONE** International
ISBN: 978-1-99-101408-5
Photocopying Prohibited

195 Spermatogenesis

Key Idea: Sperm is produced in the seminiferous tubules of the testes.

Sperm is produced via the process of **spermatogenesis** which occurs in the seminiferous tubules. Sperm production is a continual process. It takes 60-70 days for a sperm cell to fully develop, but several million sperm cells will be produced each day. A sperm cell will survive in the epididymis for about 3 weeks before being reabsorbed.

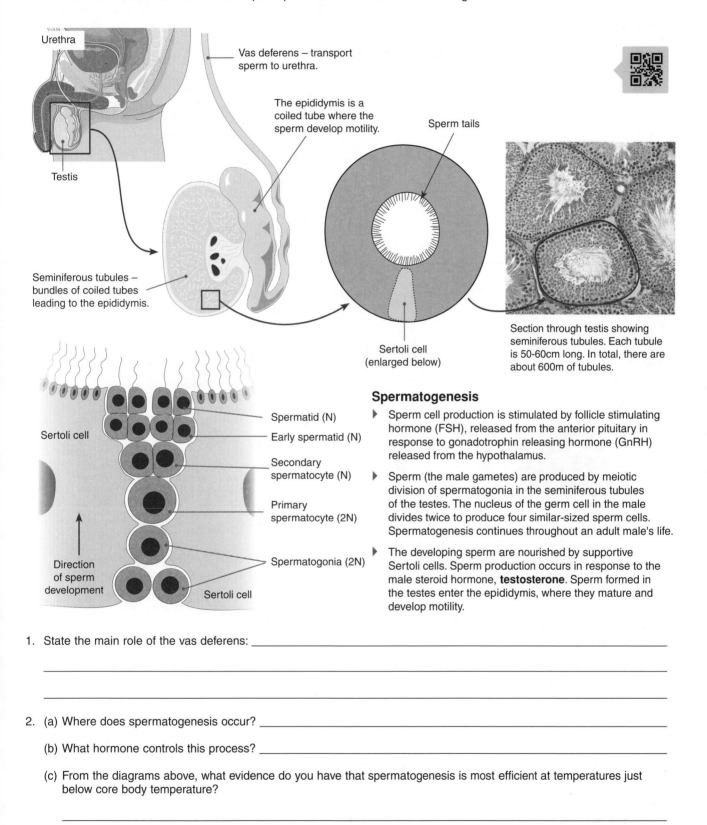

Urethra

Vas deferens – transport sperm to urethra.

Testis

The epididymis is a coiled tube where the sperm develop motility.

Sperm tails

Seminiferous tubules – bundles of coiled tubes leading to the epididymis.

Sertoli cell (enlarged below)

Section through testis showing seminiferous tubules. Each tubule is 50-60cm long. In total, there are about 600m of tubules.

Sertoli cell

Spermatid (N)
Early spermatid (N)
Secondary spermatocyte (N)
Primary spermatocyte (2N)
Spermatogonia (2N)
Sertoli cell

Direction of sperm development

Spermatogenesis

▶ Sperm cell production is stimulated by follicle stimulating hormone (FSH), released from the anterior pituitary in response to gonadotrophin releasing hormone (GnRH) released from the hypothalamus.

▶ Sperm (the male gametes) are produced by meiotic division of spermatogonia in the seminiferous tubules of the testes. The nucleus of the germ cell in the male divides twice to produce four similar-sized sperm cells. Spermatogenesis continues throughout an adult male's life.

▶ The developing sperm are nourished by supportive Sertoli cells. Sperm production occurs in response to the male steroid hormone, **testosterone**. Sperm formed in the testes enter the epididymis, where they mature and develop motility.

1. State the main role of the vas deferens: _____

_____

_____

2. (a) Where does spermatogenesis occur? _____

   (b) What hormone controls this process? _____

   (c) From the diagrams above, what evidence do you have that spermatogenesis is most efficient at temperatures just below core body temperature?

   _____

   _____

3. Are sperm cells haploid or diploid? Explain: _____

_____

196 The Female Reproductive System

Key Idea: The female reproductive system maintains female characteristics, produces egg cells for reproduction, and provides the environment for the growth and development of the fertilized egg.

The female reproductive system consists of the ovaries, Fallopian tubes, uterus, the vagina and external genitalia, and the breasts. Although both male and females have breasts, the female breasts (mammary glands) are modified so that they produce milk after childbirth. The female reproductive system produces eggs, receives the penis and sperm during sexual intercourse, protects and houses the developing fetus, and produces milk to nourish the young after birth.

The female reproductive system

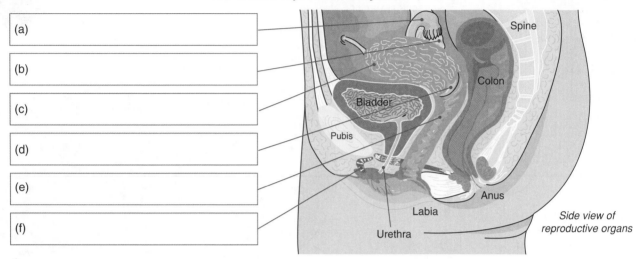

(a)

(b)

(c)

(d)

(e)

(f)

Side view of reproductive organs

Ovulation and implantation

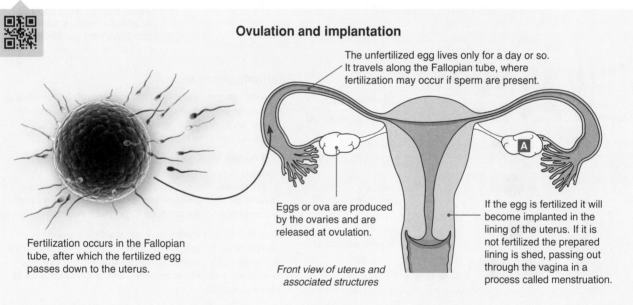

The unfertilized egg lives only for a day or so. It travels along the Fallopian tube, where fertilization may occur if sperm are present.

Eggs or ova are produced by the ovaries and are released at ovulation.

If the egg is fertilized it will become implanted in the lining of the uterus. If it is not fertilized the prepared lining is shed, passing out through the vagina in a process called menstruation.

Fertilization occurs in the Fallopian tube, after which the fertilized egg passes down to the uterus.

Front view of uterus and associated structures

1. The female human reproductive system and associated structures are illustrated above. Label the structures using the following word list and the **BIOZONE Resource Hub** links below. Word list: *ovary, uterus (womb), vagina, Fallopian tube (oviduct), cervix, clitoris*.

2. (a) Name the organ labeled (**A**) in the diagram above: _____

   (b) Name the event associated with this organ that occurs every month: _____

   (c) Name the process by which mature ova are produced: _____

3. Where does fertilization occur? _____

4. In a few words or a short sentence, state the function of each of the structures labeled (a) - (c) in the top diagram:

   (a) _____

   (b) _____

   (c) _____

©2023 **BIOZONE** International
ISBN: 978-1-99-101408-5

197 The Menstrual Cycle

Key Idea: The menstrual cycle involves cyclical changes in the ovaries and uterus to prepare for fertilization of an egg. In humans, fertilization of the ovum (egg) is most likely to occur around the time of **ovulation**. The uterine lining (endometrium) thickens in preparation for pregnancy, but is shed as a bloody discharge through the vagina if fertilization does not occur.

This event, called menstruation, characterizes the human reproductive or **menstrual cycle**. The menstrual cycle starts from the first day of bleeding and lasts for about 28 days. It involves predictable changes in response to pituitary and ovarian hormones and is divided into three phases (follicular, ovulatory, and luteal), defined by the events in each phase.

The menstrual cycle

Luteinising hormone (LH) and follicle stimulating hormone (FSH): FSH stimulates the development of the ovarian follicles, resulting in the release of **estrogen**. Estrogen levels peak, stimulating a surge in LH and triggering ovulation.

Hormone levels: One of the follicles that begins developing in response to FSH (the Graafian follicle) becomes dominant. In the first half of the cycle, estrogen is secreted by this developing Graafian follicle. Later, the Graafian follicle develops into the corpus luteum (below right) which secretes large amounts of **progesterone** (and smaller amounts of estrogen).

The corpus luteum: The Graafian follicle continues to grow and, at around day 14, ruptures to release the egg (ovulation). LH causes the ruptured follicle to develop into a corpus luteum (yellow body). The corpus luteum secretes progesterone which promotes full development of the uterine lining, maintains the embryo in the first 12 weeks of pregnancy, and inhibits the development of more follicles.

Menstruation: If fertilization does not occur, the corpus luteum breaks down. Progesterone secretion declines, causing the uterine lining to be shed (menstruation). If fertilization occurs, high progesterone levels maintain the thickened uterine lining. The placenta develops and nourishes the embryo completely by 12 weeks.

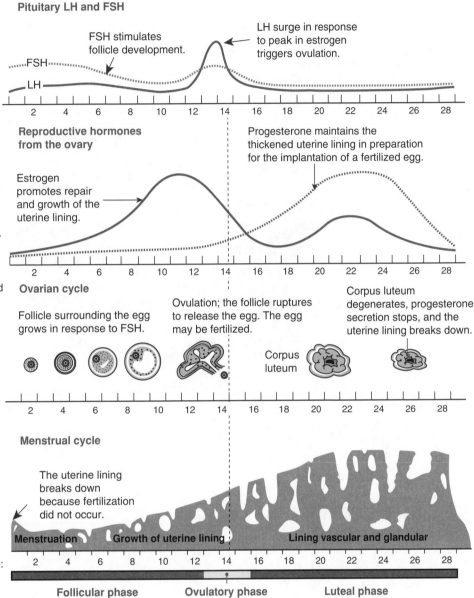

Pituitary LH and FSH

FSH stimulates follicle development.

LH surge in response to peak in estrogen triggers ovulation.

FSH

LH

Reproductive hormones from the ovary

Estrogen promotes repair and growth of the uterine lining.

Progesterone maintains the thickened uterine lining in preparation for the implantation of a fertilized egg.

Ovarian cycle

Follicle surrounding the egg grows in response to FSH.

Ovulation; the follicle ruptures to release the egg. The egg may be fertilized.

Corpus luteum degenerates, progesterone secretion stops, and the uterine lining breaks down.

Corpus luteum

Menstrual cycle

The uterine lining breaks down because fertilization did not occur.

Menstruation | Growth of uterine lining | Lining vascular and glandular

Day of the cycle:

Follicular phase | Ovulatory phase | Luteal phase

---

1. Identify the hormone responsible for:

   (a) Follicle growth: _____ (b) Ovulation: _____

2. Each month, several ovarian follicles begin development, but only one (the Graafian follicle) develops fully:

   (a) What hormone is secreted by the developing follicle? _____

   (b) What is the role of this hormone during the follicular phase? _____

   (c) What happens to the follicles that do not continue developing? _____

3. (a) What is the principal hormone secreted by the corpus luteum? _____

   (b) What is the purpose of this hormone? _____

4. What is the hormonal trigger for menstruation? _____

198 Oogenesis

Key Idea: The ova are produced by a process called oogenesis, which is only completed if the egg is fertilized.

The production of egg cells (ova) occurs by **oogenesis**. Unlike **spermatogenesis**, no new eggs are produced after birth. Instead a human female is born with her entire complement of immature eggs. These remain in prophase of meiosis I throughout childhood. After puberty, most commonly a single egg cell is released from the ovaries at regular monthly intervals (the **menstrual cycle**). This cell is arrested in metaphase of meiosis II and its second division is only completed upon fertilization. The release of egg cells from the ovaries takes place from the onset of puberty until menopause, when menstruation ceases.

Development of the ovarian follicle and egg cell within the ovary

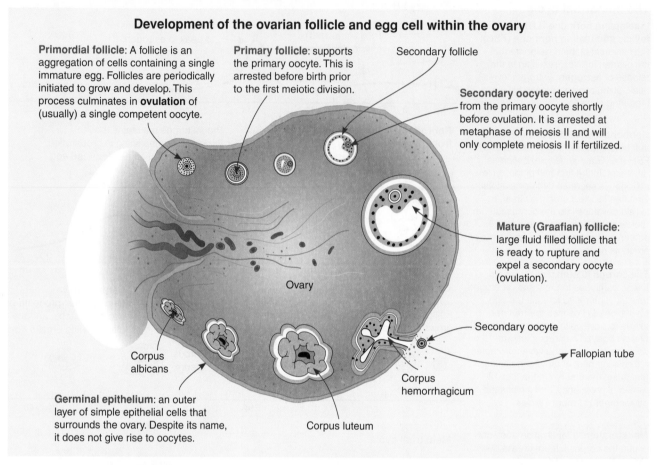

Primordial follicle: A follicle is an aggregation of cells containing a single immature egg. Follicles are periodically initiated to grow and develop. This process culminates in **ovulation** of (usually) a single competent oocyte.

Primary follicle: supports the primary oocyte. This is arrested before birth prior to the first meiotic division.

Secondary follicle

Secondary oocyte: derived from the primary oocyte shortly before ovulation. It is arrested at metaphase of meiosis II and will only complete meiosis II if fertilized.

Mature (Graafian) follicle: large fluid filled follicle that is ready to rupture and expel a secondary oocyte (ovulation).

Ovary

Secondary oocyte

Fallopian tube

Corpus albicans

Corpus hemorrhagicum

Germinal epithelium: an outer layer of simple epithelial cells that surrounds the ovary. Despite its name, it does not give rise to oocytes.

Corpus luteum

Oogenesis

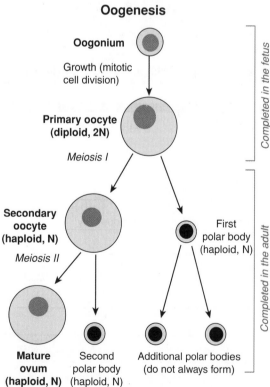

Oogonium

Growth (mitotic cell division)

Primary oocyte (diploid, 2N)

Meiosis I

Secondary oocyte (haploid, N)

First polar body (haploid, N)

Meiosis II

Mature ovum (haploid, N)

Second polar body (haploid, N)

Additional polar bodies (do not always form)

Completed in the fetus

Completed in the adult

1. Discuss the main differences between the production of male gametes and female gametes:

_____

_____

_____

_____

_____

2. Explain why males can be potentially fertile all their life, while female fertility decreases and eventually ceases with age:

_____

_____

_____

_____

_____

_____

_____

©2023 **BIOZONE** International
ISBN: 978-1-99-101408-5
Photocopying Prohibited

199 Control of the Menstrual Cycle

Key Idea: Hormones from the hypothalamus and anterior pituitary regulate the menstrual cycle. The cycles of hormonal fluctuations can be manipulated to control fertility.

The female **menstrual cycle** is regulated by several reproductive hormones. The main control centers for this regulation are the hypothalamus and the anterior pituitary gland. The hypothalamus secretes gonadotropin releasing hormone (GnRH), which is transported in blood vessels to the anterior pituitary. Here, it induces the release of two hormones: follicle stimulating hormone (FSH) and luteinizing hormone (LH). These two hormones bring about the cyclical changes in the ovaries and uterus. Regulation of blood hormone levels during the menstrual cycle is achieved through negative feedback mechanisms. The exception to this is the mid cycle surge in LH, which is induced by the rapid increase in **estrogen** secreted by the developing follicle.

Control of the menstrual cycle

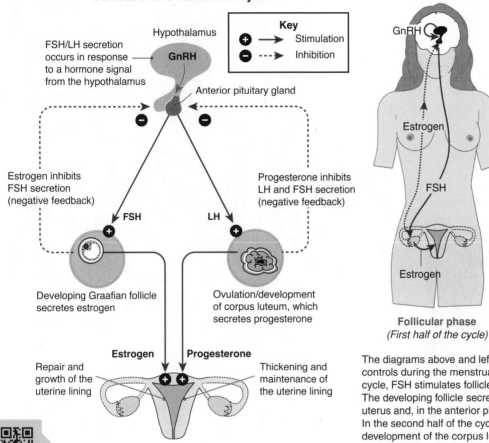

FSH/LH secretion occurs in response to a hormone signal from the hypothalamus

Key
+ → Stimulation
− - -> Inhibition

Estrogen inhibits FSH secretion (negative feedback)

Progesterone inhibits LH and FSH secretion (negative feedback)

Developing Graafian follicle secretes estrogen

Ovulation/development of corpus luteum, which secretes progesterone

Repair and growth of the uterine lining

Thickening and maintenance of the uterine lining

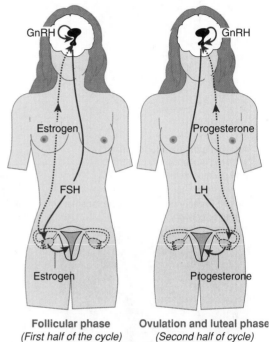

Follicular phase
(First half of the cycle)

Ovulation and luteal phase
(Second half of cycle)

The diagrams above and left summarize the hormonal controls during the menstrual cycle. In the first half of the cycle, FSH stimulates follicle development in the ovary. The developing follicle secretes estrogen which acts on the uterus and, in the anterior pituitary, inhibits FSH secretion. In the second half of the cycle, LH induces **ovulation** and development of the corpus luteum. The corpus luteum secretes **progesterone** which acts on the uterus and also inhibits further secretion of LH and FSH.

1. Summarize the role of hormones below in the control of the menstrual cycle and the site they are secreting:

   (a) GnRH: _____

   (b) FSH: _____

   (c) LH: _____

   (d) Estrogens: _____

   _____

   (e) Progesterone: _____

   _____

2. Briefly explain the role of negative feedback in the control of hormone levels in the menstrual cycle:

   _____

   _____

   _____

   _____

200 The Placenta

Key Idea: The placenta allows materials to be exchanged between the fetus and its mother. It also acts as a temporary endocrine organ, secreting hormones to maintain pregnancy. The human fetus depends entirely on its mother for nutrients, oxygen, and the elimination of wastes. The placenta is the specialized organ that performs this role, enabling exchange between fetal and maternal tissues and allowing a prolonged period of fetal growth and development within the uterus. The placenta also has an endocrine role, producing **progesterone** and **estrogen** to maintain the pregnancy.

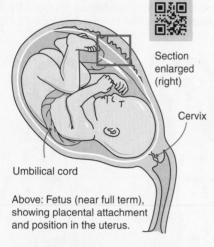

Section enlarged (right)

Cervix

Umbilical cord

Above: Fetus (near full term), showing placental attachment and position in the uterus.

Below: Photograph of a human placenta, just after delivery.

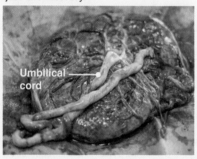

Umbilical cord

Schematic diagram showing part of the placenta in section

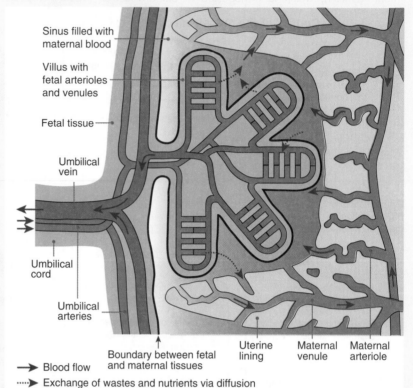

Sinus filled with maternal blood

Villus with fetal arterioles and venules

Fetal tissue

Umbilical vein

Umbilical cord

Umbilical arteries

Boundary between fetal and maternal tissues

Uterine lining

Maternal venule

Maternal arteriole

→ Blood flow

·····▶ Exchange of wastes and nutrients via diffusion

The placenta is a disk-like organ, about the size of a dinner plate and weighing about 1 kg. It develops when finger-like projections (villi) from the fetal membranes grow into the uterine lining. The villi contain the capillaries connecting the fetal arteries and vein. They continue invading the maternal tissue until they are bathed in the maternal blood sinuses. The maternal and fetal blood vessels are in such close proximity that oxygen and nutrients can diffuse from the maternal blood into the capillaries of the villi. From the villi, the nutrients circulate in the umbilical vein, returning to the fetal heart. Carbon dioxide and other wastes leave the fetus through the umbilical arteries, pass into the capillaries of the villi, and diffuse into the maternal blood. The fetal and maternal blood do not mix. The exchanges occur via diffusion through capillaries.

1. Describe the structure of the human placenta and explain its function: _____

   _____

   _____

   _____

2. The umbilical cord contains the fetal arteries and vein. Describe the status of the blood in each type of fetal vessel:

   (a) Fetal arteries: _____

   (b) Fetal vein: _____

3. Teratogens are substances that may cause malformations in embryonic development, e.g. nicotine, alcohol:

   (a) Why do substances ingested by the mother have the potential to be harmful to the fetus? _____

   _____

   (b) Why is cigarette smoking so harmful to fetal development? _____

   _____

©2023 **BIOZONE** International
ISBN: 978-1-99-101408-5
Photocopying Prohibited

201 Fertilization and Early Growth

Key Idea: The union of a male and a female gamete to form a zygote is called fertilization. It involves several distinct stages. Fertilization occurs when a sperm penetrates an egg cell at the secondary oocyte stage. The sperm and egg nuclei then unite to form the zygote. In humans, the entry of a sperm into the egg triggers specific mechanisms to prevent polyspermy (fertilization of the egg by more than one sperm). These include a change in membrane potential, and the cortical reaction (see below). A zygote resulting from polyspermy contains too many chromosomes, and is not viable, i.e. it does not develop. Fertilization is seen as time 0 in a period of gestation (pregnancy) and has five stages (below). After fertilization, the zygote begins its development, i.e. its growth and differentiation into a multicellular organism.

Fertilization (Time 0)

The stages in fertilization are represented below in a numbered sequence (1-5)

1. Capacitation

The surface of the sperm cell undergoes changes that are essential to enable the acrosome reaction and sperm entry.

2. The acrosome reaction

Enzymes from the acrosome (an enzyme-filled bag at the tip of the sperm) are released and digest a pathway through the follicle cells (not shown) and the jelly-like zona pellucida surrounding the egg cell (secondary oocyte).

3. Fusion of sperm head

The plasma membranes of the sperm and egg fuse, and the nucleus of the sperm enters the egg cytoplasm. Fusion causes a sudden membrane depolarization that acts as a 'fast block' to further sperm entry. The fusion of the two plasma membranes also triggers the completion of meiosis II in the egg cell and induces the cortical reaction (below).

4. The cortical reaction

The fusion of the two plasma membranes induces a permanent change in the egg surface that prevents further sperm entry. Cortical granules in the egg cytoplasm release their contents into the space between the plasma membrane and the vitelline layer. Substances released from the granules raise and harden the vitelline layer to form a slow and permanent block to further sperm entry.

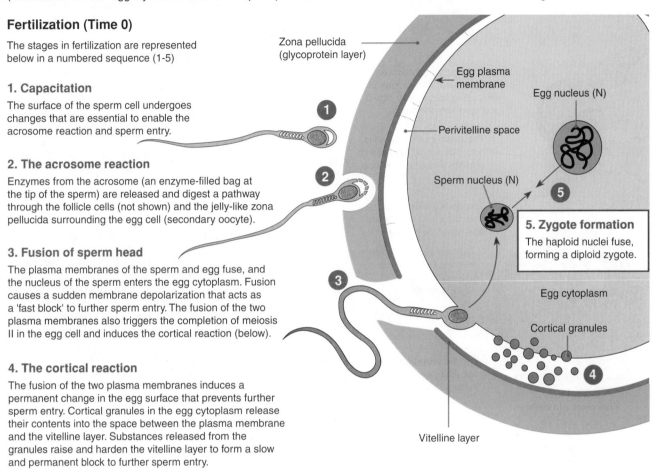

Zona pellucida (glycoprotein layer)

Egg plasma membrane

Egg nucleus (N)

Perivitelline space

Sperm nucleus (N)

5. Zygote formation
The haploid nuclei fuse, forming a diploid zygote.

Egg cytoplasm

Cortical granules

Vitelline layer

1. Briefly describe the significant events and their importance at each of the following stages of fertilization:

(a) Capacitation: _____

_____

(b) The acrosome reaction: _____

_____

(c) Fusion of egg and sperm plasma membranes: _____

_____

(d) The cortical reaction: _____

_____

(e) Fusion of egg and sperm nuclei: _____

_____

2. Why is it important that fertilization of the egg by more than one sperm (polyspermy) does not occur? _____

_____

_____

©2023 **BIOZONE** International
ISBN: 978-1-99-101408-5
Photocopying Prohibited

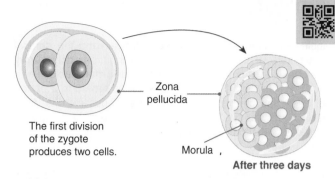

The first division of the zygote produces two cells.

Zona pellucida

Morula

After three days

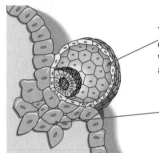

The blastocyst, a hollow ball of cells, embeds into the uterine wall, using enzymes to digest and penetrate the lining.

The uterine lining provides nourishment for the embryo until the placenta develops.

The placenta develops from the fetal membranes and maternal uterine lining.

The yolk sac is small in humans but provides more nourishment in some animals.

Umbilical cord

The fluid-filled amniotic sac encloses the embryo in the amniotic fluid.

Five week old embryo

Early growth and development

Cleavage, and the development of the morula

Immediately after fertilization, rapid cell division takes place. These early cell divisions are called cleavage and they increase the number of cells, but not the size of the zygote. The first cleavage is completed after 36 hours, and each succeeding division takes less time. After 3 days, successive cleavages have produced a solid mass of cells called the morula (left), which is still about the same size as the original zygote.

Implantation of the blastocyst (after 6-8 days)

After several days in the uterus, the morula develops into the blastocyst. It makes contact with the uterine lining and pushes deeply into it, ensuring a close maternal-fetal contact. Blood vessels provide early nourishment as they are opened up by enzymes secreted by the blastocyst. The chorion (membrane around the embryo) produces HCG (human chorionic gonadotropin), which prevents degeneration of the corpus luteum and signals that the woman is pregnant.

The embryo at 5-8 weeks

Five weeks after fertilization, the embryo is only 4-5 mm long, but already the central nervous system has developed and the heart is beating. The embryonic membranes have formed; the amnion encloses the embryo in a fluid-filled space, and the allanto-chorion forms the fetal portion of the placenta. From two months, the embryo is called a fetus. It is still small (30-40 mm long), but the limbs are well formed and the bones are beginning to harden. The face has a flat, rather featureless appearance with the eyes far apart. Fetal movements have begun and brain development proceeds rapidly. The placenta is well developed, although not fully functional until 12 weeks. The umbilical cord, containing the fetal umbilical arteries and vein, connects fetus and mother.

3. (a) Explain why the egg cell, when released from the ovary, is termed a secondary oocyte: _____

_____

(b) At which stage is its meiotic division completed? _____

4. What contribution do the sperm and egg cell make to each of the following:

(a) The nucleus of the zygote?   Sperm contribution: _____ Egg contribution: _____

(b) The cytoplasm of the zygote?   Sperm contribution: _____ Egg contribution: _____

5. What is meant by cleavage? Explain its significance to the early development of the embryo: _____

_____

_____

6. (a) What is the importance of implantation to the early nourishment of the embryo? _____

_____

(b) What is the purpose of HCG production by the embryo? _____

_____

_____

7. Why is the fetus particularly prone to damage from drugs towards the end of the first trimester (2-3 months)?

_____

©2023 **BIOZONE** International
ISBN: 978-1-99-101408-5
Photocopying Prohibited

202 Apoptosis

Key Idea: Apoptosis is a process of programmed cell death. It maintains cell numbers and sculpts body parts during development. It is a tightly regulated process.

Apoptosis, also called programmed cell death (PCD), is a natural and necessary mechanism in multicellular organisms to trigger the death of a cell. Apoptosis helps to maintain adult cell numbers and stops the multiplication of damaged or dangerous cells, such as virus-infected cells and cells with DNA damage. Apoptosis also has a role in sculpting embryonic tissue during development, e.g. in the formation of digits in developing embryos and resorption of the larval tail during amphibian metamorphosis.

An overview of apoptosis

▶ Apoptosis is a controlled process of cell death. It occurs in response to specific cell signals and involves an orderly series of biochemical events.

▶ The cell and its nucleus shrink and there is an orderly dissection of chromatin by endonucleases.

▶ Death is finalized by a rapid engulfment of the dying cell by phagocytosis. This safely disposes of the remains of the cell.

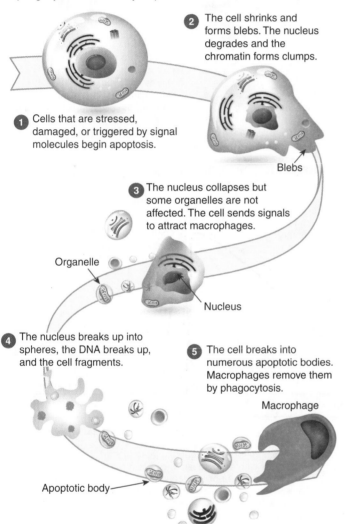

1 Cells that are stressed, damaged, or triggered by signal molecules begin apoptosis.

2 The cell shrinks and forms blebs. The nucleus degrades and the chromatin forms clumps.

Blebs

3 The nucleus collapses but some organelles are not affected. The cell sends signals to attract macrophages.

Organelle

Nucleus

4 The nucleus breaks up into spheres, the DNA breaks up, and the cell fragments.

5 The cell breaks into numerous apoptotic bodies. Macrophages remove them by phagocytosis.

Macrophage

Apoptotic body

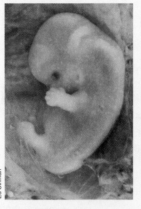 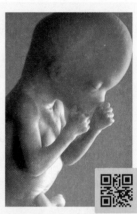

Ed Uthman

In humans, the mesoderm tissue initially formed between the fingers and toes is removed by apoptosis. Forty one days after fertilization (top), the digits of the hands and feet are webbed, appearing paddle-like. Apoptosis selectively destroys this superfluous webbing, sculpting them into digits, which can be seen in later stages of development (above).

Regulating apoptosis

Apoptosis is a complicated and tightly controlled process, distinct from cell necrosis (uncontrolled cell death), when the cell contents are spilled. Apoptosis is regulated through both:

Positive signals, which prevent apoptosis and allow a cell to function normally. They include:

▶ interleukin-2
▶ bcl-2 protein and growth factors

Interleukin-2 is a positive signal for cell survival. Like other signaling molecules, it binds to surface receptors on the cell to regulate metabolism.

Negative signals (death activators), which trigger the changes leading to cell death. They include:

▶ inducer signals generated from within the cell itself in response to stress, e.g. DNA damage or cell starvation.
▶ signaling proteins and peptides such as lymphotoxin.

1. (a) What is apoptosis? _____

_____

(b) Describe its roles in multicellular organisms: _____

_____

2. (a) How is apoptosis triggered? _____

_____

(b) Predict a possible consequence of this mechanism failing: _____

_____

203 The Hormones of Pregnancy

Key Idea: Hormones secreted during pregnancy maintain the pregnancy and prepare the body for birth.

In a non-pregnant adult human female, the levels of **estrogen** and **progesterone** regulate the secretion of the pituitary hormones that control the ovarian cycle. Pregnancy interrupts this cycle and maintains the corpus luteum and the placenta as endocrine organs, with the specific role of maintaining the developing fetus during its development. During the last month of pregnancy, the hormone, **oxytocin** induces the uterine contractions that will expel the baby from the uterus.

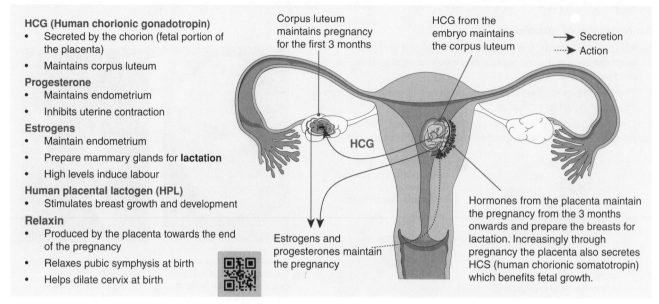

HCG (Human chorionic gonadotropin)
- Secreted by the chorion (fetal portion of the placenta)
- Maintains corpus luteum

Progesterone
- Maintains endometrium
- Inhibits uterine contraction

Estrogens
- Maintain endometrium
- Prepare mammary glands for **lactation**
- High levels induce labour

Human placental lactogen (HPL)
- Stimulates breast growth and development

Relaxin
- Produced by the placenta towards the end of the pregnancy
- Relaxes pubic symphysis at birth
- Helps dilate cervix at birth

Corpus luteum maintains pregnancy for the first 3 months

HCG from the embryo maintains the corpus luteum

→ Secretion
┈┈▶ Action

HCG

Estrogens and progesterones maintain the pregnancy

Hormones from the placenta maintain the pregnancy from the 3 months onwards and prepare the breasts for lactation. Increasingly through pregnancy the placenta also secretes HCS (human chorionic somatotropin) which benefits fetal growth.

Hormonal changes during pregnancy, birth, and lactation

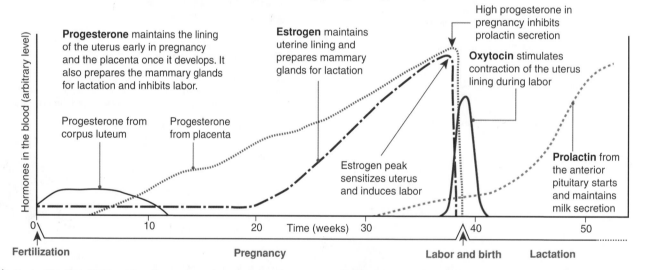

Progesterone maintains the lining of the uterus early in pregnancy and the placenta once it develops. It also prepares the mammary glands for lactation and inhibits labor.

Progesterone from corpus luteum

Progesterone from placenta

Estrogen maintains uterine lining and prepares mammary glands for lactation

Estrogen peak sensitizes uterus and induces labor

High progesterone in pregnancy inhibits prolactin secretion

Oxytocin stimulates contraction of the uterus lining during labor

Prolactin from the anterior pituitary starts and maintains milk secretion

Hormones in the blood (arbitrary level)

Time (weeks)

Fertilization   Pregnancy   Labor and birth   Lactation

▶ During the first 12-16 weeks of pregnancy, the corpus luteum secretes enough progesterone to maintain the uterine lining and sustain the developing embryo. After this, the placenta takes over as the primary endocrine organ of pregnancy. Progesterone and estrogen from the placenta maintain the uterine lining, stop further ova (eggs) developing, and prepare the breast tissue for lactation (milk production).

▶ At the end of pregnancy, the placenta begins to break down and progesterone levels fall. The uterus becomes sensitive to the high estrogen levels, triggering labor to start. The estrogen peak coincides with an increase in oxytocin, which stimulates uterine contractions in a positive feedback loop: the contractions and the increasing pressure on the cervix from the infant stimulate release of more oxytocin and more contractions, until the infant exits the birth canal.

▶ After birth, the secretion of prolactin increases. Prolactin maintains lactation during the period of infant nursing.

1. (a) Why is the corpus luteum the main source of progesterone in early pregnancy? _____

_____

(b) What hormones are responsible for maintaining pregnancy? _____

2. (a) Name two hormones involved in labor (onset of the birth process): _____

(b) Describe two physiological factors in initiating labor: _____

_____

_____

©2023 **BIOZONE** International
ISBN: 978-1-99-101408-5
Photocopying Prohibited

204 Detecting Pregnancy

Key Idea: Pregnancy can be detected by testing for HCG in the urine.

When a woman becomes pregnant, a hormone called human chorionic gonadotropin (HCG) is released by the chorion cells of the embryo. HCG accumulates in the bloodstream and is excreted in the urine. Pregnancy tests use antibodies to bind the HCG and produce a reaction that can be used to signal a positive test for pregnancy.

Pregnancy testing

▸ When a person becomes pregnant, human chorionic gonadotropin (HCG) is produced. This is excreted in the urine. In pregnancy tests HCG acts as an antigen and is acted on by antibodies (Ab) (produced against HCG, see Monoclonal Antibodies, Activity 138) in the test kit to determine if a woman is pregnant.

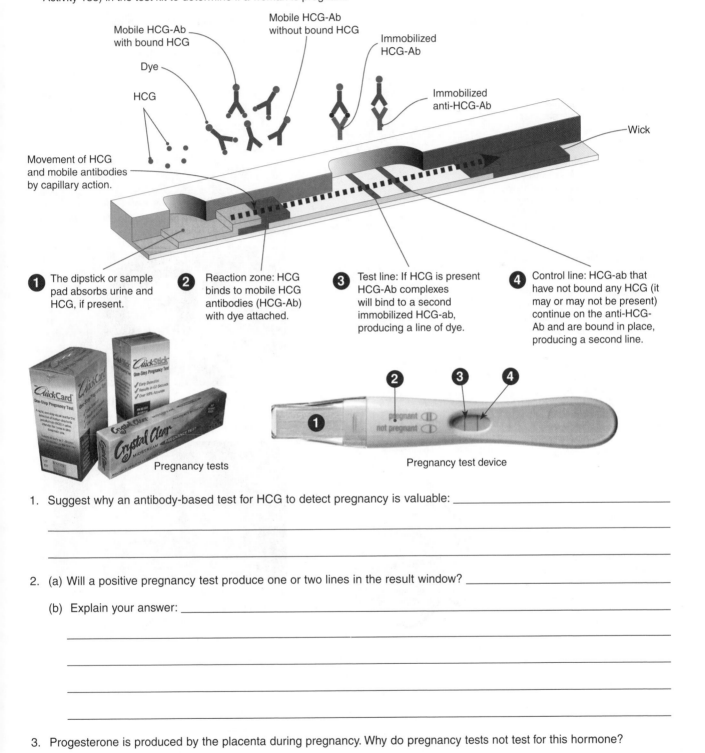

1. The dipstick or sample pad absorbs urine and HCG, if present.

2. Reaction zone: HCG binds to mobile HCG antibodies (HCG-Ab) with dye attached.

3. Test line: If HCG is present HCG-Ab complexes will bind to a second immobilized HCG-ab, producing a line of dye.

4. Control line: HCG-ab that have not bound any HCG (it may or may not be present) continue on the anti-HCG-Ab and are bound in place, producing a second line.

Pregnancy tests

Pregnancy test device

1. Suggest why an antibody-based test for HCG to detect pregnancy is valuable: _____

_____

_____

2. (a) Will a positive pregnancy test produce one or two lines in the result window? _____

   (b) Explain your answer: _____

   _____

   _____

   _____

   _____

3. Progesterone is produced by the placenta during pregnancy. Why do pregnancy tests not test for this hormone?

_____

_____

_____

205 Birth and Lactation

Key Idea: A human pregnancy is around 38 weeks. It ends in labor, the delivery of the baby, and expulsion of the placenta. During pregnancy, **progesterone** maintains the placenta and inhibits contraction of the uterus. At the end of a pregnancy, increasing **estrogen** levels overcome the influence of progesterone and labor begins. Prostaglandins, factors released from the placenta, and the physiological state of the baby itself are also involved in triggering the actual timing of labor onset. Labor itself comprises three stages (below), and ends with the delivery of the placenta. After birth, the mother provides nutrition for the infant through **lactation** (the production and release of milk from mammary glands). Breast milk provides infants with a complete, easily digested food for the first 4-6 months of life. All breast milk contains maternal antibodies, which give the infant protection against infection while its own immune system develops.

The stages of the birth process

Stage 1: Dilation

Duration: 2-20 hours

The time between the onset of labor and complete opening (dilation) of the cervix. The amniotic sac may rupture at this stage, releasing its fluid (waters breaking).

The hormone **oxytocin** stimulates the uterine contractions necessary to dilate the cervix and expel the baby. It is these uterine contractions that give the pain of labor, most of which is associated with this first stage.

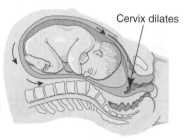
Cervix dilates

Stage 2: Expulsion

Duration: 2-100 minutes

The time from full dilation of the cervix to delivery. Strong, rhythmic contractions of the uterus pass in waves (arrows), and push the baby to the end of the vagina, where the head appears.

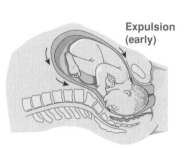
Expulsion (early)

As labor progresses, the time between each contraction shortens. Once the head is delivered, the rest of the body usually follows very rapidly. Delivery completes stage 2.

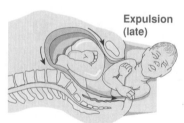
Expulsion (late)

Stage 3: Delivery of placenta

Time: 5-45 minutes after delivery

The third or placental stage, refers to the expulsion of the placenta from the uterus. After the placenta is delivered, the placental blood vessels constrict to stop bleeding.

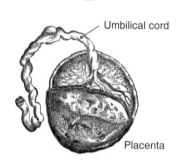
Umbilical cord
Placenta

Pain relief during childbirth

Pain during childbirth in a common experience. At some point, pain relief is normally used.

Epidural injections are given into the lining of the spinal cord. They block pain from the waist down.

Nitrous oxide is a gas frequently used for temporary pain relief. Unlike an epidural, it only reduces pain, rather than blocking it.

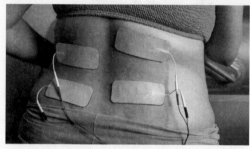
Transcutaneous electrical nerve stimulation (TENS) is a non medical electro-stimulation technique. It reduces sensitization in certain nerves.

1. Name the three stages of birth, and briefly state the main events occurring in each stage:

    (a) Stage 1: _____

    (b) Stage 2: _____

    (c) Stage 3: _____
    _____

2. Compare epidurals and nitrous oxide in pain relief: _____
    _____

©2023 **BIOZONE** International
ISBN: 978-1-99-101408-5

Lactation and its control

▶ Lactation is the production and release of milk from mammary glands. After birth, levels of the hormone prolactin increase sharply. Prolactin stimulates milk production in the alveoli, found within the lobules (right).

▶ Suckling maintains prolactin secretion and causes the release of oxytocin. This hormone induces the milk ducts to contract, resulting in milk release.

▶ The more an infant suckles, the more these hormones are produced. This is another example of positive feedback.

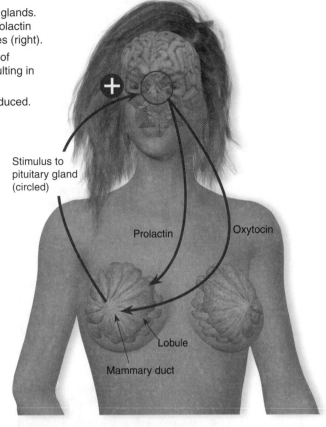

Stimulus to pituitary gland (circled)

Prolactin

Oxytocin

Lobule

Mammary duct

It is essential to establish breast feeding soon after birth, as this is when infants exhibit the strong reflexes that enable them to learn to suckle effectively. The first formed milk, colostrum, has very little sugar, virtually no fat, and is rich in maternal antibodies. Breast milk that is produced later has a higher fat content, and its composition varies as the nutritional needs of the infant change, during growth.

3. For each of the following processes, state the primary controlling hormone and its site of production:

(a) Triggers onset of labor: Hormone: _____   Site of production: _____

(b) Uterine contraction during labor: Hormone: _____   Site of production: _____

(c) Production of milk: Hormone: _____   Site of production: _____

(d) Milk ejection in response to suckling: Hormone: _____   Site of production: _____

4. Which hormone inhibits prolactin secretion during pregnancy? _____

5. Describe two benefits of breast feeding to the health of the infant:

(a) _____

(b) _____

6. (a) Describe the nutritional differences between the first formed milk (colostrum) and the milk that is produced later:

_____

_____

(b) Suggest a reason for these differences: _____

_____

_____

7. Why would the nutritional composition of breast milk change during the lactation period from birth to six months?

_____

8. Infants exhibit marked growth spurts at six weeks and three months of age. At these times, their energy intake requirements also increase sharply. With reference to what you know about the control of lactation, how could a breast-feeding mother continue to provide for the increased energy requirements of her infant?

_____

_____

206 Contraception

Key Idea: Humans have many ways in which to manage their own reproduction. There are multiple ways to prevent fertilization of the egg cell.

Contraception refers to the use of methods or devices that prevent conception (fertilization of an egg by a sperm). There are many contraceptive methods available, including physical barriers, such as condoms, that prevent egg and sperm ever meeting. The most effective methods (excluding sterilization) involve chemical interference in the normal female cycle so that egg production is inhibited. This is done by way of oral contraceptives (below, left) or hormonal implants. If taken properly, oral contraceptives are almost 100% effective at preventing pregnancy. The placement of their action in the normal cycle of reproduction (from gametogenesis to pregnancy) is illustrated below. Other contraceptive methods are included for comparison.

Hormonal contraception

The most common method by which to prevent conception using hormones is by using an oral contraceptive pill (OCP). These may be combined OCPs, or low dose mini pills.

Combined oral contraceptive pills (OCPs)

These pills exploit the feedback controls over hormone secretion normally operating during a **menstrual cycle**. They contain combinations of synthetic **estrogens** and **progesterone**. They are taken daily for 21 days, and raise the levels of these hormones in the blood so that FSH secretion is inhibited and no ova develop. Sugar pills are taken for 7 days; long enough to allow menstruation to occur but not long enough for ova to develop. Combined OCPs can be of two types:

Monophasic pills (right):
Hormones (H) are all at one dosage level. Sugar pills (S) are usually larger and differently colored.

Triphasic pills (right):
The hormone dosage increases in stages (1,2,3), mimicking the natural changes in a menstrual cycle.

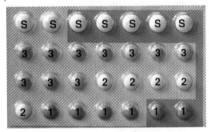

Mini-pill (progesterone only)
The mini-pill contains 28 days of low dose progesterone; generally too low to prevent **ovulation**. The pill works by thickening the cervical mucus and preventing endometrial thickening. The mini-pill is less reliable than combined pills and must be taken at a regular time each day. However, it is safer for older women and those who are breastfeeding.

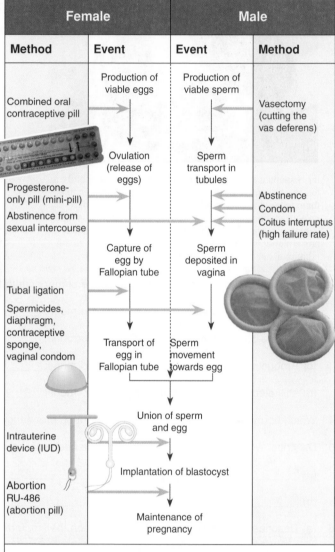

Female		Male	
Method	**Event**	**Event**	**Method**
Combined oral contraceptive pill	Production of viable eggs	Production of viable sperm	Vasectomy (cutting the vas deferens)
Progesterone-only pill (mini-pill)	Ovulation (release of eggs)	Sperm transport in tubules	
Abstinence from sexual intercourse			Abstinence / Condom / Coitus interruptus (high failure rate)
	Capture of egg by Fallopian tube	Sperm deposited in vagina	
Tubal ligation			
Spermicides, diaphragm, contraceptive sponge, vaginal condom	Transport of egg in Fallopian tube	Sperm movement towards egg	
	Union of sperm and egg		
Intrauterine device (IUD)			
Abortion RU-486 (abortion pill)	Implantation of blastocyst		
	Maintenance of pregnancy		

The flow diagram above illustrates where in the reproductive process, from gametogenesis to pregnancy, various contraceptive methods operate. Note the early action of hormonal contraceptives.

1. Explain briefly how the combined oral contraceptive pill acts as a contraceptive: _____

_____

_____

_____

2. Contrast the mode of action of OCPs with that of the mini-pill, giving reasons for the differences: _____

_____

_____

_____

©2023 **BIOZONE** International
ISBN: 978-1-99-101408-5
Photocopying Prohibited

207 Disease of the Reproductive System

Key Idea: A reproductive system disease is any condition that affects the male or female reproductive system.

There are many causes of reproductive system disease, including genetic and congenital abnormalities, abnormal hormone production, functional disorders of the genitalia, infections, and tumors. Some diseases only affect fertility, e.g. erectile dysfunction, while others, such as infections and tumors, can be life threatening. Cancers can affect any part of the reproductive system and may spread (metastasize) from there to other tissues and organs. Some common reproductive system diseases are described below.

Cancers of the female and male reproductive system

▶ Reproductive cancers affect the reproductive organs. The incidence of some cancers can be reduced by making certain lifestyle choices, e.g. not smoking, but some risk factors, including age and genetic makeup, are uncontrollable. Early detection of any cancer enables early treatment and this improves survival rates.

Female reproductive cancers

Breast cancer (below) is the most common form of cancer in females. There is a hereditary factor: 5-10% of cases are caused by the inheritance of a gene mutation.

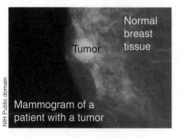

Tumor | Normal breast tissue

Mammogram of a patient with a tumor

Ovarian cancer kills more women than any other gynecological cancer because the symptoms often are not detected until the cancer is quite advanced.

Uterine (endometrial) cancer originates in the lining of the uterus (the endometrium). A hysterectomy (surgery to remove the uterus) is usually required.

Cervical cancer is strongly linked with having a human papillomavirus (HPV) infection. An HPV vaccine is available to young teenagers and may help to reduce incidence rates.

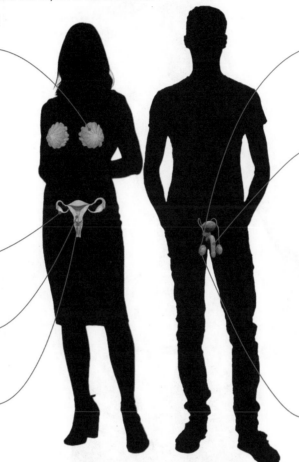

Male reproductive cancers

Prostate cancer is a slow growing tumor on the prostate gland, and mainly affects men over 40. It can be difficult to detect because it does not produce any symptoms until it becomes large enough to impair the urinary system.

Penile cancer, cancer of the penis, has a survival rate of 65% if detected early. The cause of penile cancer is unknown, but poor genital hygiene and a history of STIs are known risk factors.

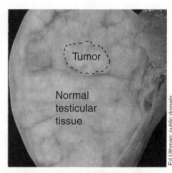

Tumor

Normal testicular tissue

Testicular cancer (above) usually occurs in young men aged 15-35. It is highly treatable and curable.

Sexually transmitted infections

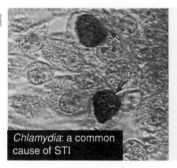

Chlamydia: a common cause of STI

Sexually transmitted infections (STIs) are passed on by unprotected sexual activity and infect both males and females. Some STIs are caused by bacteria, e.g. gonorrhea and chlamydia, and can be treated with antibiotics, but viral infections, such as genital herpes and HIV, have no cure. Some STIs can be difficult to detect because they have no symptoms. If left untreated, STIs can cause a number of related health problems, e.g. cystitis, infertility (by damaging the reproductive organs), or death.

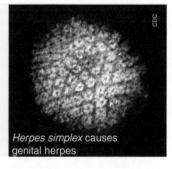

Herpes simplex causes genital herpes

1. Routine screening programs are available for some types of cancers, e.g. cervical cancer and breast cancer. Why is the early detection of cancer important?

_____

_____

2. Why are ovarian cancer in women and prostate cancer in men more likely to kill than any types of reproductive cancer?

_____

_____

208 Treating Female Infertility

Key Idea: Female infertility may occur due to many factors, including failure to ovulate or damage to the Fallopian tubes. Failure to ovulate is a common cause of female infertility. In most cases, the cause is hormonal, although sometimes the ovaries may be damaged or not functioning normally. Female infertility may also arise through damage to the Fallopian tubes as a result of infection or scarring. These cases are usually treated with hormones, followed by **IVF**. Most treatments for female infertility involve the use of synthetic female hormones, which stimulate **ovulation**, boost egg production, and induce egg release.

Treating female infertility

Cause of the infertility

Failure to ovulate because of low levels of GnRH, FSH, LH, or ovarian hormones.

Hormonal treatment successful?

Treatment may enable conception in the usual way.

Fallopian tubes blocked?

Eggs may be collected from the follicles using laparoscopy and fertilized *ex-vivo* in a glass dish (*in-vitro* fertilization or IVF).

Successful fertilization

At an early stage of cell division, the pre-embryo is transferred to the uterus. A pregnancy results if implantation is successful.

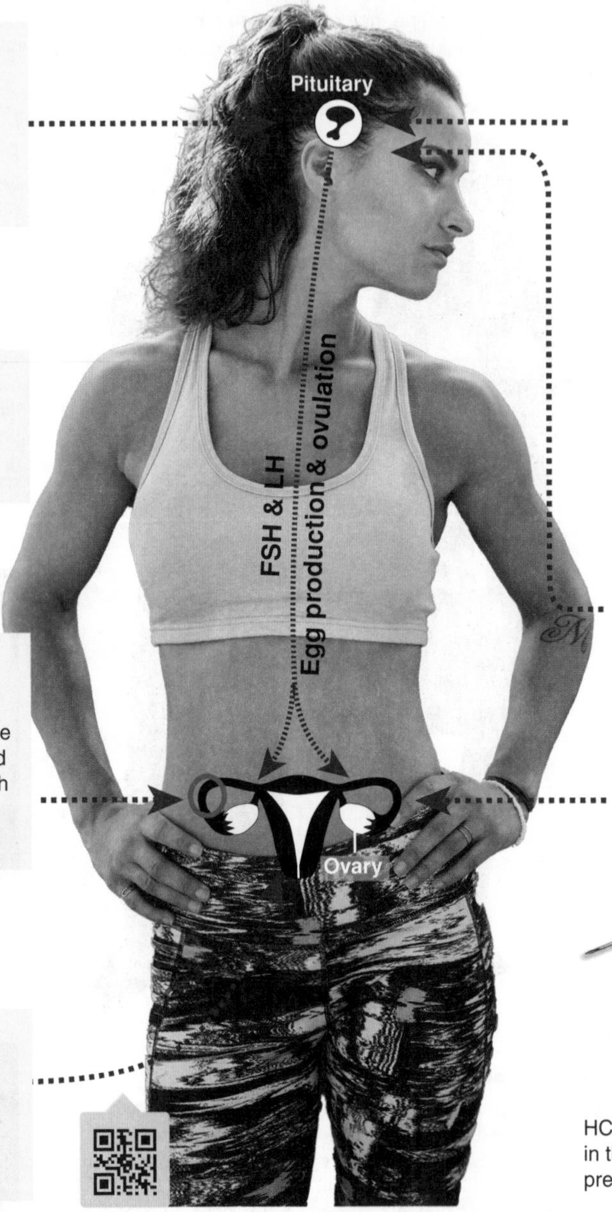

Pituitary

FSH & LH

Egg production & ovulation

Ovary

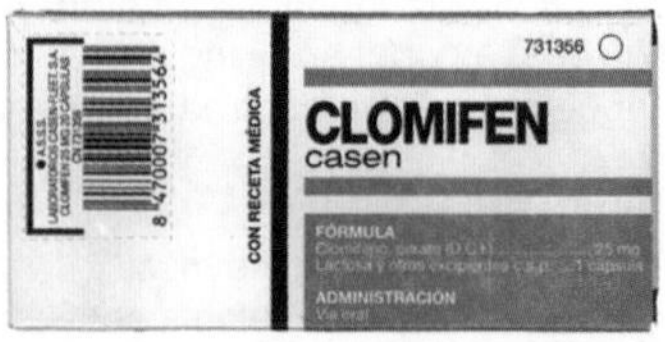

Hormone imbalance can be corrected using **estrogen**-like drugs, e.g. clomiphene (pictured here under a trade name) and tamoxifen, which induce release of FSH from the pituitary.

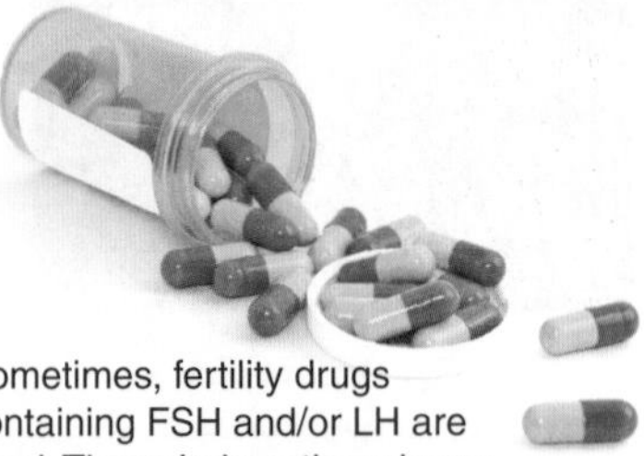

CLOMIFEN casen

Sometimes, fertility drugs containing FSH and/or LH are used. These induce the release of many ova, increasing the risk of a multiple pregnancy.

Human chorionic gonadotrophin (HCG) can replace LH and may be injected to induce egg release.

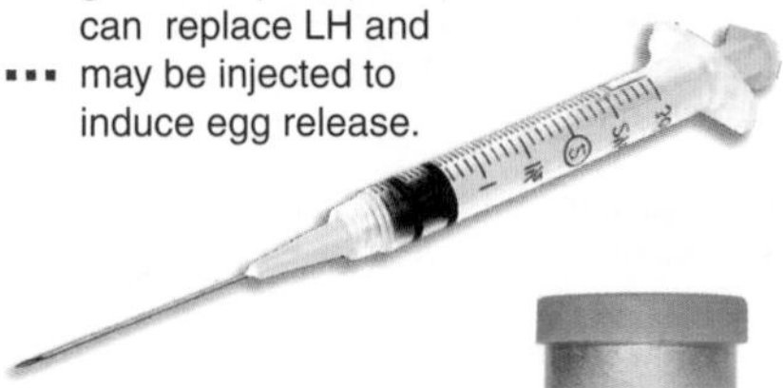

HCG is a hormone involved in the maintenance of early pregnancy.

HCG 5000iu

1. Describe two ways in which the hormonal drugs used to enhance fertility operate:

   (a) _____

   _____

   (b) _____

   _____

2. Identify two examples of female infertility where treatment using IVF would be appropriate:

   (a) _____

   (b) _____

3. Identify one risk associated with the use of fertility drugs: _____

©2023 **BIOZONE** International
ISBN: 978-1-99-101408-5
Photocopying Prohibited

209 *In Vitro* Fertilization

Key Idea: In vitro fertilization (IVF) may be used to overcome infertility which may result from a disturbance of any of the factors involved in fertilization or embryonic development. Female infertility may be due to a failure to ovulate, requiring stimulation of the ovary, with or without hormone therapy. For couples with one or both partners incapable of providing suitable gametes, it may be possible for them to receive eggs and/or sperm from donors. Fertility drugs may be used to induce the production of many eggs for use in **IVF**, although the natural cycle of **ovulation** can be used to collect the egg. Fertility drugs stimulate the pituitary gland and may induce the simultaneous release of numerous eggs; an event called superovulation. If each egg is allowed to be fertilized, the resulting embryos may be frozen after 24-72 hours culture.

Causes of infertility

Infertility is a common problem (as many as one in six couples require help from a specialist). The cause of the infertility may be inherited, the result of damage caused by disease, or psychological.

Causes of male infertility
▸ **Penis**: Fails to achieve or maintain erection; abnormal ejaculation.
▸ **Testes**: Too few sperm produced or sperm are abnormally shaped, have impaired motility, or too short lived.
▸ **Vas deferens**: A blockage or a structural abnormality may impede the passage of sperm.

Causes of female infertility
▸ **Fallopian tubes**: Blockage may prevent sperm from reaching egg; one or both tubes may be damaged (disease) or absent (congenital).
▸ **Ovaries**: Eggs may fail to mature or may not be released.
▸ **Uterus**: Abnormality or disorder may prevent implantation of the egg.
▸ **Cervix**: Antibodies in cervical mucus may damage or destroy the sperm.

In vitro fertilization

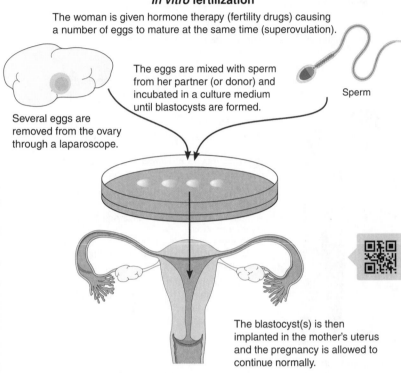

The woman is given hormone therapy (fertility drugs) causing a number of eggs to mature at the same time (superovulation).

The eggs are mixed with sperm from her partner (or donor) and incubated in a culture medium until blastocysts are formed.

Sperm

Several eggs are removed from the ovary through a laparoscope.

The blastocyst(s) is then implanted in the mother's uterus and the pregnancy is allowed to continue normally.

Biological origins of gamete donations

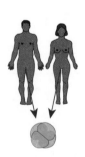

Both partners provide gametes for IVF of GIFT (they donate their own gametes).

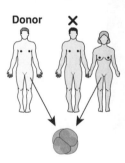

Male partner unable to provide sperm; sperm from male donor.

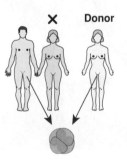

Female partner unable to provide eggs; eggs from female donor.

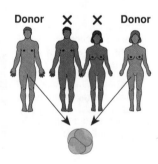

Both partners unable to provide gametes; sperm and eggs obtained from donors.

1. Describe the key stages of IVF: _____

_____

_____

_____

_____

2. Why might some of the embryos produced be frozen after culture? _____

_____

▶ IVF raises a number of ethical issues, including the concept of personhood, religious beliefs, and the rights and responsibilities of the individual, parents, and community as a whole. It also raises issues over the health and psychological effects of the offspring.

Ethical Issue 1:
The rights of the pre-embryo (blastocyst)

Multiple blastocysts are transferred to a woman's uterus to increase the chances of implantation. After implantation, many of these blastocysts are destroyed by selective pregnancy reduction.

When does personhood of the individual begin?
▶ If it begins at conception, destruction of the extra embryos technically constitutes murder.
▶ Many different ideas and definitions exist over the start of personhood or individuality.
- Can the pre-embryo technically be called an individual during the period of totipotency (about 3 weeks)? During this period, any one of its cells could develop into an individual.

Ethical Issue 2:
Underline: Possible wrongs to the couple by the use of IVF

Multiple blastocysts are transferred to a woman's uterus to increase the chances of implantation.

▶ A multiple pregnancy can have psychological and health effects on the parents.
▶ A multiple pregnancy can have health effects on the embryos.
▶ The parents may have to bear the cost of IVF, putting financial strain on them (and possible resentment towards others).
- Cost may be indirect, because the offspring may have health problems (either caused by IVF or naturally occurring).

Ethical Issue 3:
Underline: Possible wrongs to the offspring by the use of IVF

There is some medical evidence to suggest IVF babies have a higher chance of medical problems such as pre-term birth, low birth weight, spina bifida, and heart defects.

▶ Parents with genetic defects preventing them from conceiving naturally could pass these defects to the offspring via IVF.

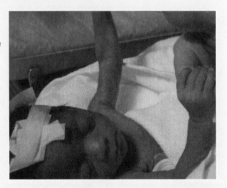

Ethical Issue 4:
Underline: Possible wrongs to the community by the use of IVF

IVF is a costly procedure.

▶ Couples who can afford IVF may be putting money and effort into conception instead of the community.
▶ The community may have to bear the cost of IVF and welfare for financially struggling parents.
▶ Offspring with health issues due to IVF may be an ongoing burden to the community.

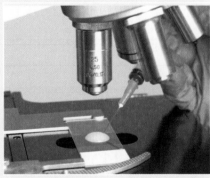

3. Evaluate the ethical and medical issues surrounding IVF treatment. In your opinion, what is the best ethical approach to using IVF? Use examples, where possible, to illustrate your ideas:

_____

_____

_____

_____

_____

_____

_____

_____

_____

_____

_____

_____

_____

_____

_____

_____

_____

_____

_____

_____

_____

_____

_____

_____

_____

_____

_____

_____

_____

_____

_____

_____

©2023 **BIOZONE** International
ISBN: 978-1-99-101408-5
Photocopying Prohibited

210 Growth and Development

Key Idea: Human body proportions change during growth. Development describes the process of growing to maturity, from zygote to adult. After birth, development continues rapidly and is marked by specific stages recognized by the set of physical and cognitive skills present. Obvious physical changes include the elongation of the bones, increasing ossification of cartilage, and changes to the proportions of the body. These proportional changes are the result of allometric growth (differential growth rates) and occur concurrently with motor, intellectual, and emotional and social development. These changes lead the child to increasing independence and maturity.

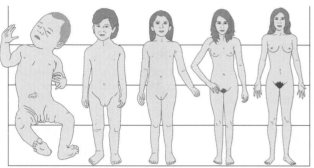

| Newborn | 2 years | 5 years | 15 years | Adult |

At birth, the cranium is very large in comparison to the face and the skull makes up around one quarter of the infant's height. During early life, the face continues to grow outward, reducing the relative proportions of the cranium, while at adulthood the size of the skull in proportion to the body is much less.

X-ray of child's skull

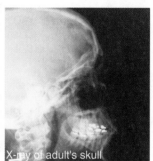

X-ray of adult's skull

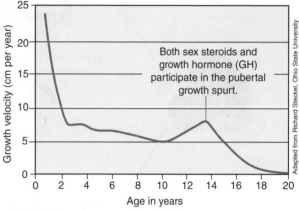

Both sex steroids and growth hormone (GH) participate in the pubertal growth spurt.

Growth velocity (cm per year) vs Age in years

Adapted from Richard Steckel, Ohio State University

By 6 weeks old, a human baby is usually able to hold its head up if placed on its stomach. At 3 months, the infant will exercise limbs aimlessly but by 5 months it is able to grasp objects and sit up. The infant may be able to crawl by 8 months and walk by 12 months. It is more or less independent by two years and undergoes changes to adulthood at around 11 years of age (puberty).

Babies are effectively born premature, compared to most other mammals, so that they complete much of their early development in the first two to three years of life. The rate of growth declines slowly through childhood, but increases again to a peak in puberty (the growth spurt). By 20 years of age the cartilage in the long bones has been replaced by bone and growth stops.

1. Describe the most noticeable change in body proportion from birth to adulthood: _____

_____

2. Describe the changes that occur in the first period of rapid growth in humans: _____

_____

_____

_____

3. Describe the changes that occur in the second period of rapid growth in humans: _____

_____

_____

4. Identify the age range (in years) marking the pubertal growth spurt: _____

5. Relate the changes in physical development to the changes occurring in the mental development of an infant:

_____

_____

_____

211 Sexual Development

Key Idea: Testosterone (males) and estrogen and progesterone (females) are responsible for the male and female characteristics.

Humans differentiate into the male or female sex by the action of a combination of different hormones. The hormones **testosterone** (in males), and **estrogen** and **progesterone**

(in females), are responsible for puberty (the onset of sexual maturity), the maintenance of sexual differences, and the production of gametes. In females, estrogen and progesterone also regulate the **menstrual cycle**, and ensure the maintenance of pregnancy and nourishment of young.

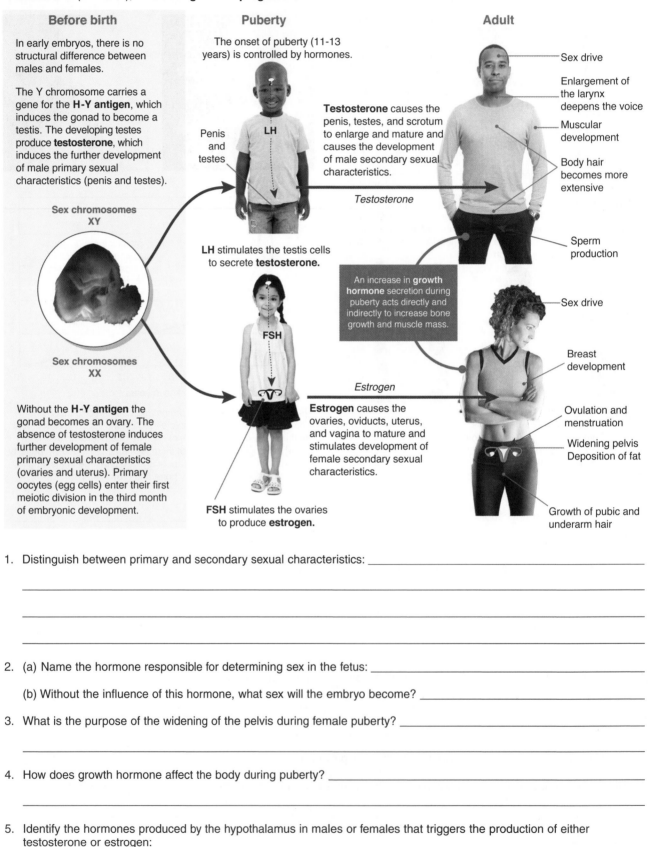

Before birth

In early embryos, there is no structural difference between males and females.

The Y chromosome carries a gene for the **H-Y antigen**, which induces the gonad to become a testis. The developing testes produce **testosterone**, which induces the further development of male primary sexual characteristics (penis and testes).

Sex chromosomes XY

Sex chromosomes XX

Without the **H-Y antigen** the gonad becomes an ovary. The absence of testosterone induces further development of female primary sexual characteristics (ovaries and uterus). Primary oocytes (egg cells) enter their first meiotic division in the third month of embryonic development.

Puberty

The onset of puberty (11-13 years) is controlled by hormones.

Penis and testes

LH

LH stimulates the testis cells to secrete **testosterone.**

Testosterone causes the penis, testes, and scrotum to enlarge and mature and causes the development of male secondary sexual characteristics.

Testosterone

An increase in **growth hormone** secretion during puberty acts directly and indirectly to increase bone growth and muscle mass.

FSH

Estrogen

Estrogen causes the ovaries, oviducts, uterus, and vagina to mature and stimulates development of female secondary sexual characteristics.

FSH stimulates the ovaries to produce **estrogen.**

Adult

Sex drive

Enlargement of the larynx deepens the voice

Muscular development

Body hair becomes more extensive

Sperm production

Sex drive

Breast development

Ovulation and menstruation

Widening pelvis Deposition of fat

Growth of pubic and underarm hair

1. Distinguish between primary and secondary sexual characteristics: _____

_____

_____

_____

2. (a) Name the hormone responsible for determining sex in the fetus: _____

   (b) Without the influence of this hormone, what sex will the embryo become? _____

3. What is the purpose of the widening of the pelvis during female puberty? _____

_____

4. How does growth hormone affect the body during puberty? _____

_____

5. Identify the hormones produced by the hypothalamus in males or females that triggers the production of either testosterone or estrogen:

_____

©2023 **BIOZONE** International
ISBN: 978-1-99-101408-5
Photocopying Prohibited

212 Aging

Key Idea: Aging (senescence) refers to the degenerative changes that occur as a result of cells dying and renewal rates slowing or stopping.

As soon as we have reached physical maturity, we begin to age. Cell renewal rates slow or stop. It is a general response, producing observable changes in structure and physiology. There is a decline in skeletal and muscular strength, and reduced immune function. Aging increases susceptibility to stress and disease, so disease and aging often accelerate together.

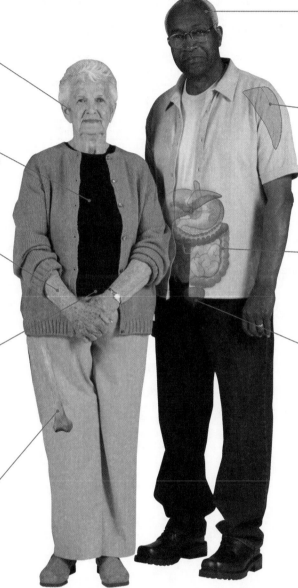

Older skin is thinner, more easily damaged, and slower to repair. Skin loses elasticity, which leads to the more obvious signs of aging: sagging and wrinkling.

Low **estrogen** levels in post-menopausal women increase the risk of cardiovascular disease (CVD) dramatically. At age 70 and beyond, men and women are equally at risk.

Reduction in glandular activity and blood flow to the skin contribute to skin aging. Skin discoloration (age or liver spots) is more common in older people, especially on areas exposed to the sun, such as the hands, face and neck.

In menopause, the ovaries stop responding to FSH and LH from the anterior pituitary. Ovarian production of estrogen and **progesterone** slows and stops, and the **menstrual cycle** becomes at first irregular and then stops altogether. At this point, a woman is no longer fertile.

Declining estrogen levels also accelerate bone loss, resulting in osteoporosis, hunching of the spine, and increased risk of fractures.

Declining levels of circulating **testosterone** affects sex drive in both men and women. Declining testosterone is also associated with age-related thinning and loss of hair.

Several cell types, including neurons, cardiac muscle, and skeletal muscle cannot be replaced.

Metabolic rate decreases with age and digestive and kidney function decline.

Aging is associated with an increase in the number of aberrant cells and an increased incidence of cancers as cellular damage accumulates. Tumors of the reproductive organs are more common in old age.

1. Explain the cause of aging, relating the physiological changes to the observable effects: _____

_____

_____

_____

2. The figure, right, shows the decline in skeletal muscle fibers with age:

   (a) At what age is number of muscle fibers at a maximum? _____

   (b) At what age have half the muscle fibers been lost? _____

   (c) Can these muscle fibers be replaced? _____

3. Aging has a number of effects on the body as a whole, but what is the main effect of aging on human reproductive capability?

   _____

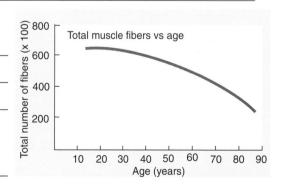

Total muscle fibers vs age

Total number of fibers (x 100)

Age (years)

213 Chapter Summary

1. What are the effects of LH and FSH on male development? _____

_____

_____

2. What type of cell division takes place during both oogenesis and spermatogenesis? _____

3. Produce a definition for each of the following terms:

    (a) Apoptosis: _____

    _____

    (b) Blastocyst: _____

    _____

    (c) Fertilization: _____

    _____

    (e) Placenta: _____

    _____

4. Label the diagram of the mature egg cell:

5. Draw and label a mature sperm cell:

6. Describe how the levels of hormones FSH, LH, estrogen, and progesterone change over a menstrual cycle:

_____

_____

_____

_____

_____

7. Which hormone can be used to detect pregnancy and why? _____

_____

A-1 Researching and Reporting

In the activities on the following pages, you will carry out a literature search on one aspect of each of the four themes on this book: disease, medicine and technology, exercise, and the effects of aging. You will need to choose appropriate sources of information and present your findings in a professional and attractive delivery style. It is important that you can critically evaluate and interpret a range of published material in both scientific publications and popular media. To analyze and evaluate the science you read about or see online you must think critically and have a good understanding of the concepts, theories, and models involved.

Opinion or evidence

As you read information to inform your study, consider carefully the source of the information. Is it a website produced by a commercial company that wants to sell specific treatments/drugs? Is it a university or research website? Is it a reputable science journal? Is it a newspaper article? Is it someone's opinion?

ANECDOTAL EVIDENCE	SCIENTIFIC EVIDENCE
Claim from memory	Claim from data
Small sample size	Large sample size
Exceptional stand-out cases reported	Everything is reported
Uncontrolled, susceptible to bias	Controlled for subject & experimenter bias
Vague outcomes	Defined outcomes

Presentation type

Below are some features to consider for the type of presentation that you choose for your study. You may have to carry out some reading research before deciding on what type of presentation best suits the subject that you choose.

POSTER	SLIDES & NARRATIVE	REPORT
Large title that can be read from a distance	Visually appealing	Clearly structured into logical sections
Visually attractive, with large, bold images hat catch the eye of the reader	All images, especially graph axes, can be read from a distance	If including images such as graphs or tables, ensure they are labelled and numbered sequentially, e.g. Figure 1, Figure 2 etc
Logical and obvious flow from one section to the next so that the reader is led from one section to the next	No distracting animations, such as text flying on to the screen	Appropriate length to cover the necessary content.
Use font that is large and easy to read at a distance	Accompanying narrative text must make sense to the reader	Clear, easy to read font chosen.

Writing a bibliography

Your bibliography should use a consistent style of presentation and be organized alphabetically according to author name or, if no author, as in a government or company website, by the name of the organization. Some common examples are given below. The key is to be consistent in the order in which you present information. You will need:

- Author
- Year of publication
- Title of the work, in italics
- Pages, issue, volume (for journal, magazine)
- Location, e.g. a URL for a website
- Publisher, for book, magazine, journal article

Book: Whitmore, SJ. 1985. *The Aging Body: Physiological Changes and Psychological Consequences.* Springer.

Website: Bazemore, N. 2022. *What's Normal Aging?* Compass, by WebMD. https://www.webmd.com/healthy-aging/guide/normal-aging.

Journal: Barnes, TL et al. 2022. Loneliness, Social Isolation, and All-Cause Mortality in a Large Sample of Older Adults. *Journal of Aging.* Vol 34, iss. 6-8. pp. 883-892 https://doi/10.1177/08982643221074857 Sage Journals.

Disease

Choose a disease or disorder that affects one of the body systems covered in this book. It could be a disease that has been mentioned in the text, that you wish to look at in more detail, such as arthritis, or some other disease that interests you, e.g. a specific form of cancer or a genetic disorder. A list of the some of the diseases/disorders covered in the body systems in the preceding chapters is given below:

BODY SYSTEM	DISEASE / DISORDER
Integumentary system & homeostasis	hypothermia, hyperthermia, effect of drugs, e.g. Ecstasy/MDMA
Muscular & skeletal systems	ankylosing spondylitis, osteoporosis, osteoarthritis, muscular dystrophy, torn muscles/sporting injuries
Nervous & endocrine systems	effect of drugs and toxins on nerve synapses, depression, Parkinson's Disease, type 1 and 2 diabetes, Graves' disease, effects of alcohol & nicotine, stress
Cardiovascular & lymphatic systems	cardiovascular diseases, effects of smoking, autoimmune diseases, infection and inflammation, HIV, allergies
Respiratory system	sleep apnea, Covid-19, COPD, asbestosis and mesothelioma, effects of smoking and vaping
Digestive system	Crohn's disease, celiac disease, malnutrition, obesity
Urinary system	kidney disease
Reproductive system and development	infertility, cancers of the reproductive system

Produce ONE of the following: a poster, a set of slides and narrative for a short presentation to your classmates, a report. Some guidance to help you produce your study, as well as space for writing notes, follows.

1. What aspect of disease or disorder are you going to study, and why does this interest you?

   _____

2. What format will you use to present your findings - poster, research report, slides and narrative, or other?

   _____

3. For your bibliography, give an example of how you will reference:

   (a) a website: _____

   _____

   _____

   (b) a journal article: _____

   _____

   _____

   (c) a book: _____

   _____

   _____

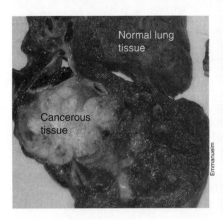

Normal lung tissue

Cancerous tissue

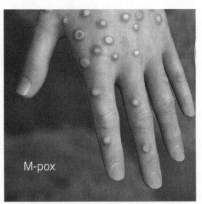

M-pox

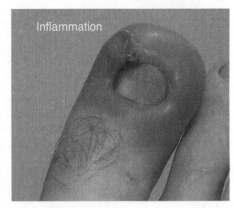

Inflammation

4. Use the following space to make rough notes, based on your reading of your chosen subject. Remember to use reliable evidence from reputable sources and bookmark or note web addresses of your chosen sites. You should aim to use a mix of resources, such as science magazines or journals, books, university research websites, government webpages or reliable industry information.

_____
_____
_____
_____
_____
_____
_____
_____

5. Use the following space to draft a structure for your report, or a list of contents of your slides, or the main points and blocks that your poster will cover. Attach your final piece of research to this page with a staple or paperclip:

_____
_____
_____
_____
_____
_____
_____
_____
_____
_____
_____
_____
_____
_____
_____
_____
_____
_____

Medicine and Technology

Choose an aspect of medicine or technology used to diagnose or treat a disease or condition that affects one of the body systems covered in this book. It could be a treatment or technology that has been mentioned in the text, that you wish to look at in more detail, such as Herceptin for breast cancer treatment, or some other subject that interests you, e.g. the discovery of X-rays and development of their use as a diagnostic tool .

BODY SYSTEM	MEDICINE / TECHNOLOGY
Integumentary system & homeostasis	blood glucose monitoring, radionuclide scanning, ultrasound, MRI, CT, endoscopy, biosensors
Muscular & skeletal systems	X Rays, hip/knee replacements,
Nervous & endocrine systems	correction of vision disorders, correction of impaired hearing, insulin injections
Cardiovascular & lymphatic systems	electrocardiograms, blood pressure monitoring, correcting heart problems, blood transfusions, vaccination,Monoclonal antibodies, organ and tissue transplants, stem cell technology, gene therapy
Respiratory system	spirometry
Digestive system	gastroscopy
Urinary system	urinalysis, dialysis, kidney transplant
Reproductive system and development	IVF, contraception, ultrasound, detecting pregnancy,

Produce ONE of the following: a poster, a set of slides and narrative for a short presentation to your classmates, a report. Some guidance to help you produce your study, as well as space for writing notes, follows.

1. What aspect of medicine or technology are you going to study, and why does this interest you?

    _____

2. What format will you use to present your findings - poster, research report, slides and narrative, or other?

    _____

3. For your bibliography, give an example of how you will reference:

    (a) a website: _____

    _____

    _____

    (b) a journal article: _____

    _____

    _____

    (c) a book: _____

    _____

    _____

 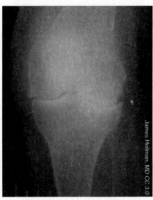 

4. Use the following space to make rough notes, based on your reading of your chosen subject. Remember to use reliable evidence from reputable sources and bookmark or note web addresses of your chosen sites. You should aim to use a mix of resources, such as science magazines or journals, books, university research websites, government webpages or reliable industry information.

_____

_____

_____

_____

_____

_____

_____

_____

5. Use the following space to draft a structure for your report, or a list of contents of your slides, or the main points and blocks that your poster will cover. Attach your final piece of research to this page with a staple or paperclip:

_____

_____

_____

_____

_____

_____

_____

_____

_____

_____

_____

_____

_____

_____

_____

_____

_____

The Effects of Aging

Choose an effect aging that affects one of the body systems covered in this book. It could be an effect that has been mentioned in the text that you wish to look at in more detail, such as hormonal effects and menopause, or some other aspect of aging that interests you, such as the effects of aging on the brain.

BODY SYSTEM	EFFECTS OF AGING
Integumentary system & homeostasis	skin wrinkling, risk of skin cancers, higher susceptibility to heat stroke
Muscular & skeletal systems	bone density changes, muscle tone and posture changes
Nervous & endocrine systems	risk of degenerative brain diseases,, e.g. Alzheimer's, Parkinson's, loss of hearing, cataracts, menopause
Cardiovascular & lymphatic systems	higher risk of stroke and cardiovascular disease, increased risk of hypertension
Respiratory system	decline in respiratory capacity, higher risk of chronic respiratory disease
Digestive system	higher risk of bowel cancer, slower food passage (constipation)
Urinary system	loss of bladder/sphincter muscle tone, reduction in nephron filtration rate
Reproductive system and development	cancers of the reproductive system, menopause, decline in sperm production. hair thinning

Produce ONE of the following: a poster, a set of slides and narrative for a short presentation to your classmates, a report. Some guidance to help you produce your study, as well as space for writing notes, follows.

1. What aspect of aging are you going to study, and why does this interest you?

   _____

2. What format will you use to present your findings - poster, research report, slides and narrative, or other?

   _____

3. For your bibliography, give an example of how you will reference:

   (a) a website: _____

   _____

   _____

   (b) a journal article: _____

   _____

   _____

   (c) a book: _____

   _____

   _____

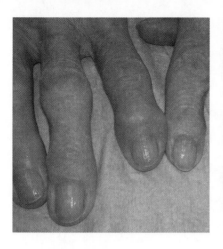

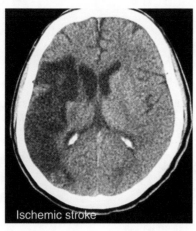

Ischemic stroke

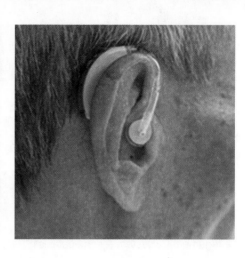

4. Use the following space to make rough notes, based on your reading of your chosen subject. Remember to use reliable evidence from reputable sources and bookmark or note web addresses of your chosen sites. You should aim to use a mix of resources, such as science magazines or journals, books, university research websites, government webpages or reliable industry information.

_____

_____

_____

_____

_____

_____

_____

_____

_____

5. Use the following space to draft a structure for your report, or a list of contents of your slides, or the main points and blocks that your poster will cover. Attach your final piece of research to this page with a staple or paperclip:

_____

_____

_____

_____

_____

_____

_____

_____

_____

_____

_____

_____

_____

_____

_____

_____

_____

Exercise

Choose an aspect of exercise that affects one of the body systems covered in this book. It could be something that has been mentioned in the text, that you wish to look at in more detail, such as cardiovascular fitness, or some other aspect of the effect of exercise on the body that interests you, such as sporting injuries or body building.

BODY SYSTEM	EFFECT OF EXERCISE
Integumentary system & homeostasis	thermoregulation
Muscular & skeletal systems	Improving muscle tone and strength, causes of muscle fatigue, eerobic training and effect on muscle performance
Nervous & endocrine systems	improved coordination, reduced risk of type 2 diabetes
Cardiovascular & lymphatic systems	exercise and cardiovascular fitness
Respiratory system	increased aerobic capacity, training for high altitude activity
Digestive system	improved digestive function
Urinary system	water balance and exercise
Reproductive system and development	reduced risk of reproductive cancers, improved muscle tone

Produce ONE of the following: a poster, a set of slides and narrative for a short presentation to your classmates, a report. Some guidance to help you produce your study, as well as space for writing notes, follows.

1. What aspect of exercise are you going to study, and why does this interest you?

   _____

2. What format will you use to present your findings - poster, research report, slides and narrative, or other?

   _____

3. For your bibliography, give an example of how you will reference:

   (a) a website: _____

   _____

   _____

   (b) a journal article: _____

   _____

   _____

   (c) a book: _____

   _____

   _____

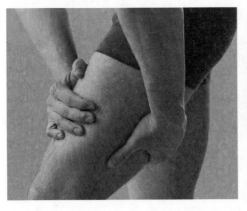 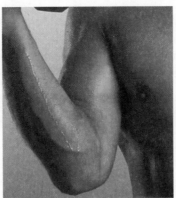 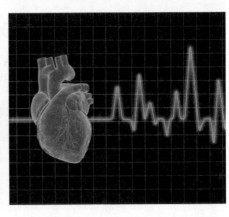

4. Use the following space to make rough notes, based on your reading of your chosen subject. Remember to use reliable evidence from reputable sources and bookmark or note web addresses of your chosen sites. You should aim to use a mix of resources, such as science magazines or journals, books, university research websites, government webpages or reliable industry information.

_____

_____

_____

_____

_____

_____

_____

_____

5. Use the following space to draft a structure for your report, or a list of contents of your slides, or the main points and blocks that your poster will cover. Attach your final piece of research to this page with a staple or paperclip:

_____

_____

_____

_____

_____

_____

_____

_____

_____

_____

_____

_____

_____

_____

_____

_____

_____

Personal Connections

For each of these body systems, list appropriate examples that you may have any direct personal connection to, either yourself, family, or friends, on the themes of: disease, medicine and technology, the effects of aging, and exercise.

	Disease	The Effects of Aging	Medicine & Technology	Exercise
Musculoskeletal system				
Integumentary system and homeostasis				
Nervous and endocrine systems				
Cardiovascular and lymphatic systems				
Respiratory system				
Digestive system				
Urinary system				
Reproductive system				

A-3 Glossary

A

abduction
Muscular movement of a joint or limb away from the midline of the main body or body structure (i.e. stretching out arm)

absorption
Process by which the products of digestion move across the gut lining into the blood or lymph.

actin
A contractile protein found in muscle cells

active transport
The energy-requiring movement of substances across a biological membrane against a concentration gradient.

adduction
Muscular movement of a joint or limb towards the midline of the main body or body structure (i.e. centre of hand)

adrenal gland
Endocrine glands that produce a variety of hormones with roles in carbohydrate metabolism, ion regulation, and response to stress.

aldosterone
Hormone produced by the adrenal gland that causes sodium and water to be retained in the body, and potassium to be secreted into the urine..

alveoli
Microscopic structures in the lungs of air-breathing vertebrates that form the terminus of the bronchioles. The site of gas exchange.

antagonistic muscles
Name given to a pair of muscles whose actions oppose each other, when one contracts the other relaxes (e.g. the biceps and triceps).

antibody
A protein produced by the body in response to a specific antigen and aimed at targeting and destroying it.

antidiuretic hormone (ADH)
The hormone released in response to low blood volumes, high sodium levels and low fluid intake.

antigen
A foreign molecule that stimulates an immune response in the body.

antigen presenting cell (APC)
Types of immune cells that process and present antigens for recognition by T cells.

aorta
Artery which carries oxygenated blood away from the heart to the head and body.

apoptosis
Also called programmed cell death. It is part of normal growth and development, and cellular regulation in multicellular organisms.

appendicular skeleton
The bones making up the limbs and the pectoral and pelvic girdles.

artery
A large blood vessel with a thick, muscled wall which carries blood away from the heart.

asthma
A respiratory disease where the airways become narrow, restricting the flow of air to the lungs.

atrium
Chamber of the heart that receives blood from the body or lungs.

Autoimmune disease
When the normal self recognition system fails to distinguish self from non-self (foreign antigens), the immune system may attack its own cells or tissues.

autonomic nervous system
A portion of the peripheral nervous system. It controls visceral functions, for example heart rate, digestion and respiration rate.

axial skeleton
The bones making up the limbs and the pectoral and pelvic girdles.

axon
The long extension of a nerve cell that conducts electrical impulses away from the cell body

B

B-cells
A type of lymphocyte that makes antibodies against specific antigens. The cell type responsible for the humoral immune response.

blood
Circulatory fluid comprising numerous cell types, which transports respiratory gases, nutrients, and wastes.

bronchi
Large air tubes that branch from the trachea to enter the lungs.

bronchitis
A respiratory disease, where excess mucus blocks the airway, leading to inflammation and infection

C

capillary
The smallest blood vessel, with an endothelium only one cell thick.

cardiac muscle
Specialized striated muscle that does not fatigue. It is found only in the walls of the heart and is not under conscious control (involuntary muscle).

cardiovascular cycle
The sequence of events of a heartbeat, and involves three main stages: atrial systole, ventricular systole and complete cardiac diastole.

cardiovascular disease
A general term used to describe diseases of the heart and blood vessels.

cartilaginous joint
Joints that are held together by cartilage. No joint cavity is present.

cell
The basic structural, functional, and biological unit of any living organism

cell cycle
The process of growth, DNA replication, mitosis, and finally cytokinesis, of a cell.

cell signaling
Communication between cells involving a chemical messenger or signal molecule (ligand) and a receptor molecule (on the target cells).

central nervous system
The portion of the nervous system comprising the brain and spinal cord.

cerebellum
A part of the hindbrain that coordinates body movements, posture, and balance.

cerebrum
The largest region of the brain. It controls and integrates motor, sensory, and higher mental functions (e.g. reason and emotion)

circulatory system
The organ system comprising of the heart, arteries, veins, capillaries, and blood.

contraception
Use of methods or devices that prevent conception (fertilization of an egg by a sperm), or implantation of the fertilized egg.

COPD
Chronic obstructive pulmonary disease causes persistent long-term respiratory symptoms, including difficulty in breathing..

cortex (kidney)
The outermost layer of an organ. The portion of the kidney between the renal capsule and medulla.

D

deficiency disease
Occurs when there is an inadequate intake of a specific nutrient.

dermis
The connective tissue layer of the skin beneath the epidermis.

Diabetes mellitus
A disease caused by the body's inability to produce or react to insulin.

diaphragm
A dome shaped muscle that works with intercostal muscles of the rib cage to bring about lung ventilation (breathing).

diffusion
The passive movement of molecules from high to low concentration.

digestive system
The body system where ingestion, digestion, absorption, and elimination of food occurs.

E

egestion
Removal of undigested food (in feces) from the gut.

Electrolyte
A substance that dissociates into ions in solution and can conduct electricity. Examples include sodium, potassium, chloride, and calcium.

endocrine gland
Ductless gland secreting hormones directly into the blood.

epidermis
The outermost layer of skin, which covers and protects the dermis.

epithelium
Linings of organs and cavities formed from epithelium and connective tissue. They include the skin, mucosa, and serosa.

esophagus
The muscular tube through which food passes from the mouth to the stomach.

estrogen
A steroid hormone, which functions as the primary female sex hormone.

excretion
Elimination of waste products of metabolism.

exocrine gland
A gland that delivers secretions via a duct.

F

fast twitch
The muscle fibre that predominates during anaerobic, explosive activity. It contains less mitochondria and myoglobin than slow twitch fibre types.

fibrous joint
A type of joint where the bones are joined by fibrous tissue. This type of joint has little or no movement, so is sometimes called a fixed or immovable joint.

G

glucagon
The hormone that brings about physiological processes to elevate blood glucose levels if they become too low.

H

hematopoiesis
The formation of blood cells.

hemoglobin
A molecule in red blood cells (erythrocytes) that oxygen is bound to and carried in the blood stream.

homeostasis
Regulation of the internal environment to maintain a stable, constant condition.

hormone
Chemical messenger that induces a specific physiological response.

hypersensitivity
The undesirable over-reaction of a sensitized person's immune system to a perceived antigen. It includes allergic reactions and autoimmune diseases.

hyperthermia
A physiological state in which the core body temperature exceeds 38.5°C without a change to the set-point of the heat control centre in the hypothalamus.

hypertonic
A common term in animal biology for a solution with a higher total solute concentration relative to another solution (across a membrane).

hypothalamus (homeostasis)
A region of the brain that controls many body mechanisms, including temperature regulation, hunger, and many other homeostatic processes.

hypothalamus (nervous system)
The region of the brain which coordinates the nervous and endocrine systems via the pituitary gland.

hypothermia
A condition experienced when the core body temperature drops below 40°C.

hypotonic
A common term in animal biology for a solution with a lower total solute concentration relative to another solution (across a membrane).

IJ

immune system
The structures and processes in the body that provide defense against disease.

inflammation
A defensive response to damage caused by physical agents, microbial infections or chemical agents. The inflammation process involves pain, redness, heat and swelling.

insulin
The hormone that lowers blood glucose, primarily through the cellular uptake of glucose, but also by promoting storage of glucose as glycogen.

integumentary system
The skin, or cutaneous membrane, and its associated structures (hair, sweat glands, nails)

ion pump
A transmembrane protein that moves ions across a plasma membrane against their concentration gradient.

isotonic
In animal biology, solutions of equal solute concentration are often termed this.

IVF
In vitro fertilization refers to a egg that has been fertilized outside of the woman's body, then the pre-embryo is transferred into the uterus.

K

kidney
Bean shaped organ which removes and concentrates metabolic wastes from the blood.

L

lactation
The production and secretion of milk from the mammary glands.

large intestine
The lower part of the gut comprising of the appendix, cecum and colon.

lymphatic system
A body system that drains fluid surrounding the tissues, which is supplying them with nutrients and oxygen, and removing wastes, and circulates through a network of lymph vessels.

lymphocyte
A group of specialized white blood cells that launch a range of specific responses to pathogens, including the production of defensive proteins called antibodies.

M

major histocompatibility complex (MHC)
A set of molecules displayed on cell surfaces that are responsible for lymphocyte recognition and antigen presentation.

malnutrition
Insufficient, excessive or imbalanced consumption of nutrients.

medulla (kidney)
The middle region of the kidney.

membrane
A thin layer of tissue that covers a structure or lines a cavity.

menstrual cycle
The cycle of changes in reproductive physiology occurring in fertile females. In humans the cycle lasts approximately 28 days.

mitosis
The phase of a cell cycle resulting in nuclear division.

N

negative feedback loop
A mechanism in which the output of a system acts to oppose changes to the input of the system. The net effect is to stabilize the system and dampen fluctuations.

nephron
The functional unit of the kidney comprising the glomerulus, Bowman's capsule, convoluted tubules, loop of Henle and collecting duct.

nerve impulse
Waves of depolarization that create action potentials moving along the axon length.

neuroglia
A class of neural cells that protect, defend, and ensure homeostatic support of nervous tissue.

neuromuscular junction
The junction between a motor neuron and a skeletal muscle fiber. It is a specialized cholinergic synapse.

neuron
A nerve cell, made up of a cell body, dendrites, and an axon.

neurotransmitter
Chemicals that transmit signals between neurons.

O

oogenesis
The process by which oocytes are produced.

organ
Structures comprising two or more tissues with related functions.

organ system
A group of organs that work together to perform a specific task.

organelle
A structural and functional part of the cell usually bound within its own membrane. An example is the mitochondria.

osmosis
Passive movement of water molecules across a partially permeable membrane down a concentration gradient.

ossification
The formation of bone tissue.

osteoarthritis
A disease characterized by the degeneration of cartilage and the formation of bony outgrowths around the edges of the eroded cartilage.

osteoblast
Cells that secrete the matrix for bone formation.

osteocyte
A bone cell.

osteoporosis
A disease characterized by loss of bone mass and increased likelihood of bone fracture. Often (but not always) associated with old age.

ovulation
Release of ova (eggs) from the ovaries during a woman's menstrual cycle.

oxygen debt
A cumulative deficit of oxygen resulting from intense exercise. The oxygen deficit is made up during the recovery (rest) period.

oxytocin
A hormone with roles in uterine contraction during labor, and milk letdown in lactating females.

P

pancreas
An abdominal organ with both endocrine and exocrine functions.

pectoral girdle
The set of bones connecting the upper limb to the axial skeleton on each side. It consists of the clavicle and scapula. Also called the shoulder girdle.

pelvic girdle
The weight-bearing girdle of the lower body, consists of the coxal (hip) bones, and sacrum.

peripheral nervous system
The part of the nervous system that comprises all the nerves and sensory receptors outside of the central nervous system.

peristalsis
Wave-like smooth muscle contractions that move food through the digestive tract.

phagocytosis
The process by which a phagocyte cell (type of white blood cell) engulfs another cell or particle.

pituitary
An endocrine gland located below the hypothalamus. It produces hormones that control other glands and many body functions.

placenta
A specialized organ, characteristic of most mammals, that enables exchanges (via the blood supply) of nutrient, gases, and wastes, between the mother and the fetus.

plasma
The non-cellular portion of the blood.

plasma membrane
Thin membrane that forms the external boundary of the cell cytoplasm.

positive feedback loop
A destabilizing mechanism in which the output of the system causes an escalation in the initial response.

progesterone
A steroid hormone involved in the female menstrual cycle, pregnancy, and embryogenesis.

puberty
The period of physical changes during which a child's body becomes a reproductively capable adult body.

Q R

renal dialysis
A medical process designed to remove wastes from the blood when the kidneys have failed.

respiratory center
A region in the medulla oblongata that controls the basic rhythm of breathing.

S

sarcomere
The contractile element of the fiber, it is contained between two Z membranes.

sensory receptors
Specialized nerve cells that detect stimuli and respond by producing an electrical discharge.

signal transduction
Conversion of a mechanical or chemical stimulus to a cell into a specific cellular response.

skeletal muscle
Muscle that is attached to the skeleton and responsible for the movement of bone around joints or movement of some organs, e.g. the eyes.

sliding filament theory
The theory of how thin and thick filaments slide past each other to produce muscles contraction.

slow twitch
The muscle fibre that predominates during aerobic, endurance activity. They contain more mitochondria and myoglobin than fast twitch fibre types.

small intestine
The upper part of the gut comprising of the duodenum, jejunum and ileum. The main site of absorption of food.

smooth muscle
The muscle responsible for automatic movements such as peristalsis. It is not under conscious control. Cells are spindle shaped with one central nucleus.

spermatogenesis
The production of male gametes. Spermatogonia develop into mature sperm cells.

sphincter
A circular muscle that closes off part of the digestive system, usually found near the stomach, to regulate the passage of food through the digestive system.

spirometry
A lung function test that measures changes in lung volume.

stomach
Large muscular digestive organ located between the esophagus and small intestine. It secretes protein digesting enzymes and strong acids to aid digestion of food.

synapse
The junction between two neurons or between a neuron and an effector.

synovial joint
A joint that allows free movement of body parts in varying directions, on one, two or three planes. A typical example is the knee joint.

T

T-cell
Cellular part of an immune response. These respond only to antigenic fragments that have been processed and presented by infected cells or macrophages.

testosterone
The principal male sex hormone.

thermoreceptor
Nerve cells that detect change in temperature (the stimulus) and sends a message to the control centre in the brain.

thermoregulation
Homeostatic control of steady internal body temperature.

tissue
A collection of cells from the same origin, which together carry out a specific function.

trachea
Tube that conveys air from the mouth to the bronchi. Also known as the windpipe.

U

ultrafiltration
Process by which small molecules and ions are separated from larger ones in the blood to form the renal filtrate (in the kidney).

Urine
Fluid containing metabolic wastes that collects in the urinary bladder.

V

vaccine
A preparation of a harmless foreign antigen that is deliberately introduced into the body to protect against a specific disease. The antigen in the vaccine is usually some part of the pathogen. It triggers the immune system to produce antibodies against the antigen but it does not cause the disease.

vein
Large blood vessels that return blood to the heart.

ventricle
Chamber of the heart that pumps blood out of the heart to the circulatory system.

villi
Intestinal lining that is folded to increase surface area and projects into the digestive tract, primarily responsible for nutrient absorption.

vital capacity
The maximum amount of air a person can expel from the lungs after a maximum inspiration.

VO$_2$ max
The amount of oxygen used by muscles during a specified interval for cell metabolism and energy production.

WXYZ

water budget
The balance of water intake and output in the body to maintain water homeostasis.

Common terms

The study of anatomy and physiology requires a good mental map of the body's different regions and a sound understanding of the terms used to describe the location of structures on the body. The following short guide lists some of the basic directional and regional terms that you will come across when you study anatomy and physiology

Commonly used anatomical terms

Abdominal:	Anterior body trunk inferior to ribs.
Anterior:	Toward or at the front of the body, (ventral).
Cephalic:	Head region.
Cervical:	Neck region.
Deep:	Away from the body surface, (internal).
Distal:	Farther from the point of attachment of a limb to the body trunk.
Dorsal:	Toward or at the back side of the body, (posterior).
Frontal plane:	Divides the body into front and back portions.
Inferior:	Toward the lower part of the body.
Lateral:	Away from the midline of the body.
Medial:	Toward or at the midline of the body.
Median plane:	A vertical plane through the midline of the body; divides the body into right and left halves, (midsagittal).
Pelvic:	Area overlying the pelvis.
Posterior:	Toward or at the back side of the body, (dorsal).
Proximal:	The point of attachment of a limb to the body trunk.
Pubic:	Genital region.
Superior:	Toward the head or upper part of the body.
Superficial:	Body surface, (external).
Thoracic:	Chest region.
Transverse plane:	Divides the body into top and bottom portions.
Ventral:	Toward or at the front of the body, (anterior).

Credits

We acknowledge the generosity of those who have provided photographs for this edition: • Danny Wann: Carl Albert State College • Berkshire Community College Bioscience Image Library • Waikato Microscope Unit • L. Howard, K Connollly Dartmouth College • University of Delaware • Danny Wann: Carl Albert State College • Prof. John Bath • D. Fankhauser, University of Cincinnati, Clermont College • LocalFitness Pty Ltd • Kent Pryor • Dr. David Wells, AgResearch • Georgetown University Hospital • Dartmouth Electron Microscope Facility • Wellington Harrier Club • Ed Uthman

We also acknowledge the photographers that have made their images available through Wikimedia Commons under Creative Commons Licences 2.0 - 4.0: • NIAID • Y tambe • NIH • Michael Berry • Emmanuelm • Wbensmith • GerryShaw • Doc. RNDr. Josef Reischig, CSc. • Ildar Sagdejev • RM Hunt • Graham Crumb • Bill Rhodes • Stevenfruitsmaak • James Heilman, MD • Drahreg01 • Woutergroen • Roadnottaken • Didier Descouens Hear hear! • Josabeth • Tourbulence • Jfoldmei • G Beard • Ed Uthman • Obli • Volker Brinkmann PLOS • Emw • Nevit Dilmen • Jacoplane • myupchar • Schaffer , Strang , Saul, et al. • BallenaBlanca • Dr D. Cooper, University of California, San Francisco •

Contributors identified by coded credits are: **BF**: Brian Finerran (University of Canterbury), **VMRCVM**: Virginia-Maryland College of Veterinary Medicine, **NIAD**: National Institute of Allergy and Infectious Diseases • **WMU**: Waikato Microscope Unit • **NIH**: National Institute of Health • **CDC**: Centers for Disease Control and Prevention • **NCI**: National Cancer Institute • **EII**: Education Interactive Imaging • **DS**: Digital Stock • **DEA**: Drug Enforcement Agency • **NASA**: National Aeronautics and Space Administration • **RCN**: Ralph Cocklin • **PIER**: Pathology Education Informational Resource • **KP**: Kent Pryor

Royalty free images, purchased by BIOZONE International Ltd, are used throughout this workbook and have been obtained from the following sources: Corel Corporation from their Professional Photos CD-ROM collection; IMSI (Intl Microcomputer Software Inc.) images from IMSI's MasterClips® and MasterPhotos™ Collection, 1895 Francisco Blvd. East, San Rafael, CA 94901-5506, USA; ©1996 Digital Stock, Medicine and Health Care collection; © 2005 JupiterImages Corporation www.clipart.com; ©Hemera Technologies Inc, 1997-2001; ©Click Art, ©T/Maker Company; ©1994., ©Digital Vision; Gazelle Technologies Inc.; PhotoDisc®, Inc. USA, www.photodisc.com. • TechPool Studios, for their clipart collection of human anatomy: Copyright ©1994, TechPool Studios Corp. USA (some of these images were modified by Biozone) • Totem Graphics, for their clipart collection • Corel Corporation, for use of their clipart from the Corel MEGAGALLERY collection • 3D images created using Bryce, Vue 6, Poser, and Pymol • iStock images • Art Today • Adobe Stock

Index